PLANT PROPAGATION

PRINCIPLES AND PRACTICES

PLANT

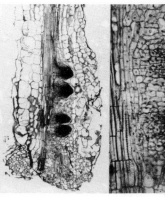

PROPAGATION

PRINCIPLES AND PRACTICES

HUDSON T. HARTMANN

Professor of Pomology
University of California at Davis

DALE E. KESTER

Associate Professor of Pomology
University of California at Davis

ENGLEWOOD CLIFFS, N.J.
PRENTICE-HALL, INC.

Third printing. . . . . September, 1960

Plant Propagation

Library of Congress Catalog Card No.: 59–7296

Printed in the United States of America

68098-C

Preface

This book provides a source of information concerning the fundamental principles involved in plant propagation and serves as a manual that describes useful techniques for propagating plants. As far as possible, these two phases of plant propagation have been considered separately and placed in consecutive chapters. For example, the basic botanical principles underlying grafting and budding are stressed in one chapter, whereas the techniques of the various grafting and budding methods are emphasized in the two succeeding chapters. Although some readers are very much concerned with the fundamental principles of plant propagation, the interest of others may lie primarily in the actual techniques involved.

The separation of these two phases of propagation makes the book more adaptable to the needs of the individual reader. The chapters dealing with the theoretical aspects of the various subjects have been written on the assumption that the reader has a knowledge of the general principles of botany and horticulture. On the other hand, the chapters describing the techniques and equipment used in the different methods of propagation have been written in terms understandable to those with little botanical background.

A rather extensive representative bibliography of the research literature is included for each subject considered, although the papers listed are by no means the only acceptable ones. In addition, suggested supplementary readings are listed for most of the subjects considered. These are generally specialized works which deal with the topic more extensively than is possible in this book. These references should be valuable for those wishing to study the subject in greater detail.

In writing this book, we depended heavily upon the help of authorities in the various fields of propagation and related subjects. They gave their time most generously in reading sections of the manuscript and in offering suggestions. We wish to acknowledge, in particular, the assistance of Dr. R. W. Allard, Dr. Lela V. Barton, Dr. W. P. Bitters, Prof. Karl Brase, Dr. R. S. Bringhurst, Dr. R. M. Brooks, Dr. W. H. Chandler, Prof. L. H. Day, Dr. Haig Dermen, Prof. W. L. Doran, Mr. R. J. Garner, Prof. C. J. Hansen, Dr. J. F. Harrington, Dr. C. O. Hesse, Dr. H. Harold Hume, Dr. A. M. Kofranek, Mr. Frank Parsons, Prof. F. I. Righter, Dr. C. A. Schroeder, Mr. H. T. Skinner, Dr. W. E. Snyder, Dr. Neil W. Stuart, Dr. K. V. Thimann, and Dr. E. H. Toole.

Numerous other research workers were also most helpful in reviewing portions of the manuscript dealing with their special fields of interest. Although it is impossible to mention them all by name here, grateful appreciation is expressed for their assistance. We appreciate also the efforts of Mrs. Joyce Houghton, who made most of the drawings.

We especially wish to thank Dr. W. P. Tufts, former chairman of the Department of Pomology, University of California, for his interest and encouragement throughout the writing of this book.

H. T. HARTMANN
D. E. KESTER

Table of Contents

I • General Aspects of Propagation

II • Sexual Propagation

III • Asexual Propagation

IV • Propagation of Selected Plants

I

GENERAL ASPECTS
OF PROPAGATION

1 | Introduction

The propagation of plants is a fundamental occupation of mankind. Civilization is largely based upon man's ability to propagate and grow specific kinds of plants which can be used for food and provide shelter, clothing, recreation, and aesthetic fulfillment.

Plant propagation may be defined as the controlled reproduction of plants by man to perpetuate selected individuals or groups of individual plants which have specific value to him. Most cultivated plants are improved forms which owe their continued existence to the fact that they are propagated under carefully controlled conditions; most would disappear in a few generations or revert to less desirable forms if allowed to reproduce naturally without control. Without the efforts of such commercial propagators as the nurseryman, seedsman, or bulb producer, the efforts of the plant breeders in producing improved forms would be limited to a few individuals, and such plants would not be generally available as they are today.

OBJECTIVES IN THE STUDY OF PLANT PROPAGATION

The study of plant propagation involves three different aspects. These may be considered as objectives in any course of study involving the propagation of plants. First of all, plant propagation requires a knowledge of mechanical manipulations and technical skills whose mastery requires a certain amount of practice and experience. This would include such things as how to bud or graft or how to make cuttings. These may be referred to as the art of propagation.

Secondly, successful plant propagation requires a knowledge of plant growth and structure. This may be said to be the science of propagation. Some of this information can be learned empirically by working with the plants themselves, but it should be supplemented, if possible, with information gained from formal courses in botany, horticulture, genetics, and so forth. Such knowledge aids the propagator in understanding why he does the things he does. It also makes it possible for him to better perform these practices.

A third important requirement of successful plant propagation is a knowledge of specific kinds of plants and the particular methods by which those plants must be propagated. To a large extent the method used must be geared to the requirements of the particular kind of plant being propagated.

METHODS OF PROPAGATING PLANTS

The propagation of plants can be accomplished by a variety of techniques depending upon the kind of plant involved and the particular purposes of the propagator. The important techniques are given below.

Outline of Methods of Propagating Plants with Typical Examples

I. Sexual
   A. Propagation by seed—annuals, biennials, and many perennial plants. Some seeds require pre-germination treatments (such as stratification or scarification), while others germinate immediately when placed in the proper environment.
II. Asexual (vegetative)
   A. Propagation by apomictic embryos—citrus
   B. Propagation by runners—strawberry
   C. Propagation by suckers—red raspberry, blackberry
   D. Layering
      (1) Tip—trailing blackberry, black raspberry
      (2) Simple—honeysuckle, spirea, filbert
      (3) Trench—apple, pear, filbert
      (4) Mound or stool—gooseberry, currant
      (5) Air (pot or Chinese)—India rubber plant, lychee
      (6) Compound or serpentine—grape
   E. Separation
      (1) Bulbs—hyacinth, lily, narcissus, tulip
      (2) Corms—gladiolus, crocus

F. Division
    (1) Rhizomes—canna, iris
    (2) Offsets—houseleek, pineapple, date
    (3) Tubers—Irish potato
    (4) Tuberous roots—sweet potato, dahlia
    (5) Crowns—everbearing strawberry, phlox

G. Propagation by cuttings
    (1) Root cuttings—red raspberry, horse-radish
    (2) Stem cuttings
        (a) Hardwood—fig, grape, gooseberry, quince, rose, forsythia
        (b) Semi-hardwood—lemon, olive, camellia, holly
        (c) Softwood—lilac, forsythia, weigela
        (d) Herbaceous—geranium, coleus, chrysanthemum
    (3) Leaf cuttings—*Begonia rex, Bryophyllum, Sansevieria,* African violet
    (4) Leaf-bud cuttings—blackberry, hydrangea

H. Grafting
    (1) Root grafting
        (a) Whip or tongue graft—apple and pear
    (2) Crown grafting
        (a) Whip or tongue graft—Persian walnut
        (b) Cleft graft—camellia
        (c) Side graft—narrow-leaved evergreens
    (3) Top grafting
        (a) Cleft graft—various fruit trees
        (b) Saw-kerf or notch graft—various fruit trees
        (c) Bark graft—various fruit trees
        (d) Side graft—various fruit trees
        (e) Whip or tongue graft—various fruit trees
    (4) Approach grafting—mango

I. Budding
    (1) T-budding—stone and pome fruit trees, rose
    (2) Patch budding—walnut and pecan
    (3) Ring budding—walnut and pecan
    (4) I-budding—walnut and pecan
    (5) Chip budding—grape

BASIC TYPES OF REPRODUCTION

There are two basic types of plant reproduction—sexual and asexual. Seed propagation is sexual, except in the case of apomixis (see p. 43). In general, propagation by seed can be expected to result in a certain amount of seedling variation, depending upon the kind of plants involved. The various vegetative methods, on the other hand, are asexual. When these are employed genetic variation during reproduction is essentially eliminated, and it is usually possible to duplicate exactly the particular genetic complex of any individual plant. The asexual reproduction of an individual plant can continue for generation after generation for hundreds of years.

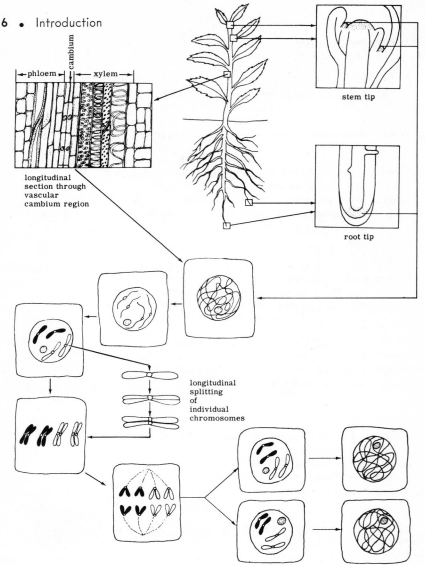

Figure 1–1. Mitosis. Diagrammatical representation of the process by which growth and asexual reproduction take place. Mitosis occurs in the three principal growing regions of the plant: the stem tip, the root tip of primary and secondary roots, and the cambium. A meristematic cell is shown dividing to produce two daughter cells whose chromosomes will be identical (usually) with those of the original cell. Details of the longitudinal splitting of each chromosome are shown.

It is important that a propagator understand the fundamental difference between these two types of reproduction. Whether or not one or the other of these two basic types can be used may determine whether or not a particular kind of plant can be maintained by propagation. Should the unique combination of characters possessed by this particular kind be lost during the propagation process, then the method would obviously be unsuccessful. It should be emphasized that the most important function of any plant propagation technique is *to preserve the characteristics of a particular kind of plant.*

Asexual Reproduction

Asexual reproduction is possible because of the normal cell division (*mitosis*) which occurs during growth. The details of the process are shown in Figure 1–1, its principal feature being that the individual chromosomes split longitudinally, the two identical parts going to the two daughter cells. As a result, the complete chromosome system of an individual cell is duplicated in each of its two daughter cells (with certain rare exceptions). The chromosomes and, consequently, the characteristics of any new plant part which arise in this way will thus be the same as the part on which it was produced.

A plant grows by cell division from three principal growing points or areas of the plant—the *shoot apex,* the *root apex,* and the *cambium.* Mitosis also occurs when *callus* forms on a wounded plant part and when new growing points are initiated on root and stem pieces. *Callus formation* refers to the production of new, unspecialized cells from a part of the plant away from the growing points in response to wounding. When new growing points are initiated on a vegetative structure, such as root, stem, or leaf, they are referred to as *adventitious shoots* or *adventitious roots.*

Adventitious roots may be defined as those that arise

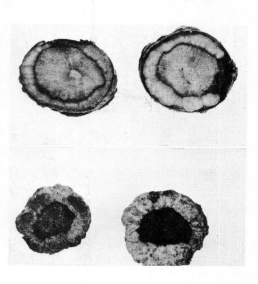

Figure 1–2. Callus tissue growing from the cut surface of stems. Note that it arises from the region of the vascular system. Olive **(above)** and quince **(below).** Courtesy Dept. of Pomology, Univ. of Calif.

from aerial plant parts, underground stems, or from relatively old roots. All roots other than those arising from the hypocotyl-root axis of the embryo and all their branches formed in normal sequence can be considered adventitious roots. *Adventitious shoots* are those appearing on

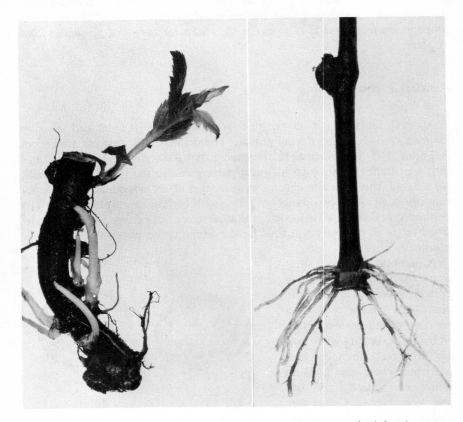

Figure 1–3. (left) Adventitious shoots growing from a root cutting. **(right)** Adventitious roots growing from the base of a stem cutting.

roots or internodally on stems after the terminal and lateral growing points are produced. Adventitious shoots should not be confused with shoots arising from *latent* growing points or buds which are present from the time that the plant part upon which they occur was originally formed but have not grown actively. The latter are common on old branches of woody plants and can be stimulated into active growth if the part terminal to it is removed.

Mitosis is the basic process of normal vegetative growth, regeneration, and wound healing which makes possible such vegetative propagation techniques as cuttage, graftage, layerage, separation, and division. These methods of propagation are important because they permit large scale multiplication of an *individual plant,* into as many separate plants as the amount of parent material will permit. Each separate plant produced by such means is (in most cases) genetically identical with the plant from which it came. The primary reason for using these vegetative propagation

Figure I–4. Cross section of branch showing a latent bud that was initiated when the shoot first developed and has continued to elongate year by year as the branch increased in diameter. A shoot that would grow from this bud now would be known as a **watersprout** and would not be adventitious.

techniques is to reproduce exactly the genetic characteristics of any individual plant, although there may be additional advantages from the standpoint of culture.

Sexual Reproduction

Sexual reproduction involves the union of male and female sex cells, the formation of seeds, and the creation of new individuals as illustrated in Figure 1–5. The cell division (*meiosis*) which produces the sex cells involves the reduction division of the chromosomes in which their number is reduced by half. The original chromosome number is restored during fertilization, resulting in new individuals containing chromosomes from both the male and female parents. Consequently, it may resemble either, neither, or both of its parents, depending upon their genetic similarities. Among the progeny from a particular combination of parents, considerable variation may occur.

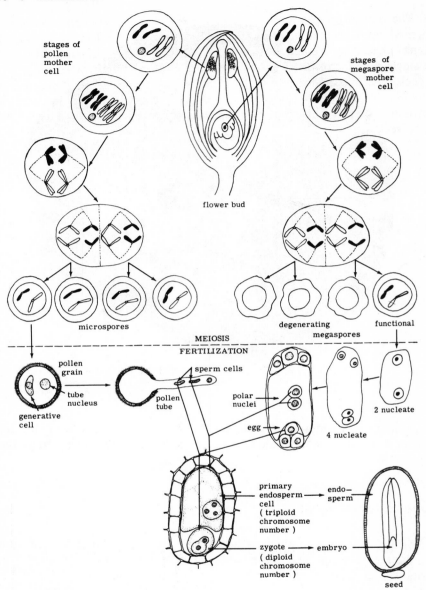

stages of
pollen
mother
cell

stages of
megaspore
mother
cell

flower bud

microspores

degenerating
megaspores

functional

MEIOSIS

FERTILIZATION

pollen
grain

sperm cells

tube
nucleus

pollen
tube

polar
nuclei

2 nucleate

generative
cell

egg

4 nucleate

primary
endosperm
cell
(triploid
chromosome
number)

endo-
sperm

zygote
(diploid
chromosome
number)

embryo

seed

Figure 1–5. Meiosis. Diagrammatical representation of the sexual cycle in higher plants. Meiosis occurs in the flower bud in the anther (male) and the pistil (female) during the bud stage. During this process the pollen mother cells and the megaspore mother cells, both diploid, undergo a reduction division in which homologous chromosomes segregate to different cells, followed immediately by a mitotic division, to produce four daughter cells, each with half the chromosomes of the mother cells. In fertilization a male gamete unites with the egg to produce a zygote in which the diploid chromosome number is restored. In angiospermous plants, a second male gamete unites with the polar nuclei to produce the endosperm.

The outward appearance of a plant and the way characteristics are inherited from generation to generation is controlled through the action of genes present on the chromosomes. A particular trait may be controlled by a single gene factor or it may be controlled through the interaction of many genes. The inheritance of a single character—pea height—is illustrated in Figure 1–6. Figure 1–7 illustrates the more complex case that exists when two independent characters affecting the appearance of peach fruit are involved.

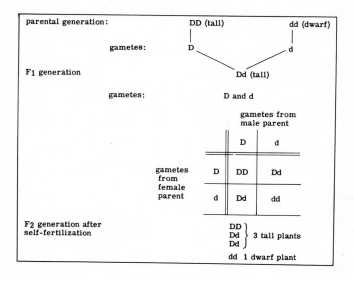

Figure 1–6. Inheritance involving a single gene pair in a monohybrid cross. This example is taken from Mendel's studies with garden peas, using the gene for tallness **(D)** which is dominant over dwarfness **(d)**. Thus a tall pea plant would either be homozygous **(DD)** or heterozygous **(Dd)**, whereas the dwarf pea plant would only be homozygous **(dd)**.

The two terms *homozygous* and *heterozygous* are very useful to describe the genetic characteristics of a particular kind of plant. If a high percentage of the genes present on one chromosome are the same as those on the opposite member of the chromosome pair (*homologous chromosomes*), the plant is homozygous and tends to "breed true" to type, providing the other parent is genetically similar. This means that the particular traits or characteristics that the plant possesses will be transmitted to its offspring, and the offspring will resemble the parent. On the other hand, if a sufficient number of genes on one chromosome differ from those on the other member of the chromosome pair, then the plant is said to be

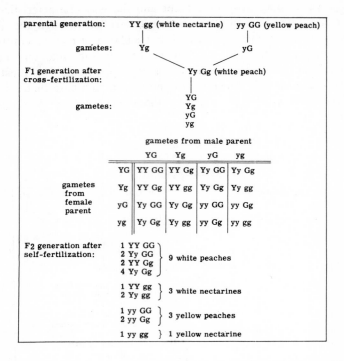

Figure 1–7. Inheritance in a dihybrid cross involving peach **(Prunus persica)**. Fuzzy skin **(G)** of a peach is dominant over the glabrous (i.e., smooth) skin of the nectarine **(g)**. White flesh color **(Y)** is dominant over yellow flesh color **(y)**. The principles are the same as in the monohybrid cross shown in Figure 1–6.

heterozygous. In such a case, important traits of the parent are not transmitted to its offspring, and the appearance of the seedlings may not only differ from that of the parent but also from each other. The amount of seedling variation may be very great in some kinds of plants.

To minimize variation and to be sure that seedlings will possess the particular characteristics for which they are to be grown, certain procedures must be followed during seed production. These procedures are discussed in Chapter 4.

PLANT NOMENCLATURE

Since plant propagation involves the controlled reproduction of plant groups selected specifically for particular purposes, it is important that such groups be specified in a way that is readily understood by everyone concerned. A uniform system of plant nomenclature is essential for proper identification and classification.

Botanical Classification

Classification of natural plant groups is based upon the increasing complexity and specialization in the structure and organization of plants which results from evolutionary processes *(4)*. The plant kingdom can be divided into fifteen *phyla* beginning with one-celled plants, i.e., Schizophyta (bacteria and blue-green algae), through somewhat more complex plants, such as the Bryophyta (mosses, liverworts), to specialized higher plants, Pterophyta.

The latter phylum includes three classes, Filicinae (ferns), Gymnospermae (gymnosperms), and Angiospermae (flowering plants). The gymnosperms (conifers and *Ginkgo*), produce seeds which are not enclosed. The angiosperms include the flowering plants, the dominant feature being the production of a seed within an enclosed structure—the ovary.

The angiosperms are divided into two sub-classes—the Monocotyledons and Dicotyledons. These sub-classes are divided into *orders,* the orders into *families,* families into *genera,* and genera into *species.* The species is usually the fundamental unit used to classify any particular kind of plant, although the *International Code of Botanical Nomenclature (2)* recognizes other categories of lesser rank than the species, i.e., *sub-species, botanical variety, sub-variety, form,* and *individual.* These latter terms refer to plants which originate in nature.

Classification of Cultivated Plants

The *International Code of Botanical Nomenclature* governs the use of botanical ("Latin") names for both cultivated and wild species *(2)*. A separate code, the *International Code of Nomenclature for Cultivated Plants,* extends these rules to cover the special categories and names of cultivated plants *(1, 3, 5)*. Thus, any kind of plant developed or maintained under cultivation has a scientific name composed of (a) the genus, (b) the species, and (c) a cultivar name, the first two in the usual Latin form, and the latter in words of a common language, such as English, French, or German, and set off either by the abbreviation *cv.* or by single quotation marks. It may also be attached to the common name. Thus:

> *Syringa vulgaris* cv. Mont Blanc
> *Syringa vulgaris* 'Mont Blanc'
> Lilac 'Mont Blanc'

A *cultivar* (a contraction of the words "cultivated variety") is defined as "an assemblage of cultivated individuals which are distinguished by any characters (morphological, physiological, cytological, chemical, or others) significant for the purposes of agriculture, forestry, or horticulture, and which, when reproduced sexually or asexually, retain their distinguishing features" *(1)*. "Cultivar" is proposed by this code as an international term for this category synonymous, however, with such older terms as "variety" (English), "variété" (French), "variedad" (Spanish), "sorte" (German), "sort" (Scandinavian), "ras" (Russian), and "razza" (Italian).

The various categories of cultivars (varieties) are important to propagators, because they represent groups of plants which are perpetuated by specific propagation techniques. The two broad types of varieties are those sexually propagated and those asexually propagated.

Specific categories are as follows:

(a) A *clone* (see p. 160), consisting of uniform material originally derived from a single individual and propagated entirely by vegetative means (cuttings, divisions, grafts, and so forth). It may be designated in the botanical name by the abbreviation *cl.*

(b) A *line,* consisting of a sexually reproducing population of uniform appearance, propagated by seeds or by spores, its stability maintained by selection to a standard (see p. 57).

(c) An assemblage of individuals, reproducing sexually or by apomixis, (see p. 43) showing genetical differences but having one or more characteristics by which it can be differentiated from other cultivars. For example, the alfalfa variety 'Ranger' is a cultivar in which the "breeders seed" (see p. 61) is derived from intercrossing five seed-propagated lines, each maintained under isolation. *Phlox drummondii* 'Sternenzauber' is a mixture of different color types, but all have the same starlike shape of the corolla.

(d) A uniform group propagated by seed which is a first generation hybrid (F_1) reconstituted on each occasion by crossing (or combining) two or more breeding stocks maintained either by inbreeding or as clones (see p. 62).

REFERENCES

1. Anonymous, International Code of Nomenclature for Cultivated Plants, Int. Union of Biol. Sci. Utrecht, Netherlands, 1958.
2. Lanjouw, J., ed., International Code of Botanical Nomenclature, Int. Union of Biol. Sci. Utrecht, Netherlands, 1956.
3. Lawrence, G. H. M. The term and category of cultivar, *Baileya,* 3:177–182. 1955.
4. Robbins, W. W., T. E. Weier, and C. R. Stocking, *Botany: An Introduction to Plant Science,* 2nd ed. New York: Wiley, 1957.
5. Stearn, W. T., International Code of Nomenclature for Cultivated Plants, *Rpt. 13th Int. Hort. Cong. 1952.* Pp. 42–68. 1953.

2

Propagating Structures, Media, Soil Mixtures, and Containers

Facilities required for propagating a number of plant species by seed, cuttings, or grafts, include two basic units. One is a heated structure with ample light, such as a greenhouse or hotbed, where seeds can be germinated or cuttings rooted. The second unit is a structure in which the young, tender plants can be moved for hardening, preparatory to planting in the field or in containers. Cold frames or lathhouses are useful for this purpose. Cold frames alone, used at the proper time of year, may serve for both purposes, at least for some species.

PROPAGATING STRUCTURES

Greenhouses

There are a number of types of greenhouses, and detailed information on their construction and management is available *(5, 6, 11, 25)*. The simplest type is of a shed roof, lean-to construction, utilizing one side, generally the south, of another building as one wall. Small, inexpensive, greenhouses can also be constructed from a number of standard 3 ft. by 6 ft. hotbed sashes fastened to a 2 by 4 wood framework.

Commercial greenhouses are usually independent structures of even-span, gable-roof construction, proportioned so that the space is well utilized for convenient walkways and propagating benches. The walks generally should be wide enough to permit the use of a wheelbarrow and the benches narrow enough so that the center can be reached from either side. In large operations, a number of single greenhouse units are often attached side by side, eliminating the cost of glassing-in the adjoining walls.

Figure 2–1. Greenhouse interior, showing good placement of walkways and benches for maximum utilization of space.

Figure 2–2. Closed greenhouse bench for rooting cuttings. The hinged frames covered with a translucent plastic sheeting admit light and allow the humidity in the bench to be kept at a high level if the cuttings are sprinkled frequently with water.

In greenhouse construction, a wood or metal framework is built to which wood sash bars are fastened in which panes of glass are embedded in putty. All-metal prefabricated aluminum greenhouses are also widely used.

A means of ventilation is necessary in all greenhouses to aid in controlling temperature and humidity. A ridge ventilator is almost always necessary and, in the larger greenhouses, side ventilators also. Automatic, thermostatically operated controls are available to open and close the ventilators as the temperature fluctuates during the day and night.

Most greenhouses have some heat source, usually steam or hot water. Banks of iron pipes are placed horizontally either under the benches or along the lower sides of the walls. Automatic, thermostatically operated controls can be obtained for either steam or hot water systems. These greatly simplify the problem of maintaining even temperatures, especially when used with automatically controlled ventilating systems.

In regions of low relative humidity, greenhouses can be artifically cooled in the summer at low cost by the use of large evaporative-type coolers. Devices are also available for automatically increasing the relative humidity. In such units, water is broken into a fog-like mist and blown through the greenhouse.

As a general practice, greenhouses are painted on the outside at the onset of warm weather in the spring with whitewash (see p. 369) or a white cold water paint. This reflects much of the radiant heat from the sun, thus preventing the buildup of excessively high temperatures within the greenhouse.

Plastic Greenhouses

Heavy-weight polyethylene sheeting can be used to cover an inexpensive, pitched-roof wood frame, thus providing a temporary-type greenhouse at a cost much less than that of conventional glass construction. Strongly supported framework is needed in northern areas, however, to withstand snow and wind *(10, 31)*. Excessive heat buildup during the day from the sun occurs less with polyethylene than with glass. There is also less heat loss at night. Two layers of plastic, 2 to 3 in. apart, give good insulating properties. Light transmission is slightly less through polyethylene than through glass. The plastic deteriorates slowly through the action of heat and light. Polyethylene applied in the fall will last until spring. The frame is then best re-covered in the fall, thus avoiding the summer period of most intense heat.

Plastic greenhouses must, of course, be provided with ventilation and heating facilities as in conventional glass construction.

Hotbeds

The hotbed is often used for the same purposes in propagating as the greenhouse but for smaller scale and less expensive operations. Seedlings can be started and leafy cuttings rooted in such structures early in the season. Heat is provided artificially below the propagating medium either by fermenting manure, electric heating cables, hot water, steam pipes, or hot air flues, the first two being the most common. As in the greenhouse, close attention must be paid to shading and ventilation, as well as temperature and humidity control.

The hotbed may consist of a large wood box or frame with a sloping, tight-fitting lid made of window sash, or, preferably, regular hotbed sash. It should be placed in a sunny but protected and well-drained location.

The size of the frame is usually constructed to conform to the size of the sash available. A standard size is 3 by 6 ft. The frame can be easily built of 1 or 2 in. lumber nailed to 4 by 4 corner posts set in the ground. Decay-resistant wood such as redwood, cypress, or cedar should be used, preferably treated with a wood preservative, such as copper naphthenate. This compound retards decay for many years and does not give off fumes toxic to plants. Creosote should not be used on wood structures in which plants will be grown since the fumes released, particularly on hot days, can be very toxic to plant tissue. Publications are available, giving in detail the construction of such equipment *(4, 24, 29)*. In most climates, hotbeds can be used throughout the year, but in areas of severe winters their use may be restricted to the spring, summer, and fall months.

Lead or plastic-covered electric soil heating cables are very satisfactory for providing bottom heat in hotbeds *(18)*. To insure safety, the wiring of these units should be done by a qualified person. The initial installation may be somewhat costly, but it is permanent and the exact temperature desired can be obtained and controlled accurately by thermostats. For a hotbed 6 by 6 ft., about 60 ft. of heating cable is required. The details of a typical installation are shown in Figure 2–3. Low voltage soil-heating systems are sometimes used. A transformer reduces the regular line voltage to about 30 v. which lessens the danger of electrical shock. The heating element consists of low cost, No. 8 bare galvanized wire.

The hotbed is filled with 4 to 6 in. of the rooting or seed germinating medium over the heating cables. Flats containing the medium can also be used, placed directly on a thin layer of sand covering the wire netting which is placed over the heating cables for protection from tools.

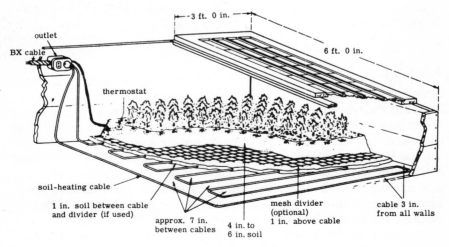

Figure 2–3. Construction of hotbed showing installation of an electric heating cable and thermostat. Courtesy General Electric Co.

Cold Frames *(4, 25)*

Cold frame construction is almost identical with that of hotbeds, except that no provision is made for supplying artificial heat. The standard glass, 3 by 6 ft. hotbed sash is ordinarily used as a covering for the frame, although lightweight, less expensive coverings can be made, utilizing frames covered with one of the flexible glass substitutes. The covered frames should fit tightly in order to retain heat and to obtain high humidity conditions. Cold frames should be placed in locations protected from winds, with the sash covering sloping from north to south.

Figure 2–4. A series of cold frames on the south side of a greenhouse. Hotbed construction would be similar except that provision would be made for bottom heat.

A primary use of these structures is in conditioning or hardening rooted cuttings or young seedlings preceding field, nursery-row, or container planting. They may also be used for starting new plants in late spring, summer, or fall when no artificial supply of heat is necessary. In cold frames only the heat of the sun is utilized, which is retained by the glass covering.

Close attention to ventilation, shading, watering, and winter protection is necessary for success with cold frames. When young, tender plants are first placed in a cold frame, the coverings would probably be kept closed tightly to maintain a high humidity, but as the plants become adjusted, the sash frames can be gradually raised to permit more ventilation and dryer conditions. Frequent sprinkling of the plants in a cold frame is essential to maintain humid conditions. During sunny weather, temperatures can build up to excessively high levels in closed frames unless some ventilation and shading is given. Spaced lath, muslin-covered frames, or reed mats are useful to lay over the glass sash to provide protection from the sun.

Plants being over-wintered in cold frames may require additional protective coverings in areas where extremely low temperatures occur.

Lathhouses

These structures are very useful in providing protection from the sun in handling container-grown nursery stock, especially in areas of high summer temperatures and high light intensity. Although protection is particularly important just after transplanting, well-established plants also require much less hand watering when grown in lathhouses. In holding shade-loving plants for any length of time, a lathhouse is almost a necessity. Such structures are also valuable in hardening certain tender species as an intermediate step between the cold frame and field planting. Removable types are often convenient, especially in the northern regions, to compensate for changing light conditions.

Lathhouse construction varies widely. Aluminum prefabricated lathhouses are available but may be more costly than wood structures. More commonly, wood or 2 in. pipe supports are used, set in concrete with the

Figure 2–5. Young plants in gallon containers in a lathhouse. Watering is by overhead, rotating sprinkler irrigation as indicated by arrows.

necessary supporting cross-members placed at a height of 7 or 8 ft. Shade is provided by 1 by 2 in. wood strips set about 2 in. apart. The sides as well as the top are usually covered. Rolls of snow fencing attached to a supporting framework can be utilized for relatively inexpensive construction. A woven plastic material—saran fabric—is widely used also in covering structures to provide shade. This material is available in different densities, thus allowing various intensities of light on the plants. It is lightweight and can be attached to heavy wire fastened to supporting posts.

Miscellaneous Propagating Structures

Mist beds for leafy cuttings. These are valuable propagating units, both in the greenhouse and out-of-doors, and are useful principally in rooting leafy cuttings. Mist propagation is discussed in Chapters 9 and 10.

Fluorescent light boxes. Young plants of many species grow satisfactorily under the artificial light from fluorescent lamp units. Sufficient light is available from these units, too, for starting young seedlings and rooting cuttings of many plant species. By enclosing the lamps in boxes, it is possible to maintain higher humidity (26, 27, 28). The "white" fluorescent tubes are generally preferable to the "daylight" color. In some basement rooms which have a fairly high humidity, a closed case may be unnecessary. The lamp fixture can be suspended over a table on which the flats of cuttings are placed. With such equipment it is often helpful to provide bottom heat, either from thermostatically controlled soil-heating cables or by the use of a socket heater or a lamp in the air space below the rooting medium. Although adequate rooting of many plant species may be obtained under fluorescent lamps, in general it is unlikely that the results will equal or surpass those obtained under proper greenhouse conditions (7).

Propagating cases. Even in a greenhouse, humidity conditions are often not sufficiently high to permit satisfactory rooting of leafy cuttings. The use of enclosed frames or cases covered with glass or glass substitutes may be necessary for successful rooting. There are many variations of such devices, sometimes called Wardian cases. Polyethylene plastic sheeting is an excellent lightweight cover for enclosing a simple framework. Such cases are also useful as a place to set completed grafts of small potted nursery stock, enabling the retention of high humidity conditions during the callusing process. In earlier days, bell jars were commonly used in propagation. These are large inverted glass jars set over a container of cuttings to be rooted. Humidity can be kept very high in such a device but attention is necessary to provide shading from the sun and to allow ventilation as soon as rooting starts.

In using such structures, great care is necessary to avoid the buildup of disease organisms. The warm, humid conditions, combined with lack of air movement and the relatively low light intensity, provide excellent conditions for the growth of various fungi and bacteria. Spraying with fungicides and disinfectants is often necessary.

Figure 2–6. Small polyethylene bags are suitable plant containers for easily-rooting species. Holes are cut in the bottoms to permit drainage. **(above)** A flat of these bags filled with vermiculite, each containing a chrysanthemum cutting. **(below, left)** Appearance of two bags of cuttings after 30 days under intermittent mist. **(right)** Root system formed on the cuttings in this time.

Plastic. Strips of polyethylene plastic can sometimes be utilized in starting cuttings of easily rooted species. Cuttings are rolled in strips filled with moist sphagnum moss and are then placed upright for rooting in a very humid location (see Figure 10–17).

Large numbers of small plastic polyethylene bags with holes punched in the bottom for drainage may be filled with a porous medium, such as vermiculite, and placed in the propagating bench with the bag tops open. A single cutting of an easily rooted species, such as chrysanthemum, is placed in each bag. These may then be rooted under mist (see p. 251) and even fertilized with a nutrient solution injected into the mist. When rooted, the plants are removed and hardened-off, then transferred in the bag for planting. This system is well adapted to certain mail order nursery operations, since the entire plant and rooting medium can be shipped at low cost.

MEDIA FOR PROPAGATING AND GROWING CONTAINER STOCK

There are several media and mixtures of different media that are widely used in propagation, not only in germinating seeds and rooting cuttings, but in growing container stock. All such media have several properties in common. (a) The medium must be sufficiently firm and dense to hold the cuttings or seeds in place during rooting or germination. Its volume must be fairly constant when either wet or dry. That is, excessive shrinkage after drying is undesirable. (b) It must be sufficiently retentive of moisture so that watering does not have to be too frequent. (c) It must be sufficiently porous so that excess water drains away permitting adequate aeration. (d) It must be relatively free from weed seeds, nematodes, and various noxious disease organisms. (e) It must have a pH level (pH is a measure of relative acidity or alkalinity) suitable for the plant being propagated or grown.

Soil

A soil is composed of materials in the solid, liquid, and gaseous state. For satisfactory plant growth these materials must exist in the proper proportions.

The solid portion of a soil is comprised of both inorganic and organic forms. The inorganic part consists of the residue from parent rock after decomposition due to the chemical and physical processes of weathering. Such inorganic components vary in size from gravel down to extremely minute colloidal particles of clay, the texture of the soil being determined by the relative proportions of particles of different size. The coarser-sized particles serve mainly as a supporting framework for the remainder of the soil, whereas the colloidal clay fractions of the soil serve as storehouses for nutrients which may be absorbed by plants. The organic portion of the soil consists of both living and dead organisms. Insects, worms, fungi, bacteria, and plant roots generally constitute the living organic matter, whereas the remains of such animal and plant life in various stages of decay make up the dead organic material. The residue from such decay (termed *humus*) is largely colloidal and assists in holding the water and plant nutrients.

The liquid part of the soil, the soil solution, is made up of water containing dissolved minerals in various quantities, as well as oxygen and carbon dioxide. Mineral elements, nitrogen, water, and possibly some carbon dioxide enter the plant from the soil solution.

The gaseous portion of the soil is important to good plant growth. In poorly drained, waterlogged soils, water replaces the air in the soil, thus depriving plant roots as well as certain desirable aerobic microorganisms of the oxygen necessary for their existence.

The texture of a soil will depend upon the relative proportions of *sand* (2 to 0.05 mm. in particle diameter), *silt* (0.05 to 0.002 mm. in particle diameter), and *clay* (less than 0.002 mm. in particle diameter). The principal texture classes are sand, loamy sand, sandy loam, silt loam, clay loam, and clay. A typical sandy loam might consist of 75 per cent sand, 14 per cent silt, and 11 per cent clay; whereas a clay loam might have 34 per cent sand, 39 per cent silt, and 27 per cent clay.

In contrast to *soil texture,* which refers to the individual soil particles, *soil structure* refers to the arrangement of those particles in the entire soil mass. These individual soil grains are held together in aggregates of various sizes and shapes. Maintenance of a favorable granular and crumb soil structure is very important. For example, working heavy clay soils when they are too wet can so change the soil structure that the heavy clods formed may remain for years.

Sand

Sand consists of small rock grains, from about 0.05 to 2.0 mm. in diameter, formed as the result of the weathering of various rocks, its mineral composition depending upon the type of rock. Quartz sand is generally used for propagation purposes, consisting chiefly of a silica complex. The type used in plastering is the grade ordinarily the most satisfactory for rooting cuttings.

Peat

Peat consists of the remains of aquatic, marsh, bog, or swamp vegetation which has been preserved under water in a partially decomposed state. Composition of different peat deposits varies widely, depending upon the vegetation from which it originated, state of decomposition, mineral content, and degree of acidity.

The light brown or yellowish brown fibrous types consist of the remains of moss, reeds, or sedges, and are usually quite acid in reaction. The brown to black, partially fibrous types are woody, lumpy, or granular and range from very acid to somewhat alkaline.

Surface layers and cultivated peat soils in an advanced state of decomposition in which plant remains are difficult to identify are generally termed "muck."

Baled peat moss as sold commercially in the United States is the brown, fibrous type. It has a very high water-holding capacity, contains some nitrogen—a little over 1 per cent—but is low in phosphorus and potassium. When peat moss is to be used in mixtures it should be broken apart and moistened well before adding to the mixture.

Sphagnum Moss

Commercial sphagnum moss is the dehydrated remains of such acid-bog plants as *Sphagnum papillosum* and *S. palustre*. It is relatively sterile, light in weight, and has a very high water-holding capacity, being able to absorb ten to twenty times its weight of water. The stem and leaf tissues of sphagnum moss consist largely of groups of water-holding cells. This material is generally shredded, either by hand or mechanically, before it is used as a propagating medium. It contains such small amounts of minerals that plants grown in it for any length of time require added nutrients.

Vermiculite

This is a micaceous mineral which expands markedly when heated. Chemically, it is a hydrated magnesium-aluminum-iron silicate. Extensive deposits in the United States are found in Montana and South Carolina. It is very light in weight (6 to 10 lbs. per cu. ft.), neutral in reaction, and insoluble in water, but it is able to absorb large quantities of water—3 to 4 gals. per cu. ft. In the crude vermiculite ore, the particles consist of thousands of very thin, separate layers which have microscopic quantities of water trapped between them. When run through furnaces at temperatures near 2000°F., the water turns to steam, popping the layers apart, forming small, porous, sponge-like kernels. Heating to this temperature gives complete sterilization. Expanded vermiculite is graded to four sizes: No. 1 has particles from 5 to 8 mm. in diameter; No. 2 from 2 to 3 mm.; No. 3 from 1 to 2 mm.; and No. 4 from 0.75 to 1 mm. Expanded vermiculite should not be pressed or compacted in any way when wet, because its desirable porous structure will be destroyed.

Perlite

This gray-white material is of volcanic origin, mined from lava flows. The crude ore is crushed and screened then heated in furnaces where the small amount of moisture in the particles changes to steam, exploding the particles to small, sponge-like kernels. It is very light, weighing only 6 to 8 lbs. per cu. ft. The high processing temperature gives a sterile product.

Leaf Mold

Maple, oak, sycamore, and elm are among the leaf types suitable for leaf mold. In preparing such a compost, layers of leaves are mixed with thin layers of soil to which small amounts of a nitrogenous compound, such as sulfate of ammonia, have been added. The mixture should be well watered to maintain decomposition action, but protection in a shed or under canvas sheets is desirable to prevent excessive leaching during heavy winter rains. Leaf mold is ready to use 12 to 18 months after preparing. It may contain nematodes as well as weed seed and noxious insects and diseases, so it should be sterilized before using.

Shredded Bark, Sawdust, and Wood Shavings

As a by-product of lumber mills, these materials of fir or pine can be used in soil mixes, serving much the same purposes as peat moss except that their rate of decomposition is slower.

SOIL MIXTURES

In propagation procedures, young seedlings or rooted cuttings are sometimes planted directly in the field, but frequently they are planted in soil in some type of a container, such as clay flower pots or metal cans. Loam soils alone are generally unsatisfactory for this for various reasons. They are often heavy, poorly aerated, and have a low moisture-holding capacity, or tend to become sticky after watering. Upon drying they may shrink rapidly, forming a hard and cracked surface. Such soils draw away from the sides of the container during drying, and subsequent added water then runs down the inner sides of the container and out the drainage holes rather than rewetting the soil mass.

To provide potting mixtures of better textures, the addition of sand and some organic matter, such as peat moss or leaf mold, is usually practiced. In preparing these mixtures, the soil should be screened to make it uniform and to eliminate large particles. If the materials are very dry, they should be moistened slightly. This applies particularly to peat which, if once mixed when dry, will absorb moisture very slowly. The soil should not be wet and sticky, however. In mixing, the various ingredients may be placed in a pile arranged in layers and turned with a shovel. Other equipment, such as a power-driven cement mixer or soil shredder, could be used in large-scale operations. Preparation of the soil mixture should preferably take place at least a day prior to use. During the ensuing 24 hours the moisture will tend to become equalized throughout the mixture. The soil mixture should be just slightly moist at the time of use so that it does not crumble; on the other hand, it should not be sufficiently wet to form a ball when squeezed in the hand.

An ideal soil mixture should (a) have an open structure which allows good aeration and holds sufficient moisture for plant growth yet permits excess water to drain away; (b) supply adequate mineral nutrients to the plants during all stages of growth; (c) be free of all harmful organisms and toxic materials; and (d) be light in weight.

Various potting mixtures that have been used for different situations and types of plants are listed below:

1. For potting rooted cuttings and young seedlings:
    1 or 2 parts sand
    1 part loam soil
    1 part peat moss (or leaf mold)
2. For general container-grown nursery stock:
    1 part sand
    2 parts loam soil
    1 part peat moss (or leaf mold)
    ½ part well-rotted manure
3. For plants which do best under acid soil conditions such as azaleas, camellias, rhododendrons, and blueberries:
    2 parts sand
    2 parts loam soil
    2 parts peat moss
    1 part leaf mold
    ½ part well-rotted manure

The U.C. Soil Mix *(8, 16, 17, 19)*

This soil mixture was developed by the Department of Plant Pathology, University of California at Los Angeles, to provide a growing medium that could be readily prepared in large quantities for the commercial nurseryman. Since the U.C. Mix is based upon materials that are uniform, generally available, and require no previous preparation, it can be easily duplicated. The basic components are (a) an inert type of fine sand, (b) finely shredded peat moss, mixed together in varying proportions, and (c) base fertilizer mixtures as described below.

The sand is composed of rounded, wind-blown particles, uniform in size and relatively small (0.5 to 0.05 mm. in diameter), thus giving it a rather high moisture-holding capacity. Such sand does not tend to compact even though the particles are small, due to their round shape and uniformity. The absence of colloidal clay particles in sand further tends to prevent compaction or shrinkage. Any ocean beach sand of high salt content would, of course, be unsuitable for soil mixes, although satisfactory sands may be found only a short distance from beaches.

The chief purpose of the peat moss in this soil mixture is to increase its moisture and nutrient-holding capacities. In a mixture of equal parts of sand and peat moss, the maximum moisture-holding capacity is about 48 per cent.

Basic fertilizer additives recommended *(17)* for use with a mixture of 50 per cent fine sand and 50 per cent peat moss are as follows:

I. *If the mix is to be stored for an indefinite period before using.* This furnishes a moderate supply of available nitrogen, but the plants will soon require supplemental feeding. To each cubic yard of the mix add:
   4 oz. potassium nitrate
   4 oz. potassium sulfate
   2½ lb. single superphosphate
   7½ lb. dolomite lime
   2½ lb. calcium carbonate lime
II. *If the mix is to be planted within one week of preparation.* This furnishes available nitrogen as well as a moderate nitrogen reserve. To each cubic yard of the mix add:
   2½ lb. horn and hoof or blood meal (13 per cent nitrogen).
   4 oz. potassium nitrate
   4 oz. potassium sulfate
   2½ lb. single superphosphate
   7½ lb. dolomite lime
   2½ lb. calcium carbonate lime

The organic nitrogen is omitted if the mix is to be stored for a time before using, since such organic forms will break down during storage, releasing a high content of water soluble nitrogen which may cause plant injury. Other forms of organic nitrogen, such as cottonseed meal (7 per cent nitrogen) or fish tankage (6 to 10 per cent nitrogen), may be sub-stituted for the horn and hoof or blood meal provided a comparable amount of nitrogen is supplied.

In using the U.C. Mix, the fine sand, shredded peat moss, and fertilizer base must be mixed together thoroughly. The peat moss should be moistened before mixing. If the mixing is done well, the peat moss will not separate and float to the top when the mixture is saturated with water. Different combinations of the sand and peat are used; 75 per cent sand and 25 per cent peat moss is suitable for bedding plants and nursery container-grown stocks; a 50 per cent sand and 50 per cent peat is satis-factory for potted plants.

This mixture, including the fertilizer, can be safely sterilized by steam or chemicals without resulting in subsequent harmful effects to the plants that often occur when other soils or mixes are sterilized.

The John Innes Soil Mixes

Two basic soil mixtures, one for seeds and one for potting, were developed at the John Innes Horticultural Institution in England *(14)*.

The John Innes Seed Compost.
2 parts loam (by volume)
1 part peat moss (by volume)
1 part clean sand (by volume)
To each cubic yard of this mixture is added:
  2 lbs. superphosphate and
  1 lb. ground limestone

The John Innes Potting Compost.
7 parts loam (by volume)
3 parts peat moss (by volume)
2 parts clean sand (by volume)
To each cubic yard of this mixture is added:
  5 lbs. John Innes Base,* and
  1 lb. ground limestone

---

* The John Innes Base consists of:
    2 parts by weight—horn and hoof meal, 1/8 in. grist (13 per cent nitrogen)
    2 parts by weight—superphosphate of lime (18 per cent phosphoric acid)
    1 part by weight—potassium sulfate (48 per cent potash)

The loam used in the John Innes mixtures should be taken from pasture turf and cut into sections 4 to 5 in. thick and 9 by 12 in. in size. These are stacked in late spring in layers 9 in. thick, each layer interspersed with a 2 in. layer of strawy manure. The layers are well moistened as stacking proceeds until a mound 6 ft. high and 6 to 8 ft. in size is formed. The stack is covered to keep off rain. Decomposition continues for about 6 months. In using, the stack is cut through from top to bottom which tends to minimize variation. The most desirable sand is one in which 60 to 70 per cent of the particles are between $\frac{1}{8}$ and $\frac{1}{16}$ in. in size. Before the compost mixture is made up, the basic loam and peat moss should be sterilized.

SOIL "STERILIZATION" (9, 23)

Soils may contain weed seeds, nematodes, and certain fungi and bacteria harmful to plant tissue. The so-called "damping off" commonly encountered in seed-beds is caused by soil fungi, such as species of *Pythium* and *Rhizoctonia*. To avoid loss from these pests, it is desirable to sterilize the soil or soil mixture before it is used for growing plants. Along with soil sterilization, use of noninfected plants, treatment of seeds with fungicides (see p. 134), disinfection of flats, greenhouse benches, soil bins, tools, and general cleanliness are also necessary to avoid recontamination. It is useless to put sterile soil in contaminated containers. Tools can be sterilized by soaking in some disinfectant such as 1 per cent carbolic acid, 2 per cent formaldehyde, rubbing alcohol, or even boiling water. Flats and benches can be sterilized with live steam, or drenched with boiling water, 2 per cent formaldehyde, or copper naphthenate.

Although the term soil "sterilization" is established by common usage, a more accurate word is "pasteurization," since during the recommended processes all organisms are not killed.

Soil sterilization can be accomplished by heat or by chemicals.

Heating soil mixes high in manure, leaf mold, or compost will hasten decomposition of the organic matter, especially if it is already partially rotted. This leads to the formation of compounds toxic to plant growth, necessitating leaching with water or a 3 to 6 weeks delay in planting. Undecomposed materials like the brown types of peat moss are relatively unaffected, however.

Certain of the complex chemical compounds in the soil are also broken down by excessive heat (above 185°F.), yielding increased amounts of soluble salts of nitrogen, manganese, phosphorus, potassium and others. Some, particularly nitrogen in the form of ammonia, may be present during the first few weeks after steaming in such quantities as to be toxic to the plants. Later, the ammonia is converted to nitrate nitrogen, which reaches a peak in about 6 weeks. The presence of superphosphate in the soil mix ties up the excessive manganese released during sterilization, preventing injury from manganese toxicity.

Soil Sterilization by Heat (1, 2, 3)

Steam is the most common heat source for soil sterilization. In fact, steam is probably the best means of sterilizing soil. The moist heat is advantageous, and it can be injected directly into the soil in covered bins or benches from perforated pipes placed 6 to 8 in. below the surface. In heating the soil, which should be moist but not wet, a temperature of 180°F. for 30 minutes is recommended, since this will kill most harmful bacteria and fungi as well as nematodes, insects, and weed seeds. Under pressure, however, temperatures harmful to the soil can be reached, e.g., 250°F. at 15 lbs. pressure, and should be avoided.

Other heat sources can be used. Small quantities of moist soil may be heated in the oven of the home cooking stove if adequate thermostatic temperature control is available to prevent excessive heating. Portable oil-burning continuous flash-flame soil pasteurizers have been developed (22) which will process 2 cu. yd. of soil per hour. Various kinds of electric soil sterilizing devices have been used. Probably the safest and most satisfactory are the indirect types in which a heating element is used containing covered resistance wires so spaced as to heat the soil mass to the desired temperature (21). Boiling water can be used to sterilize soil if a sufficient volume is applied to raise the temperature of the soil mass to at least 160°F. In this method, however, it is difficult to obtain uniform and thorough sterilization, and the treated soil becomes puddled, requiring a week or so of drying before it is suitable to use.

Soil Sterilization by Chemicals (20)

Chemical sterilization will kill organisms in the soil without disrupting the physical and chemical nature of the soil to the extent which often occurs with heat treatments. Ammonia production may increase following chemical sterilization, however, due to the removal of organisms antagonistic to the ammonifying bacteria. The soils should be moist and at temperatures of 65° to 75°F. for satisfactory chemical sterilization.

Formaldehyde. This is a good fungicide with strong penetrating powers. It also will kill some weed seeds, but is not a completely reliable nematicide. A mixture of 1 gal. of commercial formalin (40 per cent strength) to 50 gal. of water is applied to the soil at the rate of 2 to 4 qts. per sq. ft. (or 1 gal. per bu. of soil). The treated area should be covered immediately with an air tight material and left for 24 hours or more. Following this treatment, about 2 weeks should be allowed for drying and airing, but the soil should not be planted until all odor of formaldehyde has disappeared.

For small scale treatments, commercial formalin can be applied at a rate of 2½ tbs. per bu. of a light soil mixture or 1 tbs. per standard size flat. Dilute with five to six parts of water, apply to soil, and mix thoroughly. Let stand 24 hours, plant seeds, and water thoroughly.

Chloropicrin (Tear gas). This is a liquid ordinarily applied with an injector which should put 2 to 4 cc. in holes 3 to 6 in. deep, spaced 9 to 12 in. apart. It may also be applied at the rate of 5 cc. per cu. ft. of soil.

Chloropicrin changes to a gas which penetrates through the soil. The gas should be confined by sprinkling the soil surface with water and then covering it with an airtight material which is left for 3 days. Seven to 10 days is required for thorough aeration of the soil after the cover is removed before it can be planted. Chloropicrin is effective against nematodes, insects, most weed seeds, and all but the most resistant fungi. It should be used in moderately moist soils and at temperatures above 65°F. Chloropicrin fumes are very toxic to living plant tissue.

Methyl bromide *(15)*. This odorless material is very volatile and very toxic to humans; a gas mask should be worn when using it, or else ventilation conditions should be excellent. Nematodes, insects, most weed seeds, and most fungi are killed by methyl bromide. It is often used by injecting the material at 4 lbs. per 100 sq. ft. from pressurized containers into an open vessel under a plastic cover placed over the soil to be treated. The cover is sealed around the edges with soil, and should be kept in place for 48 hours. Penetration is very good, and the sterilization effect will extend to a depth of 12 in. For treating bulk soil, methyl bromide at 10 cc. per cu. ft. or 4 lbs. per 100 cu. ft., can be used. Methyl bromide is available mixed with other materials. Dowfume MC-2 contains 98 per cent methyl bromide and 2 per cent chloropicrin, which serves as a warning agent. Iscobrome contains 15 per cent methyl bromide in xylol.

Vapam (sodium N-methyl dithiocarbamate dihydrate). This is a water soluble soil fumigant which will kill weeds, germinating weed seeds, most soil fungi and, under the proper conditions, nematodes. It undergoes rapid decomposition to produce a very penetrating gas. Vapam is applied by sprinkling on the soil surface, through irrigation systems, or with standard injection equipment. For seed-bed fumigation, 1 qt. of the liquid formulation of Vapam in 2 to 3 gals. of water is used, sprinkled uniformly over 100 sq. ft. of area. After application, the Vapam is sealed with additional water or with a roller. Two weeks after application the soil can be planted. Although it has a relatively low toxicity to man, care should be taken to avoid inhaling fumes or splashing the solution on the skin.

SUPPLEMENTARY NUTRITIVE ADDITIVES

Even with a good soil mixture, complete with added mineral nutrient components, continued growth of plants in containers necessitates the addition at intervals of supplementary minerals, especially nitrogen.

A satisfactory feeding program for growing container stock is to combine a slowly available dry fertilizer, added once or twice a year, preferably in late fall, with a liquid fertilizer applied at frequent intervals through the growing season.

Suitable organic fertilizers for supplying nitrogen are blood meal or horn and hoof meal applied at a rate of about 1 heaping tsp. for a plant growing in a 1 gal. container. Twice this amount of cottonseed meal should be used.

To supply nitrogen, phosphorus, and potassium in dry form, 2 heaping tsps. of the following mixture is recommended *(17)* for plants growing in 1 gal. containers:

> 4 lbs. horn and hoof or blood meal
> 4 lbs. single superphosphate
> 1 lb. potassium sulfate or chloride

As a supplement to this, a dilute inorganic nutrient feeding at weekly intervals throughout the growing season is desirable. A simple solution may be prepared by dissolving 1 tsp. of potassium nitrate and one of ammonium nitrate in a gallon of water. Adding 2 tsps. of a mixed fertilizer, as 10-6-4, to a gallon of water will also make a satisfactory solution. Unless labeled "biuret-free," urea-containing formulations may not be suitable to use in fertilizing container-grown plants. Biuret is quite toxic, especially to conifers, ericaceous plants, pineapple, and citrus *(17, 30);* typical symptoms are leaf burning, chlorosis, and stunted growth.

Nutrient solution for fertilizing container-grown plants:

water	25 gals.
ammonium nitrate	2 ozs.
mono-ammonium phosphate	2 ozs.
potassium chloride	2 ozs.

For large scale operations, it may be more feasible to prepare a liquid concentrate and inject it into the regular watering or irrigating system by the use of a proportioner. For this, a nutrient concentrate formula such as follows could be used.

water	10 gals.
ammonium nitrate	15 lbs.
mono-ammonium phosphate	4 lbs.
potassium chloride	6 lbs.

The above chemicals should be thoroughly dissolved. *This concentrate should then be diluted—1 part to 200 parts water—before applying to the plants.*

CONTAINERS FOR GROWING YOUNG PLANTS

Flats. These are essentially shallow wood or metal trays, with drainage holes in the bottom. They are very useful for germinating seeds or rooting cuttings, since they permit young plants to be moved around easily when this is required. Standard sizes are 16 by 23 in., 11½ by 16 in., and 18 in. sq. Durable wood, such as cypress, cedar, or redwood should be used for flats. Other woods are best treated with a preservative, such as copper naphthenate, to prevent rapid decay. Metal, galvanized-iron flats are available in various sizes. They are durable, long lasting, lightweight, and will nest, thus requiring relatively little storage space.

Clay pots. The familiar red clay flower pots, although widely used in growing young plants, are far from being the ideal plant container. They are porous, lose moisture readily, and are heavy. In addition, they are easily broken, and their round shape is not economical of space. After continued use, toxic salt accumulations build up requiring soaking in water before re-use.

Plastic and aluminum pots. Although somewhat more expensive than clay pots, they have numerous advantages. They are light in weight, use little storage space, and are nonporous. They are fragile, however, and require careful handling. In aluminum pots, roots tend to grow into the creases inside the pot and cause difficulty in "knocking out" the plant and soil.

Peat fiber pots. Small pots 2 to 4 in. in size are available, pressed into shape from peat. They are completely dry and will keep indefinitely. Such pots are set in the soil right with the plant, thus acting as a fertilizer for the growing plant.

Plant bands. These are made of spruce veneer, available in various sizes, such as 2 by 2 in. up to 4 by 4 in. by 3 in. deep. They are usually set up in flats or benches and permit growing and transferring young plants individually. Plant bands may be treated with preservatives or may be impregnated with soluble nutrients which dissolve out into the soil mixture. Their square shape permits maximum utilization of space.

Paraffined paper cups. When these are punched with drainage holes they make satisfactory temporary containers for growing and transferring young plants. They are cheap, light weight, and require little storage space.

Asphalt-coated felt paper containers. These are available commercially in a number of sizes and are suitable temporary plant containers. They are inexpensive, sturdy, lightweight, and easily nested. Such containers can be easily constructed from asphalt-treated building paper, shaping the correct size paper pieces into square, open bottom cups by placing them in removable "egg-crate" cells in a flat *(12)*.

Metal containers *(13)*. Hundreds of thousands of nursery plants are grown and marketed each year in 1 gal.—and to a lesser extent—in 3 gal. cans, especially in California, Florida, and Texas. Generally, these are used containers salvaged from canneries, large restaurants, bakeries, and so forth. Such cans are also available especially prepared for growing plants. One type is crimped and tapered for nesting, and has drainage holes punched. They are enameled, which retards rusting. Machine planters

Figure 2–7. Simple type of open-bottom temporary plant container made from felt building paper. (above) Squares of paper are rolled and inserted into forms. Squared forming pegs give the containers a rectangular shape. (below) Containers are filled with a potting mixture, the metal form is removed, and young plants are inserted with a wooden dibble. Courtesy California State Division of Forestry Nursery, Davis, California.

have been developed utilizing such containers in which rooted cuttings or seedlings can be planted as rapidly as 10,000 a day. Plants are easily removed from such tapered containers by inverting and tapping. Untapered metal containers must be cut down each side with can shears or tin snips to permit removal of the plant.

Figure 2–8. Types of containers for growing small nursery plants. **(above, left to right)** Paraffined paper cups, plant bands, aluminum foil pots, square plastic pots, round plastic pots. **(below, left to right)** Peat fiber pots, gallon crimped metal pot, felt paper pot.

HANDLING CONTAINER-GROWN PLANTS

Watering of container-grown nursery stock is a major expense. Hand watering of individual cans with a large-volume, low pressure applicator on a hose several times a week is probably the best method. In some large operations overhead or travelling sprinklers are used. These are more economical but do not give as uniform results as hand watering.

In areas with severe winters, although growing nursery plants in containers is feasible, more attention must be given to the problems of winter injury. The amount of injury will vary with the species, the less hardy ones generally requiring some type of mulch around the containers to protect the roots, especially from rapidly fluctuating variations in the winter temperatures. The chances of cold injury can be lessened by having the plants well established in the containers before the onset of winter. In addition, setting the plants close together in large groups will tend to prevent the damaging rapid fluctuation of temperature.

The practice of growing and selling nursery stock in containers has much to recommend it to nurserymen. Such operations are well adapted to large scale standardization and mechanization. Nursery stock in containers is easily transported—an ordinary semi-trailer truck can load about 5000 plants in gallon containers. Plants are available to consumers at any time of the year; flowering shrubs may be offered for sale during their attractive blooming period rather than as dormant, bare-root stock. The plants are not disturbed and can be transplanted without any setback, which often occurs with balled and burlapped or bare-root stock. Rather than destroying excess quantities of some bare-root stock in the spring, the plants can be put in containers and sold during the growing season, thus greatly extending the marketing period.

REFERENCES

1. Baker, K. F., and C. N. Roistacher, Heat treatment of soil. Sect. 8 in *Calif. Agr. Exp. Sta. Man. 23,* 1957.

2. ———, Principles of heat treatment of soil. Sec. 9 in *Calif. Agr. Exp. Sta. Man. 23,* 1957.

3. ———, Equipment for heat treatment of soil. Sec. 10 in *Calif. Agr. Exp. Sta. Man. 23,* 1957.

4. Beattie, W. R., Hotbeds and cold frames, *USDA Farmers' Bul.,* 1743. 1935.

5. Beattie, J. H., Greenhouse construction and heating, *USDA Farmers' Bul.,* 1318. 1952.

6. Bouquet, A. G. B., Greenhouse management, *Ore. Ext. Cir. 499,* 1948.

7. Chadwick, L. C., Some results with the use of opaque structures for propagation by cuttings, *Proc. Amer. Soc. Hort. Sci.,* 53:567–572. 1949.

8. Chandler, P. A., The U.C. soil mix for nurseries in California, *Pac. Coast Nurseryman,* 11(1):15, 40–42. 1952.

9. Dimond, A. E., Simple procedures reduce losses from plant diseases, *Amer. Nurseryman,* 98(4):12, 76–82. 1953.

10. Emmert, E. M., Low cost plastic greenhouses, *Ky. Agr. Exp. Sta. Prog. Rpt. 28,* 1955.

11. Gray, H. E., Greenhouse heating, *Cornell Univ. Agr. Exp. Sta. Bul. 906,* 1954.

12. Herbert, F. W., and O. K. Hoglund., An improved method of making plant containers, *USDA Soil Cons. Serv. Leaflet 349,* 1953.

13. Hill, J., Plantainer growing, Hill Stock Farm, Dundee, Illinois. 1956.

14. Lawrence, W. J. C., and J. Newell, *Seed and Potting Composts.* London: Allen and Unwin, 1950.

15. Lear, B., Use of methyl bromide and other volatile chemicals for soil fumigation, *Cornell Univ. Agr. Exp. Sta. Mem. 303,* 1951.

16. Matkin, O. A., Prepared soils for container growing, *Proc. 5th Ann. Mtg. Plant Prop. Soc.,* pp. 108–113. 1955.

17. Matkin, O. A., and P. A. Chandler, The U.C. type soil mixes. Sect. 5 in *Calif. Agr. Exp. Sta. Man. 23,* 1957.

18. Moses, B. D., and J. R. Tavernetti, Electric heat for propagating and growing plants, *Calif. Agr. Exp. Sta. Cir. 335,* 1934.

19. Munnecke, D. E., and P. A. Chandler, Plants do better in treated soil, *Pac. Coast Nurseryman,* 14(9):30, 92–93. 1955.

20. Munnecke, D. E., Chemical treatment of nursery soils. Sect. 11 in *Calif. Agr. Exp. Sta. Man. 23,* 1957.

21. Newhall, A. G., Experiments with new electric devices for pasteurizing soils, *Cornell Univ. Agr. Exp. Sta. Bul. 731,* 1940.

22. Newhall, A. G., and W. T. Schroeder. New flash-flame soil pasteurizer, *Cornell Univ. Agr. Exp. Sta. Bul. 875,* 1951.

23. Newhall, A. G., and C. Chupp, Soil treatments for control of diseases in the greenhouse and the seed bed, *N. Y. Agr. Exp. Sta. Ext. Bul. 217,* 1931.

24. Post, K., Structures for starting and growing ornamental plants, *Cornell Ext. Bul. 468,* 1941.

25. Shoemaker, J. S., and A. C. Paterson, Hot beds, cold frames, and small greenhouses, *Univ. Alberta (Canada) Bul. 33,* 1940.

26. Stoutemyer, V. T., A. W. Close, and F. L. O'Rourke, Rooting greenwood cuttings without sunlight under fluorescent lamps, *Science,* 101(2639):546. 1945.

27. Stoutemyer, V. T., and A. W. Close, Rooting cuttings and germinating seeds under fluorescent and cold cathode lighting, *Proc. Amer. Soc. Hort. Sci.,* 48:309–325. 1946.

28. ———, Plant propagation under fluorescent lamps, *USDA Mimeo. Leaflet* (revised), March, 1946.

29. Ward, W. B., Hot bed construction and management, *Purdue Agr. Ext. Bul. 270,* 1952.

30. Webster, G. C., R. A. Berner, and A. N. Gansa, The effect of biuret on protein synthesis in plants, *Plant Phys.,* 32:60–61. 1957.

31. Widmoyer, F. B., and D. P. Watson, Use of a polyethylene greenhouse for rooting softwood cuttings, *Quart. Bul. Mich. Agr. Exp. Sta.,* 38:350–352. 1956.

• **Supplementary Reading**

Baker, K. F., ed., "The U.C. System for Producing Healthy Container-Grown Plants," *California Agricultural Experiment Station Manual 23,* (1957).

Duruz, W. P., *Principles of Nursery Management,* 2nd ed. New York: De La Mare, 1953.

Laurie, A., D. C. Kiplinger, and K. S. Nelson, *Commercial Flower Forcing,* 6th ed. Philadelphia: Blakiston, 1958.

Lawrence, W. J. C., *Soil Sterilization,* London: Allen and Unwin, 1956.

Post, K., *Florist Crop Production and Marketing,* New York: Orange-Judd, 1949.

Preston, F. G., *The Greenhouse,* London: Ward, Lock, 1951.

II

SEXUAL PROPAGATION

3 | The Development of Fruits and Seeds

PRODUCTION OF THE FLOWER

The life cycle of a seed-bearing plant can be divided into two broad phases—vegetative and reproductive. The seed is the end result of consecutive vegetative and reproductive stages taking place in the plant. The general sequence of steps which takes place during this cycle is the following: (a) germination of the seed; (b) vegetative growth; (c) flower bud induction; (d) flower bud initiation and development; (e) flowering—development of the male and female gametophyte, enlargement and opening of the flower, pollination, fertilization; (f) fruit and seed development; and (g) ripening of the fruit and dissemination of the seeds.

When a plant first grows from a seed it is vegetative, the predominant processes being the elongation of the stem and roots and the increase in plant volume. An individual may begin also as a rooted cutting or a grafted or a budded plant. In general, the same sequence would follow as with a seedling, although the duration of the vegetative period may be less.

The physiology of a young seedling plant differs from that of a mature plant. This is shown in some cases by the greater tendency of cuttings taken from young plants to initiate adventitious roots than those taken from older plants. In some plants, the difference in the internal state is also manifested by striking differences in morphological characters, such as differences in leaf shape or greater thorniness in younger plants. This immature condition is referred to as *juvenility (23)*. It is particularly im-

Figure 3–1. Juvenility is expressed in **Acacia melanoxylon** seedlings by leaf characteristics. The bi-pinnate leaves at the base of the seedling are characteristic of the juvenile condition; the "leaves," which are actually expanded petioles **(phyllodia)**, at the top of the seedling are characteristic of the mature form. Note the gradual change in this seedling from the juvenile to mature form.

portant in propagation by cuttings and is considered in greater detail in Chapter 9.

The vegetative period may last for only a few days or weeks in some plants, whereas in others it may persist for years. Eventually vegetative growth decreases, the reproductive phase begins, and the growing points initiate flower buds. This change may come when the plant has reached a specific age or size or as a specific response to certain environmental stimuli, particularly photoperiod or temperature. It may also be induced in woody plants by certain horticultural manipulations, as girdling, pinching or heading-back shoots, grafting or root pruning.

PRODUCTION OF THE EMBRYO

The embryo develops as a result of the union of male and female gametes. Details of the sexual cycle in plants are shown diagrammatically in Figure 1–5.

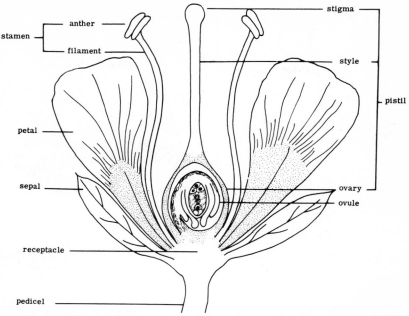

Figure 3–2. Diagrammatical sketch showing typical flower structure of an angiospermous plant.

To produce a viable seed, both pollination and fertilization must take place. In some cases, however, the fruit may mature and contain only shriveled and empty seed coats with no embryo or, if present, one that is thin and shrunken. The presence of such seeds will reduce the germination percentage of a given seed lot.

Such "seedlessness" may result from several causes: (a) *parthenocarpy,* the development of the fruit without fertilization; (b) *embryo abortion,* the death of the embryo during its development; and (c) the inability of the embryo to accumulate sufficient food reserves. If embryo abortion occurs early, it is most likely that the fruit will drop immediately or will not grow to a large size *(21, 30).*

APOMIXIS

Although a seed is generally produced by sexual reproduction, certain cases exist whereby an embryo is produced by an asexual process and not as a result of meiosis and fertilization. This is significant in that individual plants can thus be reproduced as clones by seed propagation in essentially the same manner as they would by budding, grafting, or by cuttings. The

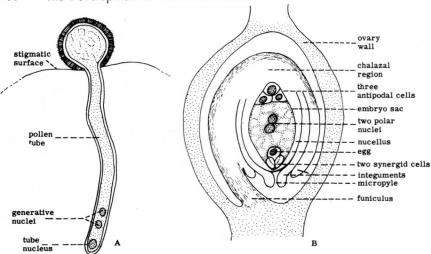

Figure 3–3. (A) Pollen grain germinating on stigma. **(B)** Ovule structure showing a mature embryo sac with its eight nuclei. In angiospermous plants one of the generative nuclei of the pollen grain combines with the egg nucleus to form the zygote; the other combines with the two polar nuclei to form the endosperm.

general phenomenon in which an asexual reproductive process occurs in place of the normal sexual reproductive process of reduction division and fertilization is known as *apomixis*. Seedlings produced in this manner are known as *apomicts*.

Types of Apomixis

Apomixis has been classified into four main types *(18)*:

Recurrent apomixis. Here the female gametophyte develops in a seemingly normal fashion except no meiosis takes place. It may originate from the egg mother-cell, as in guayule *(19)*, or from another cell of the nucellus, the egg mother-cell disintegrating, as described for *Malus hupehensis (8)*. The embryo develops directly from the egg nucleus without fertilization. Although this chain of events can occur in some cases without the stimulus of pollination, usually pollination is necessary. The single embryo will be genetically identical with the parent plant within which it is borne.

Adventitious embryony (also known as *nucellar embryony* or *nucellar budding*). This type of apomixis differs from the first in that the apomictic embryos do not arise from a gametophyte but from a cell or group of cells either in the nucellus (usually) or the integuments. A number of apomictic embryos may develop within the same ovule. A sexual embryo may also develop at the same time by the normal reproductive processes of reduction division, and fertilization. Consequently, at maturity the seed may

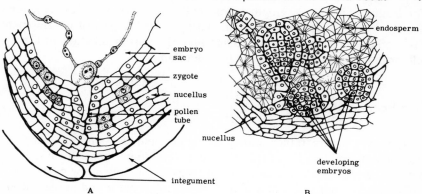

Figure 3–4. The development of nucellar embryos in **Citrus. (A)** Stage of development just after fertilization showing zygote and remains of pollen tube. Note individual active cells (those shaded) of the nucellus which are in the initial stages of nucellar embryony. **(B)** A later stage showing developing nucellar embryos. The large one may be a sexual embryo. Redrawn from Gustafsson. **(12)**

contain one, two, or more embryos enclosed within a single seed coat, only one of which would be a true sexual embryo and the others nucellar embryos.

Nonrecurrent apomixis. In this case, an embryo arises directly from the egg nucleus without fertilization. Since the egg is haploid, the resulting embryo will also be haploid. This case is rare and primarily of genetic interest. It does not consistently occur in any particular kind of plant as do recurrent apomixis and adventitious embryony.

Vegetative apomixis. In some cases vegetative buds or *bulbils* are produced in the inflorescence in the place of flowers. This occurs in *Poa bulbosa* and some *Allium, Agave,* and grass species.

Polyembryony

When two or more embryos are present within a single seed, the phenomenon is referred to as *polyembryony*. One of the important reasons for this occurrence is nucellar embryony. However, this is not the only cause.

Figure 3–5. Polyembryony in. **Citrus** seeds as indicated by two seedlings from each seed. One or both could be a nucellar seedling.

For instance, in the development of conifer embryos it is common for a cleavage of the proembryo to occur during the early part of development. Also, other nuclei in the embryo sac may develop in addition to the egg cell, or more than one embryo sac may develop.

Significance of Apomixis

Apomixis occurs rather widely in nature and is found in many different plant families (12, 22). It exists in several important cultivated plants but has been utilized as a means of propagation in only a few cases.

Outstanding horticultural examples of apomixis are found in the nucellar embryony of citrus, apple, and mango. Some grass species are at least partially apomictic. For instance, Kentucky bluegrass (*Poa pratensis*) consists of both apomictic and sexually-reproduced individuals. In one study involving a group of Kentucky bluegrass plants collected from various sources, 85 per cent were found to be apomictically reproduced (3).

FRUIT AND SEED DEVELOPMENT

Morphological Development

The relationship between the structure of the flower and the structure of the fruit and seed is as follows:

Ovary .... > fruit (sometimes additional tissues make up part of the mature fruit)

  Ovule .... > seed:

    integuments .... > testa (seed coats)

    nucellus .... > perisperm (usually absent or reduced)

    polar nuclei (2) +
      sperm nucleus .... > endosperm

    egg nucleus + sperm
      nucleus ..... > zygote ..... > embryo

Figures 3–6 and 3–7 show the relationships between the growth of the different parts of a seed and fruit. The embryo is initially a microscopically small mass of cells embedded in the endosperm, which is in turn embedded in the nucellus. The endosperm appears to function in a nutritional capacity for the embryo, although there are no vascular connections between the two tissues (10). In a few kinds of seeds, the embryo is small and undeveloped in the mature seed. Usually it undergoes considerable development. Growth of the embryo is preceded by growth of the endo-

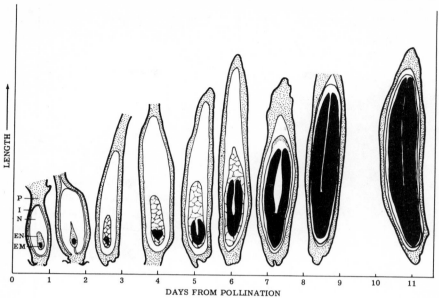

Figure 3–6. Growth of the fruit (an indehiscent achene) and seed of lettuce. P—pericarp, I—integuments, N—nucellus, EN—endosperm, EM—embryo. Redrawn from Jones (14).

sperm, which digests the inner nucellar tissue as it grows. The endosperm is in turn digested by the developing embryo. In some seeds, a large part of the endosperm is still present in the mature seed.

Sometimes the endosperm fails to properly nourish the embryo and the latter becomes abortive early in the developmental period. This phenomenon has been called *somatoplastic sterility (2)*. It commonly occurs when two genetically different individuals are hybridized, either two different species *(4, 5, 27)* or two individuals of different polyploid constitution *(6, 28)*. If such embryos are excised from the developing fruit sufficiently early and grown on a special medium (see p. 142), they can often be germinated *(1, 20)*.

Separated from the rest of the seed, a partially developed embryo does not continue to develop as an embryo (except under special cultural conditions) but begins to germinate immediately *(15, 16, 31)*. To grow into a normal seedling, it must attain a certain stage of development and must be grown in a suitable medium in which both nutritional and physical factors are supplied *(24)*. The more mature the embryo the less exacting are its requirements.

Certain external agents can prevent embryo development even though the fruit itself may continue to develop. For example, the developing seed of carrot and other Umbelliferous plants is sometimes attacked by *Lygus* bugs which can penetrate and feed on the embryo *(11, 26)*. The mature

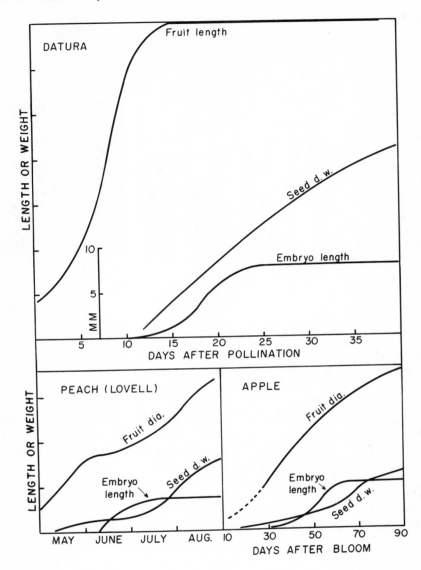

Figure 3-7. Comparative development of three different types of fruits: peach (fleshy drupe), apple (fleshy pome), and **Datura** (dry capsule). Note that changes in seed dry weight and embryo length are essentially the same for all species shown. **Datura** data from Rietsema, et al. **(25)**; apple data in part from Luckwill **(17)**.

seed is seemingly normal but contains no embryo. Cold temperatures during fruit development sometimes will kill the embryo, but the fruit itself continues to develop *(29)*.

Accumulation of Food Reserves in the Seed

The accumulation of storage materials in the seed can be measured by the changes in dry weight of the seed, although in the earlier part of the fruit development period, increase in weight may occur because of increase in size. Later, when the seed has attained its full size, the increase in dry weight is a measure of this accumulative process (25). These reserve materials originate as carbohydrates produced by photosynthesis in the leaves and translocated to the fruits and seeds where they are converted to complex storage products—carbohydrates, fats, and proteins. This process largely takes place in the later developmental period of fruit growth.

This accumulative process must take place properly if high quality seeds are to be produced. Such seeds should be plump and heavy for their size. Since the initial growth of the seedling depends upon these reserve materials, heavier seeds should result in better germination and produce more vigorous seedlings (7). If conditions interfere with this storing process so that few reserve materials accumulate, the seeds will be thin, shrunken, and light in weight. The more severe this condition, the less the seeds can survive storage periods, the poorer the germination, and the weaker are the seedlings that are produced.

Ripening and Dissemination of Seeds

Specific physical and chemical changes take place during ripening which lead to the senescence of the fruit and the dissemination of the seed. The specific criteria of seed maturity vary with different species. One of the most obvious changes is the drying of the fruit tissues. In certain fruits, this leads to dehiscence and the discharge of the seeds from the fruit. Changes may occur in the color of the fruit and the seed coats. An immature fruit is invariably green because of the presence of chlorophyll, but when the fruit ripens, the chlorophyll breaks down and may disappear so that other colors become evident as particular pigments are exposed.

THE MATURE SEED

Botanically, the seed is a matured ovule enclosed within the mature ovary, or fruit. Seeds and fruits of different species vary greatly in their appearance, size, shape, location and structure of the embryo, and the presence of storage structures. These points are useful in identification

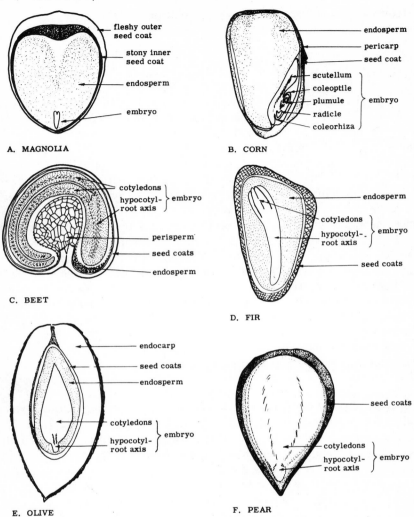

Figure 3-8. Seed structure of representative species.

(13, 19). From the standpoint of seed handling, it is not always possible to separate the fruit and seed, since they are sometimes joined in a single unit. In such cases, the fruit itself is treated as the "seed."

Parts of the Seed

The seed has three basic parts: (a) embryo, (b) food storage tissues, and (c) seed coverings.

Embryo. The embryo is a new plant resulting from the union of a male and female gamete during fertilization. Its basic structure consists of the *hypocotyl-root* axis, with growing points at each end, one for the shoot and one for the root, and one or more seed leaves (*cotyledons*) *(10)*. Plants are classified by the number of cotyledons. Monocotyledonous plants (such as the grasses or onion) have a single cotyledon, dicotyledonous plants (such as the bean or peach) have two, whereas gymnosperms (such as the pine or *Ginkgo*) may have as many as fifteen.

Storage tissues. The storage tissues of the seed may be the cotyledons, the endosperm, or the perisperm. Seeds in which the endosperm is large and contains most of the stored food are referred to as *albuminous seeds;* seeds in which the endosperm is lacking or reduced to a thin layer surrounding the embryo are referred to as *exalbuminous* seeds. In the latter case, the stored food is usually within the cotyledons, the endosperm being digested by the embryo during development. The perisperm, originating from the nucellus, occurs in only a few families of plants, such as the Chenopodiaceae and the Caryophyllaceae. Usually it is digested by the developing endosperm during seed formation.

Seed coverings. The seed coverings may consist of the seed coats, the remains of the nucellus and endosperm, and sometimes parts of the fruit. The seed coats, or *testa,* usually one or two (rarely three) in number, are derived from the integuments of the ovule. During development, the seed coats become modified and at maturity they present a characteristic appearance. Usually the outer seed coat becomes dry, somewhat hardened and thickened, and brownish or otherwise colored. On the other hand, the inner seed coat will usually be thin, transparent, and membranous. Remnants of the endosperm and nucellus are found within the inner seed coat, sometimes making a distinct, continuous layer around the embryo.

In some plants, parts of the fruit remain attached to the seed so that the fruit and seed are commonly handled together as the "seed." In certain kinds of fruits, i.e., achenes, caryopsis (grains), samaras (maple), schizocarps' (carrot), the fruit and seed layers are contiguous. In others, such as the acorn, the fruit and seed coverings separate but the fruit covering is indehiscent. In others, such as the "pit" of stone fruits or the shell of walnuts, the covering is a hardened portion of the pericarp, but it is dehiscent and can usually be removed without too much difficulty.

The seed coverings provide mechanical protection for the embryo, making it possible to handle seeds without injury, whereby they can be transported long distances and stored for long periods of time. The seed coverings may also play an important role in dormancy of some seeds, as discussed in Chapter 6.

REFERENCES

1. Blakeslee, A. F., and S. Satina, New hybrids from incompatible crosses in *Datura* through culture of excised embryos on malt media, *Science,* 99:331–334. 1944.

2. Brink, R. A., and D. C. Cooper, The endosperm in seed development, *Bot. Rev.,* 13:423–541. 1947.

3. Brittingham, W. H., Type of seed formation as indicated by the nature and extent of variation in Kentucky bluegrass, and its practical application, *Jour. Agr. Res.,* 67:225–264. 1943.

4. Buell, K. M., Developmental morphology in *Dianthus.* III. Seed failure following interspecific crosses, *Amer. Jour. Bot.,* 40:116–123. 1953.

5. Cooper, D. C., and R. A. Brink, Somatoplastic sterility as a cause of seed failure after interspecific hybridization, *Genetics,* 25:593–617. 1940.

6. ————, Seed collapse following matings between diploid and tetraploid races of *Lycopersicon pimpinellifolium, Genetics,* 30:375–401. 1945.

7. De Haas, P. G., Neue Beitrage zur Samlingsanzucht bei Kernobst, *Rpt. XIVth Int. Hort. Cong.,* pp. 1185–1196. 1955.

8. Dermen, H., Aposporic parthenogenesis in a triploid apple, *Malus hupehensis, Jour. Arn. Arb.,* 17:90–105. 1936.

9. Esau, K., Morphology of reproduction in guayule and certain other species of *Parthenium, Hilgardia,* 17:61–120. 1946.

10. ————, *Plant Anatomy.* New York: Wiley, 1953.

11. Flemion, F., and J. Olson, Lygus bugs in relation to seed production and occurrence of embryoless seeds in various Umbelliferous species. *Contrib. Boyce Thomp. Inst.,* 16:39–46. 1950.

12. Gustafsson, A., Apomixis in higher plants, Part I–III. *Lunds Univ. Arsskrift,* N. F. Avid. 2 Bd 42, Nr. 3:42(2); 43(2); 43(12). 370 pp. 1946–47.

13. Iseley, D., Investigations in seed classification by family characteristics, *Iowa Agr. Exp. Sta. Research Bul. 351:*317–380. 1947.

14. Jones, H. A., Pollination and life history studies of the lettuce (*Lactuca sativa* L.), *Hilgardia,* 2:425–479. 1927.

15. LaRue, C. D., The growth of plant embryos in culture, *Bul. Torrey Bot. Club,* 63:365–382. 1936.

16. LaRue, C. D., and G. S. Avery, Jr., The development of the embryo of *Zizania aquatica* in the seed and in artificial culture, *Bul. Torrey Bot. Club,* 65:11–21. 1938.

17. Luckwill, L. C., The hormone content of the seed in relation to endosperm development and fruit drop in the apple, *Jour. of Hort. Sci.,* 24:32–44. 1948.

18. Maheshwari, P., *An Introduction to the Embryology of Angiosperms.* New York: McGraw-Hill, 1950.

19. Martin, A. C., The comparative internal morphology of seeds, *Amer. Midland Nat.,* 36:512–660. 1946.

20. McLean, S. W., Interspecific crosses involving *Datura ceratocaula* obtained by embryo dissection, *Amer. Jour. Bot.,* 33:630–638. 1946.

21. Nitsch, J. P., Plant hormones in the development of fruits, *Quart. Rev. Biol.,* 27:33–57. 1952.

22. Nygren, A., Apomixis in the angiosperms II, *Bot. Rev.,* 20:577–649. 1954.

23. O'Rourke. F. L., The effect of juvenility on plant propagation, *Proc. 1st Ann. Mtg. Plant Prop. Soc.,* pp. 33–36. 1951.

24. Rappaport, J., *In vitro* culture of plant embryos and factors controlling their growth, *Bot. Rev.,* 20:201–225. 1954.

25. Rietsema, J., et al., Studies on ovule and embryo growth in *Datura*. I. Growth analysis, *Amer. Jour. Bot.*, 42:449–454. 1955.

26. Robinson, R. W., Seed germination problems in the Umbelliferae, *Bot. Rev.*, 20:531–550. 1954.

27. Sanders, M. E., Embryo development in four *Datura* species following self and hybrid pollinations, *Amer. Jour. Bot.*, 35:525–532. 1948.

28. Sansome, E. R., S. Satina, and A. F. Blakeslee, Disintegration of ovules in tetraploid, diploid and in incompatible crosses in *Datura, Bul. Torrey Bot. Club*, 69:405–420. 1942.

29. Shepherd, P. H., The kernel told the tale, *Amer. Fruit Grower,* 75:37. 1955.

30. Teubner, F. G., and A. E. Murneek, Embryo abortion as mechanism of "hormone" thinning of fruit, *Mo. Agr. Exp. Sta. Res. Bul. 590:*1–79. 1955.

31. Tukey, H. B., Growth patterns of plants developed from immature embryos in artificial culture, *Bot. Gaz.*, 99:630–665. 1938.

4 | Principles of Seed Selection

~~~~~

The higher plants reproduce naturally by seeds. One of the characteristics of seed reproduction is the variation which can exist within groups of seedlings. This property is very important in nature, because it makes possible the production of new kinds of plants, some of which may be of greater adaptability to different or changing environments. In propagation it can cause difficulty, because a given kind of plant cannot always be perpetuated by seed propagation. To utilize seed reproduction most successfully as a method of plant propagation it is necessary to consider the principles discussed in this chapter.

USES OF SEEDLINGS

The growing of seedlings has several specific uses in propagation.

(a) They are used to propagate many species and cultivated varieties of plants, particularly annuals and biennials. Herbaceous and woody plant species and varieties may be grown from seed, although vegetative methods might also be available. For instance, native trees and shrubs grown for reforestation, woodlots, wildlife cover, and roadsides are primarily seedlings, as are many trees too difficult to propagate vegetatively. It should be remembered, however, that many selected varieties of perennials are vegetatively propagated clones and do not "come true" from seed.

(b) Seedlings are extensively propagated in nurseries to provide rootstocks upon which to graft or bud selected clones of fruit and ornamental trees.

(c) In plant breeding, the growing of seedlings is the most important means of developing new varieties. This is due to the variability which results from segregation attending sexual reproduction.

POLLINATION REQUIREMENTS OF PLANTS

Pollination is the transfer of pollen from the anther to the stigma of the flower. A pollen tube grows down the style into the ovule where fertilization takes place. Seed development may result from (a) *self-pollination,* in which the pollen may come from the same flower, different flowers on the same plant, or from different plants of the same clone; (b) *cross-pollination,* in which pollen comes from a different plant or from a different clone; or (c) *apomixis,* in which an asexual process is substituted for a sexual one (see p. 43). In addition, in some plants, either self- or cross-pollination can occur, the amount of either varying with the kind of plant and environmental factors. In some cases, seed production is partially sexual and partially apomictic. It is important to know which process predominates in any plant being grown for the production of seed *(2).*

Self-Pollinated Plants

Important crop plants which are usually grouped here are listed in Table 4–1. Varieties of such plants can generally be maintained by seed propagation with little difficulty even when grown in close proximity to other closely related varieties. Cross-pollination is usually less than 4 per cent *(4).*

The ability of these varieties to be reproduced by seed is due to the fact that they are largely homozygous. With self-pollination, the offspring of the homozygous plants are also homozygous and inherit the characteristics of the parent. On the other hand, heterozygous plants, if self-pollinated, would segregate (for instance, like the tall and dwarf offspring in Figure 1–6). However, with continued inbreeding the proportion of homozygous plants would increase and the heterozygous decrease. After 6 to 10 generations, the group of descendents from the original parent has segregated into more or less true-breeding lines. If the unwanted lines are removed early in the process, a true-breeding *pure line* will result. This is one of the basic procedures used in breeding such varieties.

Cross-Pollinated Plants

Most kinds of plants are cross-pollinated, although in many cases either self- or cross-pollination is possible. Important economic plants in this category whose varieties are propagated by seed are listed in Table 4–1. Other plants not listed which are cross-pollinated include: sugar beet, cucurbits, cabbage and related plants (*Brassica*), most root vegetables, many flowering plants used as ornamentals, most shrubs, and fruit, nut, forest, and shade trees.

Although either self- or cross-pollination is possible with some plants, several conditions exist which completely prevent self-pollination in certain plants. This situation occurs in *dioecious* plants, such as holly (*Ilex*), in which pistillate (female) and staminate (male) flowers are produced on different plants. A similar situation occurs with *dichogamy* where the stamens do not shed pollen at a time that the pistil is receptive to it. This situation occurs in some varieties of walnuts and pecans. A third case where cross-pollination is required is *incompatibility;* that is, where the pollen tube is unable to develop properly in the style of a flower on the same plant (or clone), although the pollen is normal and will grow properly in the style of another plant. Some combinations of individual plants likewise are cross-incompatible and cannot pollinate each other. This phenomenon is based on genetic factors and occurs in such diverse species as the sweet cherry, almond, *Hemerocallis,* lily, petunia, and cabbage.

Cross-pollination is accomplished by various agencies. (a) *Wind pollination* is the rule with many plants with inconspicuous flowers. Examples are grasses, conifers, and catkin-bearing trees such as the walnut, oak, alder, and cottonwood. The pollen produced from such plants is generally light and dry, and in some cases, it is capable of being carried for long distances in wind currents. (b) *Insect pollination* is the rule with plants with brightly colored, fragrant, and otherwise conspicuous flowers which attract insects. The honey bee is one of the most important pollinating insects, although wild bees, butterflies, moths, and flies are also factors in pollination. Such insects obtain pollen and nectar from the flower. Generally, the pollen will be heavy and sticky, adhering to the body of the insect. (c) Man carries out controlled pollination by hand in some cases. This is an important practice in breeding programs and is also used in producing seed of a few kinds of plants, for instance, tuberous begonia and certain kinds of petunia. (d) Other agents which are effective in pollinating certain kinds of plants include birds, bats, snails, and water.

A cross-pollinated variety has similar capabilities of being maintained as nearly genetically pure as a self-pollinated variety, providing it is produced under properly controlled conditions. Plants of the variety should be relatively homozygous, and cross-pollination should take place only among those which would produce the desired offspring. Such varieties are *lines* of genetically similar individuals. A different procedure, however, is necessary to produce seed of hybrid varieties. Here cross-pollination takes place only between genetically different parental lines, but these are selected to produce a given type of seedling offspring. The latter procedure is described below.

If the individual plants from which seeds are to be taken are heterozygous, the seedlings from them cannot be depended upon to reproduce the characteristics of the parents. Varieties of many herbaceous and woody perennials are clones which exhibit such behavior. These include most fruit and nut varieties, such as peach, apple, and pear; many herbaceous ornamentals, such as tulip, dahlia, and chrysanthemum; and numerous woody ornamentals, such as rose and camellia. Seed propagation of such varieties is not used because they do not "breed true"—that is, the essential characteristics of the variety are not transmitted to its seedling offspring and the value of the variety is lost in the succeeding generation. Consequently, they are propagated vegetatively.

SEED PRODUCTION OF HERBACEOUS PLANT VARIETIES

To keep a variety genetically unchanged, careful control of seed production is necessary. With no control, the genetic characteristics of the variety may become somewhat different from that initially developed by the plant breeder. Contamination may result from cross-pollination with plants of a different genotype, or it may result from a mixture with other crop seed of lesser value or with weed seed. Foreign seed similar to the pure crop seed cannot be easily removed with seed cleaning equipment.

Methods of Maintaining Purity

Isolation. Isolation is used (a) to prevent the contamination by cross-pollination with a different but related variety and (b) to prevent mechanical mixing of the seed during harvest. It is primarily achieved through distance, but it also can be attained by enclosing plants or groups of plants in cages, enclosing individual flowers, or removing male flower parts and then employing artificial pollination.

Isolation obviously is not as critical in the production of self-pollinated plants as in the production of cross-pollinated plants. As a general rule, two or more closely related varieties of self-pollinated plants can be planted close to each other without one contaminating the other. The principal reason for separation here is to prevent mechanical mixing of seed during harvest. The minimum distance usually specified between plots of self-pollinated seed-producing plants is 10 ft. (see Table 4–1).

Seed of different varieties must be kept separate during harvest. Careful cleaning of the harvesting equipment when a change is made from one variety to another is required. Likewise, sacks and other containers used to hold the seed must be carefully cleaned to remove any seed which may have remained from previous lots.

Isolation is primarily a factor in the production of plants cross-pollinated by wind or insects. The minimum distance between varieties depends upon a number of factors, such as the degree of natural cross-pollination, the agency of pollination, the direction of the prevailing winds, and the number of insects present. The required distances specified by seed-regulating agencies varies with the class of seed produced. That is, greater distances should be used with seeds in which a high degree of genetic purity is desired (see Table 4–1). The minimum distance usually specified for insect-pollinated plants is ¼ mi., although for others, such as the onion, 1 mi. is specified. However, some seed producers have indicated that a minimum of ½ mi. should be used, and preferably 1 mi. or more, depending upon the location of colonies of bees *(11)*.

The distance to separate varieties of wind-pollinated plants varies with different kinds of plants. The distance usually specified for corn is 40 rd. (⅛ mi.). However, in hybrid seed corn, this distance may be reduced by planting border rows of the pollinating variety. With beets, ½ to 1 mi. is recommended, and to produce stock seed 2 mi. is preferable *(5, 13)*. Seed-producing fields of two different varieties should not be in the line of prevailing winds.

Cross-pollination takes place between certain varieties and not between others. In general, any variety can be expected to contaminate any other variety of the same species; it may or may not contaminate varieties of a different species but in the same genus; and rarely will it contaminate varieties belonging to another genus. Since the horticultural classification may not indicate taxonomic relationships, the seed producer should have some familiarity with botanical relationships among the varieties he grows.

Roguing. The existence of off-type plants, plants of other varieties, and weeds in the seed production field are other sources of contamination which should be eliminated. Although a low percentage of such plants may not seriously affect the performance of any one lot of seed, their continued presence will lead to deterioration of the variety over a period of time. The removal of such plants is referred to as "roguing."

Off-type plants may arise because of recessive genes present in a heterozygous condition. It has been previously pointed out that a completely homozygous plant is rare and some heterozygosity exists even in an apparently pure line. Additional genetic changes may occur by mutation, a process constantly occurring at a very low rate. Since many mutant genes are recessive, their effect may not be immediately apparent in the plant in which they occur. The plant becomes heterozygous for that character, and in a later generation the genes segregate and the character appears. Off-type individual plants should be rogued out of the seed production fields before pollination occurs. Regular supervision of the fields by trained personnel is required.

Volunteer plants arising from accidentally planted seed or from seed produced by earlier crops is another possible source of contamination. Regulations concerning field selection for growing seed of any particular variety usually specify that the field must not have grown a potential contaminating variety for a given number of preceding years.

Testing. Varieties being grown for seed production should be continually tested for genetic purity to be sure that they are being maintained in their true form. Many seed concerns maintain for this purpose test gardens under the supervision of trained personnel.

Although changes in a variety are primarily due to the continued existence of the above factors, some variation is still possible even with adequate control. A single variety produced by several different seed producers may represent strains which differ slightly from each other. Such changes are due to certain circumstances of production, such as the selective action of the environment or of the individual maintaining them. Any visible change would usually be detected and plants showing them rogued out. Physiological changes affecting such characteristics as yielding ability, disease resistance, and environmental adaptation are more serious and difficult to determine without testing.

Seed Certification

Seeds are produced commercially either by individual small growers or by large, commercial seed companies. Genetic purity during seed production is often maintained through *seed certification* programs *(1, 6, 9, 17)*. Such programs have been set up in most states and administered through the cooperative efforts of the state agricultural experiment station and a state crop improvement association. The crop improvement association is usually a legally designated seed certifying agency. Its members are growers who produce what is designated as "certified seed." These individual state organizations are coordinated through the International Crop Improvement Association with members in the United States and Canada.

The principal objectives of seed certification are to maintain and to make available crop seeds, tubers, or bulbs which are of good seeding value and true to variety. To accomplish these purposes, the seed certifying agency must determine the eligibility of particular varieties, which is usually based on variety testing performed by the experiment station. It must also set up standards of production as to isolation, presence of off-type plants, and quality of harvested seed, and make regular inspections of the production fields to see that the standards of production are maintained. The International Crop Improvement Association has recommended minimum standards for many crops (see Table 4–1), although these regulations

TABLE 4–1

MINIMUM ISOLATION REQUIREMENTS FOR SEED PRODUCTION OF CERTAIN SPECIES OF FIELD AND VEGETABLE CROPS.*

Type of Pollination	Species	Seed Class		
		Foundation	Registered	Certified
Self-pollinated.	barley, oats, wheat, rice, peanut, soybean, lespedeza, field pea, garden bean, cowpea, flax	Fields should be separated by a definite boundary at least 10 ft. wide.		
	grasses (self-pollinated and apomictic species)	10 ft.	10 ft.	5 ft.
Self-pollinated but to a lesser degree than those in the above list.	cotton (upland type)	100 ft. from varieties which differ markedly.		
	cotton (Egyptian type)	1320 ft.	1320 ft.	660 ft.
	pepper	200 ft.	100 ft.	30 ft.
	tomato	200 ft.	100 ft.	30 ft.
	tobacco	150 ft. or by four border rows of each variety. Isolation between varieties of different types should be 1320 ft.		
Cross-pollinated by insects.	alfalfa, birdsfoot trefoil, red clover, white clover	1320 ft.	660 or 1320 ft.†	165 ft.
	sweet clover	5280 ft.	660 or 990 ft.†	165 or 330 ft.†
	millet	1320 ft.	1320 ft.	1320 ft.
	onion	5280 ft.	2640 ft.	1320 ft.
	watermelon	2640 ft.	2640 ft.	1320 ft.
Cross-pollinated by wind.	hybrid field corn	660 ft. (may be reduced if field is surrounded by specified numbers of border rows and the varieties nearby are of same color and texture).		
	grasses	1320 ft.	660 ft.	330 ft.

* As recommended by the International Crop Improvement Association (6).
† First number if plot is less than 5 acres; second number if plot is more than 5 acres.

are set within the individual state organizations. Since specific requirements for certification may vary from state to state, the local state regulations should be examined. These usually specify the varieties which can be certified, the amount of isolation required of any particular crop, required inspections, and standards for the seed quality after harvest.

The mechanics of maintaining genetic purity are facilitated by utilizing certain classes of ·seed which are maintained at different levels of purity. These classes are given below, as defined by the International Crop Improvement Association *(6)*.

Breeder's seed. Breeder's seed is seed or vegetative propagating material which is directly controlled by the originating or, in certain cases, the sponsoring plant breeder or institution, and which provides for the initial and recurring increase of foundation seed.

Foundation seed. Foundation seed, including *elite* in Canada, shall be seed stocks that are so handled as to most nearly maintain specific genetic identity and purity, and that may be designated or distributed by an agricultural experiment station. Production must be carefully supervised or approved by representatives of the station. Foundation seed shall be the source of all other certified seed classes, either directly or through registered seed.

Registered seed. Registered seed shall be the progeny of foundation or registered seed that is so handled as to maintain satisfactory genetic identity and purity, and that has been approved and certified by the certifying agency. This class of seed should be of a quality suitable for the production of certified seed.

Certified seed. Certified seed shall be the progeny of foundation, registered, or certified seed that is so handled as to maintain satisfactory genetic identity and purity, and that has been approved and certified by the certifying agency.

Certified seed is the class grown in largest volume to be placed on the market and sold to growers. Bags of certified seed will have attached, with a metal seal, a blue tag distributed by the seed certifying agency as evidence of the genetic identity and purity of the seed contained therein. Registered seed is used to produce the plants from which certified seed is to be harvested. Bags of registered seed will be labeled with a purple tag or a blue tag marked with the word "registered." Likewise, foundation seed will be labeled with a white tag or a regular certified seed tag with the word "foundation."

Vegetable and Flower Seed Production *(5)*

Most vegetable and flower seed is produced by large commercial seed companies who either grow the seed themselves or contract with private growers to produce the seed. The company preserves genetic purity by specifying the particular variety an individual contractor will grow, by supervising the fields during production, and by maintaining test gardens.

Although such seed may not be produced through seed certification programs, similar procedures will be used to maintain genetic purity. Essentially the same classes of seed will be used, although they may be designated by different names. The primary source of seed of the variety, the foundation seed, will usually be maintained by the seed company. Trained personnel will have the responsibility of maintaining it at the highest level of purity. Seed provided by the company to the contractor-grower for growing his crop is known as *stock seed*. The seed actually harvested from the fields of the contractor-grower will be placed on the market and sold commercially by the seed company.

The Production of Seed for Hybrid Varieties

Hybrid varieties have become an increasingly important category of cultivated plants within recent years. These are the progeny produced by the repetitive crossing of two or more parental lines that are maintained either (a) by seed, such as inbred lines, or (b) asexually, such as clones. To produce commercial hybrid seed, the parental lines must be grown side by side so that cross-pollination takes place between them. The seed produced (the F_1 progeny of the cross) is the seed used to grow commercial crops. This cross must be repeated every time that the seeds are produced.

The progeny of two inbred lines is known as a *single-cross*. Combining two single-crosses produces a *double-cross,* the usual case with hybrid corn varieties.

Isolation is required of the seed-producing fields in the same manner as any seed-propagated variety that involves cross-pollination.

Hybrid plants were first utilized in the production of field corn, and almost all the field corn grown in the United States is of this type. Likewise, hybrid varieties of sweet corn and pop corn have been developed. Hybrid varieties of other plants have not been developed as rapidly as those of corn, the limiting factor in most cases being the development of methods whereby the hybrid variety can be produced on a large scale at a moderate cost. Nevertheless, a number of vegetable hybrids have become available as have hybrids of some flower plants, for instance, petunia.

Methods of cross-pollination. (a) Plants of monoecious species, e.g., corn, are readily adapted to hybrid seed production. To produce hybrid corn seed, the parental lines are planted in rows, one male row to three female rows or a similar combination *(15)*. When the tassel bearing the male flowers appears, it is removed by hand from all of the plants in the female rows so that pollen to pollinate the female flowers (the silks) can come only from the male parental lines. The hybrid seed is harvested from the female parent row.

(b) Hand pollination following emasculation of the pollen-producing stamens is a possible procedure, although it is time consuming and costly, making the seed expensive. With most plants it would not be practical on a large scale, but it has been used to obtain hybrids of some flower crops, such as petunia and tuberous begonia.

FIRST YEAR

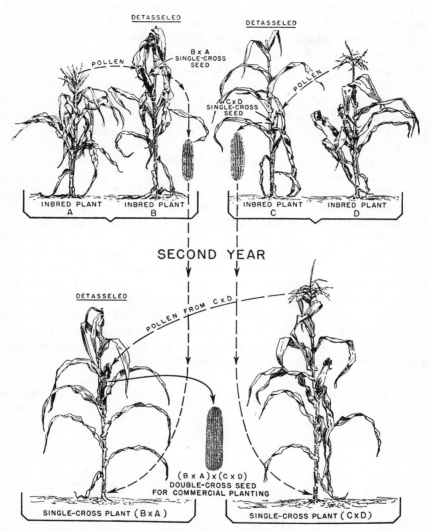

Figure 4–1. The production of hybrid corn. The seed used to grow the crop of hybrid corn is usually a combination of four inbred lines. The **single cross** between the original inbred lines is expensive to make. Seeds from two single crosses are planted to produce the **double cross.** From **U.S.D.A. Yearbook of Agriculture, 1937.**

(c) Plants which exhibit self-incompatibility also lend themselves to the production of hybrid seed, since self-pollination does not occur and all pollination must come from pollen of another plant. This has been used to produce hybrid cabbage seed *(12)*.

(d) Using as the seed parent *male-sterile* lines of plants, characterized by their inability to produce viable pollen, has become an important method in producing seed of several kinds of plants. The procedure used to develop and maintain such lines depends upon the breeding behavior of that character in the particular kind of plant in which it is found.

The inheritance of male sterility takes place in different ways *(3, 4)*. In one type, found in corn, sugar beet, and tomato, male sterility is related to a single recessive gene. Thus, if a homozygous individual is backcrossed to another heterozygous for that factor, one-half of the offspring will be male-sterile and one-half male-fertile. It is necessary to have ways to identify and eliminate these male-fertile plants before flowering, if this is to be used to produce hybrid seeds.

A second type of male sterility, reported in corn, depends upon a factor which is entirely cytoplasmic. All offspring of such plants would consequently be male sterile since the male parent would have no influence upon this characteristic in the offspring. Since any pollen source could be used, this type of sterility could be readily used to produce hybrid seed.

The third type is used in the production of hybrid onion seed *(7, 8)*. It also occurs in flax and sugar beet. Here, male-sterility results from the combination of a cytoplasmic factor S (as opposed to a normal cytoplasm N) and a recessive nuclear factor *ms* (as opposed to a dominant factor for male-fertility Ms). A male-sterile plant has a genotype of S *ms ms*, whereas a male-fertile plant can have any of the following: *N ms ms, N Ms ms, S Ms Ms,* or S *Ms ms*. The male-sterile line is maintained by continuous backcrossing to a pollen parent of *N ms ms*. Two examples of the inheritance of these factors are as follows:

(a)　　S　*ms*　*ms*　× 　N　*ms*　*ms*　　(b)　　S　*ms*　*ms*　×　N　*Ms*　*ms*
　　　　　(seed)　　　　　　(pollen)　　　　　　　　(seed)　　　　　　　(pollen)

　　　　　　　　　V　　　　　　　　　　　　　　　　　　　　V
　　　　　　　　　↓　　　　　　　　　　　　　　　　　　　　↓

　　　　　S　*ms*　*ms*　　　　　　　　　　　½　　S　*Ms*　*ms*
　　　　　(all male-sterile)　　　　　　　　　　　　　(male-fertile)
　　　　　　　　　　　　　　　　　　　　　　　　½　　S　*ms*　*ms*
　　　　　　　　　　　　　　　　　　　　　　　　　　　(male-sterile)

Use of F_1 seed for propagation. From the standpoint of continued propagation, one important point should be emphasized in regard to hybrid varieties. F_1 hybrid plants are heterozygous and will *not* breed true. The effect of hybrid vigor is greatest in the F_1 generation and declines sharply in succeeding generations. Such seed would be unreliable for propagation purposes. For each crop that is to be grown, new hybrid seed must be produced according to the procedure just described. The crop grower must rely upon the seedsman to provide him with an adequate supply of properly produced seed.

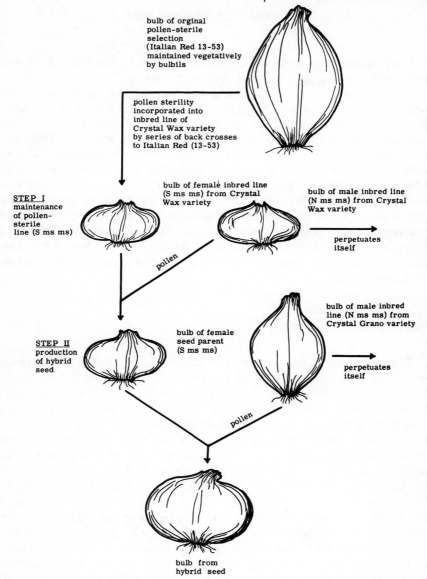

bulb of orginal
pollen-sterile
selection
(Italian Red 13-53)
maintained vegetatively
by bulbils

pollen sterility
incorporated into
inbred line of
Crystal Wax variety
by series of back crosses
to Italian Red (13-53)

STEP I
maintenance
of pollen-
sterile
line (S ms ms)

bulb of female inbred line
(S ms ms) from Crystal
Wax variety

bulb of male inbred line
(N ms ms) from Crystal
Wax variety

perpetuates
itself

pollen

STEP II
production
of hybrid
seed

bulb of female
seed parent
(S ms ms)

bulb of male inbred
line (N ms ms) from
Crystal Grano variety

perpetuates
itself

pollen

bulb from
hybrid seed

Figure 4–2. Hybrid onion seed production utilizing pollen sterility to facilitate cross-pollination as illustrated by the onion hybrids, Crystal Wax x Crystal Grano. The factors of pollen sterility, **S ms ms,** discovered in Italian Red 13-53, were incorporated by plant breeders into an inbred line of Crystal Wax by the backcross method of breeding. The pollen-sterile line is maintained by crossing it with a pollen-fertile inbred line of Crystal Wax which has the factors **N ms ms.**

Commercial seed of this hybrid is produced by planting together this pollen-sterile line of Crystal Wax with a pollen-fertile inbred line of Crystal Grano, the resulting seed from the Crystal Wax being used to grow the commercial crop of onion bulbs. Partially redrawn from Jones and Clark **(8).**

SEED SELECTION FOR WOODY PERENNIALS

Most woody plant species are heterozygous and cross-pollinated so that the possibilities of genetic variation are great.

The amount of allowable seedling variation depends upon the use for which the seedlings are to be grown. For plants to be used in reforestation, for instance, considerable variation is allowable and to some extent desirable. The young plants are originally planted much closer than will be found in the final stand of mature plants. Close spacing insures good stem form, and competition gradually eliminates the weakest trees. Those which survive will be determined by a natural selection of the most vigorous and best adapted *(16)*. On the other hand, where seedlings are grown in nurseries to provide individual shrubs or trees for landscape purposes, genetic variation can be very serious. For this reason, vegetative propagation methods are more often employed by nurserymen if possible. Seedling uniformity is desirable in the growing of rootstocks for fruit or ornamental plants.

Nursery Row Selection

Where variability involves obvious characters of vigor or appearance in the young seedling, it may be possible to select desired individuals in the nursery row and discard or otherwise dispose of the off-type seedlings. Paradox walnut seedlings resulting from the natural cross of the Persian walnut (*Juglans regia*) and the Northern California Black Walnut (*J. hindsii*) often appear in stands of *J. hindsii* seedlings when grown in the nursery to produce rootstocks for Persian walnut varieties. These hybrid seedlings, known as Paradox Hybrids, can be distinguished from the *J. hindsii* seedlings by the larger size of the leaflets and color of the bark. The "blue" form of the Colorado spruce (*Picea pungens*) is due to a genetic factor, "blue" seedlings appearing among others of the normal green form. *Liquidambar* and *Pistacia* seedling trees are widely grown on the West Coast for their brilliant fall coloring. Because of seedling variation of this characteristic, it is wise to select individual trees of these species in the fall for home landscaping when leaf coloration can be observed.

Seed Collecting from Natural Stands

Collecting seed from suitable sources can do much to minimize seedling variation *(16)*. Although some woody plant seed comes from established

Figure 4–3. (left) Paradox Hybrid **(Juglans hindsii x J. regia)** seedlings **(left)** sometimes appear among Northern California black walnut **(J. hindsii)** seedlings **(right)** being grown for rootstocks. Identification of the hybrid seedlings in the nursery row is by their lighter bark color and larger leaves. **(right)** Leaves of Persian walnut **(above)**, Paradox Hybrid **(center)**, and Northern California black walnut **(below)**. Courtesy E. F. Serr.

seed orchards, much of it is obtained wherever it may be found (i.e., in forests, woodlots, along streets or roadsides, and so forth). The genetic purity of tree and shrub species can best be achieved by collecting from *pure stands,* that is, groves or groups of plants made up of uniform plants of the same kind and with the desired characteristics. Seedlings arising from such a source, although not necessarily homozygous, would be most apt to reproduce the characteristics observed among the parent seed trees. Because of adequate cross-pollination, seed quality would usually be better than under conditions of self-pollination.

By contrast, it is usually undesirable to collect seed from an isolated plant or from single plants of a species growing near other plants of related species, such as might occur in an arboretum *(18).* Under such conditions, either self-pollination resulting in reduced seed quality or cross-pollination with different species would be apt to occur. The likelihood of producing variable seedlings unlike the parent would be greater than if collected from a pure stand.

The value of a particular seed source can best be determined by growing a population of seedlings from it. This takes time, but over a period of years a seed collector should be able to determine those particular sources which produce the best trees. When a seed source has been discovered which produces good seed and desirable seedlings, it can be used as a seed source from then on. In forestry where a pure stand is found to be particularly desirable as a seed source, it is often preserved as a seed production area or *tree seed farm*. Its value for this purpose could far outweigh any value it might have for lumber or other forest product.

Seed origin. The importance of seed origin in collecting tree seed was recognized initially by European foresters during the 19th century. Most European countries now have enacted laws which govern the use of forest tree seed, specifying that the origin of the seeds must be shown on all seed lots marketed. The recognition in the United States of the importance of seed origin has been more recent, and no uniform requirement exists for the certification of tree seed as to place of origin. Only a few states have laws which regulate the sale of tree seed.

Seed origin is important because differences can exist among members of a particular species growing in separate areas of its natural habitat. In any one environment, the individuals of the species are subject to natural selection that would eliminate unadapted plants and result in the preservation of those adapted to that particular environment. As a result, members of a particular species growing in one locality may differ markedly in certain of their heritable characteristics from members of the same species growing elsewhere. Although these differences may sometimes be recognized by morphological appearance, many are based on physiological adaptation to the area in which they grew. Important environmental factors of adaptation are climate, and soil, disease, and insect resistance. Growth rate and growth habit are also plant characteristics which may be important. Seeds collected from trees in warmer climates or at lower altitudes are likely to produce seedlings that will be injured when grown in colder regions even though the species is the same and the plants are similar in appearance. Although the reverse situation—collecting seeds from colder areas for growth in warmer regions—would be more satisfactory, it might result in a net reduction in growth due to the inability of the trees to fully utilize the growing season.

Distinct groups or races have been recognized in at least 32 American species and 35 non-American species of forest trees *(16)*. It is generally recognized, however, that more such groups exist.

In 1939 the United States Department of Agriculture adopted the following policy regarding the use of seed stocks and individual clones obtained by them for forest, shelter belt, and erosion-control plantings. It is a guide for the selection of woody plant seed from natural sources.

1. Only seed of known locality of origin or nursery stock grown from such seed is to be used.

2. Adequate evidence for the place and year of origin is to be required of the vendor when seeds are bought.

3. An accurate record of the following data is to be required of all shipments: (a) lot number; (b) year of seed crop; (c) species; (d) seed origin as to state, county, locality, and range of elevation, and (e) proof of origin.

4. Whenever available, local seed from natural stands is to be used unless it is is demonstrated that another source can give desirable plants. Local seed means seed from an area subject to similar climatic influences and may usually be considered to extend to 100 mi. of the planting and within 1000 ft. elevation.

5. When local seed is not available, seed should be used from a region having as nearly as possible the same climatic characteristics, such as length of growing season, mean temperature of growing season, same frequency of summer droughts, and same latitude *(16)*.

Mother Tree Selection

A woody plant whose seedlings possess desired characteristics can be preserved by means of vegetative propagation, such as by grafting it into a seed orchard. Such a plant is referred to as a *mother tree*. Growing it as a clone preserves the original genetic source intact. This procedure has been followed in several instances to produce rootstock seed for fruit trees. For example, important sources of seed for peach rootstocks are clones of Lovell, Yunnan, Bokhara, Shalil, and S-37. Seedlings from such sources are relatively uniform, vigorous, and (all but Lovell) have a certain degree of nematode resistance. Seedlings from such sources should show the same characteristics no matter where the mother tree is grown. The S-37 clone, used as the mother tree, has been patented (see p. 483).

Obtaining seed from particular mother trees has also been advocated in growing tung (*Aleurites*) trees *(10)*. The purpose here is not to develop rootstocks but to grow the producing tree.

REFERENCES

1. Frolik, E. F., and R. D. Lewis, Seed certification in the United States and Canada, *Jour. Amer. Soc. Agron.,* 36:183–193. 1944.

2. Fryxell, P. A., Mode of reproduction of higher plants, *Bot. Rev.,* 23:135–233. 1957.

3. Gabelman, W. H., Male sterility in vegetable breeding, in *Genetics in Plant Breeding,* Brookhaven Symposia in Biology No. 9:113–122. 1956.

4. Hayes, H. K., F. R. Immer, and D. C. Smith, *Methods of Plant Breeding.* New York: McGraw-Hill, 1955.

5. Hawthorn, L. R., and L. H. Pollard, *Vegetable and Flower Seed Production.* Philadelphia: Blakiston, 1954.

6. International Crop Improvement Association, Minimum seed certification standards, *Publ. No. 18:*1–91. 1954.

7. Jones, H. A., and A. E. Clarke, Inheritance of male sterility in the onion and the production of hybrid seed, *Proc. Amer. Soc. Hort. Sci.,* 43:189–194. 1943.

8. ———, The story of the hybrid onion, *USDA Yearbook of Agriculture, 1943–1947,* pp. 320–326. 1947.

9. LeClerg, E. L., Making sure of healthy seed, *USDA Yearbook of Agriculture, 1953,* pp. 146–151. 1953.

10. Merrill, S., Jr., et al., Relative growth and yield of budded and seedling tung trees for the first seven years in the orchard, *Proc. Amer. Soc. Hort. Sci.,* 63:119–127. 1954.

11. Morrison, G., Good breeding provides uniformity and adequate isolation maintains uniformity, *Seed World,* 58:52–56. 1945.

12. Odland, M. L., and C. L. Noll, The utilization of cross-incompatibility and self-incompatibility in the production of F_1 hybrid cabbage, *Proc. Amer. Soc. Hort. Sci.,* 55:391–402. 1950.

13. Pendleton, R. A., H. R. Fennell, and F. C. Reimer, Sugar beet seed production in Oregon, *Ore. Agr. Exp. Sta. Bul. 437,* 1950.

14. Righter, F. I., New perspectives in forest tree breeding, *Science,* 104 (2688): 1–3. 1946.

15. Sprague, G. F., Production of hybrid corn, *Iowa Agr. Exp. Sta. Bul. P48:556–582.* 1950.

16. USDA, Woody plant seed manual, *USDA Misc. Publ. 654,* 1948.

17. Wheeler, W. A., and D. D. Hill, Certification of field seeds and foundation seed program, Chap. XIV, *Grassland Seeds.* New York: Van Nostrand, 1957.

18. Wyman, D., Seeds of woody plants, *Arnoldia,* 13:41–60. 1953.

5

Techniques of Seed Production and Handling

~~~

The production of good seed is of prime importance to the propagator whether he collects or produces the seed himself or whether he obtains the seed from others. In the production of any crop, the cost of the seed is usually minor compared to other production costs. Yet no single factor is as important in determining the success of the operation.

SOURCES OF SEED

Commercial Seed Production

The commercial production of seeds is a large, specialized industry, the success of whose efforts is a vital concern of the plant propagator. The commercial seed industry produces cereal and forage crop seed, vegetable seed, and annual, biennial, and some perennial flower seeds for both commercial growers and home gardeners.

Commercial seed is raised primarily in areas where the environmental conditions are particularly suited for such production. For instance, much vegetable and flower seed is produced in somewhat limited areas that are particularly suitable but whose climate may not necessarily correspond with that of the locality in which the plants are later grown. Low humidity and lack of summer rainfall are desirable conditions for crops which must be dried for harvesting. Too low a humidity, on the other hand, may be undesirable to some plants, since it can cause premature shattering of the seed pods. For this reason, much flower seed acreage is located in the coastal areas of the West where the moist air from the nearby ocean and frequent night and morning fogs tend to prevent the pods from dehiscing during harvest.

Conditions of low atmospheric moisture also make it easier to control fungus and bacterial diseases. For instance, two seed-borne diseases, anthracnose and bacterial blight, are serious problems in bean seed production in all but the drier parts of the country. The mountain states or the central valley of California are particularly desirable for bean seed production.

Adequate isolation of cross-pollinated plants is also important and may influence the choice of seed production areas. For example, little sweet corn seed is produced in the Midwest due to the large amount of field corn grown there which could contaminate the seed.

Seed Collecting

Tree and shrub seed may be obtained from professional seed collectors either directly or indirectly through firms specializing in seed collecting or by the nurseryman collecting the seed himself. Native species of plants, used for forest planting and related uses, may be obtained from natural stands in the forests or other wild areas. Conifer seed may be harvested in conjunction with logging operations, the cones being removed from the felled trees. Some government agencies utilize their fire crews during periods of inactivity to obtain seed for governmental nurseries. Other sources of tree and shrub seeds may be parks, roadways, streets, or woodlots. In some cases, it is advantageous to maintain a seed orchard of particular selections difficult to obtain elsewhere or of selections which require close attention during harvest.

The collection of seeds is a specialized occupation. The collector must be able to identify the particular species of plant from which seed is to be collected and know when it should be harvested. He should be aware that even though he has located a particular source, has correctly identified it and ascertained that it apparently has sound seed, it may still be unsuitable genetically.

Fruit Processing Industries

Seed of many fruit plants which are used for propagating rootstocks are commonly obtained as by-products of fruit processing industries. For instance, pear seed may be obtained from canneries, apple seed from canneries or cider presses, and some varieties of apricot and peach seed from drying yards. An example of this is the Lovell peach, which is an important drying peach in California and also an important rootstock for a number of stone fruits. Peach pits are collected in large numbers at drying yards and cleaned and sold to nurserymen.

HARVESTING AND HANDLING SEEDS

The harvesting and handling of seeds is one of the most critical aspects of seed production, since it can, to a large extent, establish the propagation value of the seeds. Seeds which reach the harvesting stage in a potentially excellent condition may have their viability seriously impaired by the handling which they receive during and following harvest. The equipment and procedure used depend upon the kind of plant involved and the scope of the operation. Large-scale commercial seed harvesting operations usually require specialized equipment and machinery. The subsequent seed cleaning, processing, and sorting is also, to some extent, a specialized industry. At the other extreme, harvesting may merely involve the gathering of seeds from a few choice plants in a home garden. In either case, the over-all procedure involves the following steps: (a) determining the proper stage of maturity for harvest; (b) harvesting or collecting the seed; (c) extracting the seed from the fruit or from the plant; (d) cleaning and processing, as may be necessary; and (e) storing the seed until used. Most seeds must be dried sometime during this process, with the exception of a few kinds as pointed out later in this chapter.

Harvesting should not take place until the seeds have accumulated sufficient reserve materials. It should likewise be delayed until the state of ripeness is such that harvesting is facilitated. If delayed too long, the fruits may dehisce, drop, or be eaten or carried off by birds or animals. The tendency to "shatter" varies considerably with different kinds of plants but may be reduced by particular methods of handling. Usually it is better to harvest before the fruits become excessively dry. Cutting during the early morning hours when the dew is still present can also minimize shattering.

Uneven ripening of the fruit is another serious problem with some plants, since some seeds may become completely mature and drop while others on the same plant are only partially developed.

The optimum time to harvest most woody plant seeds is when they also are "mature." The collector must know the best criteria to indicate this condition for the particular kind of seed being obtained. These criteria may be moisture content (dryness), general appearance, or color or degree of "milkiness" of the seeds. For some pine species, the specific gravity of the freshly picked cones is a valuable characteristic used to judge their ripeness *(33)*.

With woody plant seed, there are some exceptions to the general rule of harvesting at maturity. In some cases it is better to harvest them slightly green. This is desirable with seeds, such as *Ceanothus,* which dehisce readily or when the ripe seeds may be carried off by birds or animals. Also, some seeds will germinate better in the first spring after they are produced if they are picked somewhat green and planted without being allowed to dry or their seed covering allowed to harden. Once such seeds become dry, they may not germinate until the second spring after they are produced except with special methods of handling. Some of the plants where this practice has been found to be desirable include dogwoods (*Cornus*), *Cotoneaster,* American hornbeam (*Carpinus*), redbud (*Cercis*), witch hazel (*Hamamelis*), black jetbead (*Rhodotypos*), *Viburnum, Magnolia kobus,* and *Juniperus (33, 37).*

Mechanical injuries during harvest can reduce viability and result in abnormal seedlings. Some of these injuries are internal and not noticeable at the time, but they result in low viability after storage *(31).* Although

 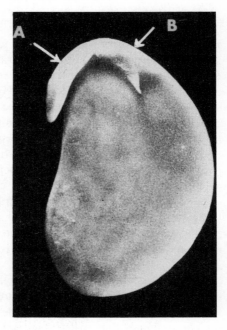

Figure 5–1. Seed injury during harvest can affect viability and produce seedling abnormalities. A break in the radicle below the cotyledons **(A)** can prevent germination. "Baldhead" in lima beans results from a break in the stem of the embryo immediately above the cotyledons **(B)**. The slower development of the shoots **(left)** arising from the cotyledon axils results in delayed maturity and lower yields. From **Calif. Agr. Exp. Sta. Cir. 423.**

damage is a potential factor in any operation including the beating or flailing of the seeds, it is probably most significant where commercial agricultural machinery is used. Such injuries can often be reduced by proper adjustment of the machinery. For instance, the amount of injury produced in combining alfalfa has been shown to be directly proportional to the peripheral speed of the threshing cylinder within the combine. An increase in the speed of the cylinder from 3500 to 6000 r.p.m. decreased the germination percentage to 80 per cent of normal *(19)*. Similar results have been produced with bean seed, which are particularly susceptible to injury because of their structure and large size *(1, 2)*. Dropping lima bean seed a single foot onto a solid surface has been shown to reduce germination about 20 per cent. Greater damage occurs if the seeds and the plants are dry than if they are moist. Higher moisture content permits higher cylinder speeds without an increase in total damage. Greater damage occurs with light feeding than with heavier feeding. These studies emphasize the need for proper machinery and correct threshing procedures as a means of minimizing seed injury.

Harvesting Procedures for Herbaceous Plants

Dry seeds and fruits. Dehiscent fruits include follicles, pods, capsules, and siliques in which the dry seed are extracted completely from their fruit enclosures. Kinds of plants involved include legumes, onion, cabbage and other cruciferous plants, okra, and a number of flower crops such as delphinium, pansy, and petunia. Indehiscent fruits include the caryopsis of cereals, grasses, and corn and the achenes characteristic of all members of the *Compositae*. Here the entire fruit is treated as a seed, but since they usually must be separated from hulls and other enclosing parts, the general procedure and equipment used are similar for the two groups.

Some field-grown grains can be cut and harvested in the same operation by the use of a combine. However, most plants are cut and allowed to dry for 1 to 3 weeks before threshing. The plants may be placed in windrows, piles, or shocks to cure. Plants whose seed pods dehisce readily, as with many flower crops, are cut (often by hand) and placed on canvas or in a tray. Where only a few plants from a backyard garden are involved, they may be cut and cured by hanging upside down in a paper bag.

Any threshing operation basically involves a procedure whereby the plants are beaten, flailed, or rolled to loosen the seed from the rest of the plant. In the combine, the essential part is a revolving cylinder which acts as a beater, combined with devices to separate the cleaned seeds from the straw. This machine is widely used for harvesting seed crops, although it may be modified to meet the requirements of the particular kind of plant involved. At one time, many vegetable seeds were threshed by large rollers pulled by horses across the plants. Rolling is still used to some extent for flower seeds. For small lots of seeds, beating, flailing, or screening by hand may be utilized. Figure 5–2 shows a small threshing box which may be convenient for such conditions.

Figure 5–2. Threshing box useful for cleaning small lots of dry seed.

Seeds must be carefully dried following harvesting. Wet seeds kept in bulk for even a few hours will begin to heat and if kept for longer periods, molds will develop. As a result, viability can be seriously impaired. Dryness is necessary for long storage periods of most seeds.

After threshing, the seeds usually require cleaning to remove dirt, chaff, extraneous plant parts, and weed and other crop seed of different shape and size. Small lots of seed can be cleaned by screening or pouring it back and forth from one container to another, letting the wind blow away the lighter materials. Commercial seed cleaning and processing utilize various kinds of specialized equipment which take advantage of differences in physical characteristics between the seeds and the materials to be removed. Characteristics include size, thickness, weight, friction, and color and utilize screens of different sizes, air blasts, gravity separators, and so forth (36).

Seeds from fleshy fruits. Herbaceous plants with fleshy fruits include tomato, pepper, eggplants, and the various kinds of cucurbits. Fruits are harvested when they have reached edible maturity or beyond in some cases (e.g., cucumber and eggplant). For small lots of seeds, the fruits may be cut open and the seeds within scooped out, cleaned, and dried. Commercial harvesting of these crops utilizes machines which macerate the fruit. The pulp and the seeds are then separated by fermentation, mechanical means, or washing through screens.

Fermentation is used in extracting tomato seed. The macerated fruits are placed in large barrels or vats and allowed to ferment for about 4 days at about 70°F., stirring occasionally. As the pulp releases the seeds, the heavy, sound seeds sink to the bottom of the vat and the pulp remains at the surface. Following extraction, the seeds are washed and dried either in the sun or in dehydrators. Additional cleaning is sometimes necessary to remove dried pieces of pulp and other materials. Extraction by fermentation is particularly desirable for tomato seed, because it controls bacterial canker.

Special machines have also been developed to extract and clean the seeds from the pulp in the case of cucumber and other vine crops. Following separation, the seeds are washed and dried as with the fermentation process.

Harvesting Procedures for Tree and Shrub Seed

Both dry and fleshy fruits can be collected from standing trees by shaking them onto canvas, by knocking with poles, by using cone hooks attached to long poles (in the case of conifers), or by hand picking. Collection may be made from felled trees in connection with logging operations. In some cases squirrel caches yield high quality cones. Seeds of some street trees, elm for instance, can be swept up from the street. Seeds on low trees and shrubs can be harvested by hand picking, clipping seed stalks, or knocking.

Seed viability of trees and shrubs varies considerably from year to year and from locality to locality. Before seeds are collected from any particular source, it is desirable to cut open a number of fruits and examine the seed contents to determine the percentage with sound, well-matured embryos. Such an examination is known as a *cutting test*. Although not necessarily a reliable viability test, it prevents taking seed from a source which produces only empty, unsound seed.

Dry, dehiscent fruits. Seeds are extracted from the pods and capsules of such plants as some woody legumes (honey locust), *Caragana, Ceanothus,* poplar, and willow. The fruits of these plants must be dried by spreading them in shallow layers on canvas, cloth, on the floor or shelves of open sheds, or in screen-bottom trays. Air drying will take 1 to 3 weeks.

Extraction may result from beating the pods with a flail, treading them under foot, or rubbing them through screens. For larger operations, commercial threshers are more suitable. The ordinary hammer-mill, as used to grind feed materials, has been used. A macerator, developed by the USDA Forest Service, has also been described for this purpose *(33)*. Made of metal, it is sufficiently watertight that running water can be used in it when macerating fleshy fruits. Fruits and seeds pass through the hopper and are macerated by means of a revolving cylinder like those of a threshing machine. Such machines will extract and clean 500 lbs. of seed per hour. Following extraction, the seeds may require additional cleaning to remove extraneous materials, using conventional screening or fanning mills.

Extraction of conifer cones requires special procedures. Cones of some species will open if they are dried in the open air for 2 to 12 weeks. Others must be force-dried at higher temperatures in special heating kilns. Under such conditions, the cones will open within several hours or at most 2 days. The temperature of artificial drying should be 115° to 140°F., depending upon the species, although a few require even higher temperatures. Jack pine (*Pinus banksiana*) and red pine (*P. resinosa*), for example, need temperatures of 170°F. for 5 to 6 hours. Caution must be used with high temperatures; overexposure will damage seeds. After the cones have been dried, the scales open exposing the seeds. The cones must then be shaken by tumbling or raking to remove the seeds. A revolving tumbler made of wire or a metal drum is used where large numbers of seeds are to be extracted. The seeds should be removed immediately upon drying or the cones may close.

Conifer seeds have appendages or wings which are removed except in the case of species whose seed coats are easily injured, such as fir (*Abies*) or incense cedar (*Libocedrus*). For small lots of seed, this can be done by rubbing them between moistened hands or trampling or beating the seeds packed loosely in a sack. For handling larger lots of seeds, special dewinging machines are used. As a final step, the seeds are cleaned to remove the wings and other light chaff.

Fleshy fruits. Fleshy fruits include berries (grape), drupes (peach, plum), pomes (apple, pear), aggregate fruits (raspberry, strawberry), and multiple fruits (mulberry, osage-orange). The flesh must be removed promptly to prevent spoilage and injury to the seeds *(16, 26)*. Cleaning by hand, treading in tubs, or rubbing through screens are suitable methods for small lots of seed. Relatively large fruits can be conveniently cleaned by placing the fruit in a wire basket and washing them with water from a high pressure spray machine. For larger lots of seed, the previously mentioned hammer mill and the USDA Forest Service macerator are convenient to use. Since the latter is constructed with a watertight feeder, running water can be conducted through it along with the fleshy fruits and the pulverized mass diverted into a tank where the pulp and seeds can be separated by flotation.

Flotation involves placing the seeds and pulp into water so that the

Figure 5–3. Power-operated seed cleaner for fleshy fruits. The whole fruits are placed in top of cleaner with side door closed. A stream of water from a hose washes over the fruit. A rapidly rotating plate with low vertical flanges which is raised slightly from the bottom of the cleaner removes the flesh from the fruit. This washes out through the bottom of the cleaner leaving the cleaned seeds inside, which can then be removed through the side door.

heavy, sound seeds will sink to the bottom and the lighter pulp, empty seeds, and other extraneous materials will float off the top. It can also be used for removing the poor seeds and other materials from dry fruits, such as acorn fruits infested with weevils.

Fruit tree seeds are often collected from the wastes from drying-yards, canneries, or cider presses. These seeds should be separated from the pulp and washed as quickly as convenient and not allowed to ferment or heat in the piles. Such seeds can be handled by flotation or washing with high pressure spray machines.

The small berries of some species, such as *Cotoneaster, Juniperus,* and *Viburnum,* are somewhat difficult to process because of their size and the inability to separate the seeds from the pulp easily. One way to handle such seeds is to crush them with a rolling pin, soak in water for several days, then remove the pulp by flotation. A better method for small-seeded fleshy fruits is to use an electric mixer of the type used in soda fountains *(27)* or a Waring blender. To avoid injuring the seeds, the metal blade of the latter machine can be replaced with a piece of rubber, 1½ in. sq., cut ·from a tire casing. It is fastened horizontally to the revolving axis of the machine *(39)*. A mixture of fruits and water is placed in the mixer and stirred for about 2 minutes. When the pulp has separated from the seed, the pulp is removed by flotation. With some seeds, such as junipers, it is necessary to crush the fruit first. This procedure has proven to be satisfactory for the following fruits *(27):*

barberry (*Berberis*)
buckthorn (*Rhamnus*)
buffalo berry (*Shepherdia*)
dogwood (*Cornus*)
elder (*Sambucus*)
hackberry (*Celtis*)
hawthorn (*Crataegus*)
holly (*Ilex*)
honeysuckle (*Lonicera*)
huckleberry (*Gaylussacia*)
juniper (*Juniperus*)
Magnolia
mountain ash (*Sorbus*)

persimmon (*Diospyros*)
privet (*Ligustrum*)
rose (*Rosa*)
Russian olive(*Elaeagnus angustifolia*)
Sassafras
serviceberry (*Amelanchier*)
silverberry (*Elaeagnus commutata*)
snowberry (*Symphoricarpos*)
strawberry (*Fragaria*)
tupelo (*Nyssa*)
Virginia creeper (*Parthenocissus*)
yew (*Taxus*)

SEED STORAGE

Seeds are usually stored for varying lengths of time after harvest. Viability at the end of any storage period is the result of (a) the initial viability at harvest, as determined by factors of production and methods of handling, and (b) the rate at which deterioration takes place. This rate of physiological change, or aging, is associated with (a) the kind or species of seed and (b) the environmental conditions of storage.

Some seeds are short-lived and normally lose viability rapidly, even within a few days or months or, at most, a year. This is particularly true of certain trees, such as poplar (*Populus*), some maple (*Acer*) species, willow (*Salix*), and elm (*Ulmus*), whose seeds ripen in the spring, drop to the ground, and germinate immediately. If conditions are not favorable for germination, loss of viability occurs within a few days or weeks. They can be most effectively handled by planting them relatively soon after harvest without drying. Seeds of some tropical plants, i.e., sugar cane (*Saccharum officinarum*) and rubber (*Hevea brasiliensis*), are short-lived if stored in the open air. Deterioration has been attributed to desiccation, but this is not the only factor involved. American elm seeds, normally short-lived, have been maintained for at least 15 years in sealed containers at low temperatures and at a low moisture content *(7)*. Desiccation is sometimes a factor, however, in other kinds of seeds.

Following are some woody plant seeds which are short-lived *(39)*:

Acer (some species) (maple)
Alnus (alder)
Amelanchier (serviceberry)
Ampelopsis (ampelopsis)
Aralia (aralia)
Asimina (paw paw)
Cedrus (cedar)
Cercidiphyllum (Katsura tree)

Magnolia (magnolia)
Mahonia (Oregon grape)
Myrica (bayberry)
Nandina (nandina)
Ostrya (hophornbeam)
Populus (poplar)
Potentilla (cinquefoil)
Rhus (sumac)

Chamaecyparis lawsoniana
(false cypress)
Clerodendron (glory bower)
Cryptomeria (cryptomeria)
Davidia (dove tree)
Diospyros (persimmon)
Franklinia (franklinia)
Halesia (silver bell)
Lindera (spice bush)
Liquidambar (sweetgum)
Lycium (wolfberry)

Salix (willow)
Sassafras (sassafras)
Shepherdia (buffalo berry)
Sophora (sophora)
Spiraea (spirea)
Staphylea (bladder-nut)
Stewartia (stewartia)
Styrax (snowball)
Ulmus (elm)
Zelkova (zelkova)

Seeds which may be considered to be medium-lived are those which would remain viable for periods of 2 or 3 up to perhaps 15 years, depending upon storage conditions. Seeds of most commercially grown vegetables, flowers, and grains fall somewhere within this range.

Seeds which are long-lived under ordinary methods of handling generally have hard seed coats that are impermeable to water and gases. If the hard seed coat remains undamaged, such seeds should remain viable for at least 15 to 20 years. The maximum life can be as long as 75 to 100 years and perhaps more. Records exist of seeds being kept in museum cupboards for 150 to 200 years, some still retaining viability. The most authentic record of maximum longevity has been reported with Indian lotus (*Nelumbo nucifera*) seeds which germinated perfectly when the impermeable seed coats were cracked after being buried in a Manchurian peat bog for an estimated 250 years *(24)*. Later tests with radioactive carbon indicated the age of these seeds to be nearly 1000 years *(22)*. Reports of seeds being viable after storage in Egyptian tombs since ancient times have never been authenticated. Certain weed seeds can retain viability for many years (50 to 70 years or more) while buried in the soil even though they have imbibed moisture *(14, 30, 32)*.

Factors Affecting Seed Storage

The storage conditions that maintain seed viability are those which slow down respiration and other life processes without injuring the embryo. The most important conditions to achieve this result are a proper moisture content of the seed, a reduced storage temperature, and a modification of the storage atmosphere. Of these, the temperature-moisture relationships have the most practical significance.

Moisture. Seeds of a few kinds of plants lose viability if the moisture content becomes low. For instance, in a study of silver maple (*Acer saccharinum*) seeds, the moisture content was found to be 58 per cent in June when the seeds matured. Viability was lost when the moisture content dropped below 30 to 34 per cent *(18)*. Citrus seeds can withstand only slight drying *(5, 10).* The same is true with some water plants, such as wild rice (*Zizania aquatica*) and the large and fleshy seeds of the oaks (*Quercus*), hickories (*Carya*), and walnut (*Juglans*) *(11).* The reduction of temperature to just above freezing will prolong the storage life of these seeds.

TABLE 5–1

ESTIMATED MAXIMUM SAFE SEED-MOISTURE CONTENTS FOR STORAGE FOR ONE YEAR AT DIFFERENT TEMPERATURES OF STORAGE (APPROXIMATE GUIDE ONLY)*

Kind of Seed	Maximum Safe Seed-Moisture Content (Per Cent) For Average Temperature of Storage Indicated		
	40°F.–50°F.	70°F.	80°F.
Bean, kidney	15	11	8
Bean, lima	15	11	8
Beet	14	11	9
Cabbage	9	7	5
Carrot	13	9	7
Celery	13	9	7
Corn, sweet	14	10	8
Cucumber	11	9	8
Lettuce	10	7	5
Okra	14	12	10
Onion	11	8	6
Pea, garden	15	13	9
Peanut (shelled)	6	5	3
Pepper	10	9	7
Spinach	13	11	9
Tomato	13	11	9
Turnip	10	8	6
Watermelon	10	8	7

* (Adapted from Table 2, USDA Leaflet 220)

On the other hand, seeds of most species of plants must have a low moisture content to survive long periods of storage. A moisture content of 4 to 6 per cent is about the most favorable for prolonged storage *(12),* although a somewhat higher moisture content is allowable if the temperature is reduced *(28).* The moisture content of seeds will vary with the relative humidity of the storage atmosphere. Different kinds of seeds vary in their actual moisture content, which is in equilibrium with any given relative humidity *(3).* Fluctuations in the moisture content of the seed, which can occur if they are exposed to the open atmosphere, reduce seed longevity *(4).* Seed storage in areas of high humidity, such as in the tropics, may be difficult because of the inability to maintain low air moisture in open storage *(25).*

Storage in sealed containers is of considerable advantage, but the moisture content must be low at the time of sealing. Seeds sealed at a moisture content of 10 to 12 per cent have had a shorter storage life than those left unsealed. Reduction of the moisture content to 4 to 6 per cent before sealing greatly increased storage life *(13)*.

Temperature. Studies by numerous investigators have consistently shown the benefits of reduced temperature in lengthening the storage life of seeds *(29)*. In general, a reduction in temperature can offset the adverse effect of a higher moisture content. However, seeds stored at low temperature but at a high relative humidity may lose viability rapidly when moved to a warmer temperature *(6)*.

Sub-freezing temperatures are usually superior to higher temperatures *(7, 29)*. The optimum cold temperature is not known, but in seeds of several conifers—*Pinus ponderosa, Pseudotsuga taxifolia, Picea sitchensis, Thuja plicata* and *Tsuga heterophylla*—stored in canvas bags at 0°F., 14°F., and 25°F., the lower the temperature the better the retention of viability *(9)*. After 4 years of storage, a temperature of 4°F. was found to be more favorable than 32°F. for a number of vegetable and flower seeds *(35)*.

The combination of low moisture content, sealed containers, and low temperature provides the most desirable seed storage conditions known. This combination of conditions is particularly valuable in prolonging the storage life of normally short-lived seeds. In studies with Douglas fir (*Pseudotsuga taxifolia*) and Western hemlock (*Tsuga heterophylla*), full viability was retained for 36 months at 0°F. in sealed containers at 5.8 and 13.6 per cent moisture and at 41°F. at 5.8 per cent moisture but not at 13.6 per cent. Viability was not retained in open storage at 0°F. or 41°F. The beneficial effect of low temperature storage was carried over into the seeds after they were removed from storage, packaged, and held preparatory to planting *(8)*.

In spite of the advantage in prolonging storage life by very low temperatures, the actual storage conditions utilized in practice would probably be those which would provide sufficient longevity for the needs of the propagator or seed handler. For the large group of medium-lived seeds, which includes most of the commonly grown crop and vegetable plants, storage at 32° to 50°F. and at a relative humidity of 50 to 65 per cent, is generally adequate to maintain full viability for at least a year and in many cases for several years *(38)*. Lower temperatures would be desirable for seeds which deteriorate rapidly or when the maximum possible storage life might be desired for a particular reason, for instance, in maintaining breeding stock *(35)*.

Storage atmosphere. The use of modified storage atmospheres has been shown experimentally to increase longevity of some seeds. Its use has been limited to those seeds which are particularly transitory in their viability. Tropical seeds such as those of sugar cane (*Saccharum officinarum*) and rubber (*Hevea brasiliensis*) deteriorate rapidly in the open air. Viability of *Hevea* seeds was prolonged by sealed storage in 40 to 45 per cent carbon dioxide *(20)*. Likewise, sugar cane seed viability was lengthened by sealing the air-dry seeds in cans with 9 gr. of calcium chloride for each liter of space, displacing the air with carbon dioxide and storing near freezing *(34)*.

Types of Seed Storage

Dry storage, without temperature control. The room or air temperature will be the temperature of storage. The difficulty of maintaining viability increases with an increase in temperature.

The moisture content of the seed should be low. Seeds should be dry (4 to 6 per cent), but in some seeds it may be higher (8 to 12 per cent—see Table 5–1). The moisture content varies with the relative humidity, and the effect on viability varies with the temperature and kind of seed.

The relative humidity of storage should be 50 per cent or less.

Containers for storage should be open bins or sacks placed in storage houses. The containers or places of storage may need to be fumigated or treated with an insecticide. Sealed containers should be used to control insects and rodents and to maintain viability if the relative humidity of the storage atmosphere is high. Seeds *must* be dry when sealed.

This type of storage can be used for a great number of commercial seeds for periods of at least 1 year if the moisture is controlled; many seeds will retain viability for considerably longer periods. Most agricultural seeds, such as cereals, grasses, or forage crops, will retain viability for 4 or 5 years or more.

Approximate storage periods for vegetable seeds are as follows *(23):*

1 year—sweet corn, onion, parsley, parsnip
2 years—beet, pepper
3 years—asparagus, bean, celery, carrot, lettuce, pea, spinach, tomato
4 years—cabbage, cauliflower, eggplant, okra, pumpkin, radish, squash
5 years—cucumber, endive, muskmelon, watermelon

The following information concerning storage of various flower seeds represents individual samples stored over a period of 10 years *(15)*. It gives an approximate guide for handling such seeds and shows the range of years of longevity represented by such seeds. These seeds retained 50 per cent of their original viability at the times indicated.

1 year or less—*Delphinium* (perennial), *Iberis umbellata* (candytuft), *Kochia* .

2 years—*Callistephus chinensis* (aster), *Helichrysum monstrosus* (straw flower), *Kochia trichophylla* (summer cypress)

3 years—*Callistephus chinensis* (aster), *Centaurea candidissima* (dusty miller), *Delphinium chinensis, Phlox drummondi, Verbena*

4 years—*Delphinium* (larkspur), *Iberis*

5 to 10 years—

Althea rosea
Alyssum maritimum
Arctotis grandis (African daisy)
Calendula
Calliopsis
Centaurea
Chrysanthemum leucanthemum
  (Shasta daisy)
C. segetum
Cosmos
Dianthus
Eschscholtzia californica
  (California poppy)
Gilia capitata

Lathyrus odoratus (sweet pea)
Mathiola (stock)
Nigella damascena (love-in-a-mist)
Papaver (Shirley poppy)
Petunia
Salpiglossis
Scabiosa grandiflora
Schizanthus (butterfly flower)
Tagetes (marigold)
Tropaeolum majus (nasturtium)
Verbena
Viola (pansy)
Zinnia

Seeds which have a water-impervious seed coat will retain viability for many years (i.e., 10 to 20 years or more) once they have been dried. Open storage is adequate. Seeds of some of the woody plants which are handled in this manner are the following:

Acacia sp. (acacia)
Albizzia sp. (albizzia)
Amorpha fruticosa (indigo bush)
Caragana arborescens
  (Siberian pea shrub)
Elaeagnus sp. (Russian olive)

Eucalyptus sp. (eucalyptus)
Koelreuteria paniculata (golden rain tree)
Rhus ovata (sumac)
Robinia pseudoacacia (locust)
Tilia (linden)

Cold, dry storage. The temperature of storage should usually be 33° to 50°F.; below freezing temperatures are useful for very long storage.

The moisture content of the seed should be low. Seeds preferably should be dry (4 to 6 per cent), but some seeds could have a moisture content of 12 to 15 per cent (see Table 5–1).

The relative humidity of storage should be 50 to 60 per cent or less.

Seeds could be stored in a cool basement, unheated shed, or even out-of-doors during the winter. The best results are achieved in refrigerated rooms with temperature control. Sealed containers with low moisture content are desirable for long storage or for some normally short-lived seed.

Almost without exception, seeds of any of the species listed for warm, dry storage would keep longer and better in cold storage. Whether or not it would be economical depends upon the difficulty of maintaining viability under less expensive conditions and the length of time that it is necessary to maintain the viability of the seed.

Cold storage of tree and shrub seeds used in nursery production is generally advisable if the seeds are to be held for longer than 1 year *(33, 39)*, except in the case of the hard-coated seeds listed previously. Specific information concerning expected longevity is lacking for many seeds, but the following have been listed as being best held cold and dry:

Abies sp. (fir)
Acer (some species) (maple)
Arbutus sp. (madrone)
Berberis sp. (barberry)
Ceanothus sp. (ceanothus)
Celtis sp. (hackberry)
Cercis sp. (redbud)
Cupressus sp. (cypress)
Fraxinus sp. (ash)
Gaylussacia (huckleberry)
Gleditsia dioca (Kentucky coffee tree)
Hamamelis sp. (witch hazel)
Juniperus sp. (juniper)
Larix sp. (larch)
Liquidambar sp. (sweetgum)
Maclura pomifera (osage orange)
Malus sp. (apple)
Picea sp. (spruce)

Pinus sp. (pine)
Platanus sp. (sycamore)
Populus sp. (poplar)
Prunus sp. (stone fruits)
Pseudotsuga taxifolia (Douglas fir)
Ptelea trifoliata (hoptree)
Rhus sp. (sumac)
Rubus sp. (blackberry)
Sambucus sp. (elder)
Sassafras albidum (sassafras)
Sequoia sp. (sequoia)
Sorbus sp. (mountain ash)
Symphoricarpos sp. (snowberry)
Thuja sp. (arborvitae)
Tsuga sp. (hemlock)
Vitex sp. (chaste tree)
Vitis sp. (grape)
Zanthoxylum (prickly ash)

Cold, moist storage. The temperature of storage should be 32° to 50°F. Seeds should be placed in a sealed container which will maintain their moisture content or else be mixed with moisture-retaining material. This procedure is similar to stratification (as described on p. 127).

Plants requiring this treatment are:

Acer sp. (maple) particularly A. *saccharinum*)
Aesculus sp. (buckeye)
Carpinus caroliniana (American hop hornbeam)
Carya sp. (hickory)
Castanea sp. (chestnut)

Corylus sp. (filbert)
Citrus sp. (citrus)
Fagus sp. (beech)
Juglans sp. (walnut)
Nyssa silvatica (tupelo)
Quercus sp. (oak)

REFERENCES

1. Allard, R. W., Production of dry edible lima beans in California, *Calif. Agr. Exp. Sta. Circ. 423*:1–27. 1953.
2. Associated Seed Growers, Inc., A study of mechanical injury to seed beans, *Asgrow Monograph No. 1.* New Haven, Conn., 1949.
3. Barton, L. V., Relation of certain air temperatures and humidities to viability of seeds, *Contrib. Boyce Thomp. Inst.,* 12:85–102. 1941.

4. ————, Effect of moisture fluctuations on the viability of seeds in storage, *Contrib. Boyce Thomp. Inst.,* 13:35–45. 1943.

5. ————, The storage of some citrus seeds, *Contrib. Boyce Thomp. Inst.,* 13:47–55. 1943.

6. ————, Seed packets and onion seed viability, *Contrib. Boyce Thomp. Inst.,* 15:341–352. 1949.

7. ————, Seed storage and viability, *Contrib. Boyce Thomp. Inst.,* 17:87–103. 1953.

8. ————, Storage and packeting of seeds of Douglas fir and Western hemlock, *Contrib. Boyce Thomp. Inst.,* 18:25–37. 1954.

9. ————, Effect of subfreezing temperatures on viability of conifer seeds in storage, *Contrib. Boyce Thomp. Inst.,* 18:21–24. 1954.

10. Childs, J. F. L., and G. Hrnciar, A method of maintaining viability of citrus seeds in storage, *Proc. Fla. State Hort. Soc.,* 64:69. 1948.

11. Crocker, Wm., Life-span of seeds, *Bot. Rev.,* 4:235–274. 1938.

12. ————, *Growth of Plants.* New York: Reinhold, 1948.

13. Crocker, Wm., and L. V. Barton, *Physiology of Seeds.* Waltham, Mass.: Chronica Botanica, 1953.

14. Darlington, H. T., The seventy-year period for Dr. Beal's seed viability experiment, *Amer. Jour. Bot.,* 38:379–381. 1951.

15. Goss, W. L., Germination of flower seeds stored for ten years in the California state seed laboratory, *Calif. Dept. Agr. Bul.* 26:326–333. 1937.

16. Haut, I. C., and F. E. Gardner, The influence of pulp disintegration upon viability of peach seeds, *Proc. Amer. Soc. Hort. Sci.,* 32:323–327. 1934.

17. Hawthorn, L. R., and L. H. Pollard, *Vegetable and Flower Seed Production.* Philadelphia: Blakiston, 1954.

18. Jones, H. A., Physiological study of maple seeds, *Bot. Gaz.,* 69:127–152. 1920.

19. Jones, L. J., et al., Alfalfa seed harvesting, *Calif. Agr.,* 2:8, 9, 16. 1950.

20. Kidd, F., The controlling influence of carbon dioxide in the maturation, dormancy and germination of seeds, Part II, *Proc. Royal Soc.,* 87:609–625. 1914.

21. Kjaer, A., Germination of buried and dry stored seed, *Proc. Int. Seed Test. Assoc.,* 12:167–190. 1940.

22. Libby, W. F., Radiocarbon dates, *Science,* 114: 291–296. 1951.

23. MacGillivray, J. H., *Vegetable Production.* Philadelphia: Blakiston, 1953.

24. Ohga, I., The germination of century old and recently harvested Indian lotus with special reference to the effect of oxygen supply, *Amer. Jour. Bot.,* 13:754–759. 1926.

25. Rodrigo, P. A., Some studies on the storing of tropical and temperate seeds in the Philippines, *Rpt. 13th Int. Hort. Cong.,* 2:1061–1066. 1952.

26. Scott, D. H., J. G. Waugh, and F. P. Cullinan, An injurious effect of peach juice on germination of the seed, *Proc. Amer. Soc. Hort. Sci.,* 40:283–285. 1942.

27. Smith, B. C., Cleaning and processing seeds, *Amer. Nurs.,* 92(11):13–14, 33–35. 1950.

28. Toole, E. H., Storage of vegetable seeds, *USDA Leaflet No. 220:*1–8. 1942.

29. ————, Relation of seed processing and of conditioning during storage on seed germination, *Proc. Int. Seed Test. Assoc.,* 16:214–227. 1950.

30. Toole, E. H., and E. Brown, Final results of the Duvel buried seed experiment, *Jour. Agr. Res.,* 72:201–210. 1946.

31. Toole, E. H., et al., Injury to seed beans during threshing and processing, *USDA Circ. 874:*1–10. 1951.

32. Toole, V. K., and E. H. Toole, Seed dormancy in relation to seed longevity, *Proc. Int. Seed Test. Assoc.,* 18:325–327. 1953.

33. USDA, Woody plant seed manual, *Misc. Pub. No. 654,* 1948.
34. Verret, J. A., Sugar cane seedlings, *Assoc. Hawaii Sugar Technol. Rpts.,* 7:15–23. 1928.
35. Weibull, G., The cold storage of vegetable seed and its significance for plant breeding and the seed trade, *Rpt. 13th Int. Hort. Cong.,* 2:1083–1090. 1952.
36. Welch, G. B., Seed processing equipment, *Miss. Agr. Exp. Sta. Bul. 520:*1–22. 1954.
37. Wells, J. S., *Plant Propagation Practices.* New York: Macmillan, 1955.
38. Wright, R. C., D. H. Rose, and T. M. Whiteman, The commercial storage of fruits, vegetables, and florist and nursery stocks, *USDA Handbook No. 66:*1–77. 1954.
39. Wyman, D., Seeds of woody plants, *Arnoldia,* 13:41–60. 1953.

Supplementary Reading

Hawthorn, L. R., and L. H. Pollard, *Vegetable and Flower Seed Production.* Philadelphia: Blakiston, 1954.

United States Department of Agriculture, *Woody Plant Seed Manual,* Miscellaneous Publication No. 654. Washington, D.C.: U.S. Government Printing Office, 1948.

United States Department of Agriculture Forest Service, *Tree Planters' Notes.* Washington, D.C.: U.S. Government Printing Office.

Wheeler, W. A., and D. D. Hill, *Grassland Seeds.* New York: Van Nostrand, 1957.

6

Principles of Seed Propagation

A seed contains an embryonic plant supplied with stored food and surrounded by protective seed coats and, in some cases, other enveloping structures. After the seed is separated from the mother plant, it remains in a state of apparent inactivity for a period of time. The process in which activity resumes in the seed, with the embryo developing into a new plant, is termed *germination;* the young plant while still dependent upon the reserve foods of the seed is the *seedling.*

Germination has three basic requirements. First, the seed must be *viable;* that is, the embryo must be alive and capable of germination. Second, the seed must be subjected to favorable *environmental conditions,* the essential factors being available water, proper temperature, and a supply of oxygen. Third, any *internal condition* which prevents germination even when the environment is favorable must be overcome. To overcome such conditions, certain pre-germination treatments may be necessary.

THE GERMINATION PROCESS

The germination process is a complex series of biochemical and physiological changes which involves the initiation of growth and the mobilization of reserve foods within the seed to be utilized by the embryo in growth. The first step in the sequence of events which takes place during germination is the imbibition of water by the seed. As the seed coats soften and the protoplasm becomes hydrated, the seed will usually swell, sometimes rupturing the seed coats. Water uptake is followed by increased enzyme activity and an increase in respiration, as measured by the uptake of oxygen. These activities are followed by cell elongation and the emergence of the radicle through the seed covering. These events are associated with the onset of germination *(68).* For germination to continue, complex insoluble storage materials must be digested enzymatically to simpler, soluble materials and translocated to the growing points where they are assimilated to provide energy for growth or for conversion into new cell material. The seedling grows by the usual processes of division, enlargement, and differentiation of cells at the growing points. The seedling depends upon reserves in the seed for continuing development until such time as the leaves can function adequately for photosynthesis. In summary, germination takes place in the following steps: imbibition, enzymatic and respiratory activity, digestion, translocation, assimilation, growth.

As germination proceeds, the structure of the seedling soon becomes evident. The embryo consists of a hypocotyl-root axis bearing one or more seed leaves, or *cotyledons.* The growing point of the root, the *radicle,* emerges from the lower end of the hypocotyl-root axis. The growing point of the shoot, the *plumule,* is at the other end of the hypocotyl-root axis, above the cotyledons. The seedling stem is divided into the section below the cotyledons—the *hypocotyl*—and the section above the cotyledons— the *epicotyl.* In practice the terms epicotyl and plumule are often used interchangeably.

The initial growth of the seedling follows two patterns. In one type— *epigeous* germination—the hypocotyl elongates and raises the cotyledons above the ground. In the other type—*hypogeous* germination—the lengthening of the hypocotyl does not raise the cotyledons above the ground and only the epicotyl emerges.

VIABILITY OF SEEDS

A supply of viable seed is an essential factor in successful seed propagation. Reduced seed viability may result from improper seed development on the plant, injuries during harvest, improper handling procedures during processing and storage, and aging. Viability is represented by the *germination percentage* which expresses the number of seedlings which can be produced by a given amount of seed.

Germination should be prompt and growth of the seedling vigorous as indicated by a rapid rate of germination. The latter characteristic is often referred to as the seed *vitality,* or *germinating power.* Embryos with a low germination rate or embryos which produce weak and abnormal seedlings are less able to withstand unfavorable environmental conditions in

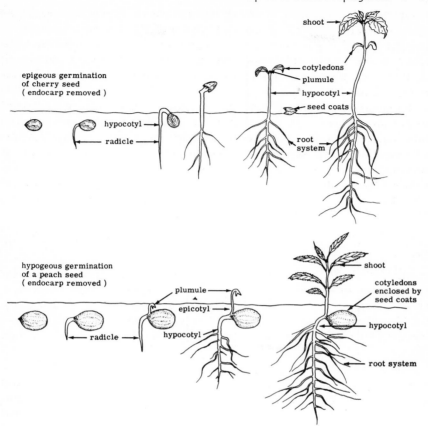

Figure 6–1. (above) Epigeous germination of cherry. The cotyledons are above ground. **(below)** Hypogeous germination of peach. The cotyledons remain below ground.

the seed bed than more vigorous seedlings. Since weak seedlings are subject to attack by disease organisms, field survival is apt to be less than a predetermined germination percentage would indicate.

MEASUREMENT OF GERMINATION

The measurement of germination involves two factors—the germination percentage and the germination rate. In seeds of low viability, these two factors are often associated. That is, if a seed lot has a low germination percentage, those which germinate will likely have a slow rate of germination. In seeds which have been stored for long periods, reduced viability is usually preceded by a period of declining vitality *(71)*.

On the other hand, the germination rate can be strongly influenced by other conditions not associated with viability. For instance, some kinds of seed naturally germinate more rapidly than others. In some cases, the rate of germination is dependent upon the degree of dormancy still present in the seed. Environmental conditions also strongly affect germination rates, as noted later in this chapter.

Germination percentage will usually involve a time element, indicating the number of seedlings produced within a specified length of time. Germination rate can be expressed by specifying the number of days required to produce a given percentage of germinated seeds. Another way of expressing germination is by the *coefficient of velocity,* according to the following formula *(44):*

$$\text{Coefficient of velocity} = \frac{\text{Total number of seedlings} \times 100}{A_1T_1 + A_2T_2 \ldots + A_xT_x}$$

where $A =$ the number of seedlings emerging on a particular number of days *(T).* Figure 6–2 compares these three methods of measurement on two vegetable seeds.

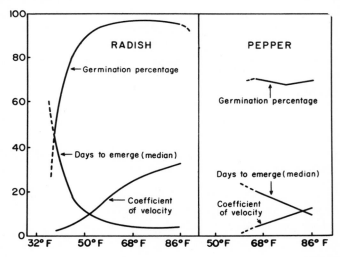

Figure 6–2. The effect of temperature upon germination as shown by three different methods of measurement: germination percentage, germination rate, and coefficient of velocity. From data of Kotowski **(44).**

SEED DORMANCY

The term *dormancy* is used in plant physiology to refer to a state of reduced activity of the plant or plant part in which readily discernible growth does not occur *(54).* It may be due to the external effects of the environment, to internal conditions within the plant part itself (the *rest period,* see p. 202), or to the inhibiting influence of adjacent plant parts, particularly buds. Likewise, the embryo of a seed remains in a state of apparent inactivity from the time it develops in the plant to the time that it germinates. Failure to germinate, assuming the embryo is viable, may be due to factors similar to those stated above, which prevent growth.

Failure to germinate may be due to a lack of one or more of the required environmental conditions—moisture, favorable temperature, or oxygen. This may be referred to as *external* dormancy caused by conditions outside the seed itself. *Internal* factors can also prevent germination even though all environmental factors are favorable. These may result from (a) conditions existing within the embryo (*embryo dormancy*) or (b) the influence of some of the enclosing seed parts on the embryo (*seed coat dormancy*).These seed coverings may mechanically inhibit water uptake, restrict movements of gases, or resist embryo expansion. Chemical inhibition by specific substances in some part of the seed or fruit may also occur (*inhibitor dormancy*). It is also possible to have combinations of two or more types of dormancy.

In some cases, it is not certain what specific factor prevents germination. Seeds of some plants (e.g., certain cereals, grasses, vegetables, and flower seeds) fail to germinate when freshly harvested but do germinate after a period of dry storage. Such conditions may disappear with normal handling, and the propagator may not know of its earlier existence. Seeds of certain plants, such as some lettuce varieties and some flowers, germinate readily at moderately cool temperatures but become dormant at temperatures of approximately 75°F. or higher. Light can control germination in seeds of some plants.

The term *dormancy* as it relates to seeds is restricted by many seed technologists to nongermination caused only by internal factors *(7, 24, 74, 75).* In this sense, a *dormant seed* is one which fails to germinate because an internal condition of some part of the seed prevents germination, even though external environmental conditions are favorable. (The term *rest* is sometimes used for this condition.) Internal dormancy is indicated if specific pre-germination treatments (as listed in Chapter 7) are necessary to induce germination or if the environmental conditions necessary for germination (see appropriate sections in this chapter) change with the age of the seed. The changes taking place in the seed which enable germination to take place promptly under "normal" growing conditions are collectively known as *after-ripening.*

Two additional terms have been used in describing seed dormancy *(14).* When dormancy can be demonstrated at the time the seeds have matured on the plant, it is termed *primary dormancy. Secondary dormancy* is that which can be induced in a seed by subjecting it to specific environmental conditions. Some forms of dormancy are therefore reversible and can be induced and overcome under appropriate conditions.

Since there has been a tendency in the development of cultivated plants to select varieties which do not have germination problems, most complex cases of dormancy are found in wild plants or in trees and shrubs. In some cases germination can occur, but it is erratic and slow and can be improved by pre-germination treatment. In others, dormancy may last for periods of several months to several years and special pre-germination treatments are necessary for successful propagation.

There is a considerable fund of knowledge available concerning methods of obtaining prompt germination of specific seeds. An understanding of the underlying physiological mechanisms involved is less satisfactory. Knowledge of both phases of the problem is incomplete, and many questions concerning seed dormancy and germination still remain unanswered. In the absence of specific information, the propagator would do well to simulate as closely as possible the natural environment of the particular plant and natural germinating conditions of its seed.

Seed dormancy is particularly significant in nature, because it contributes to natural survival. One of its most important effects in nature is to prevent germination immediately following ripening when conditions are often adverse to the survival of the seedlings. The prevention of premature germination facilitates the dissemination of plants either by natural means or by man. As a result, the species may spread to other areas with perhaps more favorable environments. Since the degree of dormancy can vary between individual seeds of a given lot, germination within a particular species may take place over a period of years. If those which germinate at a certain time are lost, other seeds will remain to germinate at a later and perhaps more favorable time.

With cultivated plants, dormancy has certain disadvantages. Some degree of dormancy is beneficial with freshly harvested seeds, since it prevents premature germination that might occur on the plant or in the harvest field. On the other hand, pre-germination seed treatments necessary for good, uniform germination are often expensive and time-consuming. Where reliable pre-germination treatments are unknown, germination may be unsatisfactory, and reduced stands of plants result. Particular difficulties are experienced in the testing of seeds for viability and may prevent the seed tester from getting quick and reliable results.

Seed Coverings Which Prevent Water Uptake

Impermeability of the seed coverings to water is a common cause of dormancy in seeds and one which is relatively easy to overcome. Species with hard seed coats are found in a number of plant families, including the Leguminosae, Malvaceae, Cannaceae, Geraniaceae, Chenopodiaceae, Convallariaceae, Convolvulaceae, Solanaceae, and others (15). The plant group most commonly associated with hardseededness is the legumes, in which are found clover, alfalfa, and similar agricultural plants, as well as locust (*Robinia*), *Acacia,* and other woody legumes. A hard, impervious coat has value in prolonging storage life, since the internal parts of such seeds, once dry, are held permanently in sealed storage until the seed coverings become modified. The seed covering which is effective may be only the hardened outer seed coat, or it may include various parts of the pericarp which are either attached to the seed or surround it.

Impermeability of the seed covering is characteristic of certain species. Yet it can sometimes be modified during seed development or by the treatment the seed receives at harvest or during storage. For instance, it is reported that white clover seeds are hard when ripened in hot, dry weather but are soft when ripened during rainy weather *(15)*. If seeds of some woody plant species are dried following harvest, a hard seed coat develops, and germination does not take place until the second spring following harvest. If, on the other hand, the seeds are fall planted without drying, germination takes place the following spring *(81)*. Changes in the degree of hardness can take place during storage. For instance, in studies of *Symphoricarpos,* as the length of the time after harvest increased, the length of the sulfuric acid treatment required to soften the coats also increased *(27)*. In some cases, seeds which normally do not have hard seed coats, such as beans, develop hardseededness with dry storage and when planted fail to germinate unless pre-treated *(51)*. These effects probably account for the fact that different lots of seeds and even seeds within a single lot may vary in the required treatment to bring about germination.

Seeds with hard seed coverings may be germinated with little difficulty by any method of breaking or modifying the seed coat, providing another type of dormancy is not also present. In nature, softening of the seed coat comes about through agencies of the environment. Exposure of hard seeds to alternate freezing and thawing outdoors over winter results in permeability of seeds in many cases. The activity of microorganisms in the soil has also been shown to be a highly significant agent of decomposition *(27)*. Fungi activity takes place at relatively warm temperatures (around 50°F. or higher) but does not occur to any appreciable amount at lower temperatures. For effective seed coat decomposition, the seeds must be held moist at warm temperatures in the soil. Addition of nitrates to the medium has increased the effect of seed softening, presumably because it stimulated fungi activity *(28)*.

Seed Coverings Mechanically Resistant to Embryo Expansion

In most seeds, once water is absorbed, the expanding pressure of the embryo during germination is sufficient to rupture the seed coats. However, the seed coverings can sometimes offer mechanical resistance to embryo expansion. In the olive, for instance, the seed is surrounded by a thick, bony, indehiscent endocarp which is both mechanically hard and water impermeable. The hard seed covering of *Symphoricarpos* is indehiscent, but water can be absorbed through the micropyle *(27)*. Other seed structures, such as the "pits" of stone fruits and the shells of walnuts and other nuts, are extremely hard and may produce temporary resistance to germination. These structures are dehiscent, and water can be absorbed through the dehiscent layer separating the two halves. Softening also takes place in this layer. The seeds of certain weeds, i.e., *Amaranthus retroflexus* and *Alisma plantago,* are also reported to have hard coats *(14)*.

The force required to overcome resistance of the freshly harvested seeds of black walnut (*Juglans nigra*) and hickory (*Carya sp.*) is considerably greater than that of the calculated breaking force of the embryo during germination *(17)*. That this was a factor in germination was shown by the fact that if the section of the shell over the radicle tip was removed, the radicle could emerge. During moist storage, the calculated shell resistance decreased markedly, but the decrease was greater at higher temperatures. This softening effect could be attributed mainly to the activity of microorganisms, since walnuts stored for 150 days under sterile conditions did not soften, whereas those stored under nonsterile conditions softened within a few weeks. Mechanical breaks or cracks in thin-walled shells may also come about during harvesting or after drying.

Seed Coats Which Restrict Gaseous Exchange to the Embryo

Dormancy in some seeds has been attributed to the restriction on the movement of gases to and from the embryo by the inner membranous seed coat or an enclosing nucellus or endosperm layer. Evidence for this is shown by the fact that prompt germination can usually be obtained by excising the embryo or altering the seed covering of freshly harvested seed which are light sensitive or temperature sensitive *(2, 11, 25)* or by increasing the oxygen content of the surrounding atmosphere *(41)*. Some investigators have attributed this effect to the accumulation of carbon dioxide arising from respiration within the seed *(32, 41)*.

One of the most extensively studied examples of the effect of the seed coats in relation to oxygen requirements is cocklebur (*Xanthium*). The cocklebur fruit contains two seeds, a lower seed and an upper seed. Normally the lower seed germinates immediately. In the field, the upper seed requires 1 or 2 years before it germinates. Prompt germination of one of the two seeds of the fruit and the delayed germination of the other has been attributed to a differential ability of the inner seed covering to restrict the movement of gases *(66)*. More recent investigations with this seed have indicated the existence of inhibitors within the embryo which are incapable of being leached out of the intact seed but disappeared if the seed is subjected to high oxygen tension or if the embryo is excised and leached *(80)*.

Dormant Embryos

Plant propagators have known for many years that seeds of certain temperate zone species must be stored—moist—over winter in the ground or in boxes between layers of moist sand or soil (*stratification*) before germination will occur. During this time, internal *after-ripening* changes take place within the seed that lead to germination.

Figure 6–3. Effect of lack of moisture or lack of oxygen during stratification upon subsequent germination of Winter Nelis pear seeds. Stratified in moist peat moss and sand at 32° F. for 110 days.
(A) Unstratified control.
(B) Stratified dry.
(C) Stratified moist.
(D) Stratified moist but in sealed container to exclude air.

Conditions required for effective stratification include (a) reduced temperatures, (b) imbibition of moisture by the seed, (c) good aeration, and (d) a certain length of time. The range of temperatures at which these changes take place is from near freezing up to 55° to 60°F., although changes take place most rapidly around 37° to 45°F. Warm temperatures, on the other hand, can reverse the process and induce secondary dormancy *(26, 77)*. The equilibrium temperature between after-ripening and the induction of secondary dormancy by warm temperatures has been determined to be 59°F. in apple seeds *(1)*. Subfreezing temperatures are not involved in after-ripening and may cause injury to moist seeds.

Drying during stratification will stop the after-ripening process and is thought to produce secondary dormancy *(36)*, although some investigators have not been able to produce it in this manner *(77)*. Reduced aeration will slow or stop after-ripening. Such treatment has been used experimentally to induce secondary dormancy, following which seeds normally not requiring stratification had to be given a cold treatment to produce germination *(18, 19, 67)*.

Figure 6–4. Effect of length of stratification period at 32° F. on germination of **Prunus mahaleb** seeds.
(A) Stratified for 127 days.
(B) Stratified for 89 days.
(C) Stratified for 39 days.
(D) Unstratified.

The time required for after-ripening varies among species, among clonal varieties within a given species, and even among different seed lots of the same kind grown in different areas or in different years *(72, 74)*. Also, individual seeds of a single lot may require longer stratification than others. It is apparent that this time requirement is a genetic characteristic, but it can be modified to some degree by other factors—perhaps by the conditions under which the seed is produced or by the methods of handling the seeds before stratification *(55, 79)*. The usual time required to stratify seeds is from 1 to 3 months although in some cases 5 to 6 months may be necessary.

The physiological changes which take place within the embryo or endosperm during after-ripening are not known. Studies measuring changes taking place in seeds being stratified have shown increasing water-absorbing power, increasing enzyme activity, increasing acidity, and a gradual change of the insoluble complex storage materials into soluble, simpler substances *(15)*. It has been pointed out, however, that such changes also occur during germination and may not represent after-ripening changes but the increasing ability of the seeds to germinate with stratification *(37)*. Some studies have correlated after-ripening changes with the hydrolysis of

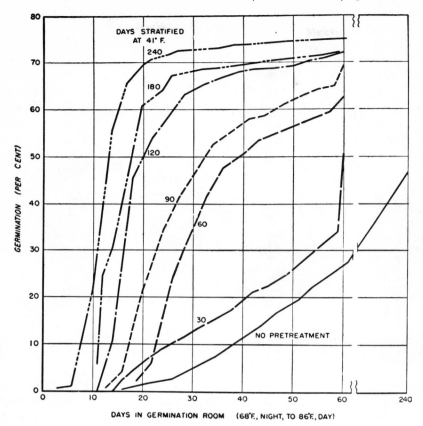

Figure 6–5. The effect of stratification for different periods of time upon the germination of **Abies balsamea** seeds. This shows that stratification may improve germination by increasing both percentage and rate of germination even though some germination can take place without it. From **USDA Misc. Pub. No. 654.**

reserve proteins to specific amino acids. In the species studied, after-ripening involved morphological growth of the embryo *(62)*.

Embryos excised from the dormant seed and placed under favorable conditions will show characteristic types of germination response *(26, 30)*. This may be used to measure viability in such seeds (see p. 120). The dormant embryo may absorb water, increase in size, become green, but produce little or no radicle or pumule growth. Unless subjected to low temperatures, the embryo can remain in this condition for some time. If, on the other hand, the embryo is nonviable at the time of excision it will become brown, flaccid, and will usually deteriorate because of fungus attack.

Some excised embryos germinate without chilling but produce abnormal seedlings. After a period of initial growth the epicotyl becomes dormant.

Figure 6–6 Appearance of Lovell peach seedlings with and without a prior seed stratification period. **(left)** Normal seedling from an after-ripened seed. **(center)** A dwarfed seedling from a nonafter-ripened seed. **(right)** A dwarfed seedling from a nonafter-ripened seed, showing the curled, abnormal leaves which often appear.

A rosetted, dwarfish seedling results due to the failure of internodes to elongate. The midribs of the leaves may also fail to elongate so that the leaves may be curled or abnormally small. The radicle, on the other hand, does not become dormant, and an extensive root system may develop.

Such dwarfed seedlings can be maintained for long periods in a warm greenhouse but resumption of shoot growth may eventually take place, often from a lateral growing point rather than the terminal bud. Although such growth may sometimes begin even with no apparent external stimulus, the most effective method to induce growth is to subject the dwarf seedlings to chilling temperatures for 6 to 8 weeks. High temperatures and increased light will encourage seedlings to continue growth without becoming dwarfed *(29, 45)*. In general, the effect of light is exerted before the dwarfing of the epicotyl becomes pronounced *(78)*. Dwarfing can be overcome and internode elongation stimulated by treating the seedling with gibberellic acid *(9)*.

The ability of an excised embryo to germinate (although abnormally) indicates that the seed covering exerts an inhibitory effect. In apple seed, this effect has been shown to come from the thin endosperm layer *(47, 76)*. Treating peach seeds with thiourea will overcome this inhibiting effect, although the resulting seedlings are dwarfed *(73)*.

Work at the Boyce Thompson Institute, Yonkers, New York, has shown that there are cases in which the pre-germination treatments required are more complex than those requiring a single cold stratification period *(15)*. In one group of plants—wild ginger *(Asarum canadense)*, several lily species *(Lilium auratum, canadense, japonicum, rubellum, superbum,* and *szovitzianum)*, herbaceous and tree peony *(Paeonia)*, and a number of *Viburnum* species—the radicle grows readily at warm temperatures. Low temperatures must follow to after-ripen the epicotyl and allow the shoot to grow. Two to 6 months (in some *Viburnums,* 17 months was necessary) at warm temperatures are required for root growth before the cold treatment of 1 to 4 months should be given. In nature these seeds require summer followed by winter temperatures in order to germinate the following spring.

Still more complex requirements were found for a number of other plants, mostly wild plants of the temperate zone—blue cohosh *(Caulophyllum)*, lily-of-the-valley *(Convallaria)*, Solomon's seal *(Polygonatum commutatum)*, bloodroot *(Sanguinaria canadensis)*, false Solomon's seal *(Smilacina racemosa)*, and *Trillium erectum* and *grandiflorum*. Their requirements were as follows: a cold period of 1 to 6 months to after-ripen the radicle; a warm period of 1 to 6 months for the radicle to grow; followed by a second cold period of 1 to 6 months to after-ripen the epicotyl.

Rudimentary Embryos

A few species of plants have seeds containing embryos which are not completely developed morphologically at the time of fruit ripening and must undergo further growth before germination will take place. Plants having seeds of this type include the *Ginkgo, Gnetum, Ranunculus ficaria,* and *Corydalis cava (14)*. Some of the seeds produced by certain of the Umbelliferae, such as the carrot, also contain immature or undeveloped embryos *(53)*.

The mature holly *(Ilex sp.)* seed consists mostly of endosperm, the embryo being small and hardly differentiated *(40)*. Development of the embryo following harvest requires moist conditions and warm temperatures, although this also has a beneficial effect in softening the tough seed coverings. The addition of a 5 per cent dextrose solution to the germinating medium has promoted embryo development. Outdoor planting in March or April may result in partial germination the following spring (1 year later) and some in ensuing years *(33)*.

The nearly microscopic seeds of orchid have a simple, undifferentiated embryo encased within transparent integuments that contain no endosperm or cotyledons and consequently little reserve food. The commercial method of propagating orchids by seed is by aseptic culture techniques, supplying the embryo with sugar and other essential nutrients from the external medium (see p. 142).

Inhibitors

Substances which inhibit germination can be extracted from a variety of plant parts, including seeds, fruits, leaf sap, bulbs, and roots. Some of these naturally occurring *germination inhibitors* have been identified as specific chemical substances: ammonia (beet seed), hydrogen cyanide (from amygdalin), ethylene (from ripe fruits), essential oils, unsaturated organic acids, alkaloids—nicotine, cocaine, caffein, unsaturated lactones —coumarin, parascorbic acid, and others *(23, 68)*. The existence of such substances in plants does not necessarily mean they have an essential role in controlling seed germination. Nevertheless, several significant cases exist where such a biological role seems to occur.

One of the common inhibiting effects of a plant structure on germination is that of the fruit or seed coverings. Most fleshy fruits, or juices from them, rather strongly inhibit germination. This occurs for instance in citrus, cucurbits, stone fruits, apples, pears, grapes, and tomatoes. Many dry fruits and fruit coverings, such as the hulls of guayule, *Pennisetum ciliare,* wheat *(Triticum)*, the capsules of mustard *(Brassica)*, and others, produce inhibition. Undoubtedly, these substances play an important biological role in preventing premature germination until such time as the seeds have separated completely from the parent plant. Where the fruit covering remains with the seed, the inhibiting effect can sometimes persist for a considerable period even after the seed is separated from the plant.

The significance of seed inhibitors in the ecology of certain desert plants has been pointed out *(43, 82)*. Seeds of certain desert plants require heavy soaking in water before germination will occur. A light soaking is insufficient. A heavy rain (which would insure survival of the seedling) is thus necessary to leach out the inhibitor and allow germination to take place.

A specific case of germination inhibition occurs in seeds of some *Iris* species. A delay of several months to a year is produced by an inhibitor in the endosperm. Even a small portion of the endosperm in contact with the embryo prevents germination. Immediate germination can be produced by growing the excised embryo in aseptic culture *(52)*.

The existence of inhibitors can be demonstrated in various seeds particularly when freshly harvested, e.g., cabbage *(13)* or lettuce *(57)*. Dormancy has also been induced experimentally in lettuce seed by treating it with an inhibitor—coumarin—and subsequently overcome by treatments required for naturally dormant seed *(50)*. The significance of inhibitors in such cases is still uncertain.

Combinations of Two or More Types of Dormancy

Germination in a number of species is complicated by the presence of more than one type of dormancy, the usual combination being that of seed coat dormancy combined with a dormant embryo. Such seeds have been recognized by nurserymen as being among the most difficult to handle because of the long period of time required to produce germination. This group has been referred to for many years as "two-year" seeds, because seeds planted in the spring will remain dormant and will not germinate until the next spring. If planted in the fall, they will not emerge until the second spring following planting.

Figure 6–7. Effect of seed treatment on germination of redbud **(Cercis occidentalis)** seeds, which exhibit both seed coat and embryo dormancy conditions. **(A)** Seeds soaked in concentrated sulfuric acid for 30 minutes. **(B)** Boiling water poured over seeds, followed by soaking in the gradually cooling water for 24 hours. **(C)** Seed scarified. **(D)** Seeds soaked in concentrated sulfuric acid for 30 minutes, followed by stratification for 90 days at 32° F. **(E)** Stratification for 90 days at 32° F.

The treatment of seeds with double dormancy involves the combination of procedures which would overcome each type of dormancy present. In nature, decomposition of the seed coverings takes place by various agencies of the environment as has been previously discussed. Warm stratification for several months, during which time microorganisms act upon the seed covering, followed by cold stratification is an effective method of handling. This explains the fact that seeds planted in the spring or summer fail to germinate until the following spring. The period of handling can be shortened by treating the seed coats artificially (as described in Chapter 7) and then stratifying. In some cases, giving the seeds a short, warm stratification period between the time of seed coat treatment and cold stratification will assist considerably in the elimination of dormancy.

EXTERNAL FACTORS AFFECTING GERMINATION

Water

Imbibition of water by the seed is the first step in the germination process. The two most important factors which affect water uptake by seeds are (a) the nature of the seed and its coverings and (b) the amount of available water in the surrounding medium. Seeds have great absorbing power due to their colloidal nature (58). In storage, seeds can absorb water from the surrounding air. Different kinds of seeds vary greatly in the amount and rate of water absorbed, either in storage or during germination (61). The rate of water uptake is also influenced by temperature, a higher temperature favoring an increased rate (59). The seed covering also plays an important role in water uptake. In some seeds, it is so impermeable to water that germination will not occur until the seed covering has been altered in some manner.

The moisture supplied to the germinating seed may affect both the germination percentage and the germination rate (20, 39). In a study of the water requirements of a group of vegetable seeds, the germination percentage was nearly equal over much of the range of available soil moisture from field capacity (FC) to permanent wilting percentage (PWP). Differences between species became evident as the moisture content of the soil approached dryness (PWP). In some seeds, germination was inhibited at moisture contents somewhat above PWP; others were able to germinate even below PWP. The rate of germination was even more sensitive to water supply than germination percentage. In the soil used—a Yolo fine sandy loam with an FC of 15.7 per cent and a PWP of 8.6 per cent—the germination rate dropped off rapidly at 11 per cent moisture or less, about halfway through the range of available moisture from 15.7 (FC) to 8.6 per cent (PWP.) From these studies, vegetable plants were grouped in regard to their moisture requirements for germination (34).

Group 1. Kinds that will germinate in soils with moisture from permanent wilting percentage or a little above to moisture content above field capacity.

Cabbage	Sweet corn	Muskmelon	Pepper
Turnip	Squash	Cucumber	Onion
Radish	Watermelon	Tomato	Carrot

Group 2. Kinds that will germinate in soils from intermediate moisture content to above field capacity.

Snap bean	Pea	Endive	Beet
Lima bean	Lettuce		

Group 3. Kinds that will germinate only in soils near field capacity.
Celery

Group 4. Kinds that germinate well at lower moisture contents but show reduced germination near field capacity.
Spinach   New Zealand spinach

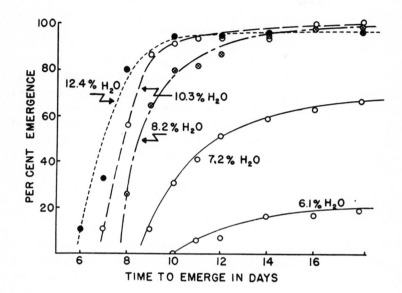

Figure 6–8. The effect of different amounts of available soil moisture on the emergence of Sweet Spanish onion seed in Pachappa fine sandy loam. From Ayers **(4).**

Excess soluble salts in the germination medium may inhibit germination and reduce seedling stands *(4).* Excess soluble salts may originate from the soil and other materials used in the germination medium, the irrigation water, or excessive fertilization. Since the effects of salinity become more acute when the moisture supply is low and the concentration of salts thereby increases, it is particularly important to maintain a high moisture supply in the seed-bed where the possibility of salinity exists. Surface evaporation from subirrigated beds can result in the accumulation of salts at the soil surface even under conditions where salinity would not be expected. Planting seeds several inches below the crown of a sloping seed-bed can minimize this hazard *(10).*

Maintaining an adequate continuous moisture supply can be difficult, because germination takes place in the upper surface of the germination medium, which is subject to fluctuations in temperature and moisture supply. The problem is greater with the necessarily shallow planting of small seeds or where the rate of germination is slow. Careful watering, deeper planting, or the application of a mulch are ways to maintain a more uniform water supply. On the other hand, excess watering accompanied by poor drainage is usually deleterious, because it reduces aeration in the germination medium and favors "damping-off" (see p. 133).

Pre-soaking seeds before planting is sometimes utilized to initiate the germination process and to shorten the time required for seedlings to emerge from the soil. Such a treatment may be advantageous with seeds normally slow to germinate, with seeds which are hard and dry, or when certain dormancy conditions exist (see p. 125). However, if the seeds ordinarily germinate without difficulty, there is little need for soaking. Seeds which have imbibed water are easily injured and more difficult to plant.

Prolonged soaking can result in injury to the seed and reduce germination (6). This harmful effect has been attributed principally to the presence of microorganisms and to poor aeration, although there seem to be other effects as well that are not understood (8). If soaking is to be prolonged, the water should be changed at least every 24 hours.

Temperature

A favorable temperature is a second requirement for germination. Seeds of some species of plants germinate over a relatively wide range; others germinate only within a certain narrow range. Temperature also affects seedling growth following germination. Usually, a temperature somewhat lower than that used in germination is best to grow seedlings.

The temperature requirements for germination of seeds are generally considered in relation to three cardinal points: minimum, maximum, and optimum (22). The designation of these actual temperatures for any one species is somewhat difficult, because temperature affects both the germination percentage and the germination rate (44). Figure 6–2 shows the effect of temperature on these two characteristics of radish and pepper seed germination. The actual germination percentage can be rather constant within the range of temperatures at which germination takes place. The rate of germination, on the other hand, as measured by days to germinate, or by the coefficient of velocity, is affected much more; an increase in temperature (up to a point) invariably results in an increase in germination rate.

Minimum temperatures are those below which germination will not occur. Table 6–1 shows that the minimum temperatures can be very low, in some cases approaching the freezing point. Since the rate of germination is decreased so much at these low temperatures, it is possible that the minimum can occur at even lower temperatures than those indicated if sufficient time is allowed.

TABLE 6–1

SOIL TEMPERATURES FOR VEGETABLE SEED GERMINATION*

Minimum

32°F.	40°F.		50°F.	60°F.	
Endive	Beet	Parsley	Asparagus	Bean, Lima	Okra
Lettuce	Broccoli	Pea	Sweet Corn	Bean, Snap	Pepper
Onion	Cabbage	Radish	Tomato	Cucumber	Pumpkin
Parsnip	Carrot	Swiss Chard		Eggplant	Squash
Spinach	Cauliflower	Turnip		Muskmelon	Watermelon
	Celery				

Optimum

70°F.	75°F.	80°F.	85°F.		95°F.
Celery	Asparagus	Bean, Lima	Bean, Snap	Pepper	Cucumber
Parsnip	Endive	Carrot	Beet	Radish	Muskmelon
Spinach	Lettuce	Cauliflower	Broccoli	Sweet Corn	Okra
	Pea	Onion	Cabbage	Swiss Chard	Pumpkin
		Parsley	Eggplant	Tomato	Squash
				Turnip	Watermelon

Maximum

75°F.	85°F.	95°F.		105°F.	
Celery	Beans, Lima	Asparagus	Eggplant	Cucumber	Squash
Endive	Parsnip	Bean, Snap	Onion	Muskmelon	Sweet Corn
Lettuce	Pea	Beet	Parsley	Okra	Turnip
Spinach		Broccoli	Pepper	Pumpkin	Watermelon
		Cabbage	Radish		
		Carrot	Swiss Chard		
		Cauliflower	Tomato		

* Data of Harrington and Minges (34).

The maximum temperatures are the highest at which germination will occur. Above this temperature, seeds of most species are actually injured; in certain others, the seeds are not injured but become dormant. The upper limits of soil temperature for the survival of the seeds listed in Table 6–1 is between 86°F. and 104°F. (34). In the experiments upon which these data are based, seeds placed at 113°F. were killed within 24 hours. During hot weather, direct sunlight striking the soil surface may raise the temperature to a level injurious to the plant tissue. Also, moisture is rapidly lost. This so-called "heat injury" affecting young seedlings resembles the "damping-off" caused by pathogenic organisms (34). For many plants shading is necessary.

Short exposures can be made to temperatures much higher than those which would be used for germination. For instance, in one study *(60)*, exposure of seeds of a number of different species to 120°F. for 1 hour did not decrease the germination percentage even though the seeds had imbibed water. At higher temperatures, the amount of injury increased but depended upon the kind of seed, the duration of exposure, and the moisture content of the seed. Dry seeds could withstand brief exposure to temperatures of 212°F., but above 250°F. all were killed.

Seeds of some species fail to germinate at temperatures over 75°F., but their ability to germinate later under other conditions is not impaired. This high temperature dormancy (*thermo-dormancy*) has practical significance in a number of cases. For instance, plantings of lettuce seed in midsummer when temperatures are high often result in reduced stands, depending upon the variety and the past history of the seed *(11, 35)*. Seed of some flower species, delphinium for instance, are also sensitive to high temperatures *(5, 38)*. This phenomenon is usually associated with dormancy present in freshly harvested seed and tends to disappear in many cases with after-ripening in dry storage. Consequently, seed testing laboratories experience difficulty with this phenomenon, since seeds are often tested for germination relatively soon after harvest. Prompt germination at higher temperatures can sometimes be induced by pre-chilling the moist seeds at 41° or 50°F. for 5 days.

Optimum temperatures are those most favorable for germination. This should be the range where the highest percentage of seedlings will be produced at the fastest rate of germination.

Germination is often much better if the seeds are subjected to daily alternating temperatures rather than a constant temperature as might be given in a germinator *(69)*. Commonly used alternations are 59°F. or 68°F. for 18 hours and 86°F. for 6 hours. The effective temperature alternations has been shown to change as the seed after-ripens in dry storage, and the effect may disappear entirely *(3)*.

Plants in general can be classified into the following groups as regard to temperature requirements: (a) those whose seeds germinate only at relatively low temperatures; (b) those which germinate only at relatively high temperatures; and (c) those which are able to germinate over a range of temperatures from cool to warm. The temperature requirement is an important factor in the adaptation of a particular species to a particular environment. Seeds of alpine plants would be expected to germinate well at low temperatures. Indeed, studies have shown that some alpines, for instance *Camassia leichtlini* and *Lewisia rediviva*, germinate only below 41°F. and 50°F. respectively *(56)*. On the other hand, seeds of most tropical plants require high temperatures.

Temperature largely determines the time of year that seeds will germinate out-of-doors. As a result, seedlings of many self-sown plants, particularly annual weeds, appear only at certain times of the year, depending upon whether they are warm-season or cool-season plants *(83)*.

Oxygen

Respiration, for which a supply of oxygen is necessary, takes place in all seeds as long as the seed is viable. In a nongerminating seed, the respiration rate is low and little oxygen is utilized. During germination, the respiration rate increases and considerably more oxygen is utilized.

Respiration may be expressed by the over-all formula:

$$\text{sugar} + O_2 = CO_2 + H_2O + \text{energy}.$$

The actual mechanics are complex, involving the transformation of the storage substances into simpler forms, their oxidation, and the transfer of the energy developed into constructive processes of growth. Part of the energy evolves as heat and can be measured by appropriate instruments. The amount of oxygen utilized depends upon the kind of stored food within the seeds. Fatty seeds will use more oxygen during germination than starchy seeds, since oxygen is utilized in the transformation of fats to carbohydrates, in which form it is translocated and utilized.

The effect of a reduced oxygen supply on germination can be important. If it becomes limiting, germination can be retarded if not completely inhibited. In poorly drained seed beds after heavy rains or excessive irrigation, the oxygen supply can be limiting because the pore spaces of the germinating medium are filled with water rather than air.

Seed of land plants vary considerably in their ability to germinate under water, but the following species germinate well: timothy, *Agrostis nebulosa,* *Axonopus compressus,* Canadian bluegrass, Bermuda grass, lettuce, wormwood, carrot, celery, portulaca, iceplant, snapdragon, *Melissa officinalis,* bittersweet, and petunia *(48)*. Seeds of water plants and rice normally germinate under water. The ability of rice to germinate at low oxygen pressures has been attributed to the presence of an anaerobic, energy-liberating system within the seeds *(65)*. Cattails (*Typha latifolia*) give poor or no germination in air but germinate promptly in water or when the oxygen supply is reduced *(49)*.

Light

Light can play an important role in seed propagation both because of its effect upon the initiation of germination and because of its controlling influence upon seedling growth.

Light and germination. The fact that visible light can stimulate or inhibit germination of seeds of some plants has been recognized since the middle of the nineteenth century. Since that time, many observations have been recorded concerning the role of light in germination *(16, 24)*. A few plants have been found whose seeds have an absolute requirement for light, and viability is lost within a few weeks without it. These include mistletoe (*Viscum album*), strangling fig (*Ficus aurea*), and *Areuthobium oxycedri,* all epiphytic plants. Germination of another group, including celery, lettuce, tobacco, and most grasses, is favored by light. Another group, e.g., species of *Phacelia, Nigella, Allium,* and *Amaranthus,* have been reported to be inhibited by light. A fourth group includes a large number which are unaffected by light. The requirement for light is not usually absolute but depends upon the previous history of the seed and the accompanying environmental conditions. Nevertheless, the light requirements of seeds form a part of the recommendations for seed testing *(75)*. Also, planting recommendations often state that light-favored seeds should be planted shallowly, light-inhibited seed more deeply.

Investigations primarily involving seed of certain lettuce varieties, tobacco, and *Lepidium* have greatly elucidated the biological role of light as a factor in germination *(12, 31)*. These have shown that the stimulating effect of visible light rays comes from the red region of the spectrum, the inhibiting effect from rays of the invisible infrared region. These two opposing effects are believed to be due to a single photochemically reversible reaction involving a pigment which is linked to some reaction that controls the onset of germination. Light of similar wave length also influences flower-bud initiation, opening of the hypocotyl hook of bean, and seedling etiolation. It is believed that this reaction is a rather general growth controlling photochemical reaction and is not necessarily specific for germination *(68, 70)*.

The response to light is associated primarily with freshly harvested seeds and tends to lessen with continued dry storage. Removing the seed covering or puncturing it in a particular manner may cause loss of light sensitivity. A favorable temperature is required; if unfavorable, the stimulus of light can be prevented. Response to light can be greatly enhanced in some cases by alternating temperatures or by treating seeds with potassium nitrate solutions *(69)*.

Light and seedling growth. Light affects the growth processes in the seedling. Under low light conditions the seedling is etiolated, the hypocotyl elongated, and the leaves unexpanded. When the seedling is exposed to light, the hypocotyl is inhibited and normal growth of the epicotyl takes place *(21)*.

In the early germination stages, the seedling utilizes the reserve supply of the seed. Later growth depends upon the production of carbohydrates and other materials resulting from photosynthesis in the leaves. Light of a relatively high intensity is necessary to produce sturdy, vigorous plants.

An extremely high light intensity, on the other hand, can result in high temperatures which may produce heat injury to the seedling. Consequently, excessively high as well as excessively low light intensities need to be avoided. Partial shading is necessary for many plants during their early seedling growth.

Supplementary artificial light is sometimes provided in growing seedlings, particularly during winter when the day length is short and cloudy weather often prevails (84). Artificial light has been used as the sole illumination in indoor propagating structures for germinating seeds as well as for rooting cuttings (63, 64). The principal problems in artificial lighting in relation to plant growth are to get a sufficiently high intensity without heating and to obtain a proper balance of light quality.

Light intensities of 700 to 1200 foot candles have been found satisfactory, although lower intensities can be used for some shade-loving plants. Placing the seedlings within a foot of the lamps should provide sufficient illumination; closer than this may result in heat injury. The length of the photoperiod should be 12 to 18 hours; below 12 hours the amount of photosynthesis becomes limiting, while photoperiods longer than 18 hours may produce poor results with some plants. Where low light intensities are used, lower temperatures should also be used. With higher light intensities, higher temperatures are permissible. Temperatures of 60° to 65°F. generally are most satisfactory.

A certain amount of blue light is necessary to produce stocky seedlings; red light alone produces tall, "leggy" plants. The most satisfactory artificial light sources are fluorescent lamps of the daylight type, 3500°K, or 4500°K white types, or a mixture of the two.

REFERENCES

1. Abbott, D. L., Temperature and the dormancy of apple seeds, *Rpt. 14th Int. Hort. Cong.*, pp. 746–753. 1955.
2. Akamine, E. K., Germination of Hawaiian range grass seeds. *Hawaii Agr. Exp. Sta. Tech. Bul.* 2:1–59. 1944.
3. ———, Germination of *Asystasia gangetica* L. seed with special reference to the effect of age on the temperature requirement for germination, *Plant Phys.*, 22:603–607. 1947.
4. Ayers, A. D., Seed germination as affected by soil moisture and salinity, *Agron. Jour.*, 44:82–84. 1952.
5. Barton, L. V., Germination of delphinium seeds, *Contrib. Boyce Thomp. Inst.*, 7:405–409. 1935.
6. ———, Relation of different gases to the soaking injury of seeds, *Contrib. Boyce Thomp. Inst.*, 16 (2):55–71. 1950.
7. ———, Dormancy in seeds, *Rpt. 13th Int. Hort. Cong.* 2:1001–1012. 1952.

8. ———, Relation of different gases to the soaking injury of seeds, II, *Contrib. Boyce Thomp. Inst.,* 17(1):7–34. 1952.

9. ———, Growth response of physiologic dwarfs of *Malus arnoldiana* Sarg. to gibberellic acid, *Contrib. Boyce Thomp. Inst.,* 18:311–317. 1956.

10. Berstein, L., A. J. MacKenzie, and B. A. Krantz, The interaction of salinity and planting practice on the germination of irrigated row crops, *Proc. Soil Science Soc. Amer.,* 19:240–243, 1955.

11. Borthwick, H. A., and W. W. Robbins, Lettuce seed and its germination, *Hilgardia,* 3 (11):275–305. 1928.

12. Borthwick, H. A., et al., Action of light on lettuce seed germination, *Bot. Gaz.,* 115:205–225. 1954.

13. Cox, L. G., H. M. Munger, and E. A. Smith, A germination inhibitor in the seed coats of certain varieties of cabbage, *Plant Phys.,* 20:289–294. 1945.

14. Crocker, W., Mechanics of dormancy in seeds, *Amer. Jour. Bot.,* 3:99–120. 1916.

15. ———, *Growth of Plants.* New York: Reinhold, 1948.

16. ———, Effect of the visible spectrum upon the germination of seeds and fruits, in *Biological Effects of Radiation.* New York: McGraw-Hill, 1930, pp. 791–828.

17. Crocker, W., N. C. Thornton, and E. M. Schroeder, Internal pressure necessary to break shells of nuts and the role of the shells in delayed germination, *Contrib. Boyce Thomp. Inst.,* 14(3):173–201. 1946.

18. Davis, W. E., Primary dormancy, after-ripening and development of secondary dormancy in embryos of *Ambrosia trifida, Amer. Jour. Bot.,* 17:58–76. 1930.

19. ———, The development of dormancy in seeds of cocklebur (*Xanthium*), *Amer. Jour. Bot.,* 17:77–87. 1930.

20. Doneen, L. D., and J. H. MacGillivray, Germination (emergence) of vegetable seed as affected by different soil conditions, *Plant Phys.,* 18:524–529. 1943.

21. Downs, R. J., Photoreversibility of leaf and hypocotyl elongation of dark grown red kidney bean seedlings, *Plant Phys.,* 30:468–472. 1955.

22. Edwards, T. J., Temperature relations of seed germination, *Quart. Rev. Biol.,* 7:428–443. 1932.

23. Evenari, M., Germination inhibitors, *Bot. Rev.,* 15:153–194. 1949.

24. ———, Seed germination, in *Radiation Biology.* New York: McGraw-Hill, 1956, III, 519–549.

25. Evenari, M., and G. Newman, The germination of lettuce seed. II. The influence of fruit coat, seed coat, and endosperm upon germination, *Bul. Res. Council, Israel,* 2:75–78. 1952.

26. Flemion, F., Physiological and chemical studies of after-ripening of *Rhodotypos kerrioides* seed, *Contrib. Boyce Thomp. Inst.,* 5:143–159. 1933.

27. ———, Physiological and chemical changes preceding and during the after-ripening of *Symphoricarpos racemosus* seeds, *Contrib. Boyce Thomp. Inst.,* 6:91–102. 1934.

28. ———, Effect of the addition of nitrogen upon germination of seeds of *Symphoricarpos racemosus, Contrib. Boyce Thomp. Inst.,* 12:485–489. 1942.

29. ———, Effects of temperature, light and nutrients on physiological dwarfing in peach seedlings, *Plant Phys.,* 31 (suppl.): III. 1956.

30. ———, and E. Waterbury, Further studies with dwarf seedlings of non-after-ripened peach seeds, *Contrib. Boyce Thomp. Inst.,* 13:415–422. 1945.

31. Flint, L. H., Light in relation to dormancy and germination in lettuce seed, *Science,* 80:38. 1934.

32. Forward, B. F., Studies of germination in oats, *Proc. Assoc. Off. Seed Anal.,* 39:83–84. 1949.

33. Giersbach, J., and W. Crocker, Germination of *Ilex* seeds, *Amer. Jour. Bot.,* 16:854–855. 1929.

34. Harrington, J. F., and P. A. Minges, Vegetable seed germination, Calif. Agr. Ext. Serv. Mimeo. Leafl., 1954.

35. Harrington, J. F., and R. C. Thompson, Effect of variety and area of production on subsequent germination of lettuce seed at high temperatures, *Proc. Amer. Soc. Hort. Sci.,* 59:445–450. 1952.

36. Haut, I. C., The influence of drying on after-ripening and germination of fruit tree seeds, *Proc. Amer. Soc. Hort. Sci.,* 29:371–374. 1932.

37. ———, Physiological studies on after-ripening and germination of fruit tree seeds, *Md. Agr. Exp. Sta. Bul. 420:1–52.* 1938.

38. Heit, C. E., Germination of sensitive flower seed kinds and varieties with suggested methods for testing in the laboratory, *Proc. Assoc. Off. Seed Anal.,* 40:107–117. 1950.

39. Hunter, J. B., and A. E. Erickson, Relation of seed germination to moisture tension, *Agron. Jour.,* 44:107–109. 1952.

40. Ives, S. A., Maturation and germination of seeds of *Ilex opaca, Bot. Gaz.,* 76:60–77. 1923.

41. Johnson, L. P. V., General preliminary studies on the physiology of delayed germination in *Avena fatua, Can. Jour. Res., Sect. C,* 13:283–300. 1935.

42. Klein, W. H., R. B. Withrow, and U. B. Elstad, Response of the hypocotyl hook of bean seedlings to radiant energy and other factors, *Plant Phys.,* 31:289–293. 1956.

43. Koller, D., Germination regulating mechanisms in some desert seeds. *Bul. Res. Council, Israel,* 4(4):379–387. 1955.

44. Kotowski, F., Temperature relations to germination of vegetable seeds, *Proc. Amer. Soc. Hort. Sci.,* 23:176–184. 1926.

45. Lammerts, W. E., Effect of photoperiod and temperatures on growth of embryo-cultured peach seedlings, *Amer. Jour. Bot.,* 30:707–711. 1943.

46. Leggatt, C. W., Germination of seeds of three species of *Agrostis. Can. Jour. Res., Sect. C,* 24:7–21. 1946.

47. Luckwill, L. C., Growth-inhibiting and growth-promoting substances in relation to the dormancy and after-ripening of apple seeds, *Jour. Hort. Sci.,* 27:53–87. 1952.

48. Morinaga, T., Germination of seeds under water, *Amer. Jour. Bot.,* 13:126–131. 1926.

49. ———, The favorable effect of reduced oxygen supply upon the germination of certain seeds, *Amer. Jour. Bot.,* 13:159–165. 1926.

50. Nutile, G. E., Inducing dormancy in lettuce seed with coumarin, *Plant Phys.,* 21:433–442. 1945.

51. Nutile, G. E., and L. C. Nutile, Effect of relative humidity on hard seeds in garden beans, *Proc. Assoc. Off. Seed Anal.,* 37:106–114. 1947.

52. Randolph, L. F., and L. G. Cox, Factors influencing the germination of iris seed and the relation of inhibiting substances to embryo development, *Proc. Amer. Soc. Hort. Sci.,* 43:284–300. 1943.

53. Robinson, R. W., Seed germination problems in the Umbelliferae, *Bot. Rev.,* 20:531–550. 1954.

54. Samish, R. M., Dormancy in woody plants, *Ann. Rev. of Plant Phys.,* 5:183–204. 1954.

55. Schander, H., Keimüngsphysiologische Studien an Kernobst. III Sortenvergleichende Untersuchungen über die Temperatureansprüche stratifizierten Saatgutes von Kernobst und über die Reversibilität der Stratifikationsvorgänge, *Sonderdruck aus Zeit. fur Pflanz,* 35:89–97. 1955.

56. Schroeder, E. M., and L. V. Barton, Germination and growth of some rock garden plants, *Contrib. Boyce Thomp. Inst.,* 10:235–255. 1939.

57. Schuck, A. K., The formation of a growth inhibiting substance in germinating lettuce seed, *Proc. Int. Seed Test. Assoc.*, 7:9–14. 1935.

58. Shull, C. A., Measurement of the surface forces in soils, *Bot. Gaz.*, 62:1–29. 1916.

59. ———, Temperature and rate of moisture uptake in seeds, *Bot. Gaz.*, 49:361–390. 1920.

60. Siegel, S. M., Effects of exposures of seeds to various physical agents. I. Effects of brief exposures to heat and cold on germination and light sensitivity, *Bot. Gaz.*, 112(1):57–70. 1950.

61. Stiles, I. E., Relation of water to the germination of corn and cotton seed, *Plant Phys.*, 23:201–222. 1948.

62. Stokes, P., The stimulation of growth by low temperature in embryos of *Heracleum sphondylium* L., *Jour. of Exp. Bot.*, 4:222–234. 1953.

63. Stoutemyer, V. T., and A. W. Close, Rooting cuttings and germinating seeds under fluorescent and cold cathode lighting, *Proc. Amer. Soc. Hort. Sci.*. 48:309–325. 1946.

64. ———, Propagation by seedage and grafting under fluorescent lamps, *Proc. Amer. Soc. Hort. Sci.*, 62:459–465. 1953.

65. Taylor, D. L., Influence of oxygen tension on respiration, fermentation and growth of wheat and rice, *Amer. Jour. Bot.*, 29:721–738. 1942.

66. Thornton, N. C., Factors influencing germination and development of dormancy in cocklebur seeds, *Contrib. Boyce Thomp. Inst.*, 7:477–496. 1935.

67. ———, Importance of oxygen supply on secondary dormancy and its relation to the inhibiting mechanism regulating dormancy, *Contrib. Boyce Thomp. Inst.*, 13:487–500. 1945.

68. Toole, E. H., et al., Physiology of seed germination, *Ann. Rev. of Plant Phys.*, 7:299–324. 1956.

69. ———, Interaction of temperature and light in germination of seeds, *Plant Phys.*, 30:473–478. 1955.

70. ———, Photocontrol of *Lepidium* seed germination, *Plant Phys.*, 30:15–21. 1956.

71. Toole, E. H., V. K. Toole, and E. A. Gorman, Vegetable-seed storage as affected by temperature and relative humidity, *USDA Tech. Bul. 972*:1–24. 1948.

72. Tukey, H. B., Differences in after-ripening requirement of several sources and varieties of peach seeds, *Proc. Amer. Soc. Hort. Sci.*, 46:199–202. 1945.

73. Tukey, H. B., and R. F. Carlson, Breaking the dormancy of peach seeds by treatment with thiourea, *Plant Phys.*, 20:505–516. 1945.

74. USDA, Woody plant seed manual, *Misc. Pub. No. 654*, 1948.

75. USDA, Manual for testing agricultural and vegetable seeds, *Agr. Handbook 30*, 1952.

76. Visser, T., The role of seed coats and temperature in after-ripening, germination and respiration of apple seeds, *Proc. Koninkl. Nederl. Akad. van Wetens*, Series C, 59:211–222. 1956.

77. ———, Some observations on respiration and secondary dormancy in apple seeds, *Proc. Koninkl. Nederl. Akad. van Wetens*, Series C, 59:314–324. 1955.

78. ———, The growth of apple seedlings as affected by after-ripening, seed maturity and light, *Proc. Koninkl. Nederl. Akad. van Wetens*, Series C, 59:325–334. 1956.

79. von Abrams, G. L., and M. E. Hand, Seed dormancy in *Rosa* as a function of climate, *Amer. Jour. Bot.*, 43:7–12. 1956.

80. Wareing, P. F., and H. A. Foda, Growth inhibitors and dormancy in *Xanthium* seed, *Physiol. Plant.*, 10(2):266–280. 1957.

81. Wells, J. S., Fall seed sowing, *Amer. Nurs.*, 96(7):15, 68–69. 1952.

82. Went, F. W., Ecology of desert plants. II. The effect of rain and temperature on germination and growth, *Ecology*, 30:1–13. 1949.

83. Went, F. W., and M. Westergaard, Ecology of desert plants. III. Development of plants in the Death Valley National Monument, California, *Ecology*, 30:26–38. 1949.

84. Withrow, A. P., Artificial lighting for forcing greenhouse crops, *Ind. Agr. Exp. Sta. Bul. 533*. 1948.

• **Supplementary Reading**

Crocker, W., *Growth of Plants*. New York: Reinhold, 1948. Chap. 3.

Crocker, W., and L. V. Barton, *Physiology of Seeds*. Waltham, Mass.: Chronica Botanica, 1953.

7

Techniques
of
Seed Propagation

Seed propagation involves careful management of germination conditions and facilities and a knowledge of the requirements of individual seeds. Its success depends upon the degree to which the following conditions are fulfilled. (a) The seed must reproduce the particular variety or species which the propagator wishes to grow. This can be accomplished by obtaining seed from a reliable dealer, buying certified seed, or—if producing one's own—following the principles of seed selection described in Chapter 4. (b) The seed must be viable and capable of germination. It also should germinate rapidly and vigorously to withstand possible adverse conditions in the seed-bed. Viability can be determined by seed tests. (c) Any inherent dormant condition of the seed which would inhibit germination must be overcome by applying any required pre-germination treatment. The propagator should know the characteristics of the seed with which he is concerned. A germination test will be helpful in indicating the necessity for any pre-germination treatment. In the absence of specific knowledge, the propagator should try to duplicate as closely as he is able the natural environmental conditions associated with this particular kind of plant. (d) Assuming that the seed is capable of prompt germination, the actual success of propagation depends upon supplying the proper environment—moisture, temperature, and oxygen—to the seed and the resulting seedling until such time as it is established in its permanent location. Proper environment also includes control of diseases and insects.

SEED TESTING

Good quality seed has the following characteristics: trueness to species or variety; a capacity for high germination; freedom from disease; and freedom from mixtures with other crop seeds, weed seeds, and inert and extraneous material. The germination capacity and the purity of the seed can be determined by conducting a *seed test* on a small representative sample drawn from the seed lot in question.

Most states have laws which regulate the shipment and sale of agricultural and vegetable seeds within that state. Likewise, seeds entering interstate commerce are subject to the Federal Seed Act adopted in 1939 *(59)*. The aim of such regulations is to require the correct labeling of commercially produced seeds by the shipper as to the following information: name and variety of seed; origin of seed; the germination percentage; and the percentage of pure seed, other crop seed, weed seed, and inert material. The regulations may set minimum standards of quality, germination percentage, and freedom from weed seeds. Testing of tree seed is required by law in only a few states. Most European countries do have this latter requirement.

Seed testing provides information for establishing the rate of sowing to obtain a given stand of seedlings. Thus, it may be desirable to conduct a seed test for seeds which have been stored for a long period subsequent to earlier tests. It may also be necessary in the case of tree seeds where there is usually no legal requirement for seed testing or for seeds obtained locally.

Procedures for testing agricultural and vegetable seeds are based on the "Rules for Testing Seeds" developed by the USDA *(59)* and the Association of the Official Seed Analysts *(6)*. Recommended methods for testing tree seeds are given by the USDA *(58)* and the International Rules for Seed Testing *(29)*.

Sampling

The first step in carrying out a seed test is to obtain a uniform sample that represents the entire lot under consideration. Equal portions are taken from evenly distributed parts of the seed lot, such as a sample from each of several sacks in lots of less than five sacks or from every fifth sack with larger lots. The seed samples are thoroughly mixed and then redivided into smaller lots to produce the *working sample,* i.e., the sample upon which the test is actually to be run. The amount of seed required for the working sample varies with the kind of seed and is specified in the Rules of Seed Testing.

Testing Purity

Purity is the percentage by weight of the pure seeds present in the sample. "Pure seed" refers to the principally named kind, variety, or type of seed present in the seed lot. After the working sample has been weighed, it is divided visually into (a) the pure seed of the kind under consideration; (b) other crop seed; (c) weed seed; and (d) inert material, including seed-like structures, empty or broken seeds, chaff, soil, stones, and other debris. In some cases, it is possible to check the genuineness of the seed or trueness to variety or species by visual inspection. Often, however, identification cannot be made except by growing the seeds and observing the plants.

At the time of making the purity test, the number of pure seeds per pound can be calculated. This data is necessary as a guide to seeding rates.

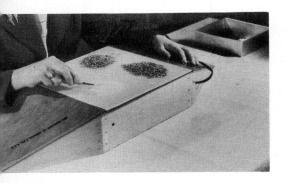

Figure 7–1. Purity of seeds is determined by visual examination of individual seeds in a weighed sample taken from the larger lot in question. Impurities may include other crop seed, weed seed, and inert, extraneous material. Courtesy E. L. Erickson Products, Brookings, S. D.

Testing Viability

The *germination percentage* refers to the relative number of pure seed of the kind under consideration which produces normal seedlings. To produce a good test, it is desirable to use at least 400 of the pure seeds picked at random and divided into lots of one hundred. If any two of these lots differ by more than 10 per cent, a retest may be carried out. Otherwise, the average of the four tests becomes the germination percentage. In addition to the actual number germinating, the rate of germination can be observed at this time.

Germination test. A germination test is one in which the seeds are placed under optimum environmental conditions of light and temperature to induce germination. The relative number of normal seedlings produced gives the germination percentage.

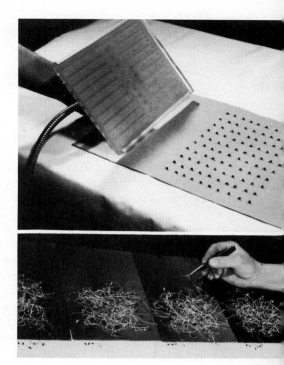

Figure 7–2. Germination testing of seeds. **(above)** One hundred seeds from the sample to be tested are placed on a moistened blotter. In this case placing the seeds evenly and quickly is made possible by an automatic vacuum counter. **(below)** After one or more weeks in a germinator the number of germinated seeds is counted. Note that this test consists of four lots of 100 seeds each. Courtesy E. L. Erickson Products, Brookings, S. D.

Various techniques are used for germinating seed. In seed testing laboratories, the seeds are commonly placed on germination trays (not galvanized steel which contains toxic zinc salts) either between two thicknesses of blotters or on top of blotters and then placed in germinators where the temperature and light are controlled. To discourage the growth of microorganisms, all materials and equipment should be kept scrupulously clean, sterilized when possible, and the water supply carefully regulated. No water film should form around the seeds; neither should the germinating medium be so wet that a film of water appears when pressed with a finger.

Covered Petri dishes are also convenient germinating containers. Standard media for them include two layers of blotters, one layer of absorbent cotton, or five layers of paper toweling; or five layers of filter paper (Whatman No. 2); or ⅝ in. of sand or soil. Paraffined cardboard boxes or small plastic boxes of the home freezer type might also be used as containers.

Another convenient method for testing seed is the *rolled towel test*. Paper toweling, 11 by 14 inches or similar size, is moistened. Seeds are spaced along one side so that the edge of the towel can cover them. More rows of seeds are spaced along the towel as it is rolled up with the seeds inside. Rolls should not be tight, about five layers being desirable. They are placed either horizontally or vertically in germinating trays. Germination blotters or flannel cloth could be substituted for the paper toweling.

Tree seed can be tested by germinating them in sterile sand in flats placed in a greenhouse. Another suggested procedure is to place the seeds on peat moss in the bottom of glass baking dishes covered with a sheet of glass. The seeds are planted uncovered in shallow grooves with enough water added so that a shallow layer remains on the bottom after the peat has absorbed all it can hold. This method is particularly desirable for seeds with a long stratification requirement (51).

A test usually runs from 10 days to 4 weeks but may continue as long as 3 months in the case of some slow-germinating seeds. A normal seedling generally should have a well-developed root and shoot, although the criteria for a "normal seedling" varies with different kinds of seeds. In addition, there may be abnormal seedlings, hard seeds, dormant seeds, and dead or decayed seeds. Abnormal seedlings can be caused by declining vitality due to age or to poor storage conditions; or to insect, disease, or mechanical injury; overdoses of fungicides; frost damage; mineral deficiencies (manganese and boron in peas and beans); or toxic materials sometimes present in metal germination trays, substrata, or tap water. Dormant seeds can usually be distinguished from nonviable seeds; the dormant seeds are firm, swollen, free from molds, or may show erratic sprouting. Any ungerminated seed should be examined to determine the possible reason.

Dormancy of freshly harvested seeds of cereals, vegetables, and flowers, and seeds of woody plants provides one of the principal difficulties of the direct test. It can prolong the testing period, impose unusual environmental requirements, and sometimes interfere with the reliability of the test. Conditions effective in overcoming dormancy which are recommended by the Rules for Testing Seeds for particular kinds of seeds include prechilling, germination at low temperatures (59°F.), germination at high (over 86°F.) or alternating temperatures, subjection to light, moistening with 0.1 or 0.2 per cent potassium nitrate, modification of seed coats, leaching with water, or pre-drying.

Excised embryo test. The excised embryo test is used to test the germination of seeds of woody shrubs and trees whose embryos require long periods of after-ripening before germination will take place (16, 23). In it, the embryo is excised from the rest of the seed and germinated alone. A viable embryo will either germinate or show some indication of germination, whereas a nonviable embryo becomes discolored and deteriorates.

The excision of the embryo must be done carefully to avoid injury to the embryo. Any hard, stony seed coverings, such as the endocarp of stone fruit seeds, must first be removed. The seeds are then soaked for 1 to 4 days, changing the water once or twice a day. Storing seeds in moist peat for 3 days to 2 weeks at cool temperatures is also satisfactory in preparing seeds for excision.

The seed coats are cut with a sharp scalpel or knife, and the embryo carefully removed. If a large endosperm is present, the seed coats may be slit, the seeds covered with water, and after about a half hour the embryo will float out or can easily be removed.

Procedures for germinating excised embryos are similar to germinating intact seeds. A procedure often used is to fill Petri dishes with ten pieces of 15 cm. filter paper and 20 to 30 cc. of tap water. The embryos are placed on the filter paper so that they do not touch. The dishes are kept in the light at a temperature of 64° to 74°F. At higher temperatures, growth of molds may become excessive and interfere with the test. The time required for the test varies from 3 days to 3 weeks rather than several months, as is sometimes required for the direct germination test.

Nonviable embryos will become soft, brown, and moldy within 2 to 10 days; viable embryos remain firm and show some indication of viability, depending upon the species. Types of response that occur include spreading of the cotyledons, development of chlorophyll, and growth of the

Figure 7–3. The excised embryo method of testing seed germination. **(above)** Germination of apple seeds showing the range of vigor from strong to weak to dead. Actual germination percentages for the four lots were **(left to right):** 100, 70, 44, and 0. **(below)** Vigor and germination of four peach stocks. **(left to right) (1)** strong seed, vigorous growth (80% viability); **(2)** good seed, fair vigor (52% viability); **(3)** old seed, weak (18% viability); and **(4)** dead seed. Courtesy C. E. Heit.

radicle and plumule. The rapidity and degree of development may give an indication of the vigor of the seed.

Tetrazolium test. The tetrazolium test is a biochemical method in which viability is tested, not by germination, but by the red color appearing when the seeds are soaked in 2,3,5-triphenyltetrazolium chloride (TTC). This chemical is absorbed within the cells where it is changed enzymatically to an insoluble red compound (chemically known as formazan). Living tissue becomes red; nonliving tissue remains uncolored. It was developed in Germany by Lakon *(33)* who referred to it as a topographical test, since loss in viability appears to begin at the extremity of the radicle, epicotyl, and cotyledon tips.

This method of analysis has not been used much for routine testing, except in some European laboratories, particularly with dormant tree seed. The International Rules for Seed Testing provides for the use of the tetrazolium test with seed of the following: *Carpinus, Fraxinus, Pinus cembra, Prunus, Pyrus, Rosa, Taxus* and *Tilia (29)*. The reaction takes place equally well in dormant and nondormant seeds. Some use has also been made of the tetrazolium method in testing freshly harvested seeds (other than tree seeds) which fail to germinate satisfactorily in direct germination tests *(7, 8, 64)*.

Results can be obtained more rapidly than with either the germination test or the excised embryo test. In some cases, viability can be determined within a few hours, although usually it will require one to several days, depending upon the kind of seed.

Since this test distinguishes between living and dead tissues within a single seed, it may indicate weakness before germination is actually impaired. Such knowledge should be valuable in research *(30)*. Lakon points out that such necrotic areas are subject to attack by pathogenic organisms, and seeds with them are subject to decay during stratification *(34)* or give reduced germination under unfavorable soil conditions *(35)*.

On the other hand, this test may not adequately measure certain types of injury which could lead to seedling abnormality—for instance, an overdose of chemicals, seedborne diseases, or frost injury *(19)*. Some difficulty may be experienced in interpreting viability where both stained and unstained portions appear on the same seed. For most seeds, the difficulty and time required in preparing the test is somewhat greater than in the germination test and about equal to the excised embryo test. Consequently, American seed laboratories have not used it for routine testing *(30)*, and some workers have preferred the excised embryo test for dormant tree seeds *(17, 23)*.

The chemical, 2,3,5-triphenyltetrazolium chloride,* is a white powder which dissolves in water to make a colorless solution. Although the solution deteriorates with exposure to light, it will remain in good condition

---

* The bromide salt has been used in some cases.

for several months if protected. It should be discarded if it becomes yellowish. A 1 per cent solution is commonly used, although concentrations as low as 0.05 per cent have given good results *(30)*. The pH should be adjusted to 6 or 7 if necessary. Seeds should be soaked in darkness.

TABLE 7–1

PROCEDURES FOR TESTING DIFFERENT TREE SEEDS
BY THE TETRAZOLIUM METHOD *(29)*

Seed	Preparation	Time of Soaking in TTC Solution (86°F)	Classes of Germinable Seeds
Carpinus	Soak 18–20 hours; cut off 1/3 of fruit at broad end opposite radicle; immerse clipped end in TTC	24 hours; extract embryo	(a) Completely stained; (b) radicle tip unstained; (c) unstained spots on cotyledon half opposite the radicle; (d) combination of (b) and (c)
Fraxinus	Soak dewinged seeds 18-20 hours, cut off 1 mm. edge around seed with fine scissors	24 hours; split seed to uncover embryo	(a) Both embryo and endosperm stained; (b) embryo stained but unstained spots on periphery of endosperm
Pinus cembra	Remove tip of dry seeds to expose radicle; soak 18–20 hours	48 hours; open endosperm and expose embryo	Completely stained well-developed embryos and endosperm
Pyrus and *Malus*	Soak 18–20 hours; excise embryo completely	18–20 hours	Same as *Carpinus*
Prunus	Remove endocarp; treat as *Pyrus*	18–20 hours	Same as *Carpinus*
Rosa	Entire procedure the same as *Carpinus*		
Taxus	Entire procedure the same as *Pinus cembra*		
Tilia	Remove fruit covering; soak 18–20 hours. Remove seed coat to excise the endosperm containing the embryo	24 hours	Same as *Fraxinus*

The procedure for carrying out the test varies slightly for different kinds of seed depending upon seed structure and other characteristics. Table 7–1 shows the recommended method of the International Rules for Seed Testing for specific tree seeds. Usually, such methods can be used with other seeds of similar structure. For instance, conifer seeds in general could be handled similarly to *Pinus cembra* except that with *Abies* both ends should be clipped *(36, 46)*.

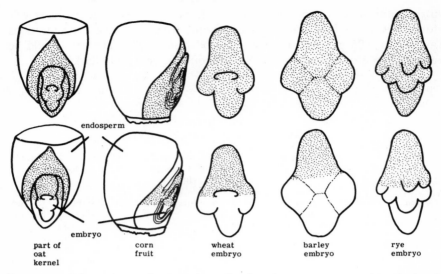

Figure 7–4. Embryo staining by tetrazolium. Oat kernels are cut transversely and placed in the solution; corn is cut longitudinally while wheat, rye, and barley embryos are excised. The top row shows the maximum staining expected; the bottom row shows the minimum staining that should occur for the seed to be classed as viable. Redrawn from Lakon **(33).**

Seeds of cereals and grasses can be tested by this method to get a rapid indication of viability *(33)*. Corn (*Zea mays*) kernels can be soaked, cut in half longitudinally to bisect the embryo, and one of the halves placed in the TTC solution for 2 to 8 hours. Oat (*Avena*) kernels are cut across and the half with the embryo is freed from the hull and placed directly into the solution without pre-soaking. Because of the thin seed coverings of timothy (*Phleum*) *(8)*, it is possible to place these seeds directly into the solution for 48 hours and to observe staining without excision. The application of a lactophenol solution (20 cc. lactic acid, 20 cc. phenol, 40 cc. glycerine, 20 cc. water) will make them even more transparent.

PRE-GERMINATION TREATMENTS TO STIMULATE GERMINATION

Mechanical Scarification

The purpose of mechanical scarification is to modify hard or impervious seed coats.

Scarification is any process of breaking, scratching, or mechanically altering the seed covering to make it permeable to water or gases. Although some scarification probably occurs during harvesting, extraction, and cleaning, germination of most hard-coated seeds is improved by additional artificial treatment.

Rubbing the seeds on sandpaper, cutting with a file, or cracking the seed covering with a hammer or between the jaws of a vise are simple methods useful for small amounts of relatively large seed. For large scale operations, special mechanical scarifiers are used. Small-seeded legumes, such as alfalfa and clover, are often treated in this manner to increase germination *(4)*. Tree seeds may be tumbled in drums lined with sandpaper

Figure 7–5. Disk scarifier used to modify hard seed coats. Construction based on one described in **USDA Misc. Pub. No. 654** for use with tree seeds. Scarifier consists of five disks covered with abrasive paper mounted on a shaft and enclosed within metal cylinder also lined with abrasive paper. The bottom third of the cylinder is filled with seeds and the disks rotated at a speed of 500 to 900 rpm. Duration of treatment must be established for the particular seed lot and kind of seed.

or in concrete mixers combined with coarse sand or gravel *(61)*. The sand or gravel should be a different size than the seed to facilitate separation.

Scarification should not proceed to the point where the seeds are injured. To determine the optimum time, a test lot can be germinated, the seeds may be soaked to observe swelling, or the seed coats examined with a hand lens. The seed coats generally should be dull but not deeply pitted or cracked enough to expose the inner parts of the seed *(31)*.

Mechanical scarification is simple and effective with many species if suitable equipment is available. The seeds are dry after treatment and may be stored or planted immediately by mechanical seeders, although scarified seed is more susceptible to injury from pathogenic organisms and will not store as well as comparable nonscarified seed.

Soaking Seeds in Water

The purpose of soaking seeds in water is to modify hard seed coats, remove inhibitors, and soften seeds and reduce the time of germination.

Soaking seeds in water will overcome seed coat dormancy and stimulate germination in some cases. Impermeable seed coats can be softened by dropping the seeds into four to five times their volume of hot water (at a temperature of 170° to 212°F.). The heat is immediately removed, and the seeds allowed to soak in the gradually cooling water for 12 to 24 hours. Following this, the unswollen seeds can be separated from the swollen ones by suitable screens and either retreated or subjected to some other method of treatment. The seeds should usually be planted immediately after the hot water treatment. However, honey locust seeds have been carefully dried and stored for later planting without impairing the germination percentage, although the rate of germination was slower (2).

Boiling seeds in water for a period of several minutes has been done in some cases, but such a procedure is hazardous. Over-exposure to these high temperatures is likely to injure the seeds.

Inhibitors present in some seeds can be removed or leached out by washing or soaking in water. For instance, the procedure for laboratory germination of beet seeds calls for pre-soaking the seeds for 2 hours in 250 cc. of water for each 100 seeds, followed by washing with water and blotting dry. This procedure is unnecessary in field planting, because the inhibitors are adsorbed by soil particles.

Soaking seeds prior to germination may shorten the time for emergence if the seeds are normally slow to germinate. This procedure has been used in germinating celery (56).

Acid Scarification

The purpose of acid scarification is to modify hard or impermeable seed coverings.

Soaking seeds in concentrated sulfuric acid is an effective method for modifying hard seed coverings. Sulfuric acid must be used with care, because it is strongly corrosive and reacts violently with water causing high temperatures and splattering. Protective clothing should be worn, and the operator should be aware of the dangers in its use.

Dry seeds are placed in glass or earthenware containers and covered with concentrated sulfuric acid (specific gravity 1.84) in a ratio of about one part seed to two parts acid. The mixture should be stirred cautiously at intervals during the treatment to produce uniform results and to prevent the accumulation of the dark, resinous material from the seed coats which is sometimes present. Since stirring tends to raise the temperature, vigorous agitation of the mixture should be avoided or injury to the seeds and splattering of the acid may result. A temperature of 60° to 80°F. is most desirable; higher temperatures shorten the necessary period of contact, and lower temperatures prolong it.

The length of treatment should be carefully standardized. It will depend upon temperature, the kind of seed, and sometimes the particular lot of seed. Large lots of seed should be thoroughly mixed prior to treatment to insure uniformity. The time of treatment may vary from as little as 10 minutes for some species to as much as 6 hours or more for other species. If a large lot of seed is to be treated, the optimum period of treatment should be determined by preliminary tests. With thick-coated seeds that require long periods, the progress of the acid treatment may be followed by drawing out samples at intervals and checking the thickness of the seed coat. When it becomes paper thin, the treatment should be terminated immediately (31).

At the end of the treatment period the acid is poured off to be reused if desired, and the seeds are washed to remove the acid. Copious amounts of water should be added immediately to dilute the acid as quickly as possible, reduce the temperature, and avoid splattering. Washing for 10 minutes with running water should be sufficient. The seeds can either be planted immediately when wet, or dried and stored for later planting.

Cold Stratification

The purposes of cold stratification are to after-ripen dormant embryos and to modify seed coverings.

Cold stratification is the subjection of moist seeds to low temperatures for a specified length of time prior to germination. This treatment is effective in bringing about prompt and uniform germination of many woody tree and shrub seeds which have dormant embryos. Without such treatment, seeds of these particular species either germinate slowly and erratically over a period of weeks or months or fail to germinate entirely.

Stratification brings about certain physiological changes within the embryo (*after-ripening*) (see p. 93). This process requires temperatures between 32° and about 50°F., moisture, aeration, and a certain amount of time.

Although cold stratification alone has some benefit in softening the seed coats, it is usually more effective to subject the seeds to a warm stratification period prior to the cold stratification treatment if hard seed coats are present.

Figure 7–6. Method of stratifying seeds in moist sand over-winter. Box may be kept under refrigeration or out-of-doors in a cool, protected place where it will not dry out. For better moisture retention cover with polyethylene plastic. Side of box has been removed to show placement of seeds in layers. However, sand and seed may be mixed together. From **Calif. Agr. Ext. Cir. 96.**

Seeds are prepared for stratification by soaking for 12 to 24 hours. The moist seeds are then mixed with a moisture-retaining stratification medium and preferably kept at temperatures of 32° to 45°F. for the prescribed period of time. Almost any medium which holds moisture, provides aeration, and contains no toxic substances should be suitable for stratification. Suitable media include well-washed sand, peat moss, chopped sphagnum, vermiculite, or well-weathered pine sawdust (fresh sawdust may contain toxic substances). An excellent material to use is a mixture of one part sand and one part peat moss, moistened and allowed to stand 24 hours before use. The stratification medium should be moist but not excessively wet.

Seeds are mixed with one to three times their volume of the stratification medium or placed in layers ½ to 3 in. thick alternating with equally thick layers of the stratification medium. Suitable containers for stratification are boxes, cans, glass jars (with perforated lids), or other containers which provide aeration, prevent drying, and protect against rodents. Polyethylene bags are also excellent stratification containers.

The proper temperature can best be maintained in refrigerated storage. Where refrigeration facilities are not available, seeds can be stratified in the same manner out-of-doors over winter in a protected location or stratified in pits 6 to 12 in. deep in the ground, alternating the seed with layers of sand. The seeds can also be placed in piles covered with straw or similar mulching material. In any case, where seeds are stratified out of doors, they should be protected from freezing, drying, and rodents.

The time required for completion of after-ripening depends on the kind of seed and sometimes upon the individual lot of seed as well. For most seeds, the required period of low temperature stratification is between 1 and 4 months. During stratification, the seeds should be examined periodically; if dry, the stratification medium should be remoistened.

At the end of the after-ripening period the seeds may begin to germinate in the stratification medium. To plant, the seeds are removed from the containers and separated from the stratification medium, using care to prevent injury to the moist seeds. A good method is to use a screen which will allow the medium to pass through while retaining the seeds. Planting should take place immediately without allowing the seeds to dry.

A method of aseptic seed stratification has been developed by Gilmore (20), which has proven useful in preparing some seeds for certain physiological investigations. Dry, dormant seeds are sterilized by soaking for 5 minutes in a Merthiolate * solution—1 part Merthiolate to 2000 parts alcohol (50 per cent strength). This is followed by 5 minutes washing in ten to twelve changes of sterile tap water. The seeds are then stratified in sterilized Erlenmeyer flasks containing just enough sterile water to keep the seeds moist.

---

* Sodium ethyl mercuricthiosalicylate.

Combinations of Two or More Pre-Germination Treatments

The purpose of combining two or more treatments is to overcome the conditions of a hard seed covering and a dormant embryo (*double dormancy*) and to promote germination of embryos with complex embryo dormancy.

The combination of mechanical scarification, acid scarification, or hot water soaking followed by cold stratification is effective for seeds which have both a hard, impermeable seed covering and a dormant embryo. Any of the three seed-coat modifying treatments could possibly be substituted for the others. An even more effective treatment in some cases is to interject several weeks of warm stratification between the seed coat treatments and the cold stratification period. The seed coat treatment must precede stratification so that water can be absorbed by the embryo. With fall-ripening seeds, this combination of treatments makes it possible to produce prompt germination the following spring.

A combination of warm and cold stratification is another suitable pre-germination treatment. A period of warm temperatures of perhaps several months followed by a period of cold temperatures (usually several months) is an effective treatment for seeds of a number of plants. The warm period results in decomposition of the seed coverings due to activity of microorganisms in the germinating or stratification medium. Temperatures should range from about 68°F. (night) to 86°F. (day); at temperatures effective for after-ripening, i.e., 32° to 50°F., microorganism activity is absent or very slow, and little decomposition occurs. A constant intermediate temperature near 50°F. may be effective in some cases, since it is within the lower temperature range of microorganism activity and also within the upper temperature range of after-ripening. The period of time would usually be somewhat greater than if the two pre-treatments were used consecutively.

The procedure for preparing seeds for warm stratification does not differ essentially from preparing seeds for cold stratification. Planting the seeds directly into greenhouse flats and keeping them at the necessary temperature for the required times might be a desirable method. For large numbers of seeds, the most practical method of handling is outdoor planting at a time when the required conditions are provided by nature. In all cases, the seeds should not dry out at any time during the process.

Timing the Planting

The purpose of timing is to provide the environmental conditions necessary to after-ripen dormant seeds and to furnish special germination requirements.

The methods so far described for treating seeds to overcome dormancy require a certain amount of handling and special equipment. Seed may also be planted out of doors directly into the seed-bed or cold frame at a time of the year when the natural environment provides the necessary conditions for after-ripening. This method of handling is particularly desirable when large lots of seeds are involved and facilities and labor supply are limited. Several difficulties arise when seeds remain for a long period in the seed-bed. They are subject to loss from drying, adverse environmental conditions, animals, birds, and disease. Weed control is also a problem until the seedlings are well established.

Several different categories of seeds can be handled this way and induced to germinate in the spring following planting. For example, seeds which require cold stratification may be fall-planted and allowed to after-ripen in the soil during the winter. Seeds which normally would require a warm stratification plus a cold stratification treatment can be planted in the summer sufficiently early to fulfill their warm temperature requirements, while the winter period in the soil satisfies the chilling requirement.

Germination can be facilitated in some cases (e.g., juniper; some *Magnolia* species) if the fruit is harvested when ripe and the seeds planted immediately without drying *(63)*. Once the seeds become dry, the seed coats become hard and germination may be delayed, perhaps until the second spring after they ripen. Seeds which ripen early in the growing season and lose their viability rapidly should be planted in spring or summer when they are collected. Where effective treatments are not known, a propagator should attempt to parallel the natural seeding habits of the plant and provide the germinating conditions of its natural environment.

Seeds are planted according to regular nursery methods, except that the seed-beds may require protection from adverse conditions during the long period of time that the seeds are in the soil before germination occurs. Application of a mulch is advantageous in maintaining a more uniform moisture supply, in controlling weeds, and in protecting against temperature extremes. Placing a screen over the seed-bed might also be worthwhile to protect against rodents or birds.

Dry Storage

The purpose of dry storage is to after-ripen certain seeds which are dormant when freshly harvested.

Freshly harvested seeds of many annual and perennial herbaceous plants fail to germinate until after a period of dry storage. This period of dormancy may last from a few days to several months, depending upon the species of plant. Since dry storage is the usual method of handling and storing most cereal, vegetable, and flower seeds, this dormant period has usually passed by the time that the seeds reach the hands of the propagator.

Where seeds are to be germinated soon after maturity, such as in seed-testing laboratories, this form of dormancy may cause difficulty. Drying for 3 days at 104°F. or 5 days at 99°F. has stimulated germination *(59)*.

Particular Temperature or Temperature Combinations

The purpose of maintaining certain temperatures is to stimulate germination of freshly-harvested seeds of certain species.

Germination of freshly-harvested dormant seeds of some species will take place only below particular temperatures, although this requirement tends to disappear after dry storage. Some vegetable seeds such as lettuce and a number of flower seeds such as delphinium have this requirement. Seeds sensitive to high temperatures can be germinated by maintaining constant, cool temperatures of approximately 55° to 65°F.; by planting seeds during favorable times of the year, for instance during spring or fall; or by germinating seeds in a cool location. If such seeds are subjected, while moist, to somewhat cooler temperatures (50°F.) for 3 to 5 days, then they can often be germinated at the higher temperatures. Since aeration is necessary, the seeds should not be submerged in water during this chilling period *(10)*.

Daily alternation of temperatures is effective in stimulating germination of freshly-harvested seeds of many species. The usual combinations of temperature are 59° to 86°F. or 68° to 86°F., with seeds being held at the lower temperature for 16 hours and at the higher temperatures for 8 hours. These conditions are a part of the normal environment at particular seasons of the year. The use of such fluctuating temperatures is of great importance in seed-testing laboratories.

A high constant temperature will overcome dormancy in freshly harvested seeds of some species *(59)*. The seed-testing rules for dormant citron melon (*Citrullus vulgaris*), for instance, specify a temperature of 86°F. Likewise, alyce clover (*Alysicarpus*) is germinated at 95°F., although this seed will respond to lower temperatures as the seed ages.

Soaking in Potassium Nitrate Solution

Soaking seeds in potassium nitrate solution stimulates germination of many freshly-harvested dormant seeds. The technique is used largely in seed-testing laboratories *(59)*.

Seeds are placed in germinating trays or Petri dishes and the substratum moistened with 0.2 per cent potassium nitrate. For Kentucky bluegrass (*Poa pratensis*) or Canada bluegrass (*P. compressa*) only a 0.1 per cent solution should be used. If rewatered, tap or distilled water is used rather than additional nitrate solution.

Light

The purpose of light is to stimulate germination of some freshly-harvested dormant seeds.

Exposure to light can stimulate or inhibit germination, depending on the kind of seed and the particular conditions. The light requirement of these seeds is strongest just following harvesting and tends to disappear with dry storage. In the Rules for Seed Testing, light is specified for the germination of a number of agricultural and vegetable seeds, particularly grasses *(59)*. Light is recommended for the germination testing of seeds of the following genera of tree seed: *Fraxinus, Juniperus, Morus, Picea, Pinus* and *Tsuga (29)*.

Although the light requirement is primarily a factor in seed testing, it should be considered in seedling production. Seeds which are known or suspected to have a light requirement should be planted shallowly, because in the absence of light with deep planting, the seeds may not germinate.

The light stimulus becomes effective after the seed has imbibed moisture. Following irradiation, the moist seeds may be dried and stored for several weeks without losing their ability to germinate in the dark.

SEED GERMINATION AND DISEASE CONTROL

The control of disease during seed germination is one of the most important tasks of the propagator. The most universally destructive disease is that which is referred to as "damping-off," which may cause serious losses of seeds, seedlings, and young plants. It is this disease with which most of the following discussion will deal. In addition, there are a great number of fungus, virus, and bacterial diseases that are seed borne and may infect certain plants *(47, 59)*. In such cases, specific methods of control may be important in propagating them.

Damping-Off

Damping-off is caused by certain fungi, primarily *Pythium ultimum* and *Rhizoctonia solani,* although other fungi—for example, *Botrytis cinerea* and *Phytophthora sp.*—may also be involved. Mycelia from these organisms occur in soil, in infected plant tissues, or on seeds, from which they contaminate clean soil and infect clean plants. In some species spores are produced. In *Pythium* and *Phytophthora,* for instance, the spores can be carried in water.

Damping-off occurs at various stages in the germination and growth of a plant. (a) The seed may decay or the seedling may rot before emergence from the soil (*pre-emergence damping-off*). (b) The seedling may develop a stem rot near the surface of the ground and fall over (*post-emergence damping-off*). (c) The seedling may remain alive and standing but the stem will become girdled and the plant stunted, eventually dying (*wire-stem*). (d) Rootlets of larger plants may be attacked; the plants will become stunted and eventually die (*root rot*).

Damping-off symptoms can also be produced by certain environmental conditions in the seed-bed. Drying, high temperatures, or high concentrations of soil solutes in the upper layers of the germinating medium can cause injuries to the tender stems of the seedling near the ground level. The collapsed stem tissues have the aspect of being "burned off." The symptoms can be confused with those caused by pathogens.

The control of damping-off involves two separate procedures: (a) the elimination of the organisms completely during propagation and (b) the control of plant growth and environmental conditions, which will minimize the effects of damping-off or give temporary control until the seedling has passed its initial stages of growth. Where possible, it is best to eliminate the organisms completely. Otherwise, there may continue to be a source of infection which can later cause difficulty if conditions become favorable to it.

Control of the organism can be obtained by sterilizing the germination medium, treating the seed, and following good sanitation practices. Soil sterilization is considered in Chapter 2, seed treatment later in this section. Seeds should always be treated if a sterile germinating medium is used, otherwise recontamination will result, and losses may be more severe than if a nonsterile medium was used in the first place. On the other hand, planting treated seed in nonsterile soil can be effective, since many of the materials used protect the seed for a time after planting.

Good sanitation in the general area where seeds are being germinated is an important means of control. Any decayed or diseased plants or other organic matter should be disposed of promptly. Walks, benches, walls, and so forth, should be kept clean and sprayed or washed with a disinfectant.

A considerable amount of benefit can be derived by using good seed and controlling the environment during germination. Many of the practices developed by seed propagators over the years have been those which have permitted seedling production despite the presence of disease organisms in the medium. The difficulty of control depends upon the quantity of the organisms present. If there is an initially high disease potential, the following controls may not be effective.

Good seed that will germinate rapidly is less likely to be attacked by damping-off fungi than weak, slow germinating seeds. A slow rate of germination could be due to age, conditions of development, or other factors affecting seed vitality. Some kinds of seeds will be more apt to be attacked than others either because of a naturally slow rate of germination or because of inherent susceptibility.

The environmental conditions which prevail during the germination period may affect the growth rate of both the fungi and the seedling. For instance, the best temperatures for the growth of *Pythium ultimum* and *Rhizoctonia solani* are between approximately 69° and 85°F. with a decrease in activity at higher or lower temperatures *(9, 39)*. Seeds which have a high minimum temperature for germination are particularly susceptible to damping-off, because at lower or intermediate temperatures (less than 75°F.) their growth rate is slow at a time when the activity of the fungi is high. At higher temperatures, the seeds not only germinate faster but also the activity of the fungi is less. Field planting of such seeds should be delayed until the soil is warm. On the other hand, seeds of cool season plants germinate (although slowly) at temperatures of less than 55°F., but since there is little or no activity of the fungi they can escape the effects of damping-off. As the temperature increases, their susceptibility increases, because the activity of the fungi is relatively greater than that of the seedling.

The moisture content of the germinating medium is of great importance in determining the incidence of damping-off. Conditions usually associated with damping-off include over-watering, poor drainage, and lack of ventilation. Experiments have shown that the damping-off fungi can grow in concentrations of soil solutes high enough to seriously inhibit the growth of seed plants *(9)*. Where salts accumulate in the germinating medium, damping-off can thus be particularly serious.

If damping-off begins in a germination container after seedlings are growing, it may sometimes be controlled by treating that area of the medium with a fungicide. The ability to control depends on the severity of the attack and the modifying environmental conditions.

Seed Treatment

Seed treatment to control diseases are of three types: disinfestation, disinfection, and seed protection *(40, 62)*. *Disinfestants* eliminate organisms present on the surface of the seed. Materials which have this sole action are useful if the seeds or embryos are to be grown in aseptic culture (see p. 142) or in some type of sterile medium. Materials which have been used for this purpose include calcium hypochlorite, Merthiolate (described on p. 128), bromine water, and mercuric chloride. Likewise, materials listed below as disinfectants or protectants are likely to be disinfestants.

Calcium hypochlorite (65). Ten gms. of calcium hypochlorite are placed in 140 cc. of water and shaken for 10 minutes or allowed to stand for an hour. The filtrate containing about 2 per cent hypochlorite is usually used, although this is sometimes diluted by half (66). The time of contact which will disinfest and still avoid injury varies with different kinds of seeds, usually being between 5 and 30 minutes. Adjusting the pH to 8 to 10 has been shown to produce most consistent results (14). Five to 10 per cent solutions of commercial bleaching preparations, such as Chlorox (containing 5.25 per cent sodium hypochlorite) have also been used (5, 41).

Disinfectants eliminate organisms within the seed itself. Treatments of this type include hot water, formaldehyde, mercuric chloride (1 part to 1000 parts water), and to some extent the organic mercury compounds.

Hot water treatment (22). The seeds are immersed in hot water (122°F.) for 15 to 30 minutes depending upon the species. After treatment, the seeds are cooled and dried rapidly by spreading out in a thin layer. Temperature and timing should be regulated precisely or the treatment may injure the seeds. Old, weak seeds should not be treated. Also, a seed protectant should be used. This treatment is effective for specific seed-borne diseases of vegetables and cereals, e.g., *Alternaria* blight in broccoli and onion, loose smut of wheat and barley.

Protectants are materials applied to the seed which protect it in the soil. Most of the recently developed fungicides used in seed treatments are protectants. These materials have also been applied as a soil drench either before or after seed planting.

Numerous materials for seed treatment are available commercially (18). Among the older materials are certain zinc and copper fungicides. Copper oxide (red or yellow) was used as a seed protectant for vegetable seeds. Machine planting is more difficult with such treated seeds, because the adhering dust slows down the flow of seed. Copper carbonate has been used for bunt control (disinfectant) in wheat.

Certain organic mercury compounds—ethyl mercury *p*-toluene sulfonanilide, methyl mercury dicyan diamide, hydroxy mercuric chlorophenol, and others—are highly effective although somewhat hazardous and require care in their use. Another group of fungicides, which are non-mercuric organic compounds—chloranil, thiram, ferbam, captan, zinc trichlorophenate and others—are less hazardous both for the operator and for the seeds, but as a group they are somewhat less effective. All of these materials are available under various trade names (18).

The combination of an insecticide and a fungicide has been found beneficial in field planting of certain crops to control attacks by wireworms and the seed corn maggot (28, 38). Insecticides used for this purpose include lindane, aldrin, dieldrin, heptachlor and benzenehexachloride. These materials should be combined with a fungicide (captan, thiram, chloranil), since they tend to increase the susceptibility of the seed to fungus attack. Various proprietary products involving such combinations are available *(18)*.

In using the various trade preparations, the directions of the manufacturer should be followed carefully. Improperly used, the materials can cause injury to the seedlings of some plants. Since they tend to be hazardous to a certain degree, depending upon the chemical, they should be handled carefully so as to avoid contact with the skin or breathing of the dust. In many cases, special machines must be used for treating the seeds.

There are several ways to apply the materials. (a) For small lots of seed, the dry or dust method is probably the most convenient. For treating large amounts of seed, the dust is applied in a rotating barrel, cement mixer, or other mechanical mixer. (b) In the liquid fixation method, $\frac{1}{4}$ pt. to $\frac{1}{2}$ gal. of water is sprayed on each 100 lbs. of seed by means of a sprayer after the dust has been applied. (c) In the "quick-wet" method, a concentrated solution of a volatile chemical is added to the seed and thoroughly mixed with it. (d) The slurry method involves the treating of the seed with a thick suspension of chemicals in a special slurry treater. (e) Soluble fungicides may be sprayed directly on the seed in a continuous or batch spray treater.

SEEDLING PRODUCTION INDOORS

The production of seedlings within some type of indoor shelter is an important method of propagating plants. Seeds are sown in special germinating media and the seedlings transferred to pots, flats, or special beds and later transplanted into their permanent location.

This technique is used, when outdoor growing conditions are unfavorable, to produce plants for pot plants or benching in greenhouses or to start plants for transplanting into out-of-door locations. It is extensively used to raise vegetables for early production, to grow plants which might not otherwise be adapted to an area of late spring and short growing season, and to produce bedding plants for landscaping purposes. It may also be used in the nursery production of trees and shrubs.

Starting seedlings indoors for outdoor growing may enable the propagator to obtain higher germination percentages, because he can control environmental conditions and reduce loss from disease, insects, and other adverse conditions.

To obtain these benefits, certain facilities are required, and somewhat more labor may be necessary in the handling of seedlings through to the transplant stage than would be required with direct seeding. It also re-

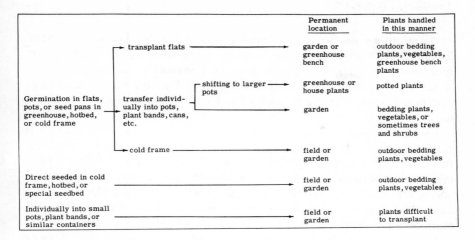

Figure 7–7. Methods of handling seedlings in relation to indoor culture.

quires rather close attention to details and a certain degree of skill and experience. On the whole, growing seedlings indoors is somewhat more expensive than direct seeding and would be justified only with valuable or expensive seeds, when seedlings are difficult to start under more rigorous outdoor conditions, or to obtain the benefits of early season production.

Facilities

The facilities required for starting seedlings indoors depends upon the number being grown. If only small lots of seedlings are to be grown, as might be done by an amateur gardener, a small box in a sunny window might be sufficient. When large numbers of seedlings are grown commercially, special propagating structures such as greenhouses, cold frames, or hotbeds are necessary.

Any container that will hold the germinating medium and provide drainage probably could be adapted for germinating seeds. Useful containers are the wooden or metal flats, individual flower pots, bulb pans, or plastic freezer boxes (see Chapter 2). Seeds which are difficult to transplant, for instance, cucumber or melon, could be planted individually into plant bands. Polyethylene plastic bags have also been suggested for germinating seeds *(55)*. The requirements of a seed germination medium are essentially the same as for any plant growing medium except that supplementary fertilization is of less consequence during germination.

Seedling Production

Germinating media. *Soil* is widely used for seeds in indoor culture. Taken directly from the field, however, most soils do not meet the requirements of a good germinating medium without modification of their structure and sterilization to free them from harmful disease organisms and insect pests. The preparation of soil mixtures is considered in Chapter 2.

Clean, sterilized containers should be used for germinating seeds. The container is completely filled with the sterilized soil mixture worked carefully around the corners to eliminate any air pockets which might be present. With a straight board drawn across the top of the flat, the excess soil is removed. The soil is then tamped firmly with a flat block of wood to a level approximately ½ in. below the rim of the container. If fine seeds are to be sown, it may be desirable to water before planting.

Sphagnum moss has been used as a germination medium either alone or as a layer on top of soil. Many kinds of plants, including azaleas, conifers, herbaceous perennials, annual flowering plants, vegetables, palms, cacti, and succulents, have been successfully propagated this way *(12, 53)*.

Since crude sphagnum is stringy, it must be shredded into smaller particles before use. With small amounts, hand screening with a 3-mesh-per-inch screen is suitable, but with larger amounts a soil shredder or hammer mill having a screen with a 1 in. opening is more practical. The moss should be dry when screened, but moistened slightly prior to use. The prepared moss is placed in the flat and mounded above the rim of the flat, then firmed to about ½ in. below the rim, watered thoroughly, and allowed to stand for a few minutes. Adding an additional layer of sphagnum about ⅛ in. thick will eliminate the smooth, compact surface produced by firming and provide a medium less favorable to the growth of algae. The moss is watered thoroughly and allowed to drain. Adding a nutrient solution to the germinating medium may be desirable to produce more vigorous growth, and if the plants are to remain in the sphagnum for a long period of time, supplemental fertilization is necessary (see p. 33).

One of the principal benefits of sphagnum moss is that it inhibits damping-off, and seed treatment is not considered necessary if it is used. Although not necessarily better than properly sterilized soil, it may be more convenient to use and does not involve the danger of recontamination *(26)*. Control of damping-off has been achieved even when the sphagnum was deliberately inoculated with the causal organisms. With the danger from damping-off reduced, watering can be frequent and heavy and the flats covered or enclosed to prevent drying during the critical early stages.

Various other materials such as *sand (13)*, *vermiculite (54)*, and *perlite* have been used as germination media. Properly used, these can give successful results. In general, these materials lack nutrients, and if seedlings are kept in them for long periods, fertilizing solutions must be added.

Vermiculite is useful because it has a high water-holding capacity and less frequent watering may be required. Good drainage should be provided, however. This can be done by putting a layer of very coarse vermiculite or coarse gravel in the bottom of the flat, filling it half full with coarse vermiculite, and planting the seeds and covering them with a medium-sized vermiculite.

Sowing. Seeds should be treated to eliminate seed-borne organisms. Where sterilized soil is used, untreated seed may result in recontamination of the germinating medium, and losses may be more severe than if non-sterile seeds were used in the first place.

The method of sowing seeds depends on the size of seed. Fine seeds can be scattered over the surface of the soil medium or planted thickly in rows. Medium-sized seeds would probably be planted in rows, and large seeds in individual holes spaced about an inch apart. To avoid planting too

Figure 7–8. Planting a seed flat. **(upper left)** The soil medium is firmed to eliminate air pockets. **(upper right)** Seed is planted thickly into shallow furrows. **(lower left)** When seedlings have produced first true leaves they are "pricked off" into a transplant flat at wider spacing or into individual pots. The peg board shown in the background is convenient to produce uniform spacing. **(lower right)** After "hardening," the seedlings are transplanted into the garden or other permanent location. A cube of soil from the flat is removed with the plant to avoid disturbing the root system.

thickly, small and medium-sized seeds can be mixed with a small amount of sand or other inert material before planting. The seeds are covered with a layer of soil to a depth of two to four times their diameter. Very fine seed may merely be dusted on the surface without covering.

After the seeds are sown, the flat should be sprinkled lightly with a fine spray of water or, particularly with fine seeds, the container may be placed in a shallow pan of water for sub-irrigation. To reduce moisture loss during the initial stages of germination, the flat can be covered with a glass pane and shaded with a strip of burlap or newspapers.

The temperature at which the flats are placed depends upon the germination requirements of the seeds. The best temperatures for seeds of most plants is around 68° to 70°F. For some, 55°F. is better, and for seeds of warm season and for tropical plants temperatures up to 86°F. are preferable. Higher temperatures (over 86°F.) result in rapid moisture loss and inhibition of germination in some seeds.

Handling of the seedlings. The primary objectives from seedling emergence until the plant is placed in its permanent location are to control damping-off and to develop stocky, vigorous plants capable of being transplanted with little check in growth. After seedling emergence, the cover over the flat is removed and the seedlings subjected to sufficient but not intense light. Temperature and light are two important factors which will affect seedling development. Moderate to low temperatures produce stocky growth. High temperatures lead to undesirable succulent growth, excessive moisture loss, and the development of damping-off organisms. General recommendations would be for a 60° to 65°F. temperature during the day and 5° to 10°F. lower at night for cool season plants, and 70° to 75°F. during the day, and 10° to 15°F. lower at night for warm season plants *(43)*. The seedlings should be subjected to adequate light to produce short, stocky plants rather than spindly, elongated seedlings, which results if they are grown in weak light. However, full sunlight during the early stages of growth should be avoided with some plants because of injury from high temperatures.

Figure 7–9. Tomato plants ready for transplanting. The two plants on the left are spindly and undesirable for transplanting. The three on the right are healthy, well-formed plants suitable for transplanting; the latter show the effects of sufficient space and desirable growing conditions. Tomato plants are transplanted bare-root. From **Calif. Agr. Ext. Cir. 167.**

The moisture supply should be constant but not excessive. Over-watering can result in poor aeration, and the resulting high humidity contributes to damping-off. When root growth is limited in the initial germinating stages, frequent light waterings are necessary to keep the upper layer of the germinating medium moist. As the root system develops, the frequency of watering can be reduced, but the medium should be wetted completely. Watering early in the day so that the plants dry before evening is desirable to reduce fungus infections. Covers of closed frames should be opened at intervals to reduce the humidity as the seedlings become larger.

If damping-off becomes a problem, it can be controlled to a certain degree by watering at intervals with a commercial fungicidal solution, although the success with which damping-off can be controlled by this means is variable.

Transplanting seedlings. When planted closely in the medium, the seedlings soon become overcrowded and a check in growth will occur if they are not promptly transplanted. This operation comes as soon as the first two to four true leaves have developed and the seedlings are large enough to handle. A seedling should be transplanted with wider spacing either into another flat or individually into pots, plant-bands, or similar containers.

A transplant flat is prepared as was done for the germinating medium. Seedlings are lifted carefully and inserted 1 to 2 in. apart into holes made with a wooden dibble in the transplant medium. The soil is then pressed firmly about the seedlings to eliminate any air pockets about it, and the flat is then thoroughly watered. For the first few days while the seedlings are becoming re-established, the flats should be shaded, held at a cool temperature, and kept from drying. When the seedlings have grown so that they are well developed and have begun to crowd, they are again transplanted either into their permanent location in the field or into pots or other containers.

Success in transplanting depends to a large extent upon the previous handling. When the permanent location is in the greenhouse, environmental conditions are controlled and are not different from that to which the seedling has been exposed during development. When movement from a greenhouse or hotbed to the open field is concerned, the operation is somewhat more critical and requires that the plant be "hardened" prior to its shift to the open field. "Hardening" involves a checking of growth resulting in the accumulation of carbohydrates which makes the plant better able to withstand adverse conditions (42). The process can be brought on by withholding the supply of moisture, reducing the temperature, and gradually shifting from the greenhouse or hotbed to the environment of the permanent location. A cold frame or lathhouse is useful for this purpose. Flats of seedlings can be moved into them and allowed to remain for 7 to 10 days prior to placing in the field.

Before moving into the field, the plants should be watered thoroughly. Planting is done in the field by hand or in some cases by transplanting machines. During transplanting, it is desirable to retain as much soil about the roots as practical to avoid disturbing the root system. Afterwards, the plant should be thoroughly watered, and if practical a temporary shade provided. For the first few days, until the plant has become established, it should be watched for wilting and watered as necessary.

The use of "booster" or "starter" solutions shortly before or after transplanting is sometimes beneficial in establishing plants in the field *(11)*. Such solutions should be used with caution, since if the soil is low in moisture at transplanting time, high concentrations of fertilizer can be injurious. This effect may vary with the soil condition (see p. 33).

Aseptic Culture

Germination in an aseptic culture is an important technique for growing seedlings when very precise control of germination is desired. It has been practiced primarily to culture embryos which are excised directly from the fruits at some stage of their development. This technique has been used to study embryo physiology *(50)*, to obtain hybrids of some plants whose seeds fail if left to develop within the fruit *(24, 44, 57)*, and to obtain prompt germination of certain dormant seeds *(5, 37, 45, 49)*. It is the usual method for germinating orchid seeds *(32, 48, 66)*.

Preparation of medium. The medium usually used is a solidified agar nutrient solution, although other standard germinating media could no doubt be used in some cases. The nutrients used depend upon the stage of embryo development—the more physiologically advanced the embryo, the less complex the medium. Numerous combinations of nutrients have been used by investigators employing this technique and several will be described here. Satisfactory results can, in general, be achieved with any of them.

Knudson's Solution B (32). Used for growing orchid seedlings.

	mgs./l.		
$Ca(NO_3)_2 \cdot 4H_2O$	1000	agar	17.5 gms.
$(NH_4)_2SO_4$	500	sucrose	20.0 gms.
KH_2PO_4	250		
$MgSO_4 \cdot 7H_2O$	250		
$FePO_4 \cdot 4H_2O$	50		

Adjust pH to 5.0 with 1.0 normal HCl.

A modification of this solution (*Knudson's Solution C*) *(32)* substitutes 250 mgs. of $FeSO_4 \cdot 7H_2O$ and 750 mgs. of $MnSO_4 \cdot 4H_2O$ for the $FePO_4 \cdot 4H_2O$. Certain other solutions have also been used for orchid culture *(3, 66)*. Ready to mix commercial materials are also available.

Modified Hoagland's Solution (20, 25). Used for mature embryos.

	mgs./l.
KNO_3	252
$Ca(NO_3)_2$	575
KH_2PO_4	136
$MgSO_4 \cdot 7H_2O$	240
Iron tartrate (1 per cent)	1 cc.
Minor element solution	1 cc.

The minor element stock solution is made up of the following:

	gms./l.
$MnSO_4 \cdot 4H_2O$	1.81
H_3BO_3	2.86
$ZnSO_4 \cdot 7H_2O$	0.22
$CuSO_4 \cdot 5H_2O$	0.08
$(NH_4)_2MoO_4$	0.09

Tukey's Solution (57). Used for mature and relatively immature embryos. Mix the following materials in the dry powder. Store in a stoppered bottle. Use 1.5 gms. per liter of water.

KCl	10.0 gms.
$CaSO_4$	2.5 gms.
$MgSO_4 \cdot 7H_2O$	2.5 gms.
$Ca_3(PO_4)_2$	2.5 gms.
$Fe_3(PO_4)_2$	2.5 gms.
KNO_3	2.0 gms.

Randolph and Cox Solution (49). Used for mature and relatively immature embryos.
Dissolve 1.0 gm. of $Na(PO_3)_n$ "Calgon" in 250 cc. of water. Dissolve O.2 gm. of $FeSO_4 \cdot 7H_2O$ and 3.6 gm. of $MgSO_4 \cdot 7H_2O$ in 250 cc. of water. Combine to form solution *B*. Mix with an equal volume of solution *A* made up of the following: 6.5 gm. of KCl, 8.5 gm. of KNO_3, and 23.6 gm. of $Ca(NO_3)_2$ in 500 cc. of water. The iron sulfate can be replaced with 3 cc. of 1.0 per cent iron citrate (50).

Sugar may be added to any of the above solutions if desired. Sucrose is usually best, although glucose can also be used. The concentration used ranges from 0.5 to 2 per cent—the older the embryo the lower the concentration needed. Additional solutions, including various growth substances and plant extracts, are used for growing very immature embryos (50).

Agar is used at the rate of 6 to 7 gms. per l., except for orchids (note above). The solution is heated to dissolve the agar and poured while still hot into culture vessels—test tubes, glass jars, or Erlenmeyer flasks stoppered with nonabsorbent cotton. The containers with the medium are sterilized in an autoclave or pressure cooker at 15 lbs. pressure for 20 minutes. The agar medium solidifies when cool.

Preparation of the cultures. The cultures must be prepared in a clean room free from dust and convection currents that might carry spores of microorganisms. Satisfactory results can sometimes be obtained in an open room if the work is done rapidly, but better results can be achieved if the manipulations are done beneath a pane of glass fastened horizontally about a foot above the table top. The best results can be achieved by doing the operations in an enclosed box or "transfer chamber," previously cleaned with a suitable disinfectant. The instruments which are used should be dipped in alcohol and flamed prior to use. Any other equipment, such as Petri dishes or similar containers used during the operations, should also be sterilized.

Asepsis of the seed or embryo can be achieved in two ways. The most effective method is to surface sterilize or clean the fruit, open it, and extract the seed with sterile instruments, placing the seed in a sterile container until the embryo is excised. Large, fleshy fruits or membranous capsules (tomato, squash, tobacco, pea) may merely be washed thoroughly. Surface sterilization with a disinfectant, such as phenol (5 per cent for 5 minutes), alcohol, or calcium hypochlorite, is more certain and is necessary in some cases.

A second method of obtaining asepsis is to treat the seed with a disinfestant (as described on p. 134). Hypochlorite is used for orchid seeds. They are placed in a small vial or flask and covered with five to ten times their volume of calcium hypochlorite solution. Adding a drop or two of a wetting agent is recommended. Shake for 5 to 20 minutes and plant im-

Figure 7–10. Seedlings growing aseptically on nutrient agar medium. **(left)** Peach seedlings. **(above)** Orchid seedlings. Photo above courtesy Shaffer Tropical Gardens, Santa Cruz, California.

mediately *(3, 66)*. Merthiolate has been used to treat *Prunus* seeds (see p. 128 for details).

The method of planting the seed and excising the embryo will vary with the kind and size of seed. For instance, very small seeds of orchids are planted directly from the solution with a wire loop or with a small medicine dropper. With larger seeds, the embryos will usually be excised and planted individually with tweezers. Standard bacteriological procedures are followed in preparing the cultures, including flame sterilizing the instruments, holding open flasks horizontal, flaming the openings of test tubes and flasks, and so forth. After the germinating containers are planted, they are kept in diffused light at room temperature.

When the embryos have germinated and the seedlings developed to a size large enough to handle, they are lifted out of the culture vessel and transplanted into a sterilized growing medium. Since the seedlings are unusually tender when they come from the enclosed flasks, particular care must be taken to protect them from strong light, high temperatures, and drying during their initial period away from the container.

DIRECT SEEDING

Direct sowing of seeds into permanent plant locations is a technique of seed propagation often preferred to the use of special seed-beds. In general, direct seeding is more economical, since it utilizes no special plant-growing facilities and involves no individual handling of seedlings. With many plants it is the only practical method to use. It is a standard method of growing field crops and many commercially-grown vegetables. The amateur vegetable and flower gardener may find direct seeding preferable to other methods, since it is simple and does not make demands on time and facilities. The lower germination percentages which might be obtained with direct sowing can be offset by increasing the rate of sowing and thinning any excess plants after germination. This procedure is feasible where the cost or value of the individual seed is not a factor. Of course, if too much thinning is necessary, the cost of production again increases. Direct seeding results in continuous and rapid development of the seedling with no check in growth associated with transplanting. The total time between seeding and harvest is less than would occur by the other methods. Some plants, such as corn, cucumbers, or beans, are difficult to transplant and are almost always planted directly in the field.

Seed-Bed Preparation

Proper seed-bed preparation is the keynote for successful field sowing. The requirements of a good seed-bed are: (a) to have an initial supply of moisture to carry the seeds through the germinating and early seedling period, (b) to have a physical condition that allows moisture to be supplied continuously to the seed, and (c) to have good aeration. A problem in seed-bed preparation is to obtain the proper balance between the extremes of low moisture, high aeration and high moisture, low aeration. This can be best obtained by a medium-textured loam which can supply moisture continuously without excessive drying. A light sandy soil dries out rapidly, whereas a heavy clay soil gives poor drainage, inadequate aeration, and tends to form a hard surface crust as it dries. Humus in the soil can be provided in the field by plowing under a cover crop or animal manure, allowing sufficient time before sowing for decomposition to take place. Incorporating peat moss, leaf mold, or other organic material may be feasible on a small scale. The ideal seed-bed would be one in which the soil is moist but not wet, finely pulverized to a depth of 6 to 10 in., particularly in the upper 3 or 4 in., and firmed to eliminate large air spaces which would increase evaporation and water loss.

The method of preparation depends upon the size of the operation and upon the crop being grown. For large-scale operations implements such as plows, disks, harrows, and land-levelers are necessary. For smaller operations the rototiller type of implement is convenient, since it loosens and pulverizes the soil in one operation. For small plots, spading or forking is the time-honored system. The soil should be spaded to a depth of 6 to 10 in. and then vigorously raked. If it is dry, irrigation several days before preparation is necessary. Working the soil when too wet destroys its structure and leads to difficulty in aeration and water penetration later. Determining the optimum soil condition is often difficult, but as a rule of thumb, if the soil forms a tight ball when squeezed with the hand, it is too wet. It should crumble when squeezed.

Seed-bed preparation may involve soil treatments to destroy harmful insects, disease organisms, and weed seeds. The modern development of specific chemicals and effective methods of application have made this phase of operation important, if the crop has sufficient economic value to justify the cost. This cost is offset to some extent by reduction in later costs of cultivation, weeding, and so forth, and the production of higher stands and improved crop yields.

Seed Planting

The time of planting is determined by the temperature requirement for germination. Cool season crops are planted early in the spring when temperatures are low; conversely, seeds requiring higher temperatures should not be planted until after the soil warms up. The time of planting is also determined by the date at which production from the plant is desired. For instance, planting small numbers of vegetable seeds at consecutive time intervals throughout the early spring and summer to produce a continuous supply from a home garden would be more desirable than a single planting to produce all of a crop at one peak harvest.

One of the problems in field planting is to determine the rate of sowing to obtain a desired stand of plants. The final stand of the plant is determined in order to produce the maximum yield of a high quality plant product. Too low a stand will reduce yields; too thick a stand will decrease size and quality. Once the desired final stand is determined, the required rate of sowing can be calculated if the germination percentage, the purity percentage, and the number of seeds per pound (or ounce) are known.

$$\frac{\text{Pounds (or ounces) of seed}}{\text{required per unit area}} = \frac{\text{Number of plants per unit area desired}}{\text{Number of seeds per pound (or ounces)} \times \text{percentage germination} \times \text{percentage purity}}$$

This figure is the minimum number of seeds to use. In practice, it is often desirable to increase the rate of sowing to offset expected losses in the seed-bed. The seedlings are thinned to a desired spacing after emergence. The depth of planting depends upon the size of the seed, the conditions of the seed-bed, and the environment at the time of planting. With too deep planting, germination may fail because the seedling is not able to emerge before the food reserves in the seed are exhausted. In addition, poor aeration may occur at lower depths. Proper depth is also related to moisture supply. Too shallow planting will place the seed in the top soil layers, which are subject to drying. In light sandy soils, or during periods of warm weather, deeper planting is best, whereas in heavier soils and during periods of cool, cloudy weather, shallower planting is permissible. A general rule is to plant seeds three to four times their thickness, being sure this depth is well within the moist layer of the seed-bed.

GROWING SEEDLINGS IN THE NURSERY

Growing trees and shrubs by seeds is an important part of nursery production. Some nurseries propagate seedlings almost entirely, dealing very little in vegetative methods. This is true in the production of trees and shrubs for reforestation, roadside planting, erosion control, and similar purposes. Nurseries producing fruit trees or ornamental shrubs and trees use seedlings extensively as rootstocks upon which to bud or graft selected clones or varieties.

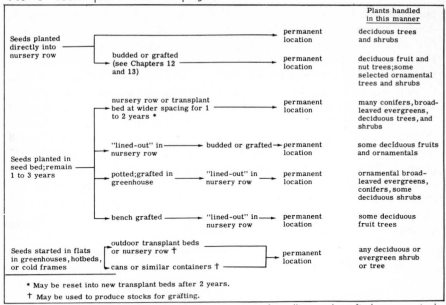

Figure 7–11. General schedules for the propagation of seedling and grafted nursery stock.

The discussion which follows can give only a general picture of the operations involved in the handling of seeds under nursery conditions. Details of operation vary from nursery to nursery depending upon various factors including the kind of plants, the size of the operation, the purposes for growing, the inclinations of the operator, and the location of the nursery. Nursery management is a specialized field involving more problems than the actual propagation of plant material.

Time of Planting

The time to plant seeds depends upon the species of plant being propagated as well as the particular method of handling used by the nursery operator. Most nurserymen either plant all of their seeds in the spring or plant part of the seeds in the fall and part in the spring (1). Seeds planted in the spring include those having no dormancy, those with hard seed coats (after pre-treatment), and those stratified in cold storage over winter. If the proper seed treatments have been given, germination should take place within several weeks after planting in all of these cases. If not properly handled, the seeds may not germinate until the second spring.

Seeds requiring cold stratification or seeds which must not be dried after harvest (e.g., acorns and walnuts) may be planted in the fall. Also, seeds which require warm plus cold stratification and those which are short-lived after harvest must be planted in the summer or fall. Fall planting is particularly useful where a large volume of seeds is to be handled and adequate cold storage facilities are not available. The seasonal labor requirement is distributed. more uniformly throughout the year if some of the planting is done in the fall. As soon as the environmental conditions are favorable in the spring, germination takes place and is not delayed by late planting. On the other hand, losses sometimes result from unfavorable winter conditions, drying, disease, or rodents. Also, weed control is a serious problem.

Seed-Bed Culture

Seedlings of many species are grown in special seed-beds during the first 1 or 2 years in the nursery. A common size of seed bed is 3½ to 4 ft. wide with a walkway between seed-beds, the length varying with the size of the operation. In some cases, sideboards are placed alongside the seed-bed after sowing to maintain the shape of the bed and to provide support for glass frames or lath shade.

Figure 7–12. Growing seedlings in seed beds. Russian olive in unshaded seed bed 6 feet wide. Seeds are thickly planted in rows six inches apart. Note sprinkler system in background.

Seed may be either broadcast over the surface of the seed-bed or drilled into closely spaced rows. Regulating the density of planting and spacing the seeds is one of the major problems in planting a seed-bed. For economical use of space, seeds should be planted as closely together as feasible. On the other hand, over-crowding leads to greater difficulty with damping-off and reduces the vigor and size of the seedlings (52).

The optimum density depends on the species and on the purposes of propagation. In other words, if a high percentage of the seedlings are to reach a desired size for field planting or for use as rootstocks for grafting, lower densities ·might be desired. If the seedlings are to be transplanted into other beds for additional growth, higher densities (with smaller seedlings) might be more practical. Once the actual density is determined, the necessary rate of sowing can be calculated from certain data obtained from a seed test and from the experiences of the operator at that particular nursery. The following formula is used *(51):*

$$W = \frac{A \times S}{D \times P \times G \times L}$$

W = weight of seeds in pounds to sow per given area.
A = area of seed-bed in square feet.
S = number of living seedlings desired per square foot at the end of the growing season.
D = average number of seeds per pound at the moisture content at which the seeds are sown.
P = average purity percentage of seeds (expressed as a decimal).
G = average effective germination percentage in the laboratory (expressed as a decimal).
L = average percentage of germinating seeds that will be living trees at the end of the season (expressed as a decimal). This is a correction factor which takes into account the expected losses which experience at that nursery indicates will occur with that species of seed.

Seeds of a particular lot should be thoroughly mixed before planting to be sure that the density in the seed-bed will be uniform. Seeds are planted either by hand or by machine. Depth of planting varies with the size of the seed. In general, a depth of about two to four times the thickness of the seed is a fairly safe estimate, but this also varies with the kind of seed. During early stages of development, seedlings generally must be protected against drying, heat, or cold. In the case of tender plants, glass frames could be placed over the beds, although with most plants a lath shade is sufficient. With some plants, shade should be provided all through the first season; with others, shade would be necessary only during the first part of the season.

A mulch applied to the seed-bed after planting helps to protect against drying, crusting, and cold, and discourages weed growth. It is particularly desirable with fall sown seeds, for seeds which are to remain for long periods in the seed-bed before germination, or for seeds sown in colder areas. Materials which have been used include sawdust, burlap, pine litter, straw, hay, ground corn cobs, wood shavings, sandpaper, canvas, shredded pine cones, sand, manure, and snow *(1).* One nurseryman reports the use of old rooting media of sand and peat as a seed-bed covering *(63).* The use of polyethylene film as a seed-bed cover has been described *(15).* In this case, the seed-bed was sown in the fall and covered lightly with sawdust, well watered, then covered with a sheet of polyethylene film on top of which burlap was placed. The following spring the film was removed as soon as germination occurred.

During the first year in the nursery, it is important to keep the seedlings growing continuously without any check in development. A continuous moisture supply, cultivation to control weeds, and proper disease and insect control are operations which contribute to successful seedling growth. Weed control is facilitated by careful seed-bed preparation, often including chemical pre-treatment. Undiluted mineral spirits (common dry cleaning fluid) derived from naphthenic petroleum has also been used effectively to control weeds in conifer seed-beds (60).

The seedlings may remain in the seed-bed for 1 to 3 years, depending upon the kind of plant. Many plants will be dug at the end of the first year and placed in transplant beds or "lined-out" in the nursery bed for further development. Deciduous plants would be planted 4 to 6 in. apart in nursery rows 18 in. to 4 ft. apart. Conifers would usually go into *transplant beds* similar to the seed-bed but at wider spacing. Spacing may be several inches apart in rows 6 to 8 in. apart. Nursery plants in rows are often undercut at the end of 1 year to stimulate the production of a more fibrous root system. Variations in the general procedure described may be followed as indicated in Figure 7–11.

Seedlings produced in a nursery are often designated by numbers to indicate the length of time in a seed-bed and the length of time in a nursery row. For instance, a designation of 1–2 would mean a seedling grown 1 year in a seed-bed and 2 years in a transplant bed or field. Similarly, a designation of 2–0 would mean a seedling produced in 2 years in a seed-bed and none in a transplant bed.

Direct Nursery Planting

Seeds of many deciduous trees are planted directly into nursery rows rather than in special seed-beds. This procedure is used to produce rootstocks for deciduous fruit and nut varieties (21). Where plants are to be budded or grafted in place, the width between rows is about 4 ft., and the

Figure 7–13. Direct seeding in the nursery row, illustrated here by Northern California black walnut seedlings planted directly in rows 4 feet apart. These seedlings will be budded or grafted to Persian walnut varieties after one season's growth.

seeds are planted 3 to 4 in. apart in the row. If the seeds show poor germinability, the seeds must be spaced closer together to get the desired stand of seedlings. Large seed (walnut) are usually planted 4 to 6 in. deep, medium-sized seed (apricot, almond, peach, and pecan) about 3 in., and small (myrobalan plum) about 1½ in. This may vary with soil type. Plants to be grown as seedlings without budding could be spaced at closer intervals and in rows closer together.

Usually, no mulch or shading is required by deciduous tree plants grown in the nursery row, although other cultural operations would be similar to seed-bed culture. Plants generally remain in place in the nursery row until they are to be transplanted into their permanent location.

A variation of this procedure is sometimes followed with species that germinate well but require some time to grow to budding size. Seeds are either planted close together to get a stand of 10 to 15 seedlings per foot or planted in a narrow band about 4 in. wide in the nursery row. The seedlings remain relatively small during the first season, at the end of which they are lifted and lined-out in a nursery row. Cherry, apple, or pear seedlings are often produced in this manner.

REFERENCES

1. Abbott, H. G., Forest tree nursery practice, *Amer. Nurs.*, 103:17–18, 130. 1956.
2. Anonymous, Locust seed treatment, *Amer. Nurs.*, 96(4):31. 1952.
3. ———, Growing your orchids from seed, *Amer. Orch. Soc. Bul. 24:*813–820. 1955.
4. Arnold, H. A., Seed scarifiers, *Tenn. Agr. Exp. Sta. Bul. 194:*1–23. 1945.
5. Asen, S., and R. E. Larsen, Artificial culturing of rose embryos, *Pa. Agr. Exp. Sta. Prog. Rpt. No. 40:*1–4. 1951.
6. Assoc. Off. Seed Anal., Rules for seed testing, *Proc. Assoc. Off. Seed Anal.*, 44:31–78. 1954.
7. Bass, L. N., 2,3,5-triphenyltetrazolium chloride as an indicator of the viability of Kentucky bluegrass seed, *Proc. Assoc. Off. Seed Anal.*, 43:131–135. 1953.
8. ———, 2,3,5-triphenyltetrazolium chloride as an indicator of the viability of timothy seed, *Proc. Assoc. Off. Seed Anal.*, 45:45–52. 1955.
9. Beach, W. S., The effects of excess solutes, temperature and moisture upon damping-off, *Pa. Agr. Exp. Sta. Bul. 509:*1–29, 1949.
10. Borthwick, H. A., and W. W. Robbins, Lettuce seed and its germination, *Hilgardia*, 3:275–305. 1928.
11. Clark, R. Ralph, Booster and starter solutions for vegetable transplants, *Ore. Agr. Ext. Bul. 703:*1–4. 1950.
12. Creech, J. L., R. F. Dowdle, and W. O. Hawley, Sphagnum moss for plant propagation, *USDA Farmers' Bul. 2085:*1–10. 1955.
13. Dunlap, A. A., Sand culture of seedlings, *Conn. Agr. Exp. Sta. Bul., 380:*133–159. 1936.

14. Eastwood, T. M., Antiseptic chemicals to inhibit the growth of microorganisms in nutrient solution cultures containing soluble carbohydrates, Ph.D. dissertation, Purdue Univ., 1948.

15. Engstrom, A., Polyethylene film for seedbed mulch, *U.S. Forest Service, Tree Planters' Notes No. 21:26–27*. 1955.

16. Flemion, F., A rapid method for determining the viability of dormant seeds, *Contrib. Boyce Thomp. Inst.*, 9:339–351. 1938.

17. ———, and H. Poole, Seed viability tests with 2,3,5-triphenyltetrazolium chloride, *Contrib. Boyce Thomp. Inst.*, 15:243–258. 1948.

18. Frear, D. E. M., *Pesticide Handbook*, 8th ed. State College, Pa.: College Science Pub., 1956.

19. Gadd, I., Report of the biochemical and seedling vigor test committee, *Proc. Int. Seed Test. Assoc.*, 18:289–306. 1953.

20. Gilmore, A. E., A technique for embryo culture of peaches, *Hilgardia*, 20:147–169. 1950.

21. Hansen, C. J., and H. T. Hartmann, Propagation of temperate zone fruit plants, *Calif. Agr. Exp. Sta. Circ. 471*, 1958.

22. Haskell, R. J., and S. P. Doolittle, Vegetable seed treatments, *USDA Farmers' Bul. 1862:1–17*. 1942.

23. Heit, C. E., The excised embryo method for testing germination quality of dormant seed, *Proc. Assoc. Off. Seed Anal.*, 45:108–117. 1955.

24. Hesse, C. O., and D. E. Kester, Germination of embryos of *Prunus* related to degree of embryo development and method of handling, *Proc. Amer. Soc. Hort. Sci.*, 65:251–264. 1955.

25. Hoagland, D. R., and D. I. Arnon, The water-culture method for growing plants without soil, *Calif. Agr. Exp. Sta. Circ. 347:1–32*. 1950.

26. Hope, C., V. T. Stoutemyer, and A. W. Close, The control of damping-off by the use of sphagnum for seed germination, *Proc. Amer. Soc. Hort. Sci.*, 39:397–406. 1941.

27. Horsfall, J. G., Combating damping-off, *N.Y. Agr. Exp. Sta. Bul. 683:1–46*. 1938.

28. Howe, W. L., W. T. Schroeder, and K. G. Swenson, Seed treatment for control of seed-corn maggot and seed decay organisms, *N.Y. Agr. Exp. Sta. Bul. 752:1–34*. 1952.

29. International Seed Testing Association, International rules for seed testing, *Proc. Int. Seed Test. Assoc.*, 21(1):1–80. 1956.

30. Isely, D., Employment of tetrazolium chloride for determining viability of small grain seeds, *Proc. Assoc. Off. Seed Anal.*, 42:143–153. 1952.

31. Koobation, M., Practical treatments to increase seed germination of woody ornamental shrubs in California, (Mimeo. publ.) Dept. Orn. Hort., Calif. State Polytech. Col., pp. 1–18, 1954.

32. Knudson, L., Nutrient solutions for orchid seed germination, *Amer. Orch. Soc. Bul. 12:77–79*. 1943.

33. Lakon, G., The topographical tetrazolium method for determining the germinating capacity of seeds, *Plant Phys.*, 24:389–394. 1949.

34. ———, Die Anwendung meines Topographischen Tetrazolium-Verfahrens zur Feststellung der Keimfähigkeit der Kern-and Steinobstsamen, *Saatgutwirstchaft*, 1:51–53. 1949.

35. ———, Die "Triebkraft" der Samen und ihre Feststellung nach dem Topographischen Tetrazolium-Verfahren, *Saatgutwirtschaft*, 2:37–39, 49–50. 1950.

36. ———, Die Feststellung der Keimfähigkeit der Koniferensamen nach dem Topographischen Tetrazolium-Verfahren. *Saatgutwirtschaft*, 2:83–87. 1950.

37. Lammerts, W. E., Embryo culture an effective technique for shortening the

breeding cycle of deciduous trees and increasing germination of hybrid seed, *Amer. Jour. Bot.*, 29:166–171. 1942.

38. Lange, W. H., C. E. Carlson, and L. D. Leach, Pest control by seed treatment, *Calif. Agr.*, 7(5):7–8. 1953.

39. Leach, L. D., Growth rates of host and pathogen as factors determining the severity of pre-emergence damping-off, *Jour. Agr. Res.*, 75:161–179. 1947.

40. Leukel, R. W., Treating seeds to prevent diseases, *Plant Diseases, Yearbook of Agriculture.* USDA, 1953, pp. 134–145.

41. Liddell, R. W., A simplified technique for germinating orchid seeds; *Amer. Orch. Soc. Bul. 15:*9–15, 69–73. 1946.

42. Loomis, W. E., Studies in the transplanting of vegetable plants, *Cornell Univ. Agr. Exp. Sta. Mem. 87:*1–63. 1925.

43. MacGillivray, John H., *Vegetable Production.* Philadelphia: Blakiston, 1953.

44. McLean, Suzanne, Interspecific crosses involving *Datura ceratocaula* obtained by embryo dissection, *Amer. Jour. Bot.*, 33:630–638. 1946.

45. Nickell, L. G., Embryo culture of weeping crab apple, *Proc. Amer. Soc. Hort. Sci.*, 57:401–405. 1952.

46. Parker, J., New methods for the determination of forest tree seed germinability, *Jour. Forest*, 51:34. 1953.

47. Porter, R. H., Recent developments in seed technology, *Bot. Rev.*, 15:221–344. 1949.

48. Post, K., *Florist Crop Production and Marketing.* New York: Orange-Judd, 1949.

49. Randolph, L. F., and L. G. Cox, Factors influencing the germination of iris seeds, *Proc. Amer. Soc. Hort. Sci.*, 43:284–300. 1943.

50. Rappaport, J., In vitro culture of plant embryos and factors controlling their growth, *Bot. Rev.*, 20:201–225. 1954.

51. Roe, E. I., and P. C. Wakeley, Seed testing, in *USDA Misc. Pub. No. 654:*41–50. 1948.

52. Scarbrough, N. M., and R. M. Allen, Better longleaf seedlings from low-density nursery beds, *U.S. Forest Service, Tree Planters' Notes No. 20:*29–32. 1954.

53. Stoutemyer, V. T., A. W. Close, and C. Hope, Sphagnum moss for seed germination. *USDA Leaf. No. 243:*1–6. 1944.

54. Stuart, N. W., Expanded vermiculite gives excellent propagation results, *Flor. Rev., 98:*33–34. 1946.

55. Sweet, D. V., Use of polyethylene film in the propagation and culture of certain horticultural plants, *Mich. Agr. Exp. Sta. Quart. Bul. 35:*265–268. 1952.

56. Taylor, C. A., Some factors affecting germination of celery seed, *Plant Phys.*, 24:93–102. 1949.

57. Tukey, H. B., Artificial culture methods for isolated embryos of deciduous fruits, *Proc. Amer. Soc. Hort. Sci.*, 32:313–322. 1934.

58. USDA, Woody Plant Seed Manual, *Misc. Pub. No. 654,* 1948.

59. USDA, Manual For Testing Agricultural and Vegetable Seeds, *Agr. Handbook No. 30:*1–440. 1952.

60. Wakeley, P. C., Planting the southern pines, *USDA Monograph No. 18:*1–233. 1954.

61. Wakeley, P. C., and P. O. Rudolf, Treatment of seed prior to sowing, in *USDA Misc. Pub. No. 654:*31–40. 1948.

62. Walker, J. C., Vegetable seed treatments, *Bot. Rev.*, 14:588–601. 1948.

63. Wells, J. S., Fall seed sowing, *Amer. Nurs.*, 96:15, 68–69. 1952.

64. Wharton, M. J., The use of the tetrazolium test for determining the viability of grass seeds, *Proc. Int. Seed Test. Assoc.*, 20:71–80. 1955.

65. Wilson, J. K., Calcium hypochlorite as a seed sterilizer, *Amer. Jour. Bot.,* 2:420–427. 1915.
66. Withner, C. L., Making orchid cultures, *Amer. Orch. Soc. Bul. 16:*98–104. 1947.

• **Supplementary Reading**

Allen, R. C., "Growing Garden Flowers from Seed," *Cornell (New York) Agriculture Extension Bulletin.* 579 (1952).

Baker, K. F., ed. "The U.C. System for Producing Healthy Container-Grown Plants," *California Agriculture Experiment Station Manual 23* (1957).

Engstrom, H. E., and J. H. Stoeckeler, "Nursery Practice for Trees and Shrubs Suitable for Planting on the Prairie Plains," *U.S. Department of Agriculture Miscellaneous Publication 434* (1941).

Post, K., *Florist Crop Production and Marketing.* New York: Orange-Judd, 1949.

Stoeckeler, J. H., and G. W. Jones, "Forest Nursery Practice in the Lake States," *U.S. Department of Agriculture Handbook No. 110* (1957).

United States Department of Agriculture, *Woody Plant Seed Manual,* Miscellaneous Publication No. 654. Washington, D.C.: U.S. Government Printing Office (1948).

———, *Manual for Testing Agricultural and Vegetable Seeds,* Agricultural Handbook No. 30 (1952).

Wakeley, P. C., "Planting the Southern Pines," *U. S. Department of Agriculture Monograph No. 18.* Washington, D.C.: U.S. Government Printing Office (1954).

Wells, J. S., *Plant Propagation Practices.* New York: Macmillan, 1955.

III

ASEXUAL PROPAGATION

General Aspects
of
Asexual Propagation

8

❧

NATURE AND IMPORTANCE OF ASEXUAL PROPAGATION

Asexual propagation is reproduction by means of vegetative parts of the plant, such as roots, shoots, or leaves. This is possible because in many plants detached vegetative parts have the capacity to regenerate either a new root system, a new shoot system, or both, or are able to unite with another plant part. For example, stem cuttings (sections of a shoot containing at least one bud) have the ability to form adventitious roots while the existing bud resumes growth. Root cuttings regenerate a new shoot system. A scion (or bud) is able to form a vascular connection when properly inserted into another plant system.

Asexual propagation involves no change (with some important exceptions as noted on p. 166) in the genetic make-up of the new plant. All the characteristics of the parent plant occur in the daughter plant, since exact duplication of the chromosome system takes place during cell division.

Environmental factors, however, such as climate, soil type, or disease attacks may modify the appearance of the plant or the flowers or fruit produced so that differences can appear even though no genetic change has occurred. Bartlett pears grown in California produce, in many years, round, apple-shaped fruits, but the same variety grown in Washington and Oregon produces fruits that are relatively long and narrow, a difference believed due to climatic factors. Even in the same orchard, a tree growing on a poor piece of soil will not have the lush, vigorous appearance of a tree of the same variety growing on a fertile piece of soil. In semi-arid regions, plants grown under irrigation may have a different appearance than the same plants grown without supplementary water.

The very existence of many of our valuable fruit and ornamental varieties depends upon the fact that they can be, and are, propagated asexually. Most of these plants are highly heterozygous and do not reproduce genetically "true" from seed. Planting seeds taken from a Jonathan apple, for example, will give a new seedling tree, but it will not be a Jonathan apple; it will be a new, unnamed, and usually inferior apple. To retain the Jonathan apple, it must be propagated asexually, not sexually. It must be propagated by some method where no genetic change, no pollination, fertilization, and germination of seeds is involved. It must be propagated asexually, as by budding, grafting, or layering. If man were, for some reason, suddenly unable to propagate further by asexual methods these varieties with their valuable tree, flower, or fruit characteristics, they would be lost as soon as the plants presently alive died. The variety would be gone forever, because planting seeds taken from their fruits would not result in the same desired variety.

THE CLONE

It is evident that in many fruit and ornamental varieties, man has large groups of plants, each originating from a single plant (a seedling) or from a single bud on a plant (a bud sport—see p. 166). Such groups of plants, including the original plant and all those that have been produced from it asexually, have been given the name *clone* (sometimes spelled *clon*). This term, pronounced *klōne,* has gained wide usage in horticultural literature *(40, 45)*. A clone can be defined as "genetically uniform material derived from a single individual and propagated exclusively by vegetative means, as cuttings, division, or grafts" *(39)*.

The Bartlett pear clone originated as a seedling in England about 1770 and has been propagated asexually ever since. The Winesap apple clone originated as a chance seedling some 200 years ago and has been propagated asexually since that time. The original tree probably died over 100 years ago. Before this occurred, buds taken from it and budded on seedling rootstocks produced new trees having tops of the same genetic constitution as the original seedling tree. By continuing this process of asexual propagation, thousands upon thousands of trees have since been grown whose budded tops collectively make up the Winesap apple clone. This same situation would hold true for all heterozygous fruit and ornamental varieties, which must be propagated asexually to perpetuate their desired characteristics.

When the concept of the clone is recognized, it is easy to understand why a discovery made with one individual member of a clone may be immediately applied to all other members of the clone. Such things as methods of propagation, cultural practices, disease resistance or susceptibility, would apply to all members of a clone, although modified, perhaps, by local environmental conditions (42). When a member plant of a certain clone is said to require cross pollination to set fruit, it must, of course, be pollinated by a member plant of another, different, clone rather than by a different member plant of the same clone, which, in reality, is just another part of the same plant.

A clone is often thought of as something entirely artificial, originally started and perpetuated by man's effort by some method of asexual propagation. Although this is true in many instances, clones do exist in nature. In some plants which reproduce naturally by asexual means, such as rhizomes, runners, or suckers, a clone could maintain and enlarge itself naturally. In fact, clones of very large size do develop; for example, the so-called species, *Lilium tigrinum,* is represented by a single clone (41). In species where apomixis occurs, a clone may exist through seed reproduction. This is fairly common in the Rosaceae, Gramineae, and Compositae families (39, 44).

MAINTENANCE OF DISEASE-FREE, TRUE-TO-TYPE CLONES

The life of a clone is theoretically unlimited. At one time it was believed that continued vegetative propagation of a clone inevitably led to a decline in vigor, renewed only by resorting to seed propagation (25). The present belief, at least with some clones, is that the decline and extinction after long-continued asexual reproduction can be attributed to virus diseases perpetuated in the clone by asexual propagation methods, which finally weaken and kill the individual plants (44). In most cases when such virus-infected clones are propagated sexually, the virus is not perpetuated, the new seedlings being virus-free. This accounts for their renewed vigor. In order to maintain valuable clones, it is essential that they be kept free from fungus, bacterial diseases, and especially virus diseases, all of which can be carried from plant to plant by asexual propagation, possibly spreading eventually throughout the clone. Many excellent varieties of the early horticulturists are now extinct curiosities due to their susceptibility to some disease which infected the entire clone. Clones such as these are replaced by others, but perhaps of lower quality, that are resistant to the prevailing disease or diseases.

One of the most promising developments in scientific horticulture is the establishment of disease-free foundation stock as sources of propagating material for nurserymen. Along with this, inspection and certification programs are set up to insure that only disease-free, true-to-name nursery stock is distributed to growers.

Pathogen-free nursery stock. There are several methods by which a start can be obtained (2). In cutting propagation, soil-borne organisms such as *Verticillium* and *Phytophthora* can often be avoided by taking only tip cuttings from tall-growing stock plants that are well off the ground. Such cuttings must, of course, be subsequently established in sterilized soil and containers.

In another method, individual pieces of propagating material, such as a cutting or bulb scale, are located that are free of pathogens. For example, to determine if such organisms are present on an individual cutting, small sections are taken from the cutting and cultured in test tubes on sterile, nutrient agar while the cutting itself is stored. Those cultures which are negative for pathogens are recorded as such and the associated cutting is planted, thus providing a source of clean propagating stock. Infected individual cuttings are discarded.

Heat treatments of previously hardened plant tissue will often eradicate pathogenic organisms on or in it, but not kill the host tissue itself. This pathogen-free tissue can then become the start for a mother-block source of propagating material. For example, *Dieffenbachia* canes can be freed of bacterial soft rot, bacterial leaf spot, and water molds by heating them to 125°F. for 30 minutes. Such treatments will kill the pathogenic organisms but, under the proper conditions, not the host plant (2).

Chemical treatments of planting stock can sometimes be used to eradicate externally carried pathogens. For example, white calla rhizomes can be freed of *Phytophthora* root rot by soaking them for an hour in a weak formaldehyde solution. The widely used treatment of seeds with a mild protective fungicide, although giving protection from pre-emergence decay, does not eradicate all pathogens from the seed.

Once disease-free propagation stock is obtained, great care should be given to prevent subsequent infection. This may be done chiefly by isolation, both of the propagating stock and the actual propagation operations. Of course, general sanitation practices and the use of sterilized soil, containers, benches, and tools is essential in maintaining the clean stock.

Since viruses sometimes move slowly through plant tissues, the extreme growing point may not contain the virus. By aseptically culturing the small growing point, it is often possible to obtain a virus-free plant from which further virus-free plants can subsequently be propagated.

General procedure for maintaining healthy clones (6, 24). Virus infection can be minimized by the following: (a) Select healthy mother-stock plants after determining their virus status by grafting or budding to indicator plants, then maintain such healthy mother plants under vector-proof conditions. (b) Multiply the tested mother plants at regular intervals on virus-free rootstocks under protected conditions in sufficient numbers to plant primary propagating beds. The nursery sites for these beds should be isolated in such a manner as to minimize the chances of the plants becoming virus-infected by natural agencies (vectors). (c) Produce planting stock at these field-propagating beds that can be supplied to nurserymen for establishing mother tree blocks, which in turn can supply budwood for propagating nursery trees that can be certified as suitable for commercial planting. If virus re-infiltration occurs, new basic foundation stock for the propagating fields should again be obtained from healthy foundation stock.

Established programs of this nature are found in potato culture. Potato clones are propagated commercially by division of stem tubers (see p. 440), an asexual method. Such reproduction would also perpetuate the various diseases attacking potatoes, such as mosaic, spindle tuber, yellow dwarf, and leaf roll. In order to have high production of marketable potatoes, it is necessary to grow plants relatively free from such diseases. Most states in the United States now have agencies that certify "seed" potatoes to be relatively disease-free, true to variety, and free from varietal mixtures. The actual production of certified potato planting stock is in cool climates where these diseases, particularly mosaic, readily appear and can be identified. In one method of starting a line of certified seed, a section of a numbered tuber is planted in a greenhouse during the winter. If no diseases appear on this plant, the remainder of the tuber—then presumed to be disease-free—is sectioned and planted out-of-doors at the normal time.

Frequent occurrence of bud mutations (see p. 166) is characteristic of certain plants, such as the various citrus species. Many of these mutations give rise to inferior, unproductive variants. In working with plants where this is likely to occur, propagators should always be on the alert to select budwood only from productive, proven, superior trees and to avoid any off-type branches *(34, 35)*. In addition, citrus trees are also susceptible to a number of bud-transmissable virus diseases, such as tristeza (quick decline), psorosis, and exocortis. It is essential that sources of budwood free of such viruses be used by nurserymen if these diseases are to be controlled in commercial plantings. To accomplish this, foundation plantings must be established as primary sources of healthy budwood, which can be guaranteed as to variety and at the same time be tested for freedom from disease. Regulating procedures must also be set up to register sources of suitable budwood and to certify nursery trees propagated from such registered parent trees.

Virus indexing. Viruses in symptomless plants are found by indexing onto varieties that will produce symptoms when infected with the virus. This is ordinarily done by grafting or budding healthy plants of a susceptible symptom-expressing variety with scions or buds from the suspected plant. This procedure is illustrated as follows in the strawberry.

Figure 8–1. Grafting procedure used in excised leaf method of transferring strawberry viruses. **(left)** Terminal leaf removed, petiole split and scion (excised leaf) inserted. **(center)** Union partly wrapped with latex tape. **(right)** Enlarged view showing healed union 40 days after grafting. Courtesy R. S. Bringhurst.

Grafting Techniques for Detecting Viruses in Strawberries (5, 23, 29, 33)

Some of the cultivated strawberry varieties are relatively tolerant of viruses and even though infected may show few or no symptoms. On the contrary, the Wood strawberry, *Fragaria vesca,* is very sensitive to viruses and shows symptoms in several weeks after inoculation. Therefore, if a runner of a commercial strawberry plant to be tested for the presence of a virus is grafted to a runner of *F. vesca,* the behavior of the *F. vesca* indicator plant after a few weeks will show any viruses present in the suspected plant. If sufficiently large runners are not available, leaf petioles of the two plants can be grafted.

The "runner" method of grafting. A thin piece of tissue, about 3/4 inch long and 1/32 inch deep, is sliced off of each runner near the top, using a sharp razor blade. Next, in one runner a slanting cut about 1/2 inch long is made, starting from one end of the first incision. The runner should not be cut through more than three-fourths of its diameter. In the other runner a similar cut is made, but in the opposite direction. With the two cut surfaces facing each other, the "tongue" of one runner is inserted into the cut of the other in the same manner as described for the "whip or tongue" graft on page 322. The runners are held together by small pieces of Scotch tape at both ends of the graft. Last, a piece of electrician's rubber tape is placed around the entire graft.

The "excised leaf" method of grafting (5).

Mature, well-developed leaves should be used. Only the terminal leaflet of the "scion" leaf is used and two-thirds of this is removed. The petiole is trimmed with a razor blade into a tapered wedge 8 to 10 mm. long. This "scion" leaf must be kept constantly moist until inserted.

The "stock" leaf is prepared by removing the terminal leaflet, and the petiole is split equally between the remaining two lateral leaflets. The scion petiole is then inserted in this split, and the union is tightly wrapped from the base upward. A self-adhesive latex bandage or crepe rubber works very well for wrapping.

REASONS FOR USING ASEXUAL PROPAGATION

Perpetuation of a Clone

It is necessary that asexual methods be used in propagating clones in order to perpetuate without change those characteristics which make the clone valuable, such as the high quality of a peach fruit, the color of a rose flower, the dwarfing effect of a clonal apple rootstock, or the resistance to viruses of a strawberry variety. If one of these particular clones is propagated from seed, its valuable attributes are immediately lost and a new, usually inferior, plant develops.

Impossibility of Seed Propagation

There are certain groups of plants which do not produce viable seed, such as some bananas, certain fig varieties, and the Navel oranges. These are said to be parthenocarpic; that is, the fruits develop without the stimulus of fertilization. Although fruits are produced, there are no seeds within them or, at most, only rudimentary seeds. There is no choice then but to propagate such varieties by asexual methods.

Ease of Propagation

Although some species may be propagated by seed with little if any change in the progeny, in many cases the seeds have such complex conditions of dormancy as to make sexual propagation difficult and slow. Propagation of privet (*Ligustrum*) is an example of this; seed germination is often slow, sometimes requiring two years, whereas stem cuttings root rapidly and in high percentages.

Often, too, with some species it is noted that after germination of the seeds the young seedlings grow slowly at first, much slower than cuttings started at the same time. Nurserymen have found, especially for many ornamental shrubs, a salable plant can be obtained much faster with propagation by cuttings (an asexual method) than by seed propagation.

GENETIC VARIATION IN ASEXUALLY PROPAGATED PLANTS

Mutations

As a general rule propagation of plants by asexual methods involves no genetic change, since no gametic union with recombination of genes occurs. Only the somatic or vegetative cells are involved, hence every cell in the new plant has the same genetic make-up as the cells in the parent plant.

However, there are still possibilities of genetic changes, even in asexual reproduction, due to *mutations*. These are changes taking place in the chromosomes during cell division. They may result from sub-microscopical changes, such as chemical alterations of the chromosomal material (the so-called "point mutations"), or from gross structural changes of the chromosomes themselves, or there may be an addition or subtraction of one or several chromosomes of a set or multiplication of the entire chromosome set (polyploidy). Any such modification of the chromosomes can result in an alteration in the characteristics of the plant.

If further cell division from a "mutated" cell in the growing point of a bud leads to the development of a shoot and, later, a complete branch, then the external characteristics controlled by the change in chromosomes may become obvious. This character could be fruit color or size or growth habit. Buds or scions taken from this altered branch would form the basis of a new clone which could be propagated asexually to give any number of identical new plants.

A part of a plant, arising from a bud, which is suddenly affected by a change in an inheritable character that can be perpetuated by asexual means is termed a *bud sport*.

Numerous bud sports have been discovered and many have formed the basis of commercially important new clones, both in fruit and ornamental species. In 1906 in Florida, pink-fleshed grapefruits were found growing on one single branch on one tree in a grove of thousands of grapefruit trees—an obvious mutation. The seedless Washington Navel orange probably arose as a bud mutation of the Brazilian orange, Laranja Selecta *(28)*. The first citrus fruit to be patented (see p. 173) originated in 1929 as a mutation—the red-fleshed Ruby grapefruit. Mutations in apples, resulting in changes in the color, size, or shape of the fruits, are also common *(27, 36, 37)*.

Undoubtedly, many valuable mutations have gone unnoticed and become lost. Some changes, such as increased sweetness of the fruit, would not be obvious and thus difficult to detect. Characteristics such as more highly colored or larger fruits are easy to observe and account for most of the recorded mutations.

Although certain authorities *(38)* believe that a somatic variant such as a bud sport is still a part of the same clone as the parent stock, in order to retain the practical value of the clonal concept, it is necessary to consider mutations as the starting point of a new clone and to give them a new name, provided, of course, that the mutations are worth preserving.

Mutations may also result from an increase in the number of chromosomes per cell (*polyploidy*). This increase may occur either in ordinary vegetative cell division (mitosis) or in the fertilization process where an unreduced chromosome number in the gametes occurs.

Polyploidy may give rise to "giant" sports in certain plants. Individual tetraploid grapevines have long been known to occur in vineyards, growers referring to such vines with prodigious growth habits and poor fruitfulness as "bulls," "males," or "giants" *(31)*. Chromosome counts have shown them to often be only partial mutations (periclinal chimeras, see p. 168), consisting of a single outer layer of diploid cells surrounding the mutated tetraploid inner tissues *(16, 17)*. Such giant sport canes in the grape are observed to arise at pruning wounds or near areas where a bud or shoot has been injured or killed. These mutant shoots seem to arise from deeply-embedded dormant bud initials *(30)*.

Spontaneous polyploidy also occurs in apples, producing giant sports *(11)*. Fruits of these sports are usually larger, flatter, and more irregular in shape than those from the parent plant. Trees bearing such fruits are vigorous with thick twigs, often having wide-angled crotches, which gives them a low flat shape.

Artificial induction of mutations. Several methods have been devised for artificially inducing mutations. An increase in the number of chromosomes per cell—polyploidy—can be caused by such treatments as application of extremely high or extremely low temperatures or applications of the auxin, indole-3-acetic acid *(21, 32)*. The most effective and widely used method, however, is treatment of the plant tissues with colchicine. The most common chromosome increase is to the tetraploid condition where the diploid complement of chromosomes is doubled. Each chromosome is then represented by a set of four in the somatic cells and two in the gametes. Higher increases also occur, from the triploid to the hexaploid and from the tetraploid to the octaploid condition, for example. These increases in chromosome number are accompanied by certain marked changes in external characteristics, chiefly an increase in the size of such parts as leaves, flowers, and fruit.

Mutations can also be induced by subjecting plants to X-rays and radioactive radiations. This causes changes in the genes and chromosomes to occur which may be manifested by marked changes in one or more characteristics of the plant.

Chimeras

The terminal meristematic growth of a bud or shoot involves a number of dividing cells rather than just one. It may happen that a mutation will affect one daughter cell and the series of cells arising from it, whereas adjacent to this series of altered cells there could be a series of nonmutated cells. Thus, a new shoot may develop consisting partly of the mutated cells (and resulting tissues) and partly of the nonmutated cells (and resulting tissues). This would then be a *chimera*. Chimeras can also be produced artificially by grafting operations. These are called *graft chimeras* (see p. 171).

Chimeras are frequently observed as the variegated foliage forms of certain herbaceous or woody plants *(13)*. They have been noted in *Citrus, Vitis, Pelargonium, Chrysanthemum, Hydrangea, Dahlia, Coleus, Euonymous, Bouvardia, Sansevieria,* and others. In such cases, the obvious change in the mutated part is the capacity to produce chlorophyll in the plastids. These variegated chimeral forms, if propagated asexually, perpetuate their distinctive characteristics almost indefinitely, although further "sporting" or reversion to the parental nonvariegated form is a common occurrence. In other words, these chimeral types are more inconstant and fluctuating during continued asexual propagation than are the nonchimeral plants which exist entirely as one genetically uniform structure. Some foliage variegations are not chimeras but are due to virus diseases, the mottled leaf conditions being a characteristic symptom.

The three main types of chimeras, as illustrated in Figure 8–3, are *sectorial, periclinal,* and *mericlinal,* although others, such as the "mixed" or "mosaic" *(18, 20)* types, do occur. Sectorial and mericlinal chimeras are unstable and are often of short duration when propagated asexually.

Sectorial chimeras. In this type, the growing point of the shoot is composed of two genetically different tissues situated side by side. Leaves and lateral buds arising from such a shoot may be composed of the two tissues combined in various ways, depending upon their location. There may be leaves and buds entirely of one tissue or of the other or of the sectorial combination as illustrated in Figure 8–3.

Periclinal chimeras. In this type, tissues of one genetic composition occur as a relatively thin "skin" one or several cell layers in thickness over a "core" of tissues of a different genetic make-up. Periclinal chimeras are found in a number of the fruit species, being especially common in the genus *Rubus (9).* The Youngberry has thornless forms which are periclinal chimeras, the cells of the outer thornless epidermal layer lacking the gene for thorniness. The Evergreen blackberry (*R. laciniatus*) also has a thornless sport, consisting of a thin layer of mutated, thornless tissue over nonmutated tissue *(10).*

Figure 8–2. A prominent sectorial chimera in the fruit of the pummelo **(Citrus maxima)**.

It can be easily demonstrated that these thornless blackberry sports are periclinal chimeras by comparing their propagation by tip layers or stem cuttings with propagation by root cuttings. In flowering plants, the shoot apex generally has three histogenic or apical layers. In stem cuttings, the shoot system arises exogenously from a bud which is usually developed or originates from all the apical layers *(12, 14)*. Since the mutation responsible for the thornless condition is presumably carried in the outermost or first apical layer (from which the epidermal tissue is derived), the thornless condition is thus perpetuated. Adventitious roots from stem cuttings are developed from the inner tissues of the stem, usually derived from the third layer, and—in the case of these thornless blackberry sports—carry the normal gene for thorniness. Thus, such a chimera propagated by stem cuttings is likely to be composed of a *shoot* system consisting of both mutated and nonmutated tissue—a chimera—and a *root* system composed wholly of nonmutated tissue. Obviously, new plants propagated by root cuttings would have no chimeral structure at all, consisting entirely of nonmutated tissues. Therefore, when root cuttings of a plant result in plants of a different appearance from those in which stem cuttings are used, it is likely that the plant is a chimera *(3)*.

Not all thornless variations are chimeras. The Austin, Burbank, and Merton thornless blackberries, for example, are not chimeras. In these plants, shoots from root cuttings as well as from stem cuttings are thornless.

In sexual reproduction involving periclinal chimeras, the progeny reproduces only the characteristics due to the genetic make-up of the cells in the sub-epidermal tissues, since the egg and pollen grain cells in the flower are derived from such tissues.

Mericlinal chimeras. This type is similar to the periclinal chimera except that the outer layer, of a different tissue, does not extend completely around the shoot, occupying only a segment of the circumference, as shown in Figure 8–3. A mericlinal chimera may appear superficially to be a sectorial chimera, differing only in that the altered tissue is just on the surface layer or layers, whereas the sectorial type occupies a complete sector from the surface into the center of a shoot or root or any other organ of the plant. Many of the supposedly sectorial chimeras that have been observed are, in reality, mericlinal chimeras.

This type of chimera is probably the most frequent to occur naturally, but it is relatively unstable during continued asexual propagation. A lateral bud arising from such a chimera could either result in a continuation of the mericlinal condition, or produce a periclinal chimera, or a completely nonchimeral shoot, depending upon its point of origin.

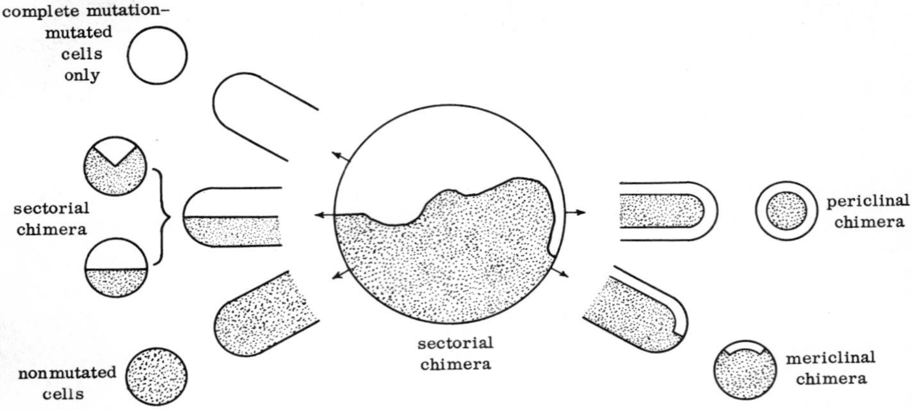

Figure 8–3. Buds arising at different positions on a sectorial chimera may produce shoots consisting entirely of mutated cells, or entirely of nonmutated cells; or the shoots may be a sectorial, mericlinal or periclinal chimera, depending upon their location. Adapted from W. N. Jones, **Plant Chimaeras and Graft Hybrids.** Courtesy Methuen & Co., London, Publishers.

The stability of a chimera varies with the different kinds. Lateral buds arising from a periclinal chimera will continue to reproduce this condition. Also, lateral buds in certain locations of mericlinal chimeras will produce periclinal chimeras. Thus, after considerable vegetative growth has occurred, these chimeral types tend to become the periclinal type. Chimeras, especially the stable periclinal type, can be reproduced vegetatively and perpetuated indefinitely.

It is probable that many of the limb mutations, the so-called bud-sports of some of the tree fruit species, as well as the trees propagated from them, are actually chimeras rather than complete mutations. A true entire mutation would always give an exact duplicate of the parent mutated tree or branch when propagated asexually. Such true reproduction does not always occur, however. In one instance, an apparent mutation of the Northern Spy apple was discovered as a tree with all the vegetative characters of the Northern Spy variety but bearing fruits varying greatly in type and coloration from branch to branch throughout the tree *(19)*. This same variation in fruit type developed in top grafts made with scions taken from this tree. Such variations in an asexually propagated plant suggest that it is a chimera, since it is typical of the variability occurring in chimeral plants. This raises the possibility that other of the well-known sports may be chimeras rather than complete mutations, and thus could not be expected to always reproduce true when propagated asexually.

Certain of the giant apple sports are known to be diploid-tetraploid periclinal chimeras, with a 2n layer (34 chromosomes per cell)—one, two, or three cell layers in thickness—over a 4n tetraploid (68 chromosomes per cell) interior. In a Delicious giant sport, for example, it was found to be tetraploid in all internal tissues but diploid in the epidermis *(15)*.

It has been demonstrated experimentally that some potatoes are periclinal chimeras in which the alteration has affected only a portion of the tissues. By removing the "eyes" of the tubers and causing adventitious shoots to arise from internal tissues, an entirely different potato results. For example, removing the eyes from the Noroton Beauty potato, which has mottled tubers, gives the Triumph, which has red tubers *(1)*. The Golden Wonder potato, which has tubers with a thick brown russet skin, is also a partial mutation, having inner tissues characteristic of the Langworthy potato, which has tubers with a thin, white, smooth skin *(7)*.

Graft Chimeras *(26)*

While most chimeras occur naturally, they also can be created artificially by the use of grafting procedures. If scions are cut back severely, adventitious buds may sometimes arise from the callus in the region of the graft union. Occasionally, a bud may develop which contains tissues of both stock and scion. The resulting structure is essentially one of the chimeral types in which the cells of the two graft components remain distinct regardless of how intermingled they become.

A thorough study of graft chimeras has been made by Winkler *(46, 47)* in Germany, who artificially produced many of them, using species in the Solanaceae family. He prepared wedge or saddle grafts of tomato (*Lycopersicon esculentum*) on black nightshade (*Solanum nigrum*) and black nightshade on tomato, both of which are easily grafted and produce callus readily. Winkler's grafts were made as shown in Figure 8–4. Following union, the graft was cut transversely at the junction, exposing tissues of both components. The cut surface soon became covered with a pad of callus derived from both the tomato and nightshade. From this callus, adventitious buds formed which developed into shoots. Most of these shoots had the appearance of either pure tomato or pure nightshade. Occasionally, however, shoots arose and grew normally which were different from either component. Some showed mixed characters, with half the shoot resembling tomato and the other half the nightshade. Winkler gave it the name "chimera," after the fabulous mythological monster that was part lion and part dragon *(46)*. Graft chimeras in the periclinal form also developed. One was found to consist mostly of nightshade tissue covered with a single layer of tomato epidermal cells. It bore fruit like that of the true nightshade and its seeds produced nightshade plants.

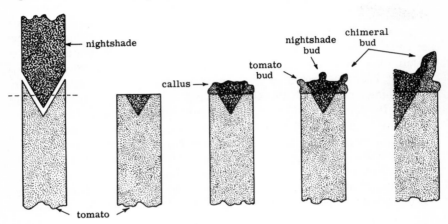

Figure 8–4. Stages in Winkler's method of producing a graft-chimera shoot between the nightshade and tomato. Adapted from W. N. Jones. **Plant Chimaeras and Graft Hybrids.** Courtesy Methuen & Co., London, Publishers.

Graft chimeras among woody perennials have long been known to exist, and some have been perpetuated indefinitely by asexual methods. Probably the earliest known "authentic" chimera is one called the "bizzarria" orange. It is described as bearing a fruit which is citron on one side and orange on the other. It originated supposedly in 1644 in a garden in Florence, Italy, from a grafting operation in which a scion of sour orange (*Citrus aurantium*) was grafted on a stock of citron (*C. medica*). According to the story, the original scion failed to grow, but in the swollen callus around the graft a shoot developed bearing the unusual "bizzarria" orange. It was propagated asexually and plants were widely distributed, leading to much controversy as to the true nature of its origin and composition. Scientific articles discussing the "bizzarria" orange were still being published 250 years after its origin, agreeing that it probably was a periclinal chimera *(18, 43)*.

The horticultural practice of grafting the medlar (*Mespilus germanica*) on a stock of the hawthorn (*Crataegus monogyna*) has led to several recorded instances of chimeral combination. The first known of these was produced near Metz, France, in 1899, when two adventitious shoots were found arising at the graft union of an old medlar tree. They had a different appearance than either the medlar or hawthorn and were different from each other. They were named *Crataegomespilus asnieresi* and *Crataegomes-pilus dardari* and were regarded for many years as true *"graft hybrids,"* believed to have resulted from a fusion of the nuclei of vegetative cells. Both of these types, sometimes called hawmedlars, have been maintained vegetatively, grafted on the hawthorn and widely distributed to botanical gardens. It is likely, however, that these two forms are periclinal chimeras *(4, 22)*.

There have been several strong proponents of the graft hybrid hypothesis. Winkler made his Solanaceae graft chimeras in the hope of gaining evidence for the graft hybrid idea. He believed that some of these unusual plant forms were true graft hybrids involving fusion of vegetative cell nuclei *(46, 47)*. Daniel is probably the most conspicuous supporter of this hypothesis and has written extensively on the subject *(8)*, although many of his views are not generally accepted.

THE PLANT PATENT LAW

On May 23, 1930, an amendment to the United States Patent Law was enacted which enabled the originators of new plant forms to obtain a patent on them. This amendment has added much impetus to the development and introduction of new and improved plants by establishing the possibility of monetary rewards to private plant breeders and alert horticulturists for valuable plant introductions. It has stimulated growers of fruit and ornamentals to be on the lookout for improved plant forms and has handsomely paid numerous fortunate or observant persons for their finds.

Essentially, what can be patented as stated in the statute is "any distinct and new variety of plant, including cultivated sports, mutants, hybrids, and newly-found seedlings, other than a tuber-propagated plant or a plant found in an uncultivated state." For a new plant to be patentable, it must be one that has been asexually reproduced and can be so propagated commercially, as by cuttings, layering, budding, grafting, inarching, and so forth, rather than sexually reproduced by seeds.

Characteristics which would cause a plant to be "distinct and new" and thus patentable include such things as growth habit; immunity from disease; resistance to cold, drought, heat, wind, or soil conditions; the color of the flower, leaf, fruit, or stem; flavor; productivity, including everbearing qualities in case of fruits; storage qualities; form; and ease of asexual reproduction.

The applicant for a plant patent must be the person who has invented and discovered and asexually reproduced the new variety of plant for which the patent is sought. If a person who is not the inventor applies for a patent, the patent, if it were obtained, would be void; in addition, such a person would be subject to criminal penalties for committing perjury. A plant found growing wild in nature is not considered patentable.

A plant patent issued to an individual is a grant consisting of the right to exclude others from asexually reproducing the plant or selling or using the plant so reproduced. Essentially, it is a grant by the United States Government, acting through the Patent Office, to the inventor (or his heirs or assigns) of certain exclusive rights to his invention for a term of 17 years throughout the United States and its territories and possessions. It affords no protection in other countries. The mere fact that a patent has been issued on a new plant does not imply any endorsement by the Government of its high quality or merit. The only implication of a patent on a plant is that it is "distinct and new."

REFERENCES

1. Asseyera, T., Bud mutations in the potato and their chimerical nature, *Jour. Gen.,* 19:1–26. 1927.
2. Baker, K. F., and P. A. Chandler, Development and maintenance of healthy planting stock, in *Calif. Agr. Exp. Sta. Man. 23,* Sect. 13. 1957.
3. Bateson, W., Root cuttings, chimeras and "sports," *Jour. Gen.,* 6:75–80. 1916.
4. Baur, E., Pfropfbastarde Periclinal Chimaeren und Hyperchimaeren, *Ber. Deuts. Bot. Ges.,* 27:603–605. 1909.
5. Bringhurst, R. S., and V. Voth, Strawberry virus transmission by grafting excised leaves, *Plant Disease Rpt.,* 40(7):596–600. 1956.
6. Cochran, L. C., et al., How nurseries get virus-free fruit stock, in *Plant Diseases,* USDA *Yearbook of Agriculture,* pp. 152–158. 1953.
7. Crane, M. B., Note on a periclinal chimera in the potato, *Jour. Gen.,* 32:73–77. 1936.
8. Daniel, L., Les hybrides de greffe, Int. Tuinbouw. Cong., Amsterdam, pp. 175–193. 1923.
9. Darrow, G. M., Notes on thornless blackberries, *Jour. Hered.,* 19:139–142. 1928.
10. ———, A productive thornless sport of the Evergreen blackberry, *Jour. Hered.,* 22:404–406. 1931.
11. Darrow, G. M., et al., The nature of giant apple sports, *Jour. Hered.,* 39:45–51. 1948.
12. Dermen, H., The mechanism of colchicine-induced cytohistological changes in cranberry, *Amer. Jour. Bot.,* 32:387–394. 1945.
13. ———, Histogenesis of some budsports and variegations, *Proc. Amer. Soc. Hort. Sci.,* 50:51–73. 1947.
14. ———, Periclinal cytochimeras and histogenesis in cranberry, *Amer. Jour. Bot.,* 34:32–43. 1947.
15. ———, A tetraploid sport of Delicious apple from Idaho, *Jour. Hered.,* 43:8. 1952.
16. ———, Colchiploidy in grapes, *Jour. Hered.,* 45:159–172. 1954.
17. Einset, J., and C. Pratt, "Giant" sports of grapes, *Proc. Amer. Soc. Hort. Sci.,* 63:251–256. 1954.

18. Frost, H. B., Polyembryony, heterozygosis, and chimeras in *Citrus, Hilgardia,* 1:365–402. 1926.

19. Gardner, V. R., Studies in the nature of the pomological variety, *Mich. Agr. Exp. Sta. Tech. Bul. 161,* 1938.

20. ———, A study of the sweet and sour apple chimera and its clonal significance, *Jour. Agr. Res.,* 68:383–394. 1944.

21. Greenleaf, W. H., Induction of polyploidy in *Nicotiana, Jour. Hered.,* 29:451–464. 1938.

22. Haberlandt, G., Das Wesen der *Crataegomespili Sitzber, Preuss. Akad. Wiss.,* 20:374–394. 1930.

23. Harris, R. V., Grafting as a method for investigating a possible virus disease of the strawberry, *Jour. Pom. and Hort. Sci.,* 10:35–41. 1932.

24. ———, The maintenance of healthy fruit clones, *Rpt. 13th Int. Hort. Cong.,* pp. 189–198. 1952.

25. Knight, Thomas Andrew, Observations on the grafting of trees, Phil. Trans. Roy. Soc., London, 85:290. 1795.

26. Krenke, N. P., Wundkompensation Transplantation und Chimären bei Pflanzen (translated from Russian). Berlin: Springer, 1933.

27. Magness, J. R., Progress in apple improvement, in USDA *Yearbook of Agriculture,* pp. 575–614. 1937.

28. Miller, E. V., The natural origins of some popular varieties of fruit, *Econ. Bot.,* 8:337–348. 1954.

29. Miller, P. W., Technique for indexing strawberries for viruses by grafting to *Fragaria vesca, Plant Disease Rpt. 36:*94–96. 1952.

30. Olmo, H. P., Breeding tetraploid grapes, *Proc. Amer. Soc. Hort. Sci.,* 59:285–290. 1952.

31. ———, Bud mutation in the vinifera grape. II. Sultanina gigas. *Proc. Amer. Soc. Hort. Sci.,* 33:437–439. 1936.

32. Randolph, L. F., Some effects of high temperature on polyploidy and other variations in maize, *Proc. Nat. Acad. Sci.,* 18:222–229. 1932.

33. Schwartz, C. D., and A. S. Myhre, Results of grafting Northwest and Marshall strawberry plants to a virus indicator, *Proc. Amer. Soc. Hort. Sci.,* 58:80–90. 1951.

34. Shamel, A. D., C. S. Pomeroy, and R. E. Caryl, Bud selection in the Valencia orange; progeny tests of limb variations, *USDA Bul. 1483,* 1927.

35. ———, Bud selection in the Washington Navel orange; progeny tests of limb variations, *USDA Tech. Bul. 123,* 1929.

36. Shamel, A. D., and C. S. Pomeroy, Bud variation in apples, *Jour. Hered.,* 23:173. 1932.

37. ———, Bud mutations in horticultural crops, *Jour. Hered.,* 27:487–494. 1936.

38. Shull, C. H., "Phenotype" and "clone," *Science,* N. S. 35:182–183. 1912.

39. Stern, W. T., International code of nomenclature for cultivated plants, *Rpt. 13th Int. Hort. Cong.,* pp. 42–68. 1952.

40. ———, The use of the term "clone," *Jour. Roy. Hort. Soc.,* 74:41–47. 1943.

41. Stout, A. B., The clon in plant life, *Jour. N.Y. Bot. Gard.,* 30:25–37. 1929.

42. ———, The nomenclature of cultivated plants, *Amer. Jour. Bot.,* 27:339–347. 1940.

43. Tanaka, T.,. Bizzarria—a clear case of periclinal chimera, *Jour. Gen.,* 18:77–85. 1927.

44. Tincker, M. A. H., Propagation, degeneration, and vigor of growth, *Jour. Roy. Hort. Soc.,* 70:333–337. 1945.

45. Webber, H. J., New horticultural and agricultural terms, *Science,* N.S. 18:501–502. 1903.

46. Winkler, H., Uber Pfropfbastarde und pflanzliche Chimaren, *Ber. Deuts. Bot. Ges.,* 25:568–576. 1907.

47. ———, Uber die Nachkommenschaft der *Solanum* Pfropfbastarde und die Chromosomenzahlen ihrer Keimzellen, *Zeits. f. Bot.,* 2:1–38. 1910.

• ## Supplementary Reading

Avery, G. S., et al., *Hormones and Horticulture.* New York: McGraw-Hill, 1947. Chap. 11.

Committee on Seed and Plant Material Certification, The American Phytopathological Society, "Development and Production of Pathogen-Free Propagative Material of Ornamental Plants," *Plant Disease Reporter Supplement 238,* (1956).

Crane, M. B., and W. J. C. Lawrence, *The Genetics of Garden Plants,* 4th ed. London: Macmillan, 1952.

Eigsti, O. J., and P. Dustin, Jr., *Colchicine—in Agriculture, Medicine, Biology, and Chemistry.* Ames: Iowa State College Press, 1955.

Jones, W. N., "Chimaeras: A Summary and Some Special Aspects," *Botanical Review,* Vol. 3 (1937), pp. 545–562.

Kneen, O. H., "Patent Plants Enrich Our World," *National Geographic Magazine,* Vol. 93 (1948), pp. 357–378.

Magness, J. R., "Vegetative Reproduction," in *Yearbook of Agriculture,* U.S. Department of Agriculture (1937).

Stearn, W. T., "The Use of the Term 'Clone,'" *Journal Royal Horticultural Society,* Vol. 74 (1949), pp. 41–47.

Swingle, C. F., "Regeneration and Vegetative Propagation," *Botanical Review* I, Vol. 6 (1940), pp. 301–355; II, Vol. 18 (1952), pp. 1–11.

Weiss, F. E., "The Problem of Graft Hybrids and Chimaeras," *Biological Review,* Vol. 5 (1930), pp. 231–271.

9

Anatomical and Physiological Basis of Propagation by Cuttings

In propagation by *stem* and *leaf-bud cuttings,* it is only necessary that a new root system be formed, since a potential shoot system—a bud—is already present. *Root cuttings* must initiate a new shoot system—from an adventitious bud—as well as an extension of the existing root piece. In *leaf cuttings,* both a new root and a new shoot system must be regenerated. Fortunately, many cells, even in mature plant parts, have the capability of returning to the meristematic condition and producing the necessary root and shoot system, thus making propagation by cuttings possible.

The various types of cuttings and methods of preparing them are discussed in Chapter 10.

THE ANATOMICAL DEVELOPMENT OF ROOTS IN CUTTINGS

Stem Cuttings

A knowledge of the internal structure of the stem is necessary in order to understand the origin of adventitious roots. In Figure 9–1 a cross section of an herbaceous stem is shown with the principal tissues indicated.

Initiation of root primordia. In most plants, the formation of adventitious roots takes place entirely after the cutting is made. In general, the origin of most adventitious roots in stem cuttings is found in groups of cells which are capable of becoming meristematic and which are located

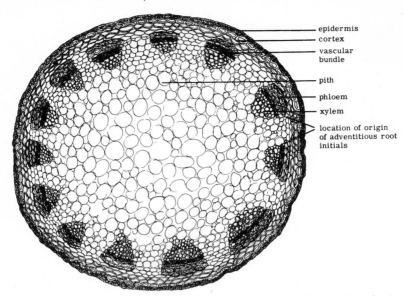

epidermis
cortex
vascular
bundle

pith

phloem

xylem

location of origin
of adventitious root
initials

Figure 9–1. Stem cross-section of a young herbaceous, dicotyledenous plant showing the region where adventitious root initials usually originate.

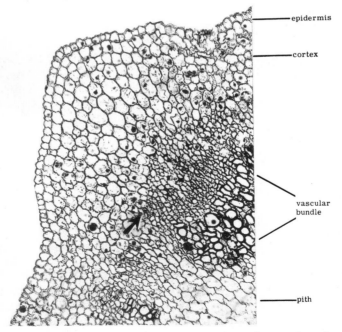

epidermis

cortex

vascular
bundle

pith

Figure 9–2. Photomicrograph of a portion of chrysanthemum stem. Arrow points to a root initial in a very early stage showing its close relationship to a vascular bundle. (Enlarged 200 times.) Courtesy B. B. Stangler.

just outside and between the vascular bundles *(89).* These small groups of cells, the *root initials,* continue dividing, forming groups of many small cells which develop into new *root primordia.* This, then, is the beginning of adventitious roots. Cell division continues and soon each group of cells takes on the appearance of a root tip. A vascular system develops in the new root primordium and becomes connected to the adjacent vascular bundle *(23).* The root tip continues to grow outward, through the cortex and epidermis, emerging at right angles to the stem. Adventitious roots on stems thus arise *endogenously;* that is, they originate within the stem tissue and grow outward.

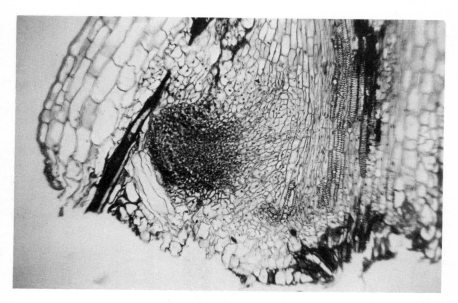

Figure 9–3. Photomicrograph of a radial section of a portion of the basal end of a carnation stem cutting. The epidermis is at the left and the pith at the right. In this species, a band of thick-walled fiber cells is present. The outward-growing root primordium has reached this band and will turn downward and emerge through the base of the cutting. (Enlarged 200 times.) Courtesy B. B. Stangler.

In young stems the root initials originate near the outer side of the vascular system, but in older stems their origin is deeper, often near the vascular cambium. In cuttings made from woody perennial plants where one or more layers of secondary xylem and phloem may be present, the roots often originate in the young secondary phloem tissue, although such roots may also arise from various tissues, such as the vascular rays, parenchyma, or pith *(13, 36, 56, 134).* Considering specific examples, in leaf-bud cuttings of black raspberry (*Rubus occidentalis*), adventitious root primordia can form almost any place along the sides of the vascular bundles although most arise from the branch and leaf traces of the buds or in the vascular

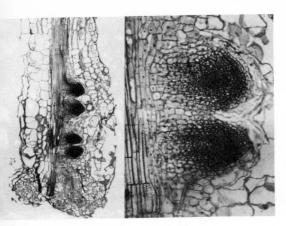

Figure 9–4. Development of adventitious roots in stem segments of tobacco. Root primordia originated in cambial region. (left) Group of four primordia. Pith is at left, cortex at right. Longitudinal section x 18. (right) Enlarged view of two primordia. Xylem is at left, phloem at right. Longitudinal section x 94. Courtesy Clarence Sterling.

supply of the leaf subtending the bud. A few occur in the vascular cylinder of the parent cane *(111)*. In softwood red raspberry (*Rubus strigosus*) tip cuttings, root initials arise in the primary rays beside certain of the vascular bundles identified as leaf traces comprising the vascular supply of the previously removed leaves. In the rose (*Rosa dilecta*), they originate close to the cambium layer in immature multiseriate ray tissue of the secondary phloem *(102)*. In white pine (*Pinus strobus*) cuttings, root initials are observed to form in association with the rays and leaf traces *(17),* whereas in *Taxus cuspidata* cuttings, adventitious roots were found to originate in secondary phloem cells and in secondary phloem ray cells and surrounding parenchyma *(44).*

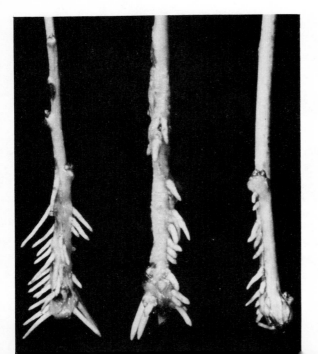

Figure 9–5. Development of adventitious roots in plum stem cuttings. Observe the tendency of the roots to form in longitudinal rows, which appear directly below buds.

Typical of cuttings taken from young herbaceous plants, adventitious roots in chrysanthemums are first observed in the interfascicular region, whereas the root initials in carnation cuttings arise in a layer of paren-chymatous cells inside a fiber sheath *(102)*. In the latter case, the developing root tips, upon reaching this band of fiber cells, are unable to push through it and turn downward and emerge from the base of the cutting.

The time for root initials to develop after the cuttings are placed in the propagating bed varies. In one study *(102)*, the initials were first observed microscopically in 3 days in chrysanthemum, 5 days in carnation, and 7 days in the rose. Visible roots emerged from the cuttings after 10 days for the chrysanthemum, but 3 weeks were required for the carnation and rose.

Preformed root initials. In some plants, initials form during stem development and are present at the time the cuttings are made *(67, 127)*. These are termed *preformed root initials* and generally lie dormant until the stems are made into cuttings and placed under environmental conditions favorable for the development and emergence of the initials as adventitious roots. Such preformed root initials occur in a number of easily-rooted genera such as willow (*Salix*), poplar (*Populus*), jasmine (*Jasminum*), and currant (*Ribes*). The position of origin of these preformed root initials is not different from that of other adventitious roots on stems. In certain species of willow and in some apple varieties, they have been observed to originate outside the cambium in rays associated with leaf and branch

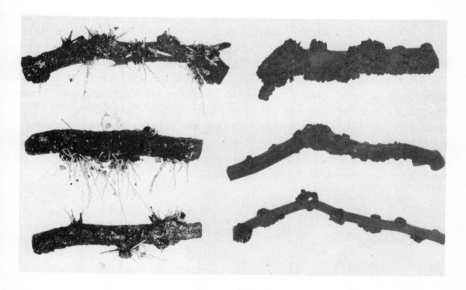

Figure 9–6. Stem sections of quince **(Cydonia oblonga)** several years old showing "burr knots." Preformed adventitious roots promptly developed on pieces at left when they were placed under warm, moist conditions.

gaps *(6, 66, 112)*. In old trees of some apple and quince varieties, these preformed latent roots cause swellings, commonly called "burr knots." The presence of preformed roots in older stems of the quince is indicated by tests in which a much higher percentage of cuttings form roots if they are made from one-year wood with a portion or "heel" of 2-year wood (containing such preformed roots at the base of the cutting) than if the cutting is made entirely of one-year wood *(128)*.

In the willow, these latent root primordia remain dormant, embedded in the inner bark for years if the stems remain intact on the tree *(7)*. Their location in this species can be observed by peeling off the bark and noting the protuberances on the wood with corresponding indentations on the inside of the removed bark. Such primordia will usually develop rapidly into roots if the stems are made into cuttings and placed in water *(67)*.

The presence of preformed root initials is not essential for rapid rooting. For example, stem cuttings of most grape varieties root easily, yet such root initials are not present. Likewise, both softwood and hardwood cuttings of many ornamental species root rapidly, although no preformed root initials are present.

Callus. Sometimes, after the cuttings have been made and placed under environmental conditions favorable for rooting, a *callus* layer will develop at the basal end of the cutting. This is an irregular mass of parenchyma cells in various stages of lignification. This callus growth arises from cells in the region of the vascular cambium and adjacent phloem, although various cells of the cortex and pith may also contribute to its formation. Frequently, the first roots appear through the callus, leading to the belief that callus formation is essential for rooting. However, it has long been known that the formation of callus and the formation of roots are independent of each other, although they often occur simultaneously, since the development of both are dependent upon similar internal and environmental conditions. Callus production may be beneficial in plants slow to root, because it provides a protective layer which retards the development of decay. On the other hand, the callus layer in some cases may interfere with the absorption of water by the cutting *(59)*.

Leaf Cuttings

A great number of plant species, including both monocots and dicots, can be started by leaf cuttings *(37)*. Although the origin of new shoots and new roots in leaf cuttings is quite varied, they can be grouped generally as developing from primary * or secondary † meristems, the latter type being the most common.

Leaf cuttings with primary meristems. In Figure 10–11 detached leaves of *Kalanchoe* (*Bryophyllum*) are shown with small plants arising from the notches around the leaf margin. These small plants originate from so-called foliar "embryos," which are formed in the very early stages of leaf development from a small group of cells at the edge of the leaf. As the leaf expands, the foliar embryo develops until it consists of two rudimentary leaves with a stem tip between them, two root primordia, and a "foot" which extends toward a vein *(152)*. As the leaf matures, cell division in the foliar embryo ceases and it remains dormant. If the leaf is detached and placed in close contact with a moist rooting medium, the young plants rapidly break through the leaf epidermis and become visible in a few days. Roots extend downward, and after several weeks many new independent plants form while the original leaf dies. The new plants thus develop from latent primary meristems—from cells that have not assumed mature characteristics. This same type of production of new plants from leaf cuttings by the renewed activity of primary meristems is found also in other species, such as the piggy-back plant (*Tolmiea*) and walking fern (*Camptosorus*).

Leaf cuttings with secondary meristems. In leaf cuttings of some plants, such as *Begonia rex, Sedum,* African violet (*Saintpaulia*), snake plant (*Sansevieria*), *Crassula,* and lilies (*Lilium*), new plants develop from secondary meristems arising from mature cells at the base of the leaf blade or from the petiole.

In *Lilium longiflorum* and *L. candidum,* the bud primordium originates in parenchyma cells in the upper side of the bulb scale, whereas the root primordium arises from parenchyma cells just below the bud primordium. Although the original scale serves as a source of food materials for the developing plant, the vascular system of the young bulblet is independent of that of the parent scale, which eventually shrivels and disappears *(136)*.

In the African violet, new roots and shoots arise by the formation of meristematic cells from mature cells in the leaves. The roots are produced endogenously from thin-walled cells lying between the vascular bundles. The new shoots arise from cells of the epidermis and the cortex immediately below the epidermis. The roots emerge, form branch roots, and continue to grow for several weeks before the shoots appear. Although the original leaf supplies nutrient materials to the young plant, it does not become a part of the new plant *(76)*.

In several species, such as the sweet potato (*Ipomoea batatas*), *Peperomia,* and *Sedum,* new roots and new shoots on leaf cuttings arise in callus

---

* *Primary meristems* are cells that are direct descendents of embryonic cells which have never ceased to be concerned with growth.

† *Secondary meristems* are cells which have differentiated and functioned as members of some mature tissue system and then again resumed meristematic activity.

tissue which develops over the cut surface through activity of secondary meristems. The petiole of leaf cuttings of *Sedum* builds up a considerable pad of callus within a few days after the cuttings are made. Root primordia are organized within the callus tissue and shortly thereafter four or five roots develop from the. parent leaf. Following this, stem primordia arise on a lateral surface of the callus pad and develop into new shoots *(153)*.

Adventitious root initials are formed on leaves much more readily than are adventitious buds. In some plants, such as the India rubber fig (*Ficus elastica*), and the camellia, the cutting must include a portion of the old stem containing an axillary bud because, although adventitious roots may develop at the base of the petiole, an adventitious shoot is not likely to form. In fact, rooted leaves of some species have been known to survive for years without producing an adventitious shoot.

Root Cuttings

In this type of cutting, the production of adventitious shoots and, in some cases, adventitious roots must take place. In many plants, adventitious buds will form readily on intact roots, especially if they are wounded. The regeneration of new root meristems often presents more difficulty than the production of adventitious buds. The usual origin of new roots on such root pieces is from latent root initials contained in old branch roots which may be present on the root piece although adventitious root initials in roots have also been observed to arise in the region of the vascular cambium *(96)*.

The actual regeneration of new plants from root cuttings takes place in different ways depending upon the species. Perhaps the most common type is for the root cutting to first produce an adventitious shoot, roots appearing later. In other plants, a well-developed root system has formed by the time the first shoots appear. In still other species, there is no consistent pattern, new roots appearing first in some individuals, new shoots forming first in others. Root cuttings of some species form a strong adventitious shoot, but no new roots develop, and the cutting eventually dies. In certain species, root cuttings will produce a strong new root system but no adventitious shoot arises, so the cutting finally dies. Root cuttings of many species, of course, regenerate neither a new root system nor a shoot system but eventually die, although the root pieces themselves may remain alive for a considerable period *(53)*.

Root cuttings taken from very young seedling trees are much more successful than those taken from older trees or from own-rooted varieties. Failures in the latter case are apparently due to the inability of the root pieces to regenerate a new root system.

One of the chief advantages claimed for asexual propagation is the faithful reproduction of all characteristics of the parent plant. However, root cuttings present an example where this does not always hold true. In periclinal chimeras (see p. 168), where the cells of the outer layers are of a different genetic make-up than those of the inner tissues, the production of a new plant by root cuttings results in a plant differing from the parent plant. This is illustrated in the Thornless Youngberry and the Thornless Loganberry, where stem or leaf-bud cuttings produce plants which retain the thornless condition, but root cuttings develop into thorny plants.

Although effective in a few cases (69), the use of root-promoting substances on root cuttings has not been of a value comparable to that obtained with stem and leaf cuttings. In cuttings of the latter types, formation of adventitious root initials occurs with relative ease, especially with the aid of auxin for stimulating this process. In root cuttings, on the other hand, formation of adventitious buds is needed, for which growth regulating chemicals of the auxin type are of little value. In fact, such materials tend to inhibit bud development.

PHYSIOLOGICAL BASIS OF ROOT INITIATION IN CUTTINGS

Undoubtedly, certain levels of the various hormonal and chemical constituents of plant tissue are more favorable than others for adventitious root initiation in cuttings. Much study has been given to determining these relationships.

A *plant hormone* is defined as " an organic substance produced naturally in higher plants, controlling growth or other physiological functions at a site remote from its place of production, and active in minute amounts (119)." There are a number of synthetic compounds which, when introduced into the plant, often give results similar to those caused by the naturally occurring hormones. These compounds have been termed *plant regulators* and are considered to be "organic compounds other than nutrients which in small amounts promote, inhibit, or otherwise modify any physiological process in plants (131)."

There are several groups of substances which have been considered, and more or less substantiated, as plant hormones. These are: (a) *auxins,* (b) *traumatic acid* or "wound hormone," (c) *calines,* (d) *reproductive hormones* or "florigen," and (e) vitamins. In considering adventitious root formation in cuttings, the *auxin* and the *caline* groups are of particular interest.

Auxins. Auxins, which have been studied more than any other group of hormones and whose existence is well established, appear to act as a sort of "master hormone," exerting a regulatory action over many plant processes and over other of the plant hormones. Auxins are involved in such diverse physiological activities as stem growth, root formation, lateral bud inhibition, abscission of leaves and fruit, fruit development, activation of cambial cells, and many others. Auxins seem to be universally present in plants, their presence having been demonstrated in a number of species. They apparently are nonspecific in their action, the same response to an auxin noted in one species usually being obtained in others. It seems likely that auxins may function as a part of some master enzyme system.

An *auxin* is defined as "an organic substance which promotes growth (*i.e.,* irreversible increase in volume) along the longitudinal axis, when applied in low concentrations to shoots of plants freed as far as practical from their own inherent growth-promoting substances *(119)*."

There are a number of diverse synthetic chemical compounds which act as auxins, but they all have certain similarities in molecular structure *(63)*. Several compounds, including indoleacetic acid, having auxin activity, have either been isolated from or shown to exist in plant tissue. There are other chemical compounds which have auxin activity but which have not been isolated from plant tissue, such as *naphthaleneacetic acid, indolebutyric acid,* and 2,4-*dichlorophenoxyacetic acid.*

Naturally occurring auxin is synthesized primarily in apical buds and young leaves. It normally moves through the plant from apex to base. However, the application of large amounts of synthetic auxin to plant material by artificial means, such as soaking the base of cuttings, apparently results in some mass translocation upward, probably mainly in the xylem.

The accumulated knowledge of the physiology of auxins has resulted in a number of practical applications, one of which is the promotion of root initiation in cuttings. It was originally shown by Went *(142)* and Thimann and Went *(115)* in 1934 that auxins stimulate adventitious root formation in stem cuttings. This was accomplished by using etiolated pea epicotyls under certain standard conditions as a biological test of the activity of the materials under study *(141, 143, 144)*.

In testing pollen extracts and other plant products, such as an auxin-rich *Rhizopus* medium, it was found *(115)* that the root-promoting hormone occurred almost always together with auxin (as measured by the *Avena* test). The activity in forming roots followed the auxin activity *(146)* through all stages of chemical tests. It was concluded that the root-forming substance was either identical with, or closely related to, auxin itself. Indole-3-acetic acid was identified as a naturally occurring compound, having considerable auxin activity in urine *(61)* and in cultures of *Rhizopus* *(117)*. Confirmation came with the proof *(62, 120)* that synthetic indoleacetic acid was as active in root formation as the natural auxin-containing *Rhizopus* preparation. Thus, it was definitely known that at least one of the hormones causing root formation was identical with auxin. Synthetic indoleacetic acid was soon tested further for its activity in promoting root initiation in cuttings, and several investigators *(10, 64, 120)* in 1935 demonstrated the practical use of this material in stimulating the rooting of cuttings. In this same year, it was shown that naphthaleneacetic, indolebutyric, and other acids were also active in promoting adventitious root formation in cuttings *(116, 161)*. Experience has since proven that these two compounds are most effective in stimulating adventitious root initiation in cuttings of many plant species.

Since application of auxin to stem tissue of many plants increases adventitious root production, it therefore seems apparent that the relative amount of auxin present, native or applied, is associated with the formation of root primordia *(22)*. In fact, it has been shown *(98, 99, 100)* that in segments of tobacco stems, when the auxin concentration is relatively high, formation of adventitious roots will be favored but bud formation prevented. When other plant constituents, adenine, or kinetin (6-furfuryl adenine) are relatively high, bud formation takes place and root formation is suppressed. When both auxin and adenine are present in nearly equal proportions, cell proliferation (callus development) occurs but without organ formation.

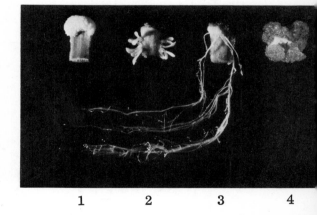

Figure 9-7. Effects of adenine sulfate and indoleacetic acid on growth and organ formation in tobacco stem segments.
1. Control.
2. Adenine sulfate, 40 mg per liter. Bud formation with decrease in root formation.
3. Indoleacetic acid, 0.02 mg per liter. Root formation with prevention of bud formation.
4. Adenine sulfate, 40 mg per liter plus indoleacetic acid, 0.02 mg per liter. Growth stimulation but without organ formation. Courtesy Folke Skoog.

1   2   3   4

In root cuttings also, the type of regeneration seems to be associated with the auxin level. In dandelion and chicory, the auxin concentration in root pieces is lower at the proximal end during the process of regeneration than at the distal end. As shown in Figure 9–8, shoot production occurs at the *proximal* (low auxin) end, whereas root production is found at the *distal* (high auxin) end, regardless of the orientation of the root segment in relation to gravity. Artificially increasing the auxin content at the proximal end causes root rather than shoot formation to take place, whereas artificially reducing the auxin level in the entire root piece causes shoot formation to occur at each end *(137)*. It seems, therefore, that the physiological basis for the initiation of adventitious root primordia may lie in the actual level of the auxin in the tissues or in the balance between auxin and certain other plant constituents such as adenine.

Calines. These are a theoretical group of plant hormones, postulated by Went *(145)* as consisting of: (a) *rhizocaline,* which is supposedly manufactured by the leaves and is necessary for root formation; (b) *caulocaline,*

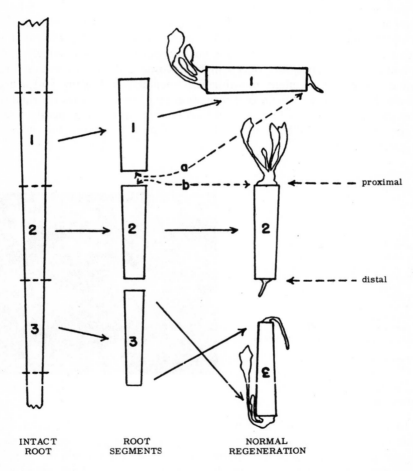

INTACT	ROOT	NORMAL
ROOT	SEGMENTS	REGENERATION

Figure 9–8. Normal regeneration of roots and shoots on root cuttings of dandelion **(Taraxacum)** and chicory **(Cichorium).** Leaves appear at the proximal ends with callus and roots at the distal ends of the cuttings regardless of their orientation to gravity. Courtesy H. E. Warmke. **(Proximal** and **distal** defined on page 285.)

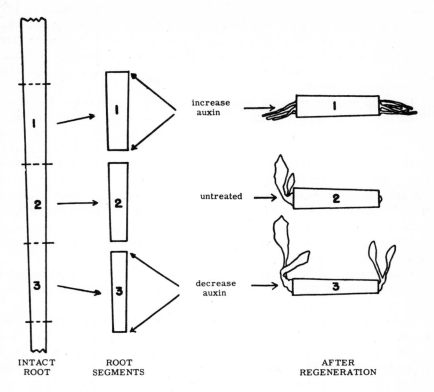

INTACT ROOT	ROOT SEGMENTS	AFTER REGENERATION

Figure 9–9. Effect of the auxin level on the type of differentiation occurring in root cuttings of dandelion (**Taraxacum**) and chicory (**Cichorium**). Added auxin (indolebutyric acid) causes roots to appear at both ends. Decreased auxin (by ethylene chlorohydrin treatments) results in shoot development at both ends. Courtesy H. E. Warmke.

synthesized in the roots and necessary for stem elongation; and (c) *phyllocaline,* made or stored in the cotyledons, but necessary for leaf growth.

Rhizocaline is believed to be synthesized in the leaves but only in the presence of light, and is considered to be specifically essential for root formation. By this theory, rhizocaline accumulates at the base of the cutting under the influence of auxin where it results in root initiation.

The belief that the leaves contribute factors of importance to root initiation in cuttings is not new. Sachs, the German plant physiologist, postulated *(94)* in 1880 the existence of a specific root-forming substance manufactured in the leaves which moves downward to the base of the stem where it promotes root formation.

It was shown *(66)* by van der Lek in 1925 that strongly sprouting buds promote the development of roots in cuttings of such plants as the willow, poplar, currant, and grape. It was assumed that hormone-like substances were formed in the developing buds and transported to the base of the cutting through the phloem where they stimulated root formation. The presence of buds is not always necessary for rooting even on species with no preformed root initials. In the grape, in which such initials are not found, the rooting of disbudded rootstock cuttings is a common practice, although disbudded stocks are more difficult to root than cuttings with the buds retained.

That the amount of some naturally occurring, root-forming substance other than auxin, as yet unidentified but essential for root initiation, may be abundant in some plants and slight or even lacking in others, is shown by other experiments. Apple and lemon cuttings were treated *(11)* with auxin, and after analysis for auxin in the two groups of cuttings, it was found that there was little difference in the amount recovered, yet none of the apple cuttings rooted whereas the lemon cuttings did. It was assumed that the apple cuttings were lacking in certain unidentified internal substances (which could be called rhizocaline) necessary for root formation. On the other hand the lemon cuttings were believed to have this substance or substances, in abundance.

Experiments *(28),* using cuttings prepared from excised asparagus stem tips, also support the belief that some substance other than auxin may limit root formation in cuttings.

From their studies on the rooting of coniferous evergreen cuttings, Thimann and Delisle *(121, 122)* agree that some unknown factor, other than auxin, consisting of a special substance or group of substances, is involved in root initiation. This factor would possibly exist in large quantities in young plants, such as one-year-old seedlings, thus accounting for the comparative ease of rooting cuttings from young plants, the "juvenility effect" (see p. 197).

Van Overbeek and others *(132, 133)* conducted experiments in rooting hibiscus cuttings from which they also concluded that some substance, or substances, in addition to auxin is definitely necessary for initiation of roots. In their tests, this substance was shown to come from the leaves. However, they could not agree with the rhizocaline theory, since the effect of the leaves in their tests was exerted equally well in darkness and light. In addition, and in contrast to the rhizocaline concept, the root-forming effect of the leaves could be replaced by nonspecific, well-known chemicals —namely, sucrose in combination with either arginine or ammonium sulfate.

In Went's pea test *(143)* for root-forming activity of various substances, it is significant that the presence of at least one bud on the pea cutting was essential for root production. A budless cutting would not form roots even when treated with an auxin-rich preparation. This indicates again that a factor other than auxin, presumably produced by the bud, is needed for root formation.

It seems clear that auxin is only one of perhaps several substances that are required for root initiation. There are other necessary factors, such as those of a nutritional and perhaps a hormonal nature. Rhizocaline may be one of these factors. In any event it seems certain that the leaves and/or buds are the source of these substances.

Plants could possibly be divided into three groups in regard to their relation to root-promoting materials: (a) Those in which the shoots contain the various native substances, including auxin, essential for root initiation. When cuttings are made and placed under the proper environmental conditions, rapid root formation occurs. (b) Those in which the internal root-promoting substances, of a hormonal or nutritional nature, are present but auxin is limiting. With the application of auxin, rooting is greatly increased. (c) Those that lack one or more of the internal factors,—hormonal or nutritional or both, whereas natural auxin may or may not be present in abundance. The external application of auxin gives little or no response due to the lack of the other as yet unidentified factors.

Anatomical relationships. Although the ease or difficulty with which cuttings develop adventitious roots may possibly be explained on the basis of physiological or biochemical factors, not to be overlooked is the relation of the anatomical structure of the stem to rooting. For example, in some plants preformed root initials are present in the stem, and in others root production follows certain patterns corresponding to the anatomical structure of the stem. This is illustrated in the grape where adventitious roots on stem cuttings often appear in longitudinal rows corresponding to the primary rays, in which they originate, running the entire length of the internode.

Certain types of stem structure or tissue relationships within the stem seem to be more favorable to the initiation of root primordia than others. This is shown by studies (72, 73) with the easily rooted citron (*Citrus medica*) which produces roots profusely along the entire stem after a short time in the rooting medium, and the sour orange (*C. aurantium*) which forms only a few roots at the base of the cutting after several weeks. In these experiments, illustrated in Figure 9–10, cylinders of bark were taken from the stem of the sour orange and were used to replace, by grafting, a similar cylinder removed from the stem of the citron. In the same manner, a cylinder of bark was taken from the stem of the citron and regrafted on the stem of the sour orange. After the bark pieces had healed in place, the stems were made into leafy cuttings with the new bark cylinder at the base. The rooting behavior of the grafted bark pieces was just as it was on intact, nongrafted cuttings. The bark cylinder of the easily rooted citron rooted readily even though grafted on the difficult-to-root sour orange. Conversely, the bark piece of the sour orange rooted sparingly and only at the base even though grafted on the easily rooted citron stem. However, the citron itself formed roots readily above the grafted bark cylinder. These studies would indicate that rooting behavior is certainly related to anatomical structure. The difficult-to-root bark piece of the sour orange, although grafted on the citron stem where it would, presumably, be able to obtain any essential rooting hormones or nutrients from the leaves of the easily rooted citron, still failed to form roots any better than it did normally. It is indicated from these studies that adventitious root formation in any particular plant may be more related to certain inherent factors in the cells than to readily conducted food materials or root-promoting hormones.

It is entirely possible, however, that interactions between certain non-transportable factors located within the cells and easily conducted nutrients and hormones could take place to establish conditions either favoring or opposing the development of adventitious roots.

FACTORS AFFECTING THE REGENERATION OF PLANTS FROM CUTTINGS

A great difference exists among species and among varieties within a species in the rooting ability of cuttings taken from them. It is difficult to predict whether or not cuttings of a certain clone will root easily. Although botanical relationships give a general indication, empirical trials of each clone are necessary. This has been done with most plants of economic importance. Stem cuttings of some varieties root so readily that the most simple facilities and care give high percentages of cuttings rooted. Other more difficult varieties can be rooted satisfactorily if all influencing factors are taken into consideration and maintained at the optimum condition. The factors to be discussed in this chapter are of great importance to this group, and the attention given to them usually means the difference between success or failure in obtaining satisfactory rooting. Cuttings of still other varieties cannot be made to root under any circumstance.

Selection of Cutting Material

Nutrition of the stock plant. There is considerable evidence that the nutrition of the stock plant exerts a strong influence on the development of roots and shoots from cuttings taken from such plants (83, 86, 88, 93, 95, 103). Kraus and Kraybill (55) observed long ago in making tomato cuttings that those with yellowish stems, high in carbohydrates but low in nitrogen, produced many roots but only feeble shoots, whereas those with greenish stems, containing ample carbohydrates but higher in nitrogen,

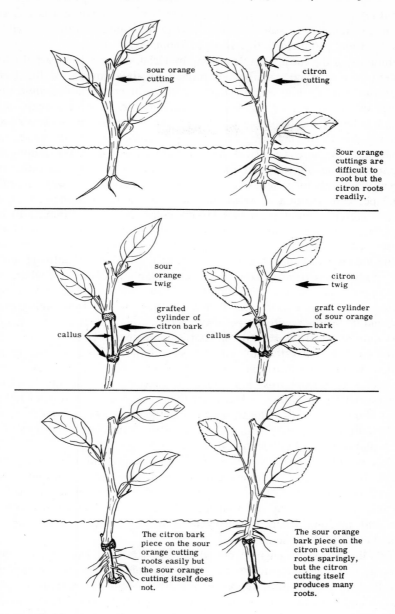

Figure 9–10. Anatomical conditions occurring in the tissues of some plants apparently are more conducive to adventitious root formation than are those found in other species. In this case, the citron roots easily but the sour orange with difficulty. Reciprocal transfers of grafted bark pieces showed that this same situation prevailed even when the bark piece was grown on the other species. Adapted from Mes **(72).** Courtesy Brooklyn Botanic Garden.

produced fewer roots but stronger shoots than the previous case. Green, succulent stems, very low in carbohydrates but high in nitrogen, all decayed without producing either roots or shoots.

Quite often the most suitable cutting material, as far as the carbohydrate content is concerned, can be determined by the firmness of the stems. Those undesirably low in carbohydrates are soft and flexible, while those higher in carbohydrates are firm and stiff and break with a snap rather than bending. This desirable condition may be confused, however, with firmness due to the maturing of the tissues, caused by the thickening and lignification of the cell walls. A more accurate method of determining cutting material having the desirable high starch content is by the iodine test. Freshly cut ends of a bundle of cuttings are immersed for one minute in a 0.2 per cent solution of iodine in potassium iodide. Cuttings having the highest starch content stain the darkest color. A rough grouping of cuttings high, medium, and low in starch can then be made. In tests with grapes *(150)*, 63 per cent of the high starch cuttings rooted, 35 per cent of the medium rooted, while 17 per cent of the low starch cuttings rooted.

Cuttings taken from slow-growing stock plants in containers where root development is restricted, carbohydrates have accumulated, and nitrogen is low, usually root more readily than cuttings taken from rank-growing field plants. Studies with grapes have shown *(84)* that it is not a general starvation effect of the stock plant that is conducive to good root formation of the cuttings, but rather the effect is specific, as far as minerals are concerned, to nitrogen nutrition. Thus, when stock plants were grown under conditions of phosphorus, potassium, magnesium, or calcium deficiency, root formation in cuttings taken from them was poorer than from full nutrient plants. But with reduced nitrogen in the stock plants, root formation of the cuttings was increased. However, extreme nitrogen deficiency of the stock plants lowered rather than increased rooting.

This is substantiated by tests *(42)* with the geranium in which stock plants were grown at three levels of nitrogen, phosphorus, and potassium. The nitrogen nutrition of the stock plants had a greater effect on the rooting response of the cuttings than did phosphorus or potassium, with the low and medium levels of nitrogen resulting in higher percentages of rooted cuttings than the high level.

This low nitrogen—high carbohydrate balance in the stock plants which, in many cases, seems to favor rooting can be achieved by several methods: (a) Reduce the nitrogen supply to the stock plants, thus reducing shoot growth and allowing for carbohydrate accumulation. This can be done by withholding nitrogenous fertilizers and allowing the stock plants to grow in full sunlight. Any type of root restriction of the stock plants, such as occurs when they are grown in containers or close together in hedge rows, tends to reduce vegetative growth and permits the accumulation of carbohydrates.

(b) Select portions of the plant for cutting material which are in the desirable nutritive stage. For example, take lateral shoots in which growth has decreased and carbohydrates have accumulated, rather than rapidly growing, succulent terminal shoots.

(c) Select regions of the shoot which are known to have a low nitrogen and high carbohydrate content. In a chemical analysis *(129)* of rose shoots of the type used for making cuttings, the total nitrogen content increased uniformly from the base of the shoot to the tip. Conversely, there was a gradient of decreasing starch content from base to tip. Basal portions of such a shoot would, therefore, have the low nitrogen—high carbohydrate balance favorable for obtaining good rooting of cuttings.

It cannot be said, however, that a high carbohydrate content in cuttings is invariably associated with ease of rooting. There may be other, stronger, influencing factors present. This is shown, for example, in rooting tests *(3)* of cuttings of four rose species, each found to store different quantities of starch through the winter. *Rosa setigera,* with abundant starch storage, failed entirely to root; *R. arvensis,* with moderate starch storage, gave 97 per cent rooting; *R. odorata,* with moderate starch storage, showed 82 per cent rooting; whereas *R. canina,* with very little starch storage, had 92 per cent of the cuttings rooted.

For plants difficult to root, there are several treatments that can be used to artificially alter the nutritive condition of the stock plant or portions of the plant. Such treatments often result in increased rooting of the cuttings taken from such plants. These include etiolation * of shoots and wiring, ringing, or notching of the shoots sometime before they are made into cuttings.

In the etiolation method *(32)* of stimulating root formation, the shoots which later are to be made into cuttings are allowed to develop during their initial stages in complete darkness, thus assuming the elongated, whitish characteristics of etiolation. The basal portion of the shoots, where the root initials develop, are retained under this etiolation treatment, but the terminal leafy portion of the shoot is allowed to develop further in the light, thus assuming a normal type of growth. After the shoots attain sufficient length, they are cut off, either immediately or at a later time, and rooted. The absence of light seems to be favorable for the initiation of root primordia in stem tissue. Although there is no conclusive evidence as to why this is so, it may be that some naturally occurring root-promoting hormone is involved either in concentration or translocation by the absence of light. Etiolation may have some effect, too, on the organic or inorganic nutrition or the internal stem structure which may lead to increased root initiation.

---

* Etiolation is the development of plants or plant parts in the absence of light. This results in such characteristics as small, unexpanded leaves, elongated shoots, and the development of a yellowish or whitish color.

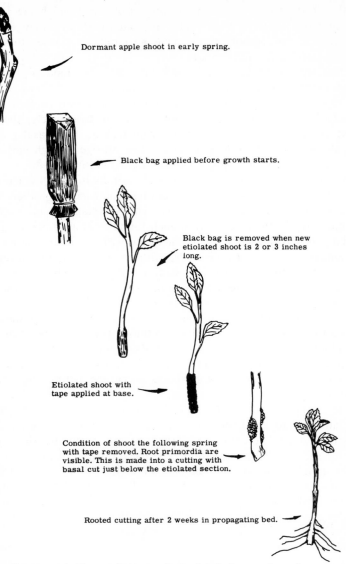

Dormant apple shoot in early spring.

Black bag applied before growth starts.

Black bag is removed when new etiolated shoot is 2 or 3 inches long.

Etiolated shoot with tape applied at base.

Condition of shoot the following spring with tape removed. Root primordia are visible. This is made into a cutting with basal cut just below the etiolated section.

Rooted cutting after 2 weeks in propagating bed.

Figure 9–11. The etiolation method of inducing rooting of cuttings of plants difficult to propagate by this method. Adapted from Gardner (32).

Since a high carbohydrate level in shoots is conducive to root formation, it would appear that treatments to block the downward movement of carbohydrates—and possibly native root-promoting hormones—such as ringing or constriction of the phloem with wire, would increase root initiation. There are some reports of success with such treatments. For example, rooting of cuttings of the rubber tree, citrus, and mango was stimulated by girdling or binding the base of the shoots with wire before taking the cuttings *(5, 54, 114)*.

Irradiation of stem segments of intact seedlings with X-rays results in the development of adventitious roots of the stems of some plants. The swelling of the stem and the production of roots just above the site of irradiation suggests the occurrence of a phloem block, which would interfere with the movement of auxins and nutritive materials *(9)*.

Grape cuttings taken from vines fertilized with zinc rooted in higher percentages and were of better quality than cuttings taken from untreated vines *(95)*. This is believed to be due, perhaps, to an increase in the native auxin production resulting from the increased level of tryptophane found in the treated plants. This same beneficial effect of zinc applications to stock plants has been noted in South Africa in the propagation of Marianna plum by hardwood cuttings.

Age of the stock plant. In plants which are easily propagated by cuttings, it makes little difference what the age or condition of the stock plant happens to be, but in plants difficult to root, this is an important factor to consider. Generally, cuttings taken from young seedling plants will root much more readily than those taken from old, mature plants *(80, 104)*. This has been termed the *juvenility factor* and applies to both stem and root cuttings. Experiments in rooting hardwood cuttings of apple, pear, cherry, and other species, including narrow-leaved evergreens, show that in a wide variety of plants root production decreases with increasing age of the plant from seed *(30)*. When cuttings were made from the tips of one-year seedlings, they rooted readily, but if the seedlings were two years old, the percentage of cuttings rooted dropped off markedly, even if one-year wood was used. It has been shown *(31, 155)*, too, that young seedling apple trees can be propagated easily by root cuttings, but root cuttings made from mature trees of most varieties usually fail to grow.

In a study *(121)* of the rooting of cuttings of certain coniferous and deciduous species known to root only with extreme difficulty, it was concluded that the most important single factor affecting root initiation was the age of the tree from which the cuttings are taken. The ease with which roots formed, using cuttings made from one-year wood, decreased steadily with increasing age of the tree. This was true whether or not the cuttings were treated with auxin.

Some old English garden books list great numbers of plants that were rooted from cuttings—plants now considered to be very difficult, if not impossible, to propagate by cuttings. It may have been that in earlier days, such plants were imported from distant countries as seeds; cuttings were subsequently made from the seedlings, the juvenility factor thus accounting for their ease in rooting.

Juvenile and mature growth phases are sometimes, but not always, accompanied by distinct morphological differences, such as leaf size and shape, thorniness, and internode length (see Figure 3–1). In the apple, for example, the juvenile condition is characterized by thin leaves with a small amount of pubescence as contrasted with thick, heavily pubescent leaves in the mature state. In other species juvenile leaves are very small, having a "wild" appearance, whereas leaves in the mature phase are much larger.

Little is known of the underlying causes of this juvenility effect, even though many examples can be cited. It is probable that the difference between juvenile and mature shoots in their ability to produce root primordia is due to biochemical factors, rather than differences in anatomical structure. Generally, the internal stem structure of plants in the juvenile and the mature growth phases is very similar. The fact that successful rooting of nonjuvenile apple cuttings can be obtained *(45, 51)* by the use of treatments with indolebutyric acid, together with proper timing, indicates that the necessary anatomical structure for root formation is present. Biochemical conditions favorable for root initiation found within juvenile shoots probably disappears with increasing age of the plant. In the apple, at least, the application of auxin to cuttings of mature growth stages seems to restore these favorable conditions. This may be due to a direct action of auxin itself, or possibly to the activation of some other naturally occurring substance by the auxin application.

Easily rooted juvenile forms of stems may be obtained from mature trees by inducing adventitious shoot production from roots which may then be made into softwood stem cuttings. In the apple, adventitious shoots develop if the root pieces are packed lightly in a layer of moist, well-aerated sphagnum moss and placed over sand in a closed propagating frame with high humidity and bottom heat of about 70°F. *(104)*.

Another method of obtaining juvenile wood from mature plants is by the use of the juvenile growth originating from sphaeroblasts (wart-like growths containing meristematic and conductive tissues). These are induced to form on stem tissue by disbudding and heavily cutting back stock plants. The sphaeroblasts then give rise to adventitious shoots. These juvenile type shoots then may be easily rooted under the proper conditions *(140)*. By using the mound layering (stooling) method (see p. 409) on these rooted sphaeroblast cuttings, rooted shoots are produced which continue to possess the morphological juvenile characteristics. It has been pointed out that in the stooling method of propagation the juvenile growth phase is continually maintained *(27)*.

Type of wood selected for cuttings. In taking cutting material, there are, of course, many choices of the type of material to use, ranging (in woody perennials) from the very succulent terminal shoots of current growth to large hardwood cuttings several years old. Here, as with most of the other factors affecting rooting of cuttings, it is impossible to state any one type of cutting material that would be best for all plants. What may be ideal for one plant would be a failure for another. What has been found to hold true for certain species, however, often may be extended to other related species.

(a) *Differences between individual seedling plants.* In rooting cuttings taken from individual plants of a species which ordinarily is propagated by seed, experience has shown that wide differences may exist among individuals in the ease with which cuttings taken from them form roots. Just as seedlings differ in many respects, it is not surprising that this difference in root-forming ability should also exist. Differences in the rooting ability of clones are, of course, recognized. Likewise, such differences should be anticipated when woody plants usually propagated by seed— as most forest tree species—are propagated by cuttings. In rooting cuttings taken from old trees of Norway spruce (*Picea abies*), white pine (*Pinus strobus*), and red maple (*Acer rubrum*) marked differences occurred in the rooting capacity of wood from individual trees *(18, 101)*.

(b) *Differences between lateral and terminal shoots.* Experiments *(60)* in rooting plum stem cuttings compared the rooting of different types of softwood cuttings taken in June. The results obtained showed a marked superiority in the rooting of the lateral shoots. In averaging two varieties, the terminal tips had 10 per cent rooting, the laterals in active growth 19 per cent, and the laterals which had ceased active growth 35 per cent.

Similarly, lateral branches of white pine and Norway spruce, both with and without auxin treatments, gave consistently higher percentages of rooted cuttings than did terminal shoots *(18, 26, 121)*. In the rhododendron, also, thin cuttings made from lateral shoots consistently gave higher rooting percentages than those taken from vigorous, strong, terminal shoots. In the Greek juniper (*Juniperus excelsa*), it has also been observed that much better rooting is obtained from cuttings taken near the base of the plant than when the cutting material is selected from the top.

Certain plants with a large pith in the main shoot, such as the ash (*Fraxinus*), bottle-tree (*Sterculia*), and some *Rhododendron* species are difficult to root if this pithy main axis is used for cutting material, but when lateral branches with a higher proportion of wood to pith and more stored foods are used, rooting is much more successful *(35)*.

In some species, plants started from cuttings taken from lateral branches will exhibit a different type of growth than plants started from cuttings taken from upright terminal growth. It was pointed out *(35)* many years ago that plants which exhibit marked horizontal branching will produce very diverse plants, depending upon whether vertical or horizontal cutting material is used. For example, to obtain the desirable, upright type of plant of *Taxus cuspidata capitata,* cuttings should be taken only from erect terminals or upright growing laterals, rather than from horizontal side shoots. Another example of this is shown by Norway spruce cuttings *(121)*. The new growth of lateral shoots after rooting is at an angle to the vertical, while that of terminal shoots is erect. This phenomenon is also very noticeable in rooting cuttings of coffee (*Coffea arabica*). If the cuttings are made from upright-growing shoots, they will produce the desired vertical plants, but if taken from drooping lateral branches the cuttings, after rooting, produce only branches spreading along the ground.

(c) *Differences between different parts of the shoot.* In some woody plants, hardwood cuttings are often made by sectioning shoots several feet long and obtaining perhaps four to eight cuttings from a single shoot. Marked differences in the chemical composition of such shoots are known to occur from base to tip. Variations in root production on cuttings taken from different portions of the shoot are often observed, with the highest rooting, in many cases, found in cuttings taken from the basal portions of the shoot. In the propagation of the olive (*Olea europaea*) from one-year-old, leafy stem cuttings, basal portions of the shoot root more readily than terminal sections *(38, 87)*. This also is true for leafy tung (*Aleurites fordii*) cuttings where basal cuttings, treated with various concentrations of growth substances, consistently gave higher percentages of cuttings rooted and roots per cutting than did cuttings taken from the tip or middle portions of the shoot *(156)*. In the same manner, cuttings prepared from one-year-old shoots of three varieties of the highbush blueberry (*Vaccinium corymbosum*) were significantly more successful if taken from the basal portions of the shoot rather than from the terminal portions *(78)*. The number of preformed root initials in woody stems has been determined (in some plants at least) as distinctly decreasing from the base to the tip of the shoot *(67)*. Consequently, the rooting capacity of basal portions of such shoots would be considerably higher than that of the more apical parts.

To the contrary, however, in studies with a different type of wood, cherries (*Prunus cerasus, P. avium, P. mahaleb*) rooted by softwood cuttings under mist gave the following percentages of rooted cuttings: Stockton Morello, basal—30 per cent, tip—77 per cent; Bing, basal—0 per cent, tip—100 per cent; and Montmorency, basal—10 per cent, tip—90 per cent *(40)*.

It may well be that in the woody type of stem, a year or more in age, where carbohydrates have accumulated at the base of the shoots and, perhaps, where some root initials have formed in the basal portions, possibly under the influence of root-promoting substances from buds and leaves, the best cutting material would be found in the basal portions of the shoots. An entirely different physiological situation exists in the succulent shoots of deciduous plants which would be used for softwood cuttings. Here, carbohydrate storage and preformed root initials would not be present. The better rooting of shoot tips may be explained by the possibility of a higher concentration of some root-promoting hormone found in the terminal sections.

This factor is of little importance, however, with most easily rooted, woody ornamental species. Entirely satisfactory rooting usually is obtained regardless of the position of the cutting on the shoot.

(d) *Flowering or vegetative wood.* In most plants, cuttings could be made from shoots that are either in a flowering or vegetative condition. With easily rooted species, it would make little difference which was used, but in difficult-to-root species, this may be an important factor. For example, in the blueberry (*Vaccinium atrococcum*), hardwood cuttings taken from shoots bearing flower buds do not root as well as those bearing only leaf buds (77, 78). When vegetative wood was used, 39 per cent of the cuttings rooted, but when cuttings were made containing one or more flower buds, not a single cutting rooted. Removing the flower buds prior to rooting did not increase the rooting percentage, indicating that the actual presence of the flower buds does not inhibit rooting, but rather some physiological or anatomical condition associated with the presence of flower buds. In rooting *Rhododendron* cuttings, it has been observed that removal of flower buds stimulates rooting, but removal of vegetative buds reduces rooting (16).

It has been rather consistently noted for both root and stem cuttings of many species that better regeneration takes place when the cuttings are taken either before or after, rather than during, the flowering period (21). In some instances (140), cuttings taken any time during the year when the stock plants were in the vegetative state rooted very well, but as soon as the stock plants started initiating flower buds, the cuttings failed to root. Some antagonism apparently exists between vegetative regeneration and flowering. The basis for this is probably found in auxin relationships, since it is known that the high auxin levels, which are favorable for adventitious root formation in stem cuttings, may inhibit flower initiation (118, 125).

(e) *Heel vs. non-heel cuttings.* In preparing cuttings, it is often recommended that a "heel" (a small slice of older wood) be retained at the base of the cutting in order to obtain maximum rooting. For hardwood cuttings of some plants, this may be true. In the quince (*Cydonia oblonga*), considerably better rooting was obtained with the heel type of cutting, due probably in this case to the presence of preformed root initials in the older wood (128). Narrow-leaved evergreen cuttings are often said to root more readily if a heel of old wood is retained at the base of the cuttings, but tests (151) using cuttings with and without a heel showed no significant differences in rooting. It is sometimes difficult to obtain the proper type of cutting material to make heel cuttings, and the number of cuttings prepared from a given amount of cutting material would thus be reduced. This may be compensated for, however, if an increased rooting percentage is obtained by using such cuttings.

In softwood cuttings, with the wood in a different physiological condition, heel cuttings and "mallet" cuttings (those with a short segment of old wood at the base of the cutting) are generally not as successful as the straight cuttings (45).

When considerable difficuly is being experienced in rooting cuttings of a certain variety, it may be that one of these different types of cuttings may root easier than the others and would justify its use.

Time of year the cuttings are taken. It is possible, of course, to make cuttings at any time during the year. In propagating deciduous species, hardwood cuttings could be taken during the dormant season, or leafy softwood or semi-hardwood cuttings could be prepared during the growing season, using succulent or partially matured wood. The narrow and broad-leaved evergreen species have one or more flushes of growth during the year, and cuttings could be obtained at various times in relation to these flushes of growth.

Certain species, such as the privets, can be rooted readily if cuttings are taken almost any time during the year; on the other hand, some can be rooted satisfactorily only if they are made at definite times of the year when the cutting material is in the required stage of development (156). Softwood cuttings of deciduous woody species taken during the spring or summer usually tend to root more readily than hardwood cuttings procured in the winter. For plants difficult to root, it is thus often necessary to resort to the use of softwood cuttings. For example, in tests (40, 60) with cherries, not one hardwood cutting taken in winter was induced to root, whereas softwood cuttings made in the spring gave satisfactory rooting with most varieties. This situation is also well illustrated in the lilacs (*Syringa sp.*). About the only way cuttings of these plants can be rooted is to make softwood cuttings during a short period in the spring when the shoots are several inches long and in active growth. The Chinese fringe tree (*Chionanthus retusus*) is notoriously difficult to root from cuttings, but by taking the cuttings during a short period in early June, high rooting percentages can be obtained, if other good practices are observed (106).

It is possible for hardwood cuttings of deciduous species to be taken at any time from just before leaf fall until the buds start development in the spring; for easily rooted species, it makes little difference when the cuttings are made during the dormant season. Rapidly developing buds sometimes tend to promote root formation, whereas buds in the "rest period" * may inhibit root development (68).

A common practice in England in rooting hardwood cuttings is to plant them in the nursery in the fall, even though leaves may still be present.

---

* The "rest period" is a physiological condition of the buds of many woody perennial species beginning shortly after the buds are formed. While in this condition, they will not expand into flowers or leafy shoots even under suitable growing conditions. But after exposure to sufficient cold, the "rest" influence is broken, and the buds will develop normally with the advent of favorable temperatures.

They remain in the soil during the winter, with a callus forming at the base of the cutting shortly after planting. Rooting does not occur generally, however, until spring when roots and shoots develop simultaneously. In the United States, hardwood cuttings are not often planted in the fall, but are ordinarily collected at various times during the fall or winter and stored under cool, moist conditions until spring, or they may be collected and planted in early spring *(1)*.

In trials *(39, 41)* of various methods of handling hardwood cuttings of the Marianna plum (*Prunus cerasifera* × *P. munsoniana ?*) in California, best rooting occurred when the cutting material was gathered in mid-November, treated with indolebutyric acid, then stored under moist conditions at 60°F. for 6 weeks. They were then transferred to cold storage (36°F.) until being planted in the spring. In handling cuttings by this method, root initials are formed during the warm storage conditions following auxin treatments, yet the buds do not open, since they are in the rest period. The subsequent low temperature storage slows further root activity and overcomes the influence of the rest in the buds. Upon planting in the spring, the previously formed roots emerge promptly and are able to supply water to the developing leaves.

For softwood cuttings of deciduous species, the best results are generally secured if the cuttings are taken as early as possible, but after the leaves are fully expanded and the shoots have attained some degree of maturity. Excellent results are often obtained *(60)* when softwood cuttings are taken from potted plants that have started growth early in the spring after being moved into a greenhouse.

In tests *(51)* on the rooting of softwood cuttings of several apple varieties, it was found that the effectiveness of the optimum treatments with root-inducing chemicals generally decreased with increasing age of cuttings, even during a one-month period. The best results were obtained when the cuttings were made in early May when the shoots were 4 to 7 inches long. This effect of timing is also strikingly shown by experiments *(57)* on the rooting of deciduous azalea cuttings, which are notoriously difficult to propagate.

Broad-leaved evergreens usually root most readily if the cuttings are taken after a flush of growth has been completed and the wood is partially matured. This occurs, depending upon the species, from spring to late fall.

In rooting cuttings of narrow-leaved evergreens, the best results may be expected if the cuttings are taken during the period from late fall to late winter; exposure of the stock plants to a certain amount of winter chilling seems to stimulate rooting *(18)*. Cuttings of many species of this type can be rooted successfully when taken any time over a period of several weeks or several months, whereas for others, the time limits are more exacting.

In addition, in propagation by root cuttings, the season of the year when the cuttings are taken may be very important in obtaining a high percentage of success. In the red raspberry *(53)*, for instance, timing was found to be quite critical. Root cuttings taken in midsummer invariably failed, with success increasing as they were taken through the fall, with a peak reached in the winter months. Decreasing percentages of successful regeneration occurred on through the spring into summer.

Treatment of Cuttings

Presence of buds and leaves. The presence of buds often greatly promotes root formation in cuttings, especially if the buds are starting growth. Removal of the buds has been shown *(66, 141)* in certain plants to stop root formation almost completely, especially in species without preformed root initials. In some plants if a ring of bark is removed down to the wood just below the bud, root formation is reduced, indicating that some influence travels through the phloem from the bud to the base of the cutting, where it is active in promoting root production. If cuttings are taken in midwinter when the buds are dormant, their stimulating effect is not present, but if the cuttings are made in the spring when the buds are out of the rest period and more active, their favorable root-growing influence again appears *(68)*. Bench-grafted grape rootstock cuttings are frequently disbudded to prevent subsequent suckering. Rooting still occurs but with greater difficulty, and the type of root system produced is altered. In cuttings made from shoots with preformed root initials, the further development of the roots seems to be little influenced by the presence or absence of buds *(113)*.

It has long been known, and there is considerable supporting experimental evidence *(11, 92, 141)*, that the presence of leaves on cuttings exerts a strong stimulating influence on root initiation. The carbohydrates resulting from the photosynthetic activity of the leaves undoubtedly contribute to root formation. In cacao (*Theobroma cacao*), for example, carbohydrates seem to be the principal contribution of the leaves. By adding sucrose to leafless cuttings treated with indolebutyric acid, 80 to 90 per cent rooting could be obtained, but without added sucrose, practically no cuttings rooted *(24)*. However, in general, the root-promoting effects of leaves and buds are due chiefly to auxins. These organs are known to be powerful auxin producers, and the effects are observed directly below the leaf or bud, showing that polar apex to base transport is involved. The action is complicated by the fact that leaves produce photosynthate as well, but this strong effect of leaves and buds cannot be simply ascribed to their production of nonauxin factors.

Experiments by van Overbeek, *et al.,* using an easily rooted red hibiscus (*Hibiscus rosasinensis*) variety and a difficult-to-root white variety have given considerable information on the internal factors controlling root formation in cuttings *(132, 133).* Abundant roots could be obtained on leafy cuttings of the red variety by indolebutyric acid treatments, but this did not cause rooting of the white variety. Cuttings of the white variety failed to root even though they had a scion of the easily rooted red variety grafted onto them, but when such grafts were treated with indolebutyric acid, abundant roots formed. This gave clear evidence that two factors were necessary for root formation on the white variety: (a) the applied growth substance, and (b) an unknown factor, or complex, present in the leaves of the red hibiscus. It was concluded from this that the white hibiscus failed to root because it not only lacked auxin, but its leaves failed to produce the other factor, or factors, which in addition to auxin, were necessary for root initiation.

Figure 9–12. Effect of leaves on the rooting of Lisbon lemon cuttings. Both groups rooted under intermittent mist and treated with indolebutyric acid at 4000 ppm by the concentrated-solution-dip method.

Figure 9-13. The presence of leaves together with growth-regulator treatments gives best root production in many plants as shown by the olive (**Olea europaea**). (A) Leaves plus indolebutyric acid treatment. (B) Leaves only. (C) No leaves but treated with indolebutyric acid. (D) Neither leaves nor indolebutyric acid treatment.

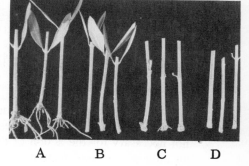

A   B   C   D

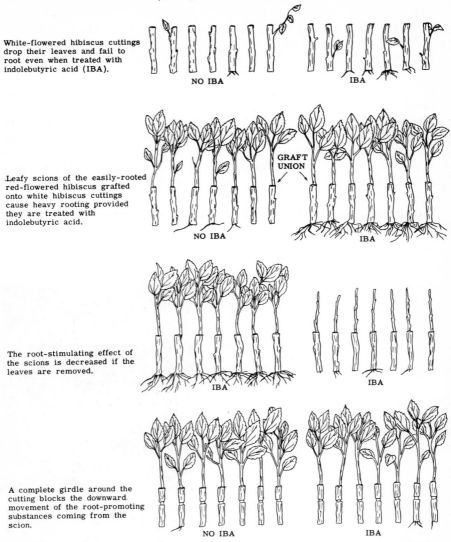

White-flowered hibiscus cuttings drop their leaves and fail to root even when treated with indolebutyric acid (IBA).

NO IBA   IBA

Leafy scions of the easily-rooted red-flowered hibiscus grafted onto white hibiscus cuttings cause heavy rooting provided they are treated with indolebutyric acid.

GRAFT UNION

NO IBA   IBA

The root-stimulating effect of the scions is decreased if the leaves are removed.

IBA   IBA

A complete girdle around the cutting blocks the downward movement of the root-promoting substances coming from the scion.

NO IBA   IBA

Figure 9–14. White-flowered hibiscus cuttings fail to root due to the deficiency of two essential factors. One is an unknown factor (or complex of factors) which is not supplied by its own leaves but can be furnished by leaves on scions of the easily-rooted red-flowered hibiscus. The other factor is an auxin which can be supplied to the base of the cutting artificially as indolebutyric acid. Redrawn from van Overbeek and Gregory **(132).**

Further investigations *(133)* on the nature of the root-promoting factor, or complex, present in the leaves of the red hibiscus showed that light was not necessary for the action of the leaves to be exerted, for nearly as great an influence on root formation was obtained when the cuttings were maintained in the dark as in diffuse light. After trying a large number of compounds, it was found that the root-forming action of the red hibiscus leaves could be replaced quantitatively but not qualitatively by a treatment consisting of a 24-hour soaking of the base of the cuttings in a 4 per cent sucrose solution plus a nitrogenous material (either arginine at 10 ppm, or ammonium sulfate at 1000 ppm). However, treatments with indolebutyric acid were still required in addition to the sucrose and nitrogen in order to obtain rooting. Either of these substances by itself was ineffective, just as either the presence of leaves or the indolebutyric acid treatment alone was ineffective. It was concluded that the main function of the leaves, in root initiation, is to supply the cuttings with sugars and nitrogenous substances. Quantitative chemical analyses showed that the leaves do actually supply such nutritional substances, even in the dark.

Polarity. The polarity inherent in shoots and roots is strikingly shown in the rooting of cuttings. Stem cuttings form shoots at the distal end (nearest the shoot tip), and roots at the proximal end (nearest the crown of the plant). Root cuttings form roots at the distal end and shoots at the proximal end. Changing the position of the cuttings in respect to gravity does not alter this tendency.

Figure 9–15. Results of planting a cutting of red currant **(Ribes sativum)** upside down (reversed polarity). **(left)** Several months after starting. **(right)** One year later. The shoot from the center bud with new roots at its base has become the main plant and is growing with correct polarity. The shoot from the top bud, while still alive, has failed to develop normally.

In early studies *(135)* on the rooting of cuttings, it was pointed out that a stem cutting is polarized, and the theory was advanced that this property could be attributed to the individual cellular components and ultimately to their molecular structure. When a root piece is cut into two segments, the two surfaces touching before the cut must be very similar in all respects. Yet upon regeneration of roots and shoots, one surface of the cut produces a shoot and the other surface produces callus tissue and roots. When the segments are cut, the physiological unity of the root is disturbed which must cause a redistribution of some substance, probably auxin, thus accounting for the different responses observed at previously adjacent surfaces. An inherent polarity of the individual cells is probably responsible for the redistribution of this substance *(33, 90)*. This auxin relationship to the type of regeneration is emphasized by the experiments illustrated in Figures 9–8 and 9–9 *(137)*.

Wounding. The technique of making basal wounds, as described on page 243, has proved to be very beneficial in rooting cuttings of certain species, especially those with older wood at the base of the cutting. Following wounding, callus production and root development frequently are much heavier along the margins of the wounds. Evidently, wounded cells or adjacent ones near the base of the cutting are stimulated into cell division and production of new root primordia. This is due, perhaps, to a natural accumulation of hormones and carbohydrates in the wounded area. There is evidence *(15)* that wounded cuttings are able to absorb more water from the rooting medium than unwounded cuttings. This practice would also provide opportunity for a much greater uptake of applied growth regulators by the tissues at the base of the cutting.

Growth regulators and other materials. Before the use of synthetic root-promoting growth regulators (auxins) in rooting stem cuttings, many other chemicals were tried with varying degrees of success. In some of the earlier studies *(14)* of this type, treatments of tomato and privet cuttings with sugar as well as compounds of manganese, iron, and phosphorus were tried. Improved rooting often resulted, especially with potassium permanganate. Similar treatments of hardwood cuttings *(59)* failed to show any uniform benefit, except when sucrose was used, which sometimes resulted in a marked increase in callus and root development, although considerable variation occurred. The effect of these compounds has in general been so slight and variable that they are rarely used.

It has long been known that certain unsaturated gases, such as carbon monoxide, acetylene, and ethylene, stimulate the initiation of adventitious root primordia, as well as the development of latent, pre-existing root initials *(159)*. Cuttings of many herbaceous plants respond to these gases with increased rooting. It is believed *(146)* that the probable effect of these gases is the activation of naturally-occurring root-forming hormones already in the cutting, rather than a direct effect.

The discovery in 1934 and 1935 that auxins, such as indoleacetic acid, were of real value in stimulating the production of adventitious roots in stem and leaf cuttings, and in a few cases, root cuttings *(69),* was a major milestone in propagation history (see p. 187).

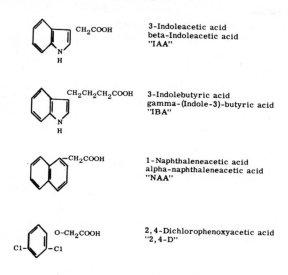

3-Indoleacetic acid
beta-Indoleacetic acid
"IAA"

3-Indolebutyric acid
gamma-(Indole-3)-butyric acid
"IBA"

1-Naphthaleneacetic acid
alpha-naphthaleneacetic acid
"NAA"

2,4-Dichlorophenoxyacetic acid
"2,4-D"

Figure 9–16. Structural formulas of some growth regulators active in initiating adventitious roots in cuttings.

An ancient practice of European gardeners was to embed grain seeds into the split ends of cuttings to promote rooting. This seemingly odd procedure has a sound physiological basis, for it is now known that germinating seeds produce large amounts of auxin, which, of course, would materially aid in root formation in the cuttings.

Some of the phenoxy compounds are extremely active in promoting root formation even at very low concentrations *(47, 50, 52, 108, 162).* The well-known *2,4-dichlorophenoxyacetic acid* (2,4-D) is quite potent in inducing rooting of certain species, but it has the disadvantage of tending to inhibit shoot development. Four other phenoxy compounds, *2,4,5-trichlorophenoxyacetic acid, 2,4,5-trichlorophenoxypropionic acid, 2,4,5-trichlorophenoxybutyric acid,* and *2,4-dichlorophenoxybutyric acid,* are more promising than 2,4-D in that they do not seem to materially affect the normal development of shoots or cause abnormalities in the roots, provided they are used at very low concentrations. The effective range for these compounds seems to be very narrow, however.

Mixtures of root-promoting substances are sometimes more effective than either component alone. Thus, a mixture of equal parts of indolebutyric acid and naphthaleneacetic acid was found when used on a number of widely diverse species to induce a higher percentage of cuttings **to** root and more roots per cutting than either material alone *(24, 48, 130)*.

Adding a small percentage of certain of the phenoxy compounds to either indolebutyric acid or naphthaleneacetic acid has caused excellent rooting in some species *(50)* and has produced qualitatively better root systems than obtained with phenoxy compounds alone.

The use of the salts of some of the growth regulators rather than the free acid may be quite desirable in some instances due to their comparable activity and greater solubility in water *(160)*. The acid form of most of these compounds is relatively insoluble in water, but can be used by dissolving the acid in a few drops of alcohol or ammonium hydroxide before adding to the water. In some species, the amide derivatives of indoleacetic and naphthaleneacetic acids are more effective than the acids in rooting cuttings, whereas in other species, the amides are ineffective or even inhibit root production *(105)*.

For general use in rooting stem cuttings of the majority of plant species, indoleacetic acid (IAA), naphthaleneacetic acid (NAA), and indolebutyric acid (IBA), particularly the latter two, are recommended. To determine the best material and optimum concentration for rooting any particular species under a given set of conditions, actual empirical trials are necessary (see p. 244).

In using the various root-promoting materials, there is often a question as to how long the preparations will keep without losing their strength. It has been reported *(12)* that talc preparations lose their effectiveness over a period of about 8 months, even if kept in closed containers or held under refrigeration. Bacterial destruction of indoleacetic acid occurs readily in unsterilized solutions. A 9 ppm concentration was found to disappear in 24 hours and a 100 ppm concentration in 14 days. In sterile solutions, this material remains active for several months. A widely distributed species of *Acetobacter* destroys IAA, but the same organism has no effect on indolepropionic (IPA) or indolebutyric acid. Uncontaminated solutions of naphthaleneacetic acid and 2,4-dichlorophenoxyacetic acid maintain their strength for as long as a year. Indoleacetic acid is also sensitive to light, strong sunlight destroying a 10 ppm concentration in about 15 minutes. IBA and IPA are much more light-stable than IAA, a 20-hour exposure to strong sunlight causing only a slight change in concentration. Both NAA and 2,4-D seem to be entirely light-stable. With their resistance to bacterial decomposition and light destruction, the latter two compounds would be more likely to maintain their effectiveness over a longer period of time than the indole compounds. When indoleacetic acid solutions are prepared, they should be used immediately due to their rapid deterioration *(73)*.

In some cases the use of fungicides, such as *ferbam* (ferric dimethyl-dithiocarbamate) or *Phygon XL* (50 per cent 2,3-dichloro-1,4-naphthoquinone), either alone or in conjunction with root-promoting substances, have been beneficial in rooting cuttings *(20, 148)*.

Tests have been conducted by research workers all over the world, using most of the species of plants whose propagation is of interest, to determine the value of the various root-promoting substances in inducing roots on cuttings. Several compilations *(2, 74, 85, 124)* listing the results of this vast amount of work are available.

(a) *Methods of application of root-promoting growth regulators.* (For detailed directions see page 244.)

(b) *Treatments with vitamin B_1 (thiamin chloride).* It is known *(4, 149)* that vitamin B_1 is necessary for the growth in sterile culture media of detached roots of many species. In intact plants, this vitamin is produced in the leaves and is transported to the roots where it enters into the root growth processes. Some investigators *(138, 147)* have suggested that in certain plants, roots on cuttings which have been initiated by treatments with root-inducing substances fail to grow satisfactorily due to lack of vitamin B_1 and would thus respond to vitamin B_1 treatments applied following the initiation of root primordia. However, further trials *(34, 49 82)* involving a number of plant species failed to show consistent benefits to root growth by applications of this material to cuttings. Although necessary for root growth, apparently in most plants an ample supply is already stored in the cutting or can be manufactured by the leaves.

(c) *Treatments with mineral nutrients.* The rooting of cuttings has been distinctly promoted by the addition of nitrogenous compounds in a number of different plants. The addition of several nitrogen compounds, both organic and inorganic, was found *(19)* to have a beneficial effect on the rooting response of *Rhododendron* cuttings. Also, in experiments *(123)* on rooting of bean leaf cuttings, treatments with two organic forms of nitrogen—asparagine and adenine—were found to be very effective in promoting rooting. Leafless *Hibiscus* cuttings, when treated with arginine or ammonium sulfate in combination with sucrose, were stimulated markedly in initiating root primordia, provided they were also treated with auxin *(133)*. The fact that concentrations as low as 0.05 ppm are sometimes quite effective, supports the possibility that the role of these nitrogenous materials may be of a hormonal nature.

As was pointed out on page 194, a deficiency of nitrogen in the stock plant, at least with certain species, is beneficial to root initiation in cuttings made from such plants. Why treatments of cuttings with nitrogen should, on the other hand, promote rooting is not clear. It must be realized, however, that different steps are involved—first, the actual formation of root initials, and second, the growth of these initials into functioning roots. A deficiency of nitrogen in relation to carbohydrates may benefit one of the steps, whereas the addition of nitrogen, perhaps in a certain form, may benefit the other.

The presence of boron in the rooting medium may be necessary for rooting, at least for some plants. This is indicated by experiments *(43)* in rooting cuttings prepared from bean hypocotyls. It was found that when cuttings were placed for rooting in nutrient solutions completely lacking in boron, visible roots failed to appear, although when rooted in complete nutrient solutions or in solutions lacking in certain other trace elements, adequate rooting took place.

Environmental Conditions During Rooting

Humidity. Although the presence of leaves on cuttings is a strong stimulus to root formation, the loss of water from the leaves may possibly reduce the water content of the cuttings to such a low level as to cause them to die before root formation can take place. In cuttings, the natural water supply to the leaf from the roots has been cut off, yet the leaf is still capable of carrying on transpiration. In species which root rapidly, quick root formation soon permits water uptake to compensate for that removed by the leaves, but in more slowly rooting species, transpiration of the leaves must be reduced to a very low rate to keep the cuttings alive until roots form. To reduce transpiration of the leaves on cuttings to a minimum, the vapor pressure of the water in the atmosphere surrounding the leaves should be maintained as nearly equal as possible to the water vapor pressure in the intercellular spaces within the leaf.

It has long been a standard practice in propagating frames and greenhouses to sprinkle the cuttings frequently as well as the walls and floors so as to maintain a high humidity. Automatically operated devices which disperse a fog-like mist are available for use in greenhouses or other closed structures. These methods of humidification give a beneficial effect primarily in increasing the amount of water vapor in the air *(58, 81)*.

Mist propagation. A definite advance occurred with the development of techniques for rooting leafy cuttings under *mist (25, 29, 79, 91, 107)*. Such sprays maintain a film of water on the leaves which not only results in a high water vapor pressure surrounding the leaf but also lowers the air and leaf temperature—all factors tending to lower the transpiration rate. In tests where leaf temperatures were recorded by thermocouples, leaves under mist were found to be 10° to 15°F. cooler than leaves not under mist *(65)*. In other comparisons, the air temperature in a mist bed in the greenhouse was very uniform, averaging about 70°F., whereas in an adjacent polyethylene-covered, closed propagating frame, wide temperature fluctuations occurred, reaching almost 90°F. during the hottest part of the day. These cooling effects of the water sprays are so effective that propagating beds can be placed in full sun without an appreciable temperature increase of the leaves. The high light intensity obtained by cuttings in the sun desirably increases the photosynthetic activity of the leaves in comparison with that occurring in the usual shaded propagating beds.

A clear distinction should be made between humidification and mist. Under systems which only increase the relative humidity, the water vapor pressure in the area around the leaves is increased. Under mist systems this also occurs, but the leaf itself is covered with a film of water, which has the additional benefit of reducing the temperature of the leaf and thus reducing the internal water vapor pressure, and consequently the transpiration rate.

Under mist, conditions are ideal for growth and rooting of leafy cuttings. Transpiration is reduced to a low level, but the light intensity can be high, thus promoting full photosynthetic activity; the temperature of the entire cutting is relatively low, thereby reducing the respiration rate. On the other hand, in the closed propagating bed, temperatures tend to build up and some ventilation and shading are necessary. Otherwise the cuttings would burn up. Under these conditions of higher temperature, the transpiration rate goes up. The low light intensity resulting from shading reduces photosynthesis, whereas the higher temperature increases respiration. The cutting may actually be using up its reserve food faster than it is being manufactured, which of course will soon result in its death. The cutting under mist, conversely, can be synthesizing food in excess of that used in respiration, such nutrients being very important in promoting the initiation and development of new roots.

Although mist nozzles should maintain a film of water on the leaves at all times, at least during the daylight hours, the application of additional water as mist seems to be of no advantage; in fact, it is likely to be harmful. The large amounts of water used in mist systems operating continuously may reduce the temperature of the rooting medium to that of the water, which is usually too low for optimum rooting. Under *intermittent mist* systems, where the water is applied at frequent but short intervals, relatively little water is used and the temperature of the rooting medium is not adversely low. Temperatures in the rooting area of cuttings under intermittent mist are likely to be higher than those under constant mist, thus being more favorable for rooting.

The leaves of cuttings of certain species deteriorate to some extent under mist, and much more so under constant than intermittent mist. Various studies *(25, 71),* including work with radioactive isotopes, have shown that subjecting leaves to natural or artificial rains, or just soaking in water, will remove mineral nutrients from the leaves. It would be expected then that leafy cuttings, after prolonged periods under mist, would lose considerable amounts of nutrients.

Development of disease conditions on cuttings under mist propagation might be expected, but such has not been the case; in fact, the reverse has been true. For example, in greenhouse roses, no mildew was found to develop on leaves under mist, but mildew did develop on those not under mist. This is explained by the failure of mildew spores to germinate in free water *(65)*. It has been shown *(154)* that water sprays inhibit the development of powdery mildew (*Sphaerotheca pannosa*), and it may be that other disease organisms are held in check in the same manner.

Under mist sprays, softwood cuttings may be taken very early in the season at the stage most favorable for rooting. If started under conventional equipment, such succulent cuttings would be difficult to maintain without wilting. However, excessively immature growth of some plants cannot be used, even under mist, without collapsing. (For details of setting up mist propagating equipment, see page 251.)

Figure 9–17. Propagation under mist enables the use of long cuttings with greater leaf area. This often causes stronger rooting thus resulting in a larger rooted plant. These cuttings of the olive were treated with indolebutyric acid at 4000 parts per million by the concentrated-solution-dip method.

Temperature. In the cutting bed, daytime air temperatures of 70° to 80°F. with night temperatures of 60° to 70°F. are satisfactory for rooting of most species, although some root better at lower temperatures. Excessively high air temperatures should be avoided, because this tends to promote bud development in advance of root development and to increase water loss from the leaves. Temperature can regulate the production of adventitious roots. It is important to have root development ahead of shoot development. In cutting beds, some type of heat artificially applied below the cuttings, as described on page 18, is often used in maintaining the temperature at the base of the cutting higher than that of the buds at the top of the cutting, thus inducing root initiation before the buds open.

Thermostatically controlled equipment which will provide a uniform temperature near 70°F. at the base of the cuttings gives much better rooting than is obtained with widely fluctuating temperatures.

Light. The effect of light on root formation in cuttings varies according to the type of cutting being rooted. It is well known that the absence of light on stem tissue (etiolation) is conducive to the initiation of root primordia in some plants. On the other hand, leafy cuttings require exposure of the leaves to light for root formation to occur.

In experiments *(145, 146)* using etiolated pea cuttings without leaves and treated with indoleacetic acid, it was found that light of any wave length reduced the number of roots formed below the number formed in darkness. White light had the greatest effect, and blue light the least. However, if one leaf was left on each cutting and no auxin applied, the greatest root formation was in white light and the least amount in darkness. Greater root formation occurred under red light than under yellow, green, or blue light. Thus, with ample auxin present (in the case of the etiolated cuttings which had indoleacetic acid added), light inhibited initiation of root primordia. But with no external auxin applied (depending only upon its manufacture in the leaves), white light gave maximum rooting, with almost no roots in darkness. Hence, in this case at least, it may be that light was necessary for the manufacture of auxin, which in turn promotes root initiation. If the auxin requirement is satisfied externally, however, the presence of light appears to have an inhibitory effect on root initiation. Deciduous hardwood cuttings, which probably store previously manufactured auxin, initiate roots best in darkness. Small, leafy cuttings, however, with little or no auxin or carbohydrate storage, require light for food and auxin formation and subsequent root production.

White fluorescent lamps providing light intensities of 150 to 200 footcandles as a light source have given excellent rooting of cuttings *(109)*. Although this is relatively low (full sunlight is about 10,000 foot-candles), it seems to be sufficient for satisfactory root formation in some species.

It has been shown *(8, 109)* that radiation in the orange-red end of the spectrum favors rooting of cuttings more so than does the blue region. However, in one test *(110)* when the stock plants were exposed for 6 weeks to light sources of different quality before taking the cuttings, those from plants exposed to blue light rooted most readily.

There is some evidence that the photoperiod under which the stock plant is grown exerts an influence on the rooting of cuttings taken from it. This may be related to carbohydrate accumulation, the best rooting being obtained under photoperiods promoting carbohydrate increase. The photoperiod under which the cutting is actually rooted does, in some species, also have an effect on initiation of root primordia, long days or continuous illumination being more effective than short days *(75, 97, 109, 139, 158)*.

Another effect of photoperiod, which could have important commercial value, is its control of growth after the cuttings have been rooted. Certain plants more or less cease active vegetative growth due to the normal change in day length. The chrysanthemum, for example, ceases vegetative activity and initiates flower buds as the day length shortens in the fall. For rapid production of nursery stock, artificial maintenance of long day conditions which would keep the plants constantly vegetative may shorten the time required to produce a salable plant by many months *(139)*. The effect of photoperiod on growth of woody plants can become quite complicated, however, as many such species enter a rest period which requires exposure to a low temperature chilling period before active vegetative growth will resume.

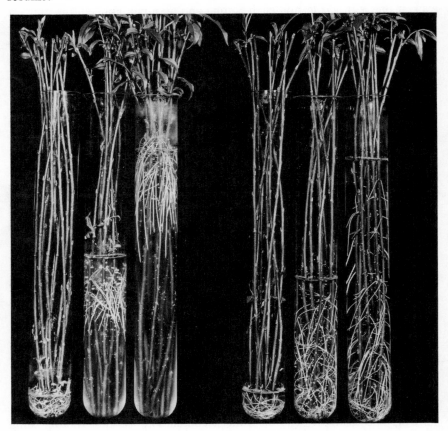

Figure 9–18. Necessity of oxygen for adventitious root development in willow cuttings. Started October 24 and photographed November 16. Water depths in tubes 2, 8, and 15 inches. **(left)** Water not aerated. **(right)** Water aerated with oxygen from a commercial gas cylinder. Roots on cuttings in tubes at the left developed only at the water surface where oxygen is available. Cuttings in oxygenated water at the right produced roots throughout their length. Courtesy P. W. Zimmerman.

Rooting medium. The rooting medium has three functions: (a) to hold the cutting in place during the rooting period, (b) to provide moisture for the cutting, and (c) to provide air to the base of the cutting.

An ideal rooting medium is one that provides sufficient porosity to allow for good aeration, has a high water-holding capacity, and yet is well drained. For tender softwood and semi-hardwood cuttings, it should have comparative freedom from fungi and bacteria.

It has been known for many years that the kind of rooting medium used may affect the type of root system arising from cuttings. For example, cuttings of a number of plant species when rooted in sand produce long, unbranched, coarse, and brittle roots; but when rooted in peat moss, the roots are well branched, slender, and more flexible. The latter type, of course, is more desirable during digging and repotting.

Experiments *(70)* designed to determine which of the characteristic differences between peat moss and sand are responsible for the different types of root system produced indicate that it is the difference in the moisture content. Determinations of the air and moisture content of peat moss and sand when each was at a point considered optimum for rooting cuttings showed that, on a volume basis, peat moss contains over twice as much air and three times as much moisture as sand. These studies indicate that the more desirable, fine type of root system is associated with an increased amount of moisture of the rooting medium.

Available oxygen in the rooting medium is essential for root production, although the requirement varies with different species. For example, willow cuttings form roots readily in water with an oxygen content as low as 1 ppm, but English ivy requires about 10 ppm for adequate root growth *(157)*. Carnation and chrysanthemum cuttings increased markedly in root production as the water in which they were rooted was aerated with increasing amounts of oxygen, from 0 to 21 per cent *(126)*. When roots are produced only near the surface of the rooting medium, it is likely that the oxygen supply in the medium is inadequate.

The different kinds of rooting media commonly used are discussed on page 241.

REFERENCES

1. Auchter, E. C., American experiments in propagating deciduous fruit trees by stem and root cuttings, *Proc. IX Int. Hort. Cong.,* pp. 287–296. 1930.
2. Avery, G. S., Jr., *et al., Hormones and Horticulture.* New York: McGraw-Hill, 1947.
3. Brandon, R., Seasonal variations in the starch content of the genus *Rosa,* and their relation to propagation by stem cuttings, *Jour. of Pom. and Hort. Sci.,* 17:233–253. 1939.
4. Bonner, J., Vitamin B$_1$, a growth factor for higher plants, *Science,* 85:183–184. 1937.

5. Bobiloff, W., Stekken van *Hevea braziliensis. Meded. alg. Proefst. Avros. Rubberserie,* 94:123–126. 1934.

6. Carlson, Margery C., The formation of nodal adventitious roots in *Salix cordata, Amer. Jour. Bot.,* 25:721–725. 1938.

7. ———, Nodal adventitious roots in willow stems of different ages, *Amer. Jour. Bot.,* 37:555–561. 1950.

8. Chadwick, L. C., Some results with the use of opaque structures for propagation by cuttings, *Proc. Amer. Soc. Hort. Sci.,* 53:567–572. 1949.

9. Christensen, E., Root production in plants following localized stem irradiation, *Science,* 119: 127–128. 1954.

10. Cooper, W. C., Hormones in relation to root formation on stem cuttings, *Plant Phys.,* 10:789–794. 1935.

11. ———, Hormones and root formation, *Bot. Gaz.,* 99:599–614. 1938.

12. ———, The concentrated-solution-dip method of treating cuttings with growth substances, *Proc. Amer. Soc. Hort. Sci.,* 44:533–541. 1944.

13. Corbett, L. C., The development of roots from cuttings, *W. Va. Agr. Exp. Sta. Ann. Rpt.,* 9(1895–96):196–199. 1897.

14. Curtis, O. F., Stimulation of root growth in cuttings by treatment with chemical compounds, *Cornell Univ. Agr. Exp. Sta. Mem. 14,* 1918.

15. Day, L. H., Is the increased rooting of wounded cuttings sometimes due to water absorption? *Proc. Amer. Soc. Hort. Sci.,* 29:350-351. 1933.

16. De Boer, S., Some aspects of propagation by cuttings of ornamental trees and shrubs, *Rpt. 13th Int. Hort. Cong.,* pp. 443–446. 1952.

17. Delisle, A. L., Histological and anatomical changes induced by indoleacetic acid in rooting cuttings of *Pinus strobus* L., *Va. Jour. Sci.,* 3:118–124. 1942.

18. Deuber, Carl G., Vegetative propagation of conifers, Trans. Conn. Acad. Arts and Sci., 34:1–83. 1940.

19. Doak, B. W., The effect of various nitrogenous compounds on the rooting of rhododendron cuttings treated with naphthaleneacetic acid, *New Zealand Jour. Sci. and Tech.,* 21:336A–343A. 1940.

20. Doran, W. L., Effects of treating cuttings of woody plants with both a root inducing substance and a fungicide, *Proc. Amer. Soc. Hort. Sci.,* 60:487–491. 1953.

21. Dore, J., Seasonal variation in the regeneration of root cuttings, *Nature,* 172:1189. 1953.

22. Dorn, H., Histologische Studien über die Entwicklung sprossbürtiger Wurzeln nach Heteroauxinbehandlung, *Planta,* 28:20–42. 1938.

23. Esau, K., *Plant Anatomy.* New York: Wiley, 1953.

24. Evans, H., Physiological aspects of the propagation of cacao from cuttings, *Rpt. 13th Int. Hort. Cong.,* pp. 1179–1190. 1953.

25. ———, Investigations on the propagation of cacao, *Trop. Agr.,* 28:147–203. 1951.

26. Farrar, J. H., and N. H. Grace, Vegetative propagation of conifers. XI. Effects of type of cutting on the rooting of Norway spruce cuttings. *Can. Jour. Res.,* 20, Sec. C:116–121. 1942.

27. Fritzsche, R., Untersuchungen über die Jugendformen des Apfel und Birnbaumes und ihre Konsequenzen für die Unterlagen und Sortenzüchtung, *Ber. Schweiz. Bot. Ges.,* 58:207–268. 1948.

28. Galston, A. W., On the physiology of root initiation in excised asparagus stem tips, *Amer. Jour. Bot.,* 35:281–287. 1948.

29. Gardner, E. J., Propagation under mist, *Amer. Nurs.,* 73(9):5–7. 1941.

30. Gardner, F. E., The relationship between tree age and the rooting of cuttings, *Proc. Amer. Soc. Hort. Sci.,* 26:101–104. 1929.

31. ———, The vegetative propagation of plants, *Md. Agr. Exp. Sta. Bul. 335,* 1932.

32. ———, Etiolation as a method of rooting apple variety stem cuttings, *Proc. Amer. Soc. Hort. Sci.,* 34:323–329. 1937.

33. Gautheret, R. J., Plant tissue culture, *Growth,* 10:21–43. 1946.

34. Grace, N. H., Responses of plant stem cuttings treated with chemicals in a carrier dust, *Can. Jour. Res. C.,* 23:115–126. 1945.

35. Graham, R. J. D., and L. B. Stewart, Special methods of practical utility in vegetative propagation of plants, *Proc. IX Int. Hort. Cong.,* pp. 159–164. 1930.

36. Harrison, B. F., Histological responses of *Iresine lirdenii* to indoleacetic acid, *Bot. Gaz.,* 99:301–338. 1937.

37. Hagemann, A., Untersuchungen an Blattstecklingen, *Gartenbauwiss,* 6:69–202. 1932.

38. Hartmann, H. T., The use of root-promoting substances in the propagation of olives by soft-wood cuttings, *Proc. Amer. Soc. Hort. Sci.,* 43:303–308. 1946.

39. ———, and C. J. Hansen, Effect of season of collecting, indolebutyric acid, and pre-planting storage treatments on rooting of Marianna plum, peach, and quince hardwood cuttings, *Proc. Amer. Soc. Hort. Sci.,* 71:57–66. 1958.

40. ———, and R. M. Brooks, Propagation of Stockton Morello cherry rootstock by softwood cuttings under mist sprays, *Proc. Amer. Soc. Hort. Sci.,* 71:127–134. 1958.

41. ———, and C. J. Hansen. Rooting pear and plum rootstocks. *Calif. Agr.* 12(10):4, 14, 15. 1958.

42. Haun, J. R., and P. W. Cornell, Rooting response of geranium (*Pelargonium hortorum,* Bailey, var. Ricard) cuttings as influenced by nitrogen, phosphorus, and potassium nutrition of the stock plant, *Proc. Amer. Soc. Hort. Sci.,* 58:317–323. 1951.

43. Hemberg, T., Rooting experiments with hypocotyls of *Phaseolus vulgaris* L., *Physiologia Plantarum,* 4:358–369. 1951.

44. Hiller, Charlotte, A study of the origin and development of callus and root primordia of *Taxus cuspidata* with reference to the effects of growth regulator, Master's thesis, *Cornell Univ.,* 1951.

45. Hitchcock, A. E., and P. W. Zimmerman, Relation of rooting response to age of tissue at the base of green wood cuttings, *Contrib. Boyce Thomp. Inst.,* 4:85–98. 1932.

46. ———, Effects of growth substances on the rooting response of cuttings, *Contrib. Boyce Thomp. Inst.,* 8:63–79. 1936.

47. ———, A sensitive test for root formation, *Amer. Jour. Bot.,* 24:735–736. 1937.

48. ———, Effects obtained with mixtures of root-inducing and other substances, *Contrib. Boyce Thomp. Inst.,* 11:143–160. 1940.

49. ———, Further tests with Vitamin B_1 on established plants and on cuttings, *Contrib. Boyce Thomp. Inst.,* 12(2):143–156. 1941.

50. ———, Root inducing activity of phenoxy compounds in relation to their structure, *Contrib. Boyce Thomp. Inst.,* 12:497–507. 1942.

51. ———, Root-inducing substances effective on apple cuttings taken in May, *Proc. Amer. Soc. Hort. Sci.,* 40:292–297. 1942.

52. ———, Methods of rating the root-inducing activity of phenoxy acids and other growth substances, *Contrib. Boyce Thomp. Inst.,* 14:21–38. 1945.

53. Hudson, J. P., Factors affecting the regeneration of plants from roots, Ph.D. dissertation, Univ. of Nottingham, 1956.

54. Hunter, R. E., The vegetative propagation of citrus, *Trop. Agr.,* 9:135–140. 1932.

55. Kraus, E. J., and H. R. Kraybill, Vegetation and reproduction with special reference to the tomato, *Ore. Agr. Exp. Sta. Bul. 149,* 1918.

56. Kraus, E. J., N. A. Brown, and K. C. Hamner, Histological reactions of bean plants to indoleacetic acid, *Bot. Gaz.,* 98:370–420. 1936.

57. Kraus, E. J., Rooting azalea cuttings, *Nat. Hort. Mag.*, 32:163–164. 1953.

58. Kiplinger, D. C., Humidity in the greenhouse, *Monthly Bul. Ohio Florists Assoc. No. 196*:2–8. 1946.

59. Knight, R. C., and A. W. Witt, The propagation of fruit tree stocks by stem cuttings. Observations on the factors governing the rooting of hardwood cuttings. *Jour. Pom. and Hort. Sci.*, 5:248–266. 1926.

60. ———, The propagation of fruit tree stocks by stem cuttings. II. Trials with hard- and soft-wood cuttings, *Jour. Pom. and Hort. Sci.*, 6:47–60. 1927.

61. Kögl, F., A. J. Haagen-Smit, and H. Erxleben, Über ein neues Auxin ("Heteroauxin") aus Harn. XI. *Mitteilung. Z. physiol. Chem.*, 228:90–103. 1934.

62. Kögl, F., Über Wüchsstoffe der Auxin- und der Bios-gruppe, *Ber. Deuts. chem. Ges.*, 68:16–28. 1935.

63. Koepfli, J. B., K. V. Thimann, and F. W. Went, Phytohormones: structure and physiological activity. I. *Jour. Biol. Chem.*, 122:763–780. 1938.

64. Laibach, F., and O. Fischnich, Künstliche Wurzelneubildung mittels Wuchsstoffpaste, *Ber. Deuts. bot. Ges.*, 53:528–539. 1935.

65. Langhans, R. W., Mist for growing plants, *Farm Res.* (Cornell Univ.), 21(3):3. 1955.

66. Lek, H. A. A. van der, Root development in woody cuttings, *Meded. Landbouwhoogesch. Wageningen,* 38(1). 1925.

67. ———, Anatomical structure of woody plants in relation to vegetative propagation, *Proc. IX. Int. Hort. Cong.,* pp. 66–76. 1930.

68. ———, Over den invloed der knoppen op de wortelvorming der stekken, *Meded. Landbouwhoogesch. Wageningen,* 38(2):1–95. 1934.

69. Lindner, R. C., Effects of indoleacetic acid and naphthaleneacetic acid on development of buds and roots in horseradish, *Bot. Gaz.,* 100:500–527. 1939.

70. Long, J. C., The influence of rooting media on the character of roots produced by cuttings, *Proc. Amer. Soc. Hort. Sci.,* 29:352–355. 1933.

71. Long, W. G., D. V. Sweet, and H. B. Tukey, The loss of nutrients by leaching of the foliage, *Quart. Bul. Mich. Agr. Exp. Sta.* 38:528–532. 1956.

72. Mes, M. G., Cuttings difficult to root, *Plants and Gardens,* 7(2):95–97. 1951.

73. ———, Plant hormones, Prog. Rpt. Plant Phys. Res. Inst. 1950–51, Univ. of Pretoria, 1951.

74. Mitchell, J. W., and R. R. Rice, Plant growth regulators, *USDA Misc. Publ. 495,* 1942.

75. Moskov, B. S., and I. E. Koschezhenko, Rooting of woody cuttings as dependent upon photoperiodic conditions, *Compt. Rend. (Doklady) Acad. Sci. URSS,* 24(4):392–395. 1939.

76. Naylor, E. E., and B. Johnson, A histological study of vegetative reproduction in *Saintpaulia ionantha, Amer. Jour. Bot.,* 24:673–678. 1937.

77. O'Rourke, F. L., The influence of blossom buds on rooting of hardwood cuttings of blueberry, *Proc. Amer. Soc. Hort. Sci.,* 40:332–334. 1940.

78. ———, Wood type and original position on shoot with reference to rooting in hardwood cuttings of blueberry, *Proc. Amer. Soc. Hort. Sci.,* 45:195–197. 1944.

79. ———, Mist humidification and the rooting of cuttings, *Mich. Agr. Exp. Sta. Quart. Bul.* 32:245–249. 1949.

80. ———, The effect of juvenility on plant propagation, *Proc. 1st Plant Prop. Soc. Ann. Mtg.,* pp. 33–37. 1951.

81. O'Rourke, F. L., and J. E. Moulton, The use of new type atomizers in the propagation greenhouse, *Mich. Agr. Exp. Sta. Quart. Bul.* 30:92–95. 1947.

82. Pearse, H. L., Response of fruit tree cuttings to treatment with synthetic rootforming substances, *Rep. East Malling Res. Sta. for 1938,* pp. 157–166. 1939.

83. ———, The effect of nutrition and phytohormones on the rooting of vine cuttings, *Ann. of Bot.*, N. S. 7:123–132. 1943.

84. ———, Rooting of vine and plum cuttings as affected by nutrition of the parent plant and treatment with phytohormones, *Sci. Bul. 249, Dept. of Agr. Union of S. Afr.*, 1946.

85. ———, Growth substances and their practical importance in horticulture, *Commonwealth Bur. Hort. and Plant. Crops, Tech. Comm. No. 20, 1948.*

86. Preston, W. H., J. B. Shanks, and P. W. Cornell, Influence of mineral nutrition on production, rooting and survival of cuttings of azaleas, *Proc. Amer. Soc. Hort. Sci.*, 61:499–507. 1953.

87. Podluzhnii, D. F., Propagation of the olive tree by cuttings, *Soviet Sub-tropics*, No. 11–12, pp. 41–43. 1940.

88. Pridham, A. M. S., Factors in the rooting of cuttings and the growth of young plants, *Proc. Amer. Soc. Hort. Sci.*, 40:579–582. 1942.

89. Priestley, J. H., and C. F. Swingle, Vegetative propagation from the standpoint of plant anatomy, *USDA Tech. Bul. 151*, 1929.

90. Prokofiev, A. A., On the mechanism of the action of heteroauxin, *Compt. Rend. (Doklady) Acad. Sci. URSS*, 42:233–237. 1944.

91. Raines, M. A., Some uses of a spray chamber in experimentation with plants, *Amer. Jour. Bot.*, Suppl. to Vol. 27, No. 10, p. 185. 1940.

92. Rappaport, J., The influence of leaves and growth substances on the rooting response of cuttings, *Natuurw. Tijdschr.*, 21:356–359. 1940.

93. Reid, Mary E., The influence of nutritive conditions of seeds and cuttings upon the development of roots, *Proc. IX Int. Hort. Cong.*, pp. 165–169. 1930.

94. Sachs, J., Stoff und Form der Pflanzenorgane. I and II. *Arb. bot. Inst. Würzburg*, 2:452–88 and 689–718. 1880 and 1882.

95. Samish, R. M., and P. Spiegel., The influence of the nutrition of the mother vine on the rooting of cuttings, *Ktavim*, 8:93–100. 1957.

96. Siegler, E. A., and J. J. Bowman, Anatomical studies of root and shoot primordia in 1-year apple roots, *Jour. Agr. Res.*, 58:795–803. 1939.

97. Skinner, H. T., Further observations on the propagation of rhododendrons and azaleas by stem and leaf-bud cuttings, *Proc. Amer. Soc. Hort. Sci.*, 37:1013–1018. 1940.

98. Skoog, F., Growth and organ formation in tobacco tissue cultures, *Amer. Jour. Bot.*, 31:19–24. 1944.

99. Skoog, F., and C. Tsui, Chemical control of growth and bud formation in tobacco stem and callus, *Amer. Jour. Bot.*, 35:782–787. 1948.

100. ———, Growth substances and the formation of buds in plant tissue, *Plant Growth Substances*. Madison: Univ. of Wis. Press, 1951.

101. Snow, A. G., Jr., Clonal variation in rooting response of red maple cuttings, *USDA Northeastern Forest Exp. Sta. Tech. Note 29*, 1939.

102. Stangler, B. B., An anatomical study of the origin and development of adventitious roots in stem cuttings of *Chrysanthemum morifolium* Bailey, *Dianthus caryophyllus* L., and *Rosa dilecta* Rehd., Ph.D. dissertation, Cornell Univ., 1949.

103. Starring, C. C., Influence of the carbohydrate-nitrate content of cuttings upon the production of roots, *Proc. Amer. Soc. Hort. Sci.*, 20:288–292. 1923.

104. Stoutemyer, V. T., Regeneration in various types of apple wood, *Iowa Agr. Exp. Sta. Res. Bul.* 220:309–352. 1937.

105. ———, A comparison on rooting induced by acid and by amide growth substances, *Proc. Amer. Soc. Hort. Sci.*, 39:253–258. 1941.

106. ———, The propagation of *Chionanthus retusus* by cuttings, *Nat. Hort. Mag.*, 21 (4):175–178. 1942.

107. Stoutemyer, V. T., and F. L. O'Rourke, Spray humidification and the rooting of greenwood cuttings, *Amer. Nurs.*, 77(1):5–6, 24–25. 1943.

108. ———, Rooting of cuttings from plants sprayed with growth-regulating substances, *Proc. Amer. Soc. Hort. Sci.,* 46:407–411. 1945.

109. Stoutemyer, V. T., and A. W. Close, Rooting cuttings and germinating seeds under fluorescent and cold cathode light, *Proc. Amer. Soc. Hort. Sci.,* 48:309–325. 1946.

110. ———, Changes of rooting response in cuttings following exposure of the stock plants to light of different qualities, *Proc. Amer. Soc. Hort. Sci.,* 49:392–394. 1947.

111. Sudds, R. H., The origin of roots in several types of red and black raspberry stem cuttings, *Proc. Amer. Soc. Hort. Sci.,* 33:380–385. 1935.

112. Swingle, C. F., Burr knot formation in relation to the vascular system of the apple stem, *Jour. Agr. Res.,* 34:533–544. 1927.

113. ———, A physiological study of rooting and callusing in apple and willow, *Jour. Agr. Res.,* 39:81–128. 1929.

114. Thakurta, A. G., and B. K. Dutt, Vegetative propagation of mango from gootes (marcotte) and cuttings by treatment of high concentration auxin, *Cur. Sci.,* 10:297. 1941.

115. Thimann, K. V., and F. W. Went, On the chemical nature of the root-forming hormone, *Proc. Kon. Akad. Wetensch,* Amsterdam, 37:456–459. 1934.

116. Thimann, K. V., On an analysis of activity of two growth-promoting substances on plant tissues, *Proc. Kon. Akad. Wetensch,* Amsterdam, 38:896–912. 1935.

117. ———, On the plant growth hormone produced by *Rhizopus suinus, Jour. Biol. Chem.,* 109:279–291. 1935.

118. ———, On the nature of inhibitions caused by auxins, *Amer. Jour. Bot.,* 24:407–412. 1937.

119. ———, Plant growth hormones, in G. Pincus and K. V. Thimann, eds., *The Hormones: Physiology, Chemistry, and Applications.* New York: Academic Press, 1948. Vol. I, Chap. 2.

120. Thimann, K. V., and J. B. Koepfli, Identity of the growth-promoting and root-forming substances of plants, *Nature,* 135:101–102. 1935.

121. Thimann, K. V., and A. L. Delisle, The vegetative propagation of difficult plants, *Jour. Arnold Arb.,* 20:116–136. 1939.

122. ———, Notes on the rooting of some conifers from cuttings, *Jour. Arnold Arb.,* 23:103–109. 1942.

123. Thimann, K. V., and E. F. Poutasse, Factors affecting root formation of *Phaseolus vulgaris, Plant Phys.,* 16:585–598. 1941.

124. Thimann, K. V., and J. Behnke-Rogers, The use of auxins in the rooting of woody cuttings, M. M. Cabot Foundation, *Publ. No. 1,* Harvard Forest, Petersham, Mass. 1950.

125. Thurlow, J., and J. Bonner, Inhibition of photoperiodic induction in *Xanthium, Amer. Jour. Bot.,* 34:603–604. 1947.

126. Tinga, J. H., The effect of five levels of oxygen on the rooting of carnation cuttings in tap water culture, Master's thesis, Cornell Univ., 1952.

127. Trécul, A., Recherches sur l' origine des racines, *Ann. Sci. Nat. Bot. Ser.,* 3:340–350. 1846.

128. Tukey, H. B., and K. Brase, Experiences in rooting soft- and hard-wood cuttings of hardy fruits, *Proc. Amer. Soc. Hort. Sci.,* 28:460–464. 1931.

129. Tukey, H. B., and E. L. Green, Gradient composition of rose shoots from tip to base, *Plant Phys.,* 9:157–163. 1934.

130. Van Onsem, J. G., Synergistic effects of hormone mixtures on the rooting of cuttings, *Rpt. 13th Int. Hort. Cong.,* pp. 506–514. 1953.

131. Van Overbeek, J. et al., Nomenclature of chemical plant regulators, *Plant Phys.,* 29:307–308. 1954.

132. Van Overbeek, J., and L. E. Gregory, A physiological separation of two factors necessary for the formation of roots on cuttings, *Amer. Jour. Bot.*, 32:336–341. 1945.

133. Van Overbeek, J., S. A. Gordon, and L. E. Gregory, An analysis of the function of the leaf in the process of root formation in cuttings, *Amer. Jour. Bot.*, 33:100–107. 1946.

134. Van Tieghem, P., and H. Douliot, Recherches comparatives sur l'origine des membres endogènes dans les plantes vasculaires, *Ann. Sci. Nat. Bot.*, VII., 8:1–160. 1888.

135. Vöchting, H., *Über Organbildung im Pflanzenreich.*, I., 1–258. Bonn, 1878.

136. Walker, R. I., Regeneration in the scale leaf of *Lilium candidum* and *L. longiflorum*, *Amer. Jour. Bot.*, 27:114–117. 1940.

137. Warmke, H. E., and G. L. Warmke, The role of auxin in the differentiation of root and shoot primordia from root cuttings of *Taraxacum* and *Cichorium*, *Amer. Jour. Bot.*, 37:272–280. 1950.

138. Warner, G. C., and F. W. Went, *Rooting of Cuttings with Indoleacetic Acid and Vitamin B_1.* Pasadena, Calif.: Plant Culture Publishing Co., 1939.

139. Waxman, S., and J. P. Nitsch, Influence of light on plant growth, *Amer. Nurs.*, 104(10):11–12, 1956.

140. Wellensiek, S. J., Rejuvenation of woody plants by formation of sphaeroblasts, *Proc. Kon. Akad. Wetensch.*, Amsterdam, 55:567–573. 1952.

141. Went, F. W., On a substance causing root formation, *Proc. Kon. Akad. Wetensch.*, Amsterdam, 32:35–39. 1929.

142. ———, A test method for rhizocaline, the root-forming substance, *Proc. Kon. Akad. Wetensch.*, Amsterdam, 37:445–455. 1934.

143. ———, On the pea test method for auxin, the plant growth hormone, *Proc. Kon. Akad. Wetensch.*, Amsterdam, 37:547–555. 1934.

144. ———, Hormones involved in root formation, *Proc. 6th Int. Bot. Cong.*, 2:267–269. 1935.

145. ———, Specific factors other than auxin affecting growth and root formation, *Plant Phys.*, 13:55–80. 1938.

146. Went, F. W., and K. V. Thimann, *Phytohormones.* New York: Macmillan, 1937.

147. Went, F. W., J. Bonner, and G. C. Warner, Aneurin and the rooting of cuttings, *Science*, 87:170–171. 1938.

148. White, H. E., Fermate and its effect on rooting of geranium cuttings, *Proc. Amer. Soc. Hort. Sci.*, 47:522–524. 1946.

149. White, P. R., Vitamin B_1 in the nutrition of excised tomato roots, *Plant Phys.*, 12:803–811. 1937.

150. Winkler, A. J., Some factors influencing the rooting of vine cuttings, *Hilgardia*, 2:329–349. 1927.

151. Wyman, D., The influence of the heel in the rooting of narrow-leaved evergreen cuttings, *Flor. Exch.*, 75(14):25. 1930.

152. Yarborough, J. A., Anatomical and developmental studies of the foliar embryos of *Bryophyllum calycinum*, *Amer. Jour. Bot.*, 19:443–453. 1932.

153. ———, Regeneration in the foliage leaf of *Sedum*, *Amer. Jour. Bot.*, 23:303–307. 1936.

154. Yarwood, C. E., Control of powdery mildews with a water spray, *Phytopath*, 29:288–290. 1939.

155. Yerkes, G. E., Experiments in the propagation of fruit tree stocks, *Proc. Amer. Soc. Hort. Sci.*, 20:241–244. 1923.

156. Yin, H. C., and C. H. Liu, Experiments on the rooting of tung tree cuttings, *Amer. Jour. Bot.*, 35:540–542. 1938.

157. Zimmerman, P. W., Oxygen requirements for root growth of cuttings in water, *Amer. Jour. Bot.,* 17:842–861. 1930.

158. Zimmerman, P. W., and A. E. Hitchcock, Vegetative propagation of holly, *Contrib. Boyce Thomp. Inst.,* 2:205–219. 1929.

159. ——, Initiation and stimulation of adventitious roots caused by unsaturated hydrocarbon gases, *Contrib. Boyce Thomp. Inst.,* 5:351–369. 1933.

160. ——, Comparative effectiveness of acids, esters, and salts as growth substances and methods of evaluating them, *Contrib. Boyce Thomp. Inst.,* 8:337–350. 1937.

161. Zimmerman, P. W., and F. Wilcoxon, Several chemical growth substances which cause initiation of roots and other responses in plants, *Contrib. Boyce Thomp. Inst.,* 7:209–229. 1935.

162. ——, Substituted phenoxy and benzoic acid growth substances and the relation of structure to physiological activity, *Contrib. Boyce Thomp. Inst.,* 12:321–343. 1942.

• Supplementary Reading

Audus, L. J., *Plant Growth Substances.* London: Hill, 1953. Chap. 5.

Garner, R. J., and E. S. J. Hatcher, "The Interplay of Factors Influencing the Rooting Behavior of Shoot Cuttings," Report 14th International Horticultural Congress (1955), pp. 204–214.

Leopold, A. C., *Auxins and Plant Growth.* Berkeley: University of California Press, 1955. Chap. 10.

Pearse, H. L., "Growth Substances and Their Practical Importance in Horticulture," Technical Communication No. 20 (Commonwealth Bureau of Horticulture and Plantation Crops, East Malling, England, 1948).

Thimann, K. V., and J. Behnke-Rogers, *The Use of Auxins in the Rooting of Woody Cuttings.* Petersham, Mass.: Harvard Forest, 1950.

Went, F. W., and K. V. Thimann, *Phytohormones.* New York: Macmillan, 1937. Chap. 11.

10

Techniques of Propagation by Cuttings

In propagation by cuttings, a portion of a stem, root, or leaf is cut from the parent plant, after which this plant part is placed under certain favorable environmental conditions and induced to form roots and shoots, thus producing a new independent plant which, in most cases, is identical with the parent plant.

THE IMPORTANCE AND ADVANTAGES OF PROPAGATION BY CUTTINGS

This is the most important method of propagating ornamental shrubs—deciduous species as well as the broad and narrow-leaved types of evergreens. Cuttings are also used widely in the commercial greenhouse propagation of many florists' crops and are commonly used in propagating several fruit species.

For species that can be easily propagated by cuttings, this method has numerous advantages. Many new plants can be started in a limited space from a few stock plants. It is inexpensive, rapid, simple, and does not require the special techniques necessary in grafting or budding. There is no problem of compatibility with rootstocks or of poor graft unions. Greater uniformity is obtained by the absence of the variation which sometimes appears due to the variable seedling rootstocks of grafted plants. The parent plant is usually reproduced exactly with no genetic change.

It is not always desirable, however, to produce plants on their own roots

by cuttings even if it is possible to do so. It is often advantageous or necessary to use a rootstock resistant to some adverse soil condition or to soil-
borne organisms.

TYPES OF CUTTINGS

Cuttings are almost always made from the vegetative portions of the
plant, such as stems, modified stems (rhizomes, tubers, corms, and bulbs),
leaves, or roots. The reproductive parts of the plant are not ordinarily
used, although such parts as the ovary, pedicel, petals, and cotyledons have
been reported to form roots *(1, 9, 19)*.

Several types of cuttings can be made, classified according to the part
of the plant from which they are obtained:

> Stem cuttings
>> Hardwood
>>> Deciduous
>>> Narrow-leaved evergreen
>> Semi-hardwood
>> Softwood
>> Herbaceous
> Leaf cuttings
> Leaf-bud cuttings
> Root cuttings

Many plants can be propagated by several of the different types of
cuttings with equally satisfactory results. The type used would depend
upon the individual circumstances, the least expensive and easiest usually
being selected.

If the particular plant being propagated will root well by hardwood
stem cuttings in an outdoor nursery, this method would ordinarily be used
due to its simplicity and low cost. Root cuttings are also easily prepared.
For species more difficult to propagate, it is necessary to resort to the
more expensive and elaborate facilities required for rooting the leafy types
of cuttings.

In selecting cutting material it is important to use parent plants that
are healthy, moderately vigorous, and of known variety, if the latter is of
importance. Stock plants that are diseased or injured by frost or drought,
prematurely defoliated by insects or diseases, stunted by excessive fruiting, or that have made rank, overly vigorous growth should be avoided.
Generally, nothing is gained or lost by selecting cutting material from high
yielding plants. The past performance of the stock plants *(3)* will usually
make little difference in the performance of the new plants except when
a mutation (bud sport—see p. 166) occurs. Differences in yields or fruit
and flower size are generally due to variations in soil, climate, or cultural
practices (except where seedling variation occurs).

A commendable practice for commercial nurserymen is the establishment of stock blocks as a source of propagating material, where uniform, true-to-variety, disease-free plants can be maintained and held under the proper nutritive condition for the best rooting of cuttings taken from them.

Stem Cuttings

This is the most important type of cutting and can be divided into four groups according to the nature of the wood used in making the cuttings: *hardwood, semi-hardwood, softwood,* and *herbaceous.* In propagation by stem cuttings, segments of shoots containing lateral or terminal buds are obtained with the expectation that, under the proper conditions, adventitious roots (see p. 177) will develop and thus produce independent plants.

The type of wood, stage of growth used in making the cuttings, the time of year the cuttings are taken, and several other factors can be very important in securing satisfactory rooting of some plants. Information concerning these factors is given in Chapter 9, although much of this knowledge can be obtained by actual experience in propagating plants.

Hardwood cuttings (deciduous species). This is one of the least expensive and easiest methods of vegetative propagation. Hardwood cuttings are easy to prepare, are not readily perishable, may be shipped safely over long distances if necessary, and require no special equipment during rooting.

The cuttings are usually prepared during the dormant season—late fall, winter, or early spring—from wood of the previous season's growth, although with a few species, such as the fig or the olive, two-year or older wood is used. This type of cutting is most often found in the propagation of deciduous woody plants, although some broad-leaved evergreens, such as the olive *(12),* can be propagated by leafless hardwood cuttings. Many deciduous ornamental shrubs are started readily by this type of cutting. Some common ones are privet, forsythia, wisteria, honeysuckle, and spirea. Rose rootstocks, such as *Rosa multiflora,* are propagated in great quantities by hardwood cuttings. A few fruit species are propagated commercially by this method—for example, the fig, quince, olive, mulberry, grape, currant, gooseberry, pomegranate, and some plums.

The propagating material for hardwood cuttings should be taken from healthy, vigorous stock plants, growing in full sunlight. The wood selected should not be from extremely rank growth with abnormally long internodes, or from small, weakly growing interior shoots. Wood of moderate size and vigor is the most desirable. The cuttings should have an ample supply of stored foods to nourish the developing roots and shoots until the new plant becomes self-sustaining.

Hardwood cuttings vary in length according to the species involved, but generally they are prepared 4 to 12 inches long. At least two nodes are included; the basal cut is just below a node and the top cut ½ to 1 inch above a node. The diameter of the cuttings may range from ¼ inch to 1 or even 2 inches, depending upon the species. Three different types of cuttings can be prepared as shown in Figure 10–1, the "mallet," the "heel," and the straight cutting. The mallet includes a short section of stem of the older wood, whereas the heel cutting includes only a small piece of the older wood. The straight cutting, not including any of the older wood, is most commonly used, giving satisfactory results in most instances.

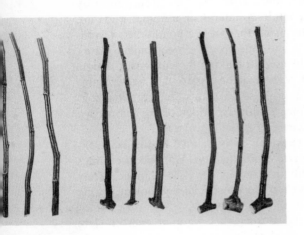

Figure 10–1. Types of hardwood cuttings: (left) Straight—the type ordinarily used. (center) "Heel" cuttings. A small piece of older wood is retained at the base. (right) "Mallet" cuttings. An entire section of the branch of older wood is retained.

In cases where it is difficult to distinguish between the top and base of the cuttings, it is advisable to make all the basal cuts at a slant rather than at right angles. In large scale operations, bundles of cutting material are cut to the desired lengths by band saws or other types of mechanical cutters rather than making the cuttings individually by hand.

There are several methods commonly used for handling hardwood cuttings before planting:

(a) Prepare the cuttings to a uniform length, tie them with wire into convenient-sized bundles, placing the tops all one way, and store them under cool, moist conditions until spring. During this so-called "callusing" period, the bundles of cuttings may be buried out-of-doors in sandy soil, sand, or sawdust in a well-drained location. They may be placed horizontally or, more often, they are buried in a vertical position, but upside down with the basal end of the cuttings several inches below the surface of the soil. The basal ends are, therefore, somewhat warmer than the upper ends. This probably tends to promote root initiation at the base, while retarding bud development at the top. At planting time in the spring, the bundles of cuttings are dug up and the cuttings planted right side up. In

(A) Preparing the cuttings from dormant and leafless one-year-old shoots. A common length is 6 to 8 inches and the basal cut is generally made just below a node.

(B) Treating the cuttings with a root-promoting substance. On the left a bundle of cuttings is being dipped in a commercial talc preparation. On the right another method is illustrated. The basal ends of the cuttings are being soaked for 24 hours in a dilute solution of the chemical. With easily-rooted plants such treatments are unnecessary.

(C) The cuttings may be planted immediately but with some plants it is helpful to callus the cuttings for several weeks in a box of moist shavings or peat moss before planting.

(D) Planting the cuttings in the nursery row. A **dibble** (a heavy, pointed, flat-bladed knife) is a useful tool for inserting the cutting and at the same time firming the soil around the previously-planted cutting.

(E) The cuttings should be planted deeply enough so that just one bud shows above-ground. A loose, sandy loam is best for starting hardwood cuttings.

(F) Several weeks after planting, the cuttings start to grow. They must be watered frequently if rains do not occur and, of course, weeds must be controlled.

Figure 10–2. How to make hardwood cuttings.

regions with mild winters, the bundles of cuttings are often stored during this callusing period in large boxes of moist sand, sawdust, peat moss, or shavings, either in an unheated building or out-of-doors. This probably would not be enough protection for the cuttings, however, in regions where severe, sub-zero winter temperatures are experienced. A cool, but above freezing cellar would be satisfactory for such climates. If refrigerated rooms are available, the cuttings can be safely stored during the callusing period at temperatures of 40° to 50°F. until they are ready to plant.

(b) It is often sufficient with easily rooted species to merely gather the cutting material during the dormant season, wrap it in paper-covered bundles with slightly damp peat moss, and store at 32° to 40°F. until spring. The cutting material should not be allowed to dry out or to become excessively wet during storage. At planting time, the cuttings are made into proper lengths and planted in the nursery.

Stored cuttings or cutting material should be examined at frequent intervals to watch for excessive bud development. If this should take place, lower storage temperatures should be used or the cuttings made and planted without delay. If the buds are far developed when the cuttings are planted, leaves will form before the roots appear and the cuttings will dry up and die due to water loss from the leaves.

(c) Cuttings may be taken in the fall and planted immediately. A callus often develops at the base of the cutting before the dormant season starts and, with quick-rooting plants, some roots develop in the fall, but with most species, the formation of roots and shoots probably occurs simultaneously in the spring *(17)*. Cuttings handled this way, however, are subject to heaving out of the ground in regions where the soil intermittently freezes and thaws during the winter. Fall-planted cuttings may be injured by rodents during the winter and weed growth may be considerable before the soil can be cultivated in the spring.

(d) A successful method with some species is to take the cuttings in the fall, treat them with a root-promoting compound (see p. 244), then store them under moist conditions at relatively high temperatures—65° to 70°F. for 4 to 6 weeks to stimulate root initiation. After this, the cuttings may be planted in the nursery (in mild climates) or held in cold storage (35° to 40°F.) until planted in the spring.

Hardwood cuttings (narrow-leaved evergreen species). Cuttings of this type are often slow to root, taking several months to a year or more. Some species root much more readily than others. In general, the *Chamaecyparis* and the low-growing *Juniperus* species root easily, the yews (*Taxus* sp.) fairly well, whereas the upright junipers, the spruces (*Picea* sp.), and hemlocks (*Tsuga* sp.) are more difficult to root. Cuttings of the firs (*Abies* sp.) and pines (*Pinus* sp.) are very difficult to root *(18)*. As with many other plants, cuttings taken from young, juvenile stock plants root much more readily than those taken from older trees *(39)*. Treatments with root-promoting substances, particularly indolebutyric acid (see p. 249), are usually beneficial in increasing the percentage of cuttings rooted and in obtaining heavier root systems (23, 33).

Narrow-leaved evergreen cuttings are best taken when fully dormant in late fall or early winter after the stock plants have experienced one or more sharp frosts. They can be started out-of-doors in cold frames or preferably on benches in the greenhouse (41).

Figure 10–3. Narrow-leaved evergreen cuttings. These rooted juniper cuttings are about five inches long.

The best type of wood to use in making the cuttings varies considerably in this group with the species being rooted. As shown in Figures 10–3 and 10–16, the cuttings are made 4 to 8 inches long with all the leaves removed from the lower half of the cutting. Mature terminal shoots of the previous season's growth are usually used. In some instances, such as with *Juniperus chinensis pfitzeriana,* older and heavier wood can also be used, thus resulting in a larger plant when rooted. In some species, such as *Juniperus excelsa,* older growth taken from the sides and lower portion of the stock plant roots better than the more succulent tips. Cuttings of *Taxus* root best if they are taken with a piece of old wood at the base of the cutting. Such cuttings are also less subject to fungus attacks (40). In most of the narrow-leaved evergreen species, some type of basal wounding (see p. 249) is beneficial in inducing rooting.

Semi-hardwood cuttings. Cuttings of this type are usually made from woody, broad-leaved evergreen species, but leafy summer cuttings taken from partially matured wood of deciduous plants could also be considered as semi-hardwood. Cuttings of broad-leaved evergreen species are generally taken during the summer months from new shoots just after a flush of growth has taken place and the wood is partially matured. Many ornamental shrubs, such as the camellia, pittosporum, euonymus, the evergreen azaleas, and holly are commonly propagated by semi-hardwood cuttings. A few subtropical types of fruit, such as citrus and the olive, can also be started in this manner.

The cuttings are made 3 to 6 inches long with leaves retained at the upper end but removed from the lower end. If the leaves are very large, they should be reduced in size to lower the water loss and to allow closer placing in the cutting bed. The terminal ends of the shoots are often used in making the cuttings, but the more basal parts of the stem will usually root also. The basal cut is usually just below a node. The cutting wood should be obtained in the cool, early morning hours when the stems are turgid, and kept wrapped in moist burlap and out of the sun at all times until the cuttings are made. It is necessary that leafy, semi-hardwood cuttings be rooted under conditions of high humidity; bottom heat and growth regulator treatments are also beneficial (see pp. 18 and 244).

Figure 10–4. Semi-hardwood cuttings as illustrated by the **Camellia.** (above) Cuttings made in late summer from partially-matured wood. (below) Cuttings starting to root.

Softwood (greenwood) cuttings. Cuttings prepared from the soft, succulent, new spring growth of deciduous or evergreen species may properly be classed as softwood cuttings. Many ornamental woody shrubs can be started by softwood cuttings. Typical examples are the hybrid French lilacs, forsythia, magnolia, weigela, and spirea. Some deciduous ornamental trees such as the maples can also be started in this manner. Although fruit tree species are not commonly propagated by softwood cuttings, apple, peach, plum, apricot, and cherry will root, especially under mist (see p. 251).

Softwood cuttings generally root easier and quicker than the other types, but require more attention and equipment. This type of cutting is always made with leaves attached. They must, consequently, be handled carefully to prevent drying and be rooted under conditions of very high humidity.

Figure 10–5. Softwood cuttings of several ornamental species. (above) Cuttings made in late spring from young shoots. (below) Cuttings after rooting. (left to right) Myrtus, Pyracantha, Oleander, and Veronica.

Temperature should be closely observed during rooting, approximating 75° to 80° F. at the base and 70° F. at the leaves for most species. Softwood cuttings produce roots in a fairly short time—2 to 4 or 5 weeks in most cases. They also generally respond markedly to treatments with root-promoting substances (see p. 244).

It is important in making softwood cuttings to obtain the proper type of cutting wood from the stock plant. This will vary greatly, however, with the species being propagated. Extremely fast-growing, soft, tender shoots generally are not desirable, as they are likely to rot before rooting. At the other extreme, old, woody stems are slow to root in most cases. The best cutting material has some degree of flexibility, but is mature enough to break when bent sharply. Weak, thin, interior shoots should be avoided as well as very vigorous, abnormally thick, or heavy ones. Average growth from portions of the plant in full light is the most desirable to use. Some of the best cutting material is the lateral or side branches of the stock plant. Heading back the main shoots will usually force out numerous lateral shoots from which cuttings can be made. Softwood cuttings ordinarily are 3 to 5 inches long with two or more nodes. The basal cut is made just below a node. The leaves on the lower portion of the cutting are removed, but those at the upper portion are retained. If the upper leaves are very large, they should be reduced in size to lower the transpiration rate and to use less space in the propagating bed, although, for the best rooting, it is desirable to retain the maximum leaf area that is possible without wilting. All flower buds should be removed. In some large nurseries where quantities of cuttings are prepared, bundles of cutting material are rapidly chopped into uniform lengths by paper cutters.

The cutting material is best gathered in the early part of the day and should be kept moist, cool, and turgid at all times by wrapping in damp burlap or mixing with moist sphagnum moss or some similar material. Soaking the cuttings in water to keep them fresh is undesirable. Laying the cutting material or prepared cuttings in the sun for even a few minutes will cause serious damage.

Figure 10–6. Typical herbaceous cuttings. (left to right) Chrysanthemum, begonia, and geranium. It is often necessary with large-leaved plants, such as the begonia, to trim back some of the leaves in order to prevent wilting and to conserve space in the propagating bench.

Herbaceous cuttings. This type of leafy cutting is made from such succulent, herbaceous, greenhouse plants as geraniums, chrysanthemums, coleus, and carnations. They are 3 to 5 inches long with leaves retained at the upper end. Most florists' crops are propagated by herbaceous cuttings. They are rooted under the same conditions as softwood cuttings, requiring high humidity. Bottom heat is also helpful. Under proper conditions, rooting is rapid and in high percentages. Although root-promoting substances are beneficial, they are usually unnecessary. Herbaceous cuttings of some plants that exude a milky sap, such as the geranium, pineapple, or cactus, do better if the basal ends are allowed to dry for a few hours in the air before they are inserted in the rooting medium. This allows the wounded tissues to dry and heal over which tends to prevent the entrance of decay organisms.

Figure 10–7. How to make softwood and herbaceous stem cuttings.

(A) Leaves should be trimmed off the lower portion of each cutting. Several upper leaves are retained but if they are very large they should be reduced in size.

(B) With some plants it is desirable to make a clean basal cut with a sharp knife. This is to avoid bruising or injuring the area at the base of the cutting which may provide a start for decay organisms. With other easily-rooted plants this is not important and the basal cut can be made with pruning shears.

(C) While softwood cuttings of many plants root readily, in most cases some stimulation may be obtained by the use of root-promoting chemicals. Here a commercial preparation is used which contains indolebutyric acid dispersed in talc. The base of the cutting is dipped into the powder.

(D) Inserting the cuttings into the rooting medium. The cuttings should be placed far enough apart so as to avoid much over-lapping of the leaves. The cuttings must be kept damp at all times while handling to prevent wilting and should never be laid down in the direct sunlight.

(E) In inserting the cuttings into the rooting medium a short length of 2 x 4 serves to press the medium around the cuttings previously planted and is used as a spacer and guide for the next row. A large butcher knife cuts a narrow slit to aid in inserting the cuttings.

(F) After the cuttings have been inserted in the flat they should be well watered. This is to wet the rooting medium thoroughly and to settle it around the cuttings. Holes in the bottom of the flat provide drainage of any excess water.

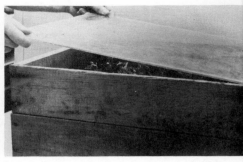

(G) Leafy cuttings should always be rooted under conditions of high humidity. Here a bottomless flat is placed over the original flat and a pane of glass is laid over this.

(H) The glass will let light through to the cuttings and will aid in maintaining high humidity. The flat should be placed in a shady location—never exposed to full sunlight. The cuttings should be lightly sprinkled with water frequently to maintain the humidity at a high level.

Leaf Cuttings

In this type of cutting, the leaf blade or leaf blade and petiole are utilized in starting a new plant. In most cases, adventitious roots and an adventitious shoot (see p. 8) form at the base of the parent leaf. Rarely does this original leaf become a part of the new plant.

One type of propagation by leaf cuttings is illustrated by *Sansevieria*. The long tapering leaves are cut into sections 2 to 3 inches long as shown in Figure 10–8. These leaf pieces are inserted for three-fourths of their length into sand, and after a period of time, a new plant forms at the base of the leaf piece. The original leaf cutting does not become a part of the new plant. The variegated form of *Sansevieria, S. trifasciata laurenti,* is an example of a periclinal chimera (see p. 168) which will not reproduce true to type from leaf cuttings; to retain its characteristics, it must be propagated by division of the original plant.

Figure 10–8. Leaf cuttings of **Sansevieria. (left)** The thick, leathery leaves are cut into pieces 3 or 4 inches long. To avoid trying to root upside down, the basal end can be marked by cutting on a slant as shown with two of the cuttings. **(right)** Development of the plant. The original cutting does not become a part of the new plant.

Figure 10–9. Propagation of **Begonia rex** by leaf cuttings. New plants arise at wounds made in the large veins of the leaf which is laid flat on the surface of the rooting medium.

In starting plants with thick, fleshy leaves, such as *Begonia rex,* by leaf cuttings, the large veins are cut on the undersurface of the mature leaf which is then laid flat on the surface of the propagating medium. The leaf is pinned or held down in some manner, with the natural upper surface of the leaf exposed. As shown in Figure 10–9, after a period of time under shaded, humid conditions, new plants will form at the point each vein was cut. The old leaf blade will gradually dry up.

Another method, sometimes used with the fibrous-rooted begonias, is to cut large, well-matured leaves into triangular sections each containing a piece of a large vein. The thin, outer edge of the leaf is discarded. These leaf pieces are then inserted upright in sand with the pointed end down. The new plant develops from the large vein at the base of the leaf piece. The original leaf dies, not becoming a part of the new plant.

The African violet (*Saintpaulia*) is typical of leaf cuttings which can be made of an entire leaf (leaf blade plus petiole), the leaf blade only, or just a portion of the leaf blade. The new plant forms at the base of the petiole or midrib of the leaf blade.

Figure 10–10. Leaf cuttings of African violet **(Saintpaulia) (above)** and **Peperomia (below). (left)** Each cutting consists of a leaf blade and petiole. **(right)** Leaf cuttings after rooting. One or more new plants will form at the base of the petiole. The original leaf can be cut off and used again for rooting.

Leaf cuttings should be rooted under the same conditions of high humidity that are used for softwood or herbaceous cuttings. Root-promoting chemicals are sometimes helpful *(16)*.

Figure 10–11. Leaf cuttings of **Bryophyllum. (left)** New plants arise from "foliar embryos" in the notches at the margin of the leaf. **(right)** Leaves ready to lay flat on the rooting medium. They should be partially covered or pegged down to hold the leaf margin in close contact with the rooting medium.

Figure 10-12. Boysenberry leaf-bud cuttings. **(top)** Untreated. **(bottom)** Basal ends treated with indolebutyric acid at 4000 parts per million by the concentrated-solution-dip method.

Leaf-Bud Cuttings

This type of cutting consists of a leaf blade, petiole, and a short piece of the stem with the attached axillary bud.

Such cuttings are of particular value for species that are able to initiate roots but not shoots from detached leaves. In such cases, the axillary bud at the base of the petiole provides for the essential shoot formation. A number of plant species such as the black raspberry (*Rubus occidentalis*), blackberry, boysenberry, lemon, camellia, and rhododendron can be readily started by leaf-bud cuttings, as well as many tropical shrubs and most herbaceous greenhouse plants usually started by stem cuttings. Red raspberries *(Rubus idaeus)* apparently do not reproduce by leaf-bud cuttings.

This method is particularly valuable when propagating material is scarce, because it will produce at least twice as many new plants from the same amount of stock material as can be started by stem cuttings. Each node can be used as a cutting. Leaf-bud cuttings should only be made from material having well-developed buds and healthy, actively growing leaves. This method of making cuttings is shown in Figure 10–12.

Treatment of the cut surfaces with one of the root-promoting substances may stimulate root production *(38, 45)*. The cuttings should be inserted in the rooting medium with the bud about ½ inch below the surface. High humidity is essential and bottom heat is desirable for rapid rooting. Clean quartz sand is generally satisfactory as a rooting medium for leaf-bud cuttings, but with some plants, such as rhododendrons and blackberries, a mixture of sand and peat moss may be preferable *(27, 30)*.

For large-scale commercial propagation by this method, the cuttings may be rooted in out-of-door, glass-covered cold frames during the summer months, preferably July, August, and September. Earlier than this, there probably would be insufficient numbers of leaves from the stock plants to provide cutting material in large quantities. Leaf-bud cuttings made later than September may not be rooted before the onset of cold weather *(11)*.

Root Cuttings

The best results are likely to be attained if the cuttings are taken in late winter or early spring when the roots are well supplied with stored foods but before new growth starts. The period during the spring when the parent plant is rapidly making new shoot growth should be avoided.

It should also be remembered that when propagating grafted plants by root cuttings taken below the graft union, the rootstock will be reproduced rather than the top portion of the grafted plant.

Figure 10–13. Root cuttings of the red raspberry. **(left)** Cuttings just made and ready for planting. **(right)** After several weeks in the rooting medium. Adventitious shoots have developed and an extension of the roots is beginning.

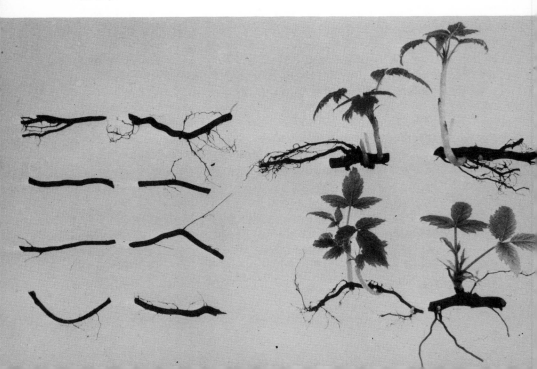

Propagation by root cuttings is very simple, but the best procedure may vary according to the size of the roots of the plant being propagated.

Plants with small, delicate roots. Root cuttings of such plants should be started in flats or shallow boxes of sand or finely screened soil in the greenhouse or hotbed. The roots are cut into short lengths, 1 to 2 inches long, and scattered horizontally over the surface of the soil. They are then covered with a ½ inch layer of fine soil or sand. After watering thoroughly, a pane of glass should be placed over the flat until the plants get started in order to prevent excessive drying. The flats are set in a shaded place, and adventitious shoots will soon develop. After the new plants become well formed, the stronger ones can be transplanted to other flats or lined-out in nursery rows for further growth.

Plants with somewhat fleshy roots, propagated indoors. This type of root cutting is best started in a flat or box of sandy soil in the greenhouse or hotbed. The root pieces should be 2 to 3 inches long and planted vertically. To avoid planting them upside down, the proximal end (nearest the crown of the plant) may be made with a straight cut and the distal end (away from the crown) with a slanting cut. The proximal end of the root piece should always be up. In planting, insert the cutting vertically so that the top is just level with the top of the soil. New adventitious shoots should form rapidly and as soon as the plants become well established with good root development they can be transplanted to their permanent location.

Plants with large roots, propagated out-of-doors. Root cuttings of this type are generally prepared in late fall or winter and are made 2 to 6 inches long. They are tied in bundles, using care to keep the same ends together to avoid planting upside down later. The cuttings are then packed in boxes of moist sand, sawdust, or peat moss until the soil is suitable for planting in the spring. During this storage period, the root cuttings should be kept cool (35° to 40° F.), but not allowed to freeze. The cuttings should be planted in a well prepared nursery soil with the tops of the cuttings level with the top of the soil. It is important in vertical planting that the end of the root cutting which is nearest the crown of the plant be placed up. With some species, it is just as satisfactory to plant the cuttings horizontally about 2 inches deep.

ROOTING MEDIA

Cuttings of many plant species will root so easily that it makes little difference what rooting medium is used. Plants more difficult to root may be greatly influenced by the rooting medium, not only in the percentage of cuttings rooted, but in the type of root system formed *(21)*.

Deciduous hardwood cuttings and root cuttings are ordinarily started in *soil*. A well-aerated sandy loam is usually preferable to a heavy clay soil, a higher percentage of the cuttings forming roots, which are usually of better quality. Also, in the lighter, sandy soils, cuttings may be planted and—after rooting—dug much sooner following rains than when heavy soils are used. The soil should, of course, be free from such organisms as nematodes, *Verticillium,* and crown gall. Soil is usually not considered to be a suitable rooting medium for the more succulent softwood, and semi-hardwood type of cuttings, but some commercial nurserymen have used it very successfully. Cuttings of certain easily rooted plants, such as chrysanthemums and geraniums, are sometimes started directly in small flower pots or plant bands, using a mixture of 2 parts coarse sand to 1 part soil. This mixture preferably should be sterilized before using (see p. 30).

Sand is the most widely accepted rooting medium for cuttings. It is relatively inexpensive and is readily available. Clean, sharp, plaster sand, free from organic matter and soil, such as is usually supplied to the building trade, is excellent. Sand is not as retentive of moisture, however, as some of the other rooting media, necessitating more frequent watering. The sand should be fine enough to retain some moisture around the cuttings yet coarse enough to allow water to drain freely through it. Used alone, very fine particle sand or very coarse sand does not give good results with cuttings of most woody ornamentals. As with other rooting media, it is best to use the sand only once for rooting cuttings unless it can be sterilized (see p. 30).

For such evergreens as the yews, junipers, and the arborvitaes, sand is probably the most satisfactory rooting medium to use. With some species, however, cuttings rooted in sand produce a long, unbranched, brittle root system in contrast to the more desirable fibrous and branched systems developed in other media *(4, 12, 21)*.

Peat moss (see p. 25) is often added to sand in varying proportions, mainly to increase the water-holding capacity of the mixture. This combination makes an excellent rooting medium for cuttings of most species. Mixtures used vary from 2 parts sand to 1 of peat moss to 1 part sand to 3 parts of peat moss.

Including peat moss in a rooting medium increases the water-holding capacity of the mixture considerably and consequently the danger of overwatering. High proportions of peat moss in the mixture, if kept too wet, will sometimes cause rotting of the roots soon after they are formed.

Shredded sphagnum moss (see p. 25) is sometimes used as a rooting medium for stem, leaf, and root cuttings when mixed with an equal part of sand *(7)*.

Vermiculite (see p. 25) is widely used as a rooting medium. Tests *(5, 24)* have shown that cuttings of a number of plants root better in the larger particle sizes, whereas some do better in the smaller sizes. A mixture of equal parts of vermiculite and a medium grade sand sometimes gives more satisfactory results than either one of these materials used alone.

There are several other proprietary materials especially prepared for rooting cuttings. These are mostly mineral ore derivatives that have been expanded by heat and graded to uniform particle size. Some of these may eventually come into wide use for rooting cuttings but will probably have their best application when mixed with other materials, such as peat moss, sand, or vermiculite.

Water has long been used for small scale rooting of cuttings of easily propagated species. Its great disadvantage is lack of aeration. Tests have shown that by artificially aerating water with air or oxygen, excellent rooting of cuttings of some species can be obtained *(28, 46)*. In aerated water, the best roots are produced near the basal end of the cuttings, whereas in nonaerated water, the best roots are produced on the cuttings near the surface of the water where the oxygen content is higher. Sufficient oxygen may be supplied by the use of running tap water.

Moisture-saturated air can possibly be used as a rooting medium by placing cuttings in closed frames in which the relative humidity is maintained close to 100 per cent. This method has resulted in satisfactory root formation with some plants and is especially successful with root cuttings *(26, 31)*.

WOUNDING

In a number of plant species, root production on stem cuttings is markedly promoted by wounding the base of the cutting. Cuttings of juniper, arborvitae, rhododendron, maple, magnolia, and holly species seem to be greatly helped by basal wounding. There are several ways of making the wounds. In preparing cuttings of some of the narrow-leaved evergreen species, such as arborvitae, stripping off the lower side branches of the cuttings produces satisfactory wounds. A simple vertical cut with a tip of a sharp knife down each side of the cutting, for an inch or two, penetrating through the bark and into the wood may be enough. A more drastic wound is made with a razor blade device. This consists of 4 single-edge blades soldered together along their backs. Four wound cuts are then made simultaneously with this equipment.

Larger cuttings, such as would be made with magnolias, may be more effectively wounded by removing a thin slice of bark down each side of the cutting, exposing the cambium but not cutting deeply into the wood. For the greatest benefits, immediately after wounding the cuttings should be treated with one of the root-promoting compounds, either a talc or a concentrated-solution-dip preparation (see p. 247), working the material into the wounds.

DIRECTIONS FOR TREATING CUTTINGS WITH GROWTH REGULATORS

The purpose of treating cuttings with "hormones," or more correctly termed, plant growth regulators, is to increase the percentage of cuttings which form roots, hasten root initiation, and increase the number of roots produced per cutting (see p. 208). Plants whose cuttings root very easily present no problem, and the additional expense and effort of using these materials is not justified. The best use of these materials is with plant species that can be propagated by cuttings, but with difficulty. The use of these root-promoting substances, however, does not permit the other good practices in cutting propagation, such as the maintenance of proper humidity, temperature, and light conditions, to be ignored. The value of these chemicals in propagation is well established, as shown by the tremendous number of reports in the scientific journals of tests made on the rooting of cuttings of almost all plant species of economic importance *(25, 35)*. Although treatments of cuttings with root-promoting substances are useful in the propagation of plants, the ultimate size and vigor of such treated plants seem to be no better than occurs with untreated plants *(6)*.

Materials

The synthetic root-promoting chemicals that have been found to be the most reliable in stimulating adventitious root production in cuttings are indolebutyric acid, naphthaleneacetic acid, and indoleacetic acid although there are others which can be used (see p. 209). Indolebutyric acid is probably the best material for general use, because it is nontoxic over a wide range of concentrations and is effective in promoting rooting of a large number of plant species. Some of these chemicals are available in commercial preparations dispersed in a powder (usually talc) into which the base of the cutting is dipped before inserting into the rooting medium.

Figure 10—14. Methods of wounding cuttings. **(top)** Use of razor blade tool (four single-edge blades soldered together along top). **(center)** Wounding with point of knife. **(bottom)** Making a heavy wound by slicing off a section of bark and wood.

The pure chemicals are also available from several chemical manufacturers so that it is possible for the propagator to prepare his own solutions.

Methods of Application

Commercial powder preparations. Complete directions come with these materials together with a list of plants which are likely to respond to the particular preparation. The woody, difficult-to-root species should be treated with the more concentrated preparations, whereas the more tender, succulent, and easily rooted species should be used with lower strength preparations. Fresh cuts should be made at the base of the cuttings shortly before they are dipped into the powder. The operation is speeded up if a bundle of cuttings is dipped at once rather than each cutting individually, although the inner cuttings in the bundle may not receive as much powder as those on the outside. The powder adhering to the cuttings after they are lightly tapped is expected to be sufficient to produce the desired effect. If there is little or no natural moisture at the base of the cuttings, they may be immersed in water or pressed against a damp sponge before dipping in the powder, thus causing more to adhere.

It is advisable in using these powder preparations to remove a small portion of the stock material, sufficient for the work at hand, and discard any remaining portion, rather than to dip the cuttings into the entire stock of powder, which may lead to its early deterioration due to contamination with foreign material and moisture.

A satisfactory method is to spread a thin film of the powder on a piece of waxpaper or aluminum foil. A convenient sized handful of cuttings is then dipped and rotated in the powder after the bases are evened.

The cuttings should be inserted into the rooting medium immediately after treatment. To avoid brushing off the powder during insertion, a thick knife may be used to make a trench in the rooting medium before the cuttings are inserted.

The commercial talc preparations have the advantage of being readily available and easy to use, but uniform results may be difficult to obtain due to the variability in the amount of the material adhering to the cutting. This is influenced by such factors as the amount of moisture at the base of the cutting and the texture of the stem—hairy or smooth.

Dilute solution soaking method. The basal 1 inch of the cuttings are soaked in a dilute solution of the material for about 24 hours just before they are inserted into the rooting medium. Such solutions are not difficult to prepare. The concentrations used vary from about 20 ppm for easily rooted species to about 200 ppm for the more difficult species.

To prepare 100 cc. of a 100 ppm solution of a root-promoting substance, 10 mgs. of the pure chemical is dissolved in a few drops of alcohol. To this add 100 cc. of water. Naphthaleneacetic acid dissolves best in a few drops of ammonium hydroxide before adding to the water. The acid form of these growth substances is not directly soluble in water.

An approximate 100 ppm solution of indolebutyric acid can be prepared by dissolving a level 1/4 teaspoonful of the chemical in a small amount of alcohol and adding to 1 gal. of water, stirring thoroughly.

During the soaking period, the cuttings should be held at ordinary room temperature but not placed in the sun. The amount of the chemical absorbed by the cuttings depends somewhat upon the surrounding conditions during this period, which may lead to some variation in the results obtained.

Concentrated-solution-dip method. A concentrated solution of the chemical in alcohol is prepared (500 to 10,000 ppm) and the basal ends of the cuttings are dipped in it for a short time (about five seconds), and then the cuttings are inserted immediately into the rooting medium. This method of application has a number of advantages over the others. It eliminates the necessity of providing equipment for soaking the cuttings and returning later to insert them in the rooting medium. In addition, more uniform results are likely to be obtained, because the uptake of the chemical by the cuttings is not influenced as much by surrounding conditions as is the case with the other two methods. The same solution can be used over and over for many thousands of cuttings, but it must be tightly sealed when not in use, because the evaporation of the alcohol will change its strength. It is best to use only a portion of the material at a time, just sufficient for the immediate needs, discarding it after use rather than pouring it back into the stock solution.

To prepare 100 cc. of a 4000 ppm solution of a root-promoting substance, weigh out 400 mgs. of the chemical and dissolve it in 100 cc. of 50 per cent alcohol.

An approximate 4000 ppm solution of indolebutyric acid can be prepared by dissolving a level 1/4 teaspoon of the pure crystals in 3-1/3 fluid ounces of 50 per cent alcohol.

Growth regulators used in excessive concentrations for the species may result in injury. This may merely inhibit bud development *(6),* or it may cause yellowing and dropping of leaves, blackening of the stem, and eventual death of the cuttings. An effective, nontoxic concentration has been used if the basal portion of the stem shows some swelling, accompanied by profuse root production just above the base of the cutting. Usually, a concentration just below the toxic point is considered to be the most favorable for root promotion.

Some of the negative results obtained in using growth regulators as an aid in rooting cuttings may have occurred due to the use of old or deteriorated chemicals. A simple test using tomato leaf cuttings makes it possible to determine in a few days whether the preparation planned for use still retains its root-promoting properties *(15).* Tomato leaf cuttings, of the type shown in Figure 10–15, are treated with the material, then inserted in moist sand in a glass-covered box together with a group of untreated cuttings for comparison. At the end of a week, the cuttings should be observed. Tomato cuttings are very sensitive to growth regulators and will give a good indication of the effectiveness of the material by the extent of their root production.

Figure 10–15. Tomato leaf cuttings provide a sensitive test for the effectiveness of root-promoting substances. **(left to right)** **(1)** No treatment; **(2)** treated with indolebutyric acid in talc at 1000 parts per million; **(3)** at 3000 ppm; and **(4)** at 8000 ppm. Marglobe variety after 12 days in sand.

The use of fresh preparations is advisable whenever possible. Dilute solutions (such as 25 to 50 ppm) of indoleacetic or indolebutyric acid are likely to lose their activity within a few days, especially if they become contaminated with foreign material. Growth-regulator preparations dispersed in talc will keep their activity for several months, whereas the solutions used in the concentrated-solution-dip method of application, which contain a high percentage of alcohol, will retain their activity almost indefinitely.

RESPONSE OF PLANTS TO TREATMENTS WITH ROOT-PROMOTING SUBSTANCES

Herbaceous plants. Cuttings of most plants of this type have shown a definite increase in rooting when treated with growth regulators. The chief effect has been to speed the rate of rooting and to produce heavier clumps of roots. Plants which have shown good response include chrysanthemums, geraniums, carnations, begonias, poinsettias, English ivy, and African violets. Cuttings of such herbaceous plants usually root so easily under proper care without growth-regulator treatments, however, that it is debatable whether their use is justified.

Broad-leaved evergreens. Propagation of this type of plant, by softwood or semi-hardwood cuttings, is often considerably improved by growth-regulator treatments, provided the other necessary requirements for rooting are satisfied. The citrus species—orange, lemon, and grapefruit—as well as the olive are evergreen tree fruits that respond well to treatment. A great many ornamentals in this group have also given good response, including the camellia, holly, rhododendron, box, daphne, euonymus, gardenia, oleander, escallonia, pittosporum, and pyracantha.

Narrow-leaved evergreens. Reports are quite variable concerning the benefits of the use of root-promoting chemicals with this type of plant. For most species, however, if the cuttings are taken at the right time of year, and the proper material and concentration used, improved results can be expected. Species found to respond to treatments include the fir, juniper, spruce, pine, yew, arborvitae, and hemlock.

Deciduous plants. Cuttings may be made of this type of plant either as hardwood cuttings during the dormant season or softwood cuttings during the active growing period. Experience has shown that in most cases the response to growth-regulator treatments is greater with softwood cuttings than with the dormant hardwood cuttings. Plants of this type that have responded to treatments include the apple, apricot, pear, peach, plum, filbert, cherry, maple, birch, beech, and mulberry.

ENVIRONMENTAL CONDITIONS FOR ROOTING LEAFY CUTTINGS*

For the successful rooting of leafy cuttings, the essential environmental requirements are proper temperature (65° to 75° F.), a very humid

---

* Also see page 212.

Figure 10–16. Effect of wounding and auxin treatment on the rooting of cuttings of **Juniperus sabina tamariscifolia** under intermittent mist in the greenhouse. **(top)** Wounded. **(bottom)** Not wounded. **(left)** Treated with indolebutyric acid at 4000 ppm by the concentrated-dip method. **(center)** Treated with indolebutyric acid in talc, at 8000 ppm. **(right)** Not treated. Cuttings started March 5, dug April 23.

atmosphere, ample light, and a clean, moist, well-aerated, and well-drained rooting medium. There are many possible types of equipment that are satisfactory for providing these conditions—from a simple fruit jar placed over a few cuttings stuck in sand to elaborate greenhouse benches with automatic humidity control and automatically controlled electric soil cables below the cuttings. Probably one of the simplest devices, which is entirely satisfactory for rooting a limited number of cuttings, is an ordinary wooden box with a pane of glass or a sheet of polyethylene film over the top. If this is placed in a heated room in the winter under a window, cuttings of many species can be rooted in it. Such a box can also be used successfully in the summer for rooting cuttings of some plants, if placed out-of-doors in the shade. Cuttings of some plants can be rooted successfully with only artificial light, if placed under an ordinary large fluorescent lamp fixture (see p. 21).

In commercial operations, large-scale rooting of leafy cuttings is done in hotbeds, cold frames, or in beds in greenhouses or plastic houses. In these structures, proper humidity and temperature conditions can be maintained and controlled (see Chapter 2).

PREPARING THE ROOTING FRAME AND INSERTING THE CUTTINGS

The frames or benches should preferably be raised or, if on the ground, equipped with drainage tile, so there is never any question of perfect drainage of excess water.

The frames should be deep enough so that at least 6 inches of rooting medium can be used. Several days before the cuttings are to be inserted, the bench should be prepared. This consists of filling it with the desired

Figure 10–17. Polyethylene plastic sheeting can be used for starting cuttings of easily-rooted species. The basal ends of the cuttings are inserted in damp sphagnum or peat moss and rolled in the polyethylene as shown here. The roll of cuttings should then be set upright in a very humid location for rooting.

material (see p. 241) to a depth of about 5 inches, leveling with a flat board, and firming it in place with slight pressure. The final depth should be enough so that an average length cutting—4 or 5 inches—can be inserted to at least half its total length and still have the end of the cutting an inch or more above the bottom of the frame. The rooting medium should be watered thoroughly at this time.

After the cuttings have been made, they should be inserted in the bed as soon as possible. It is very important that the cuttings be protected from drying at all stages during their preparation and insertion. A convenient method of holding the cuttings until insertion in the rooting medium is to place them in shallow boxes or flats covered with damp burlap.

A satisfactory method of inserting the cuttings is to lay a narrow wood strip—1½ to 3 inches wide—cut to the width of the bed, on top of the rooting medium. A flat, wide-bladed knife is drawn along the edge of this wood strip deeply into the medium. The cuttings may then be set into this narrow cut, spaced so the leaves just touch. After one row is finished, the wood strip is gently pushed down to firm the medium against the row of cuttings. It is then lifted and moved to the other side of the inserted row and the process repeated. Each time the strip is pressed down, firming the rooting medium against the cuttings. If vermiculite is used, the firming should be very gentle, because this material loses its structure if compressed when wet.

After a section of the rooting bench is filled, it is thoroughly watered. The cuttings are "flooded-in" with a large volume, low pressure sprinkler head. This completely settles the rooting medium around the cuttings, especially at their bases, rather than leaving them suspended in a hole.

MIST SYSTEMS FOR ROOTING CUTTINGS
(8, 10, 29, 32, 42, 43, 44) *

In the propagation of plants by leafy cuttings, one of the chief problems is to maintain the cuttings without wilting until roots are produced. This is ordinarily accomplished by keeping the relative humidity of the air surrounding the cuttings at a high level. Sprinkling the foliage, benches, and floors by hand several times a day during the rooting period is a usual practice in greenhouses to assist in maintaining a high humidity. Automatic control of the humidity by various types of mechanical humidifiers is of considerable value where quantities of cuttings are to be rooted in the greenhouse (2).

---

* Also see page 212.

A type of humidity control, which also incorporates other advantages, is the practice of rooting leafy cuttings under *water mist sprays*. This provides a film of water over the leaves, which lowers their temperature, reduces transpiration, and with many species results in better rooting.

This mist technique enables the rooting of cuttings of plants previously considered to be very difficult or impossible to root. This is probably true because it permits the use of soft, succulent, fast-growing cutting material early in the season which, in some species, is much more likely to root than older, more mature, hardened wood.

Mist beds can be built either in a greenhouse for use in summer and winter, or out-of-doors in a lath house or in open sun for use during the warmer months of the year. Over these beds, nozzles are placed which produce a fine fog-like mist spaced so as to give complete coverage of the bed.

Installation. Two basic types of spray nozzles are: (a) the oil burner, whirling action type, and (b) the deflection type.

The oil burner nozzle produces an evenly distributed, fine spray and uses a relatively small amount of water. The mist is produced in this nozzle by water passing through small grooves set at an angle to each other. A modification of the oil burner nozzle is the self-cleaning type in which a spring-loaded pin cleans the aperture each time the nozzle shuts off.

The deflection nozzle develops a mist by a fine stream of water striking

Figure 10–18. Mist beds for rooting leafy cuttings. (above) Bed in open sun with overhead nozzles. (below) Bed in lath house with nozzles directed upward.

a flat surface. The larger aperture used in this type greatly reduces clogging but uses considerably more water. This nozzle covers a larger area than the oil burner type so that fewer need to be used. It also operates on a low water pressure more effectively than the oil burner type. Some makes can be shut off individually which facilitates working in the propagating beds.

There are various possible methods of placing the water pipes to which the nozzles are attached. One is to lay the main feeder pipe down the center of the bed, either below, at, or above the surface of the rooting medium, with the nozzles at the end of risers from this pipe. Another method is to place the feeder pipe well above the cuttings—either one pipe down the center of the bed or two pipes, one along each side—with the nozzles directed downward into the bed. Whatever arrangement is used, the nozzles should be placed close enough together and the water pressure should be high enough so that the entire bed is completely under the mist. Unless the mist actually wets the leaves, rooting is likely to be unsatisfactory.

In outdoor installations, some type of protection, such as shown in Figure 10–18, is usually necessary around the bed to prevent strong winds

Figure 10–19. Two basic types of nozzles used in mist propagation systems. **(left)** Deflection type. **(right)** Whirling action type. Nozzles taken apart in lower view showing filter screens.

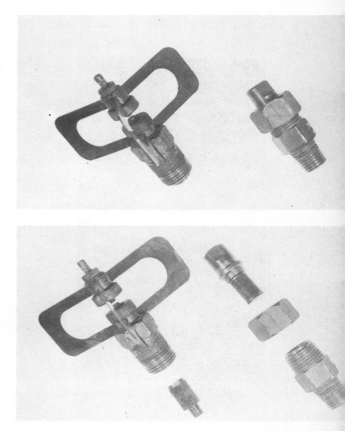

from blowing the mist away and drying the cuttings. In some of the early installations, the mist operated continuously; later, it was found that better results were generally obtained by shutting the water off at night. Further tests *(14)* showed that even during the daylight hours, interrupted mist, which supplied water at intervals frequent enough to keep a film of water on the leaves, gave better results than constant mist. Obviously, it being impractical to turn the mist on and off by hand, electrical control devices became necessary. Several types are available, all operating to control a magnetic solenoid valve inserted in the water line to the nozzles.

Controls. In a mist installation, especially the outdoor type, damage to the cuttings will result if the leaves are allowed to become dry for very long. Even 10 minutes without water on a hot, sunny day can be disastrous. In setting up the control system to provide an intermittent mist, every precaution should be taken to guard against accidental failure of the mist applications. This includes the use of a "normally-open" solenoid valve— that is, one constructed so that when electric power is not connected, the valve is open and water passes through it. Application of electricity closes the valve and shuts off the water. Then, if an accidental power failure occurs or any failure in the electrical control mechanism takes place, the mist

Figure 10–20. Commercial out-of-door mist installation for rooting cuttings. Courtesy C. W. Stuart and Co., Inc., Newark, New York State.

would just remain on continuously and no damage to the cuttings would result. On the other hand, in using a normally-closed solenoid, which requires an electric current to open it and allow the passage of water, any failure of the power would mean complete stoppage of the mist and, if not detected very soon, a possible total loss of the cuttings.

Electrically operated timer mechanisms are available commercially which will operate the mist as desired. A successful type uses two timers acting together—one turns the entire system on in the morning and off at night; the second timer operates the system during the daylight hours to produce an intermittent mist—at any desired combination of timing intervals, such as 40 seconds ON and 60 seconds OFF. This type of control mechanism is relatively foolproof, and although it does not automatically compensate for variations in humidity conditions, it can be adjusted closely enough to give entirely satisfactory results. Various types of time clocks can be easily constructed or purchased for regulating the application of water *(13, 20)*.

In another type of control mechanism, the so-called electronic "leaf," a small piece of plastic containing two terminals is placed under the mist along with the cuttings as shown in Figure 10–21 *(14, 34)*. Wires from the terminals lead to the control box. When a film of water covers the plastic, permitting electrical contact between the terminals, the solenoid valve is activated and the mist is shut off. When the film of water evaporates so that there is no electrical connection, the mist is turned on by the solenoid. As soon as the plastic leaf is again wet, the mist is again shut off. In practice, the ON period may vary from a few seconds to several minutes. This would, theoretically, maintain a film of water on the leaves of the cuttings at all times, automatically compensating for changes in the evaporating power of the air. This system can be used with either a normally-open or normally-closed solenoid valve. The behavior of this type of control varies considerably according to the placement of the leaf in the propagating bed. In out-of-door installations where considerable drifting of the mist is caused by the wind, it sometimes becomes quite difficult to place the leaf properly so that it will provide the desired amount of mist. A disadvantage of the electronic leaf appears in areas having water of a high mineral content. Salt deposits will gradually accumulate between the contact points, thus completing the circuit and keeping the water off. This can be overcome by disconnecting the power source from the leaf and scraping this precipitate from the plastic. This system uses much less water than the other methods.

Other types of controls have been tried for providing an interrupted mist, such as humidistats and units based on the action of a photoelectric cell. Satisfactory results have been obtained with a control unit whose action depends upon the alternate evaporation from and the absorption of water by a hollow, porous clay globe (a Livingston atmometer) *(22)*.

Figure 10–21. Electronic "leaf" (indicated by arrow) installed in a mist propagating bed. Water on the "leaf" contacts the two terminal points completing a circuit to the control unit thus shutting off the mist. When the water on the "leaf" evaporates, the circuit is opened to the control unit which then turns on the mist, again wetting the "leaf," repeating the cycle.

The hazard of electrical shock should always be kept in mind when working with any electrical control unit in a mist bed where considerable water is present. The complete installation should be done by a competent electrician.

Operation. Difficulties may arise in operating a mist propagation bed. One of these is lack of sufficient water pressure to operate the nozzles properly. This can be overcome by installing a small electrically operated rotary booster pump between the water source and the solenoid valve.

If there is much sand in the water, it is advisable to install filters in the supply line, which will reduce the clogging of the strainers in the nozzles. Figure 10–22 shows two such filters in parallel in an installation where the water carried an excessive amount of sand.

In propagating cuttings under mist, it is essential that a well-drained

water supply line

two filters in parallel

rotary booster pump

electric motor

solenoid valve line to mist be

oneway valve in bypass line

supply line to second mist be

Figure 10–22. Water pipe connections for an intermittent mist installation. Two filters in parallel may be used if the water has a high sand content. A booster pump may be necessary if water pressures are low. Installed in the line this pump gave 60 to 70 lbs. pressure which is desirable for good misting by the nozzles. A by-pass valve around the pump permits normal pressures if the pump is not in operation. A solenoid valve operated by the control timer is in the line going to the mist bed.

rooting medium be used and the bed raised, equipped with drainage tile, or otherwise provided for adequate removal of any excess water.

Hardening off. Moving the rooted cuttings from the very moist conditions under mist to a dryer environment presents a considerable problem and must be carefully done. With some plants, *Prunus* sp. for example, it seems to be essential to remove the cuttings immediately from the mist once they are rooted. Otherwise, rapid defoliation and deterioration of the roots occurs.

There are several possible ways of successfully taking the rooted cuttings from the mist conditions: (a) The cuttings may be left in place in the mist bed but with the duration of the misting periods gradually decreased, either by lessening the ON periods and increasing the OFF periods or by leaving the misting intervals the same but gradually decreasing the time the mist is in operation each day. (b) In some operations, the rooted cuttings are left in place and allowed to send their roots on through the rooting medium to the soil beneath. The propagating frame may then be moved to a different location to root another set of cuttings. (c) Another possibility is to root the cuttings in flats and move the flats after rooting to another mist frame where they are "hardened off." In these methods, the cuttings may be left in place until the dormant season, when they can be dug more safely, to either be lined-out in the nursery row for further growth or potted and brought into the greenhouse. If the rooted cuttings are left in the rooting medium for a considerable time, it may be advisable to water them at intervals with a nutrient solution (see p. 33). Mist systems have been successfully used in which soluble fertilizers are injected into the mist line thus feeding the cuttings during and after the rooting period *(36)*. (d) Some propagators root the cuttings directly in wood plant bands set up in flats. After rooting, the plants may then be easily removed for transplanting without disturbing the roots. (e) Another method is to pot the cuttings immediately after rooting and hold them for a time in a humid, shaded location, e.g., a fog chamber, closed frame, or greenhouse.

It is a common experience to have the buds of cuttings that are rooted under mist enter an apparent dormant or physiological rest condition in which they do not continue further growth that season even though they are well rooted.

CARE OF CUTTINGS DURING ROOTING

Hardwood stem cuttings or root cuttings started out-of-doors in the nursery row require only the usual care given to other crop plants, such as adequate soil moisture, freedom from weed competition, and insect and disease control. The best results with most species are likely to be obtained if the nursery is established in full sun where shading and root competition from large trees or shrubbery do not occur.

Leafy softwood or semi-hardwood stem cuttings and leaf-bud or leaf cuttings being rooted under high humidity require close attention throughout the rooting period. The temperature should be controlled carefully. The cuttings must not be allowed to show wilting for any length of time. Glass-covered frames, exposed even for a few hours to strong sunlight, will build up excessively high and injurious temperatures due to the radiant heat accumulating under the glass. Such equipment should always be protected by cloth screens, whitewash on the glass, or some other method of reducing the light intensity.

If bottom heat is provided, thermometers should be inserted in the rooting medium to the level of the base of the cutting and checked at frequent intervals, especially at first. A temperature of 65° to 75°F. at the base of the cuttings is desirable. Excessively high temperatures in the rooting medium even for a short time are likely to result in death of the cuttings.

It is very important to maintain humidity conditions as high as possible in rooting leafy cuttings. Syringing the leaves with a spray nozzle at frequent intervals is a common practice especially during hot weather. Although more time consuming, several light sprinklings with water each day are better than heavy soakings at less frequent intervals. A nozzle should be used that breaks the water into a fine mist. Provision for automatic mist applications is highly desirable where large scale propagation operations are involved. A drop of the humidity to a low level with a consequent pronounced wilting of the cuttings, if prolonged for any length of time, may so injure the cuttings that rooting will not occur, even though high humidity conditions are subsequently resumed.

Although high humidity in the propagating frame is important while roots are forming, it is also necessary that adequate drainage be provided so that excess water can escape and not cause the rooting medium to become soggy and waterlogged. When peat or sphagnum moss is used as a component of the rooting medium, it is especially important to see that it does not become excessively wet.

It is also necessary to maintain sanitary conditions in the propagating frame. Leaves that drop should be removed promptly, as well as any obviously dead cuttings. If difficulty is experienced with infection of the leaves by decay producing organisms, it may prove helpful to dip the cuttings before rooting into a mild fungicide solution, such as Fermate (1 tbs. to 1 gal. of water). Spraying the entire cutting bed with a fungicide, such as Semesan, shortly after the cuttings are inserted and several additional times during the rooting period is helpful in controlling fungus diseases. Organisms find ideal conditions in a highly humid, closed propagating frame with a low light intensity and, if not controlled, can destroy thousands of cuttings overnight.

If insects, such as red spiders, aphids, or mealy bugs, appear on the leaves of the cuttings immediate control measures are necessary.

HANDLING CUTTINGS AFTER ROOTING

Hardwood Cuttings

Rooted hardwood cuttings in the nursery row are usually dug during the dormant season after the leaves have dropped. With fast growing species, the cuttings may be sufficiently large to dig after one season's growth. Slower growing species may require 2 or even 3 years to become large enough to transplant.

The digging should take place on cool, cloudy days, when there is no wind. If possible, digging should not be done when the soil is wet, especially if it has a high clay content. Most of the soil should drop readily from the roots after the plants are removed. After the plants are dug, they should be quickly heeled-in in a convenient location or else replanted immediately in their permanent location. "Heeling-in" is to place dug, bare-rooted deciduous nursery plants close together in trenches with the roots well covered. This is a temporary provision for holding the young plants until they can be set out in their permanent location.

Commercial nurseries often store quantities of deciduous plants for several months in cool, dark rooms with the roots protected by damp wood shavings, shingle tow, or some similar material. Nursery stock to be kept for extended periods should be held under refrigerated conditions at 32° to 35°F.

If only a few plants are to be removed from the nursery row they can be dug with shovels, but in large-scale nursery operations some type of mechanical digger, such as shown in Figure 10–24, is generally used, which

Figure 10–23. Method of "heeling in" large quantities of dormant nursery stock in wood shavings or similar material.

"undercuts" the plants. This is a sharp U-shaped blade, which travels 1 to 2 feet below the soil surface under the nursery row, cutting through the roots. Sometimes a horizontal "lifting" blade is attached to and travels behind the cutting blade. This slightly lifts the plants out of the soil, making them easy to pull by hand.

Figure 10–24. A large, specially constructed power digger used for "under-cutting" rows of nursery stock in a commercial nursery. After the roots are cut with the large U-shaped blade the trees can be pulled out by hand. Courtesy Oki Nursery, Sacramento, Calif.

Unless very small, plants of evergreen species usually cannot be successfully handled bare-rooted, as is done with dormant and leafless deciduous plants. The presence of leaves on evergreen plants requires the continuous contact of the roots with soil. Therefore, large, salable plants of broad- or narrow-leaved evergreens and occasionally deciduous plants are either grown in containers or dug and sold "balled and burlapped." By

Plants ready to be moved and transplanted. This method is widely used for all types of evergreen plants which have not been grown in containers.

Burlap is wrapped around soil ball and tied with heavy cord.

Plant is carefully removed with a ball of soil adhering to the roots. Soil must be at proper moisture level so it does not fall apart.

Figure 10–25. Steps in "ball and burlapping" nursery stock, being used here in digging "tree" roses.

the latter method, the plants are removed from the soil by carefully digging a trench around each individual. The soil mass around the roots is sometimes tapered at top and bottom, resulting in a ball of soil in which the roots are embedded. It is important that the soil be at the proper moisture level—not too wet and not too dry—otherwise it will fall apart. The ball is tipped gently onto a large square of burlap, which is then pulled tightly and sewed in place with heavy twine. If properly done, this adequately holds the soil to the roots and the plant can then be moved safely for considerable distances and replanted successfully.

Softwood, Herbaceous, Semi-Hardwood, Leaf-Bud, Leaf-Cuttings

Cuttings such as these, rooted with leaves attached and under conditions of high humidity, require considerable care in being removed from the rooting medium. After rooting has started, the humidity should be lowered and ventilation of the bed provided. They should be dug as soon as a substantial root system with secondary roots has formed. Many propagators have experienced rapid rooting of cuttings only to have them die when they are dug and potted. Sometimes this trouble may be overcome by leaving the cuttings in the rooting bed longer, until after the first-formed primary roots have branched to develop a dense, fibrous, secondary root system to which the rooting medium clings in a ball.

Most of the rooting media used contain little or no mineral nutrients available to the plants, hence the cuttings are dependent upon the nutrients already stored in the stems and leaves at the time the cuttings were made. This is generally sufficient to maintain the cuttings during the period of root formation. With some species, however, it may be helpful to water the cuttings with a nutrient solution about 10 days before they are to be removed, especially if digging has been delayed until a secondary root system has developed.

If for any reason the cuttings are to be kept for a prolonged period in the rooting medium, they should be watered several times with a nutrient solution (see p. 33).

In digging, the cuttings should be lifted gently from the rooting medium with a trowel or some similar device, taking care not to break off the roots. It is desirable for the cuttings to be lifted out with a mass of the rooting medium still adhering to the roots. This can be done if some material such as peat moss or vermiculite is included in the rooting medium. The cuttings are ready for potting when most of the roots are 1 to 2 inches long. (See page 26 for potting mixtures.)

Often, when cuttings are well rooted, field conditions are such that they cannot be planted. It is possible to hold rooted cuttings of some species in polyethylene bags for prolonged periods under cold storage. Temperatures of 35° to 40°F. seem to be the most suitable *(37)*.

The rooted cuttings should be watered thoroughly shortly after potting. It is very important that potted cuttings be moved gradually from the protected conditions under which they were rooted (high humidity, low light intensity) to out-of-doors conditions (low humidity, high light intensity, and wind). It is often best to leave the cuttings for several days after they have been potted under the same conditions in which they were rooted. If they were rooted in mist, they must be given especially close attention and moved gradually to the dryer atmosphere. Before placing the rooted cuttings in full sun, they should be hardened-off for 1 or 2 weeks in a cold frame or lathhouse or under some partial protection from the sun (see p. 19).

REFERENCES

1. Akamine, E. K., Effect of 2,4-dichlorophenoxyacetic acid on root development in bean cotyledons, *Science, 108*:209. 1948.
2. Bailey, V. K., Controlled humidity in greenhouses, *Proc. 4th Ann. Mtg. Plant Prop. Soc.,* pp. 121–128. 1954.
3. Bioletti, F. T., Selection of planting stock for vineyards, *Hilgardia, 2*:1–23. 1926.
4. Chadwick, L. C., Studies in plant propagation, *Cornell Agr. Exp. Sta. Bul. 571, 1933.*
5. ————, The effect of certain mediums and watering methods on the rooting of cuttings of some deciduous and evergreen plants, *Proc. Amer. Soc. Hort. Sci., 53*:555–566. 1949.
6. Chadwick, L. C., and D. C. Kiplinger, The effect of synthetic growth substances on the rooting and subsequent growth of ornamental plants, *Proc. Amer. Soc. Hort. Sci., 36*:809–816. 1938.
7. Creech, J. L., R. F. Dowdle, and W. O. Hawley, Sphagnum moss for plant propagation, *USDA Farmers' Bul. 2085, 1955.*
8. Fillmore, R. H., Open frame propagation of cuttings under mist, *Amer. Nurs., 100*(4):12–13, 67. 1954.
9. Erickson, L. C., and P. DeBach, Rooting lemon cuttings with fruit attached, *Science, 117*:102–103. 1953.
10. Gardner, E. J., Propagation under mist, *Amer. Nurs., 73*(9):5–7. 1941.
11. Garner, R. J., and D. H. Hammond, "Leaf-bud" propagation of loganberry, youngberry, and blackberries, *Gard. Chron.,* 105 (Ser. B):9–11. 1939.
12. Hartmann, H. T., Further studies in the propagation of the olive by cuttings, *Proc. Amer. Soc. Hort. Sci., 59*:155–160. 1952.
13. Hess, C. E., and W. E. Snyder, A simple and inexpensive time clock for regulating mist in plant propagation procedures, *Proc. 3rd Ann. Mtg. Plant Prop. Soc.,* pp. 56–61. 1953.
14. ————, Interrupted mist found superior to constant mist in tests with cuttings, *Amer. Nurs., 100*(12):11–12, 82. 1954.
15. Hitchcock, A. E., and P. W. Zimmerman, The use of green tissue test objects for

determining the physiological activity of growth substances, *Contrib. Boyce Thomp. Inst.,* 9:463–518. 1938.

16. Joyner, J. F., et al., The vegetative propagation of *Sansevieria, Agron. Jour.,* 43:128–130. 1951.

17. Knight, R. C., and A. W. Witt, The propagation of fruit tree stocks by stem cuttings, *Jour. Pom. and Hort. Sci.,* 5:248–266; 6:47–60. 1926, 1927.

18. Kumlien, L. L., *The Friendly Evergreens.* Dundee, Ill.: D. Hill Nursery, 1946.

19. LaRue, C. D., Root formation on flowers in sterile culture, *Amer. Jour. Bot.,* 24:739. 1937.

20. Langhans, R. W., Mist propagation and growing, *N.Y. State Flower Growers' Bul. 103,* March, 1954.

21. Long, J. C., The influence of rooting media on the character of the roots produced by cuttings, *Proc. Amer. Soc. Hort. Sci.,* 29:352–355. 1932.

22. May, C., and E. Hacskaylo, New control unit developed for intermittent misting of cuttings, *Amer. Nurs.,* 103(8):18. 1956.

23. Myhre, A. S., and C. D. Schwartze, Rooting evergreen cuttings with hormones, *Proc. Amer. Soc. Hort. Sci.,* 51:639–650. 1948.

24. O'Rourke, F. L., and M. A. Maxon, Effect of particle size of vermiculite media on the rooting of cuttings, *Proc. Amer. Soc. Hort. Sci.,* 51:654–656. 1948.

25. Pearse, H. L., Growth substances and their practical importance in horticulture, *Commonwealth Bur. of Hort. and Plant. Crops, Tech. Comm. No. 20,* 1948.

26. Potter, J. M. S., Propagation of blackberries, *Jour. Roy. Hort. Soc.,* 61:637–638. 1936.

27. Skinner, H. T., A new propagation method for hybrid rhododendrons, *Jour. N.Y. Bot. Gard.,* 40:83–89. 1939.

28. Smith, P. F., Rooting of guayule stem cuttings in aerated water, *Proc. Amer. Soc. Hort. Sci.,* 44:527–528. 1944.

29. Snyder, W. E., and C. E. Hess, Recommendations for the installation of a mist system for rooting cuttings of nursery crops, Dept. of Flor. and Orn. Hort., N.Y. State Univ. Mimeo. Leaf., 1955.

30. Stoutemyer, V. T., T. J. Maney, and B. S. Pickett, A rapid method of propagating raspberries and blackberries by leaf-bud cuttings, *Proc. Amer. Soc. Hort. Sci.,* 30:278–282. 1933.

31. ———, Some observations on the production of own-rooted apple stocks from root cuttings, *Proc. Amer. Soc. Hort. Sci.,* 33:350–354. 1936.

32. Stoutemyer, V. T., and F. L. O'Rourke, Spray humidification and the rooting of cuttings, *Amer. Nurs.,* 77(1):5–6. 1943.

33. Swartley, J., and L. C. Chadwick, Synthetic growth substances as aids to root production on evergreen and softwood deciduous cuttings, *Proc. Amer. Soc. Hort. Sci.,* 37:1099–1104. 1939.

34. Templeton, H. M., The Phytotektor method of rooting cuttings, *Proc. 3rd Ann. Mtg. Plant Prop. Soc.,* pp. 51–56. 1953.

35. Thimann, K. V., and J. Behnke-Rogers, The use of auxins in the rooting of woody cuttings, *M. M. Cabot Foundation Publ. No. 1,* Harvard Forest, Petersham, Mass. 1950.

36. Vanderbrook, C., Mist spray growing and nutriculture, *Amer. Nurs.,* 102(9):13–14. 1955.

37. ———, The storage of rooted cuttings, *Amer. Nurs.,* 103(9):10, 76–77. 1956.

38. Watkins, J. V., and G. H. Blackman, Leaf-bud cuttings for multiplying tropical shrubs, *Proc. Amer. Soc. Hort. Sci.,* 37:1109–1111. 1939.

39. Wells, J. S., Pointers on propagation: young wood and old, *Amer. Nurs.,* 96(9):11, 68–69. 1952.

40. ———, Pointers on propagation: propagation of *Taxus, Amer. Nurs.,* 96(11):**13,** 37–38–43. 1952.

41. ———, Variations in propagation procedure, *Amer. Nurs.,* 97(3):13, 51–53. 1953.

42. ———, Outdoor propagation under constant mist, *Amer. Nurs.,* 97(11):14, 55. 1953.

43. ———, Further notes on constant mist, *Amer. Nurs.,* 98(11):12–13, 62. 1953.

44. ———, Where do we stand on the use of mist, *Amer. Nurs.,* 101(5):17, 108–109. 1955.

45. Williams, H. H., Studies on the propagation of certain broad-leaf evergreens with special reference to leaf-bud cuttings and root inducing substances, *Proc. Amer. Soc. Hort. Sci.,* 43:323–330. 1943.

46. Zimmerman, P. W., Oxygen requirements for root growth of cuttings in water, *Amer. Jour. Bot.,* 17:842–861. 1930.

• **Supplementary Reading**

Avery, G. S., *et al., Hormones and Horticulture.* New York: McGraw-Hill, 1947. Chap. II.

Brooklyn Botanic Garden. Handbook on Propagation. *Plants and Gardens.* Vol. 13, No. 2 (1957).

Creech, J. L., ed., "Vegetative Propagation," *National Horticultural Magazine,* Vol. 33, No. 1 (1954).

Doran, W. L., "Propagation of Woody Plants by Cuttings," *Massachusetts Agricultural Experiment Station Bulletin 491* (1957).

Free, M., *Plant Propagation in Pictures.* Garden City, New York: Doubleday, 1957.

King, E. J., *The Propagation of Plants.* London: Hutchinson's, 1950.

Laurie, A., D. C. Kiplinger, and K. S. Nelson, *Commercial Flower Forcing,* 6th ed. Philadelphia: Blakiston, 1958.

Post, K., *Florist Crop Production and Marketing.* New York: Orange-Judd, 1949.

Stoutemyer, V. T., "Encouragement of Roots by Plant Regulators," in H. B. Tukey, ed., *Plant Regulators in Agriculture.* New York: Wiley, 1954. **Chap. 4.**

11

Theoretical Aspects of Grafting and Budding

Grafting is the art of joining parts of plants together in such a manner that they will unite and continue their growth as one plant. The part of the graft combination which is to become the upper portion or top of the new plant is termed the *scion* (*cion*), and the part which is to become the lower portion or root is termed the *rootstock* or *understock* or more commonly the *stock* (*129*). The term "stion" has been suggested for the combination of a scion and stock growing as one plant (*146*). All methods of joining plants are properly termed *grafting*, but when the scion part is a small piece of bark (and sometimes wood) containing a single bud, the operation is termed *budding*. Most of the conditions and factors mentioned in this chapter affecting grafting would, therefore, apply equally well to budding, although the techniques involved in each are somewhat different.

REASONS FOR GRAFTING AND BUDDING

Perpetuating clones (see p. 160) **that cannot be conveniently reproduced by cuttings, layers, division, or other asexual methods.** Clones of many species such as the apple, almond, pear, walnut, and certain woody ornamentals are not propagated commercially by cuttings, simply because they cannot be rooted in high enough percentages by the methods now in use. A limited number of additional individuals can be started by layering or division, but for propagation in considerable quantities, the nurseryman is forced to resort to budding or grafting scions of the desired variety on rootstocks with which they are compatible (see p. 290).

Obtaining the benefits of certain rootstocks. In some instances, varieties can be propagated easily by cuttings, yet it is still preferable to graft or bud them on certain stocks which have desirable root characteristics not obtained when the scion variety is on its own roots. For many plant species, rootstocks are available which will tolerate unfavorable conditions, such as heavy, wet soils, or resist soil-borne pests or disease organisms. Also, rootstocks are available for some species which cause the grafted tree to have exceptional vigor or to become dwarfed. Some stocks, particularly in the citrus species, have a pronounced effect on the size and quality of the fruit of the scion variety.*

Rootstocks can be divided into two groups, *seedling* and *clonal*. The latter is started either by cuttings or layers. Variation among seedlings can possibly make them undesirable as rootstocks, because such variability may lead to considerable variability in the growth and performance of the grafted trees.

Nurserymen in the United States, however, generally use seedling rootstocks for fruit tree species due to the ease of growing and the fact that they have not encountered enough variability in trees propagated on such seedlings to cause much concern. It is the usual procedure to discard any obviously off-type seedlings in the nursery row, thus eliminating pronounced variability. Actually, other unavoidable environmental differences in an orchard, principally soil factors, may be greater than the smaller variations encountered in seedling rootstocks.

On the other hand, much effort, especially in England, has been given to the development of clonal rootstocks. These are propagated vegetatively and, of course, each individual rootstock plant is the same genetically as all the other plants in the clone and can be expected to have identical growth characteristics in a given environment. Clonal rootstocks are desirable not only to produce uniformity but, equally important, to perpetuate specific characteristics of a particular stock, such as nematode resistance or an influence on plant size, which ordinarily would not be perpetuated by seedling stocks.

Obtaining the benefits of certain intermediate stocks. There are several cases where the simple grafting of a scion variety upon a rootstock does not produce the desired plant. In some instances, the scion and the particular stock used are not completely compatible; that is, the grafted tree fails to grow or the union is weak and sooner or later breaks. This can often be overcome by using a short piece of stem tissue of a variety compatible with both scion and rootstock, inserted between the two—termed *double-working*. Such a plant would have two graft unions instead of one. Or a certain growth habit may be desired for the section between the roots and the desired top of the plant, as in the development of "tree" roses where

---

* Detailed discussions of the rootstocks available for the various fruit and ornamental species are given in Chapters 16 and 17.

a strong upright growing section is inserted to give the tree effect, a form not usually obtained with roses. Also, trees of certain very desirable fruit varieties have trunks which are susceptible to diseases or winter injury. By double-working and using a resistant variety for the trunk, this trouble can be overcome. It is also known that some degree of rootstock effect of certain stocks can be obtained by using such stocks as an intermediate stem piece rather than as the rootstock. For example, the dwarfing Malling IX apple rootstock will result in some dwarfing of the top scion variety when a stem piece of it is inserted between a vigorous rootstock and a vigorous scion variety.

Figure 11-1. A commercial application of double-working. **(left)** Rubber trees in Brazil of a high-yielding, **blight-susceptible** East India clone budded on seedling rootstocks have been injured by attacks of leaf blight. **(right)** Trees of same high-yielding clone but double-worked so as to use a **blight-resistant** top. These trees consist of seedling rootstock, high-yielding stem, and blight-resistant top. Courtesy M. H. Langford **(74).**

Changing varieties of established plants (topworking). A tree, or an entire orchard, may be of a variety that is undesirable. It could be an old variety no longer in demand, or unproductive, or one with poor growth habits, or possibly susceptible to prevalent diseases or insects. As long as a compatible scion variety is used, the top may be regrafted to a more desirable variety—if such exists—which will overcome the existing trouble.

Provision for adequate cross-pollination can be obtained by topworking scattered trees throughout the orchard to the proper pollinizing variety.

Or, if one isolated tree is unfruitful due to lack of cross-pollination, a branch of the tree may be grafted to the proper pollinizing variety.

A pistillate (female) plant of dioecious (pistillate and staminate flowers borne on separate individual plants) species, such as the hollies (*Ilex*), may be unfruitful due to the lack of a nearby staminate (male) plant to provide proper pollination. This can be corrected by grafting a scion taken from a staminate plant on one branch of the pistillate plant.

Of interest to the home gardener is the fact that several varieties of almost any fruit species can be grown on a single tree of that species by topworking each scaffold branch to a different variety. In a few cases, different species can be worked on the same tree. For example, on a single citrus rootstock it would be possible to have oranges, lemons, grapefruit, tangerines, and limes.

Hastening the growth of seedling selections. In various fruit breeding projects, the young seedling selections, if left to grow on their own roots, may take 5 to 10 or more years to come into bearing. This can be speeded up, however, by taking the shoot of the seedling as soon as it is sufficiently large to be used as a scion and grafting it on a larger, established tree with a strong root system. Grafting such as this becomes an aid in hastening breeding programs, particularly with species which are slow to start bearing *(136)*. It is possible to graft several seedling selections on one mature tree, but this is often considered to be inadvisable due to the danger of virus contamination coming either from the old tree or one or more of the seedling scions and spreading to the others.

Sometimes, desirable new seedling plants developed in breeding programs never attain the ability to grow well on their own roots, but when grafted on a vigorous, compatible rootstock they develop into a plant of the desired form and stature *(23)*. Examples of this are given by crosses of *Syringa laciniata* $\times$ *S. vulgaris* which produce new types of the Chinese lilac. Many of the seedlings lack sufficient vigor to survive more than 2 or 3 years, but if they are budded on the tree lilac, *Syringa amurensis japonica,* they survive and grow vigorously *(107)*.

Repairing damaged parts of trees. Occasionally the roots, trunk, or large limbs of trees become severely damaged by winter injury, cultivation implements, certain diseases, or rodents. By the use of bridge-grafting or inarching such damage can be repaired. This is discussed in detail on page 344.

Studying virus diseases. It is characteristic of virus diseases that they can be transmitted from plant to plant by grafting. One of the problems encountered in propagating clones is that virus-infected propagating wood may unknowingly be used, thus spreading the disease throughout the clone. Transmission of viruses by grafting makes possible testing for the presence of the virus in varieties or species which may carry the disease but show few or perhaps no symptoms. By grafting scions from a plant suspected of carrying the virus on a plant known to be highly susceptible to the virus, with prominent symptoms, detection of the disease is easily accomplished *(52, 82, 112)*. This procedure is known as *indexing*.

In order to detect the presence of a latent virus in a symptomless carrier, it is not necessary to use only combinations which make a permanent, compatible graft union. For example, the Shiro-fugen flowering cherry is used to detect viruses in peach, plum, almond, and apricot. A temporary, incompatible union is often a sufficient bridge for a virus *(72)*.

FORMATION OF THE GRAFT UNION

Briefly, the healing of a normal graft union is as follows:

(a) Freshly cut scion tissue is brought into secure, intimate contact with freshly cut stock tissue in such a manner that the cambial regions of each are in close proximity. Temperature and humidity conditions must be such as to promote activity in the newly exposed and surrounding cells.

(b) The outer exposed layers of cells in the cambial region of both scion and stock produce parenchyma cells which soon intermingle and interlock; this is commonly called *callus tissue.*

(c) Certain cells of this newly formed callus tissue which are in line with the cambium layer of the intact scion and stock differentiate into new cambium cells.

(d) These new cambium cells produce new vascular tissue, xylem toward the inside and phloem toward the outside, thus establishing vascular connection between the scion and stock, a requisite of a successful graft union.

The healing of a graft union can be considered as the healing of a wound. Such injured tissue as might occur if the end of a branch was split longitudinally would heal quickly if the split pieces were bound tightly together. New parenchyma cells would be produced by abundant proliferation of cells of the cambium region of both pieces, forming callus tissue. Some of the interlocking parenchyma cells would differentiate into cambium cells, which subsequently would produce xylem and phloem tissue.

If, between the two split pieces, a third detached piece was interposed which had been cut so that a large number of its cells in the cambial region could be placed in intimate contact with cells of the cambial region of the two split pieces, proliferation of cells from all cambial areas would soon result in complete healing, with the foreign, detached piece joined completely between the two original split pieces. A graft union is essentially then a healed wound, with an additional, foreign, piece of tissue incorporated into the healed wound.

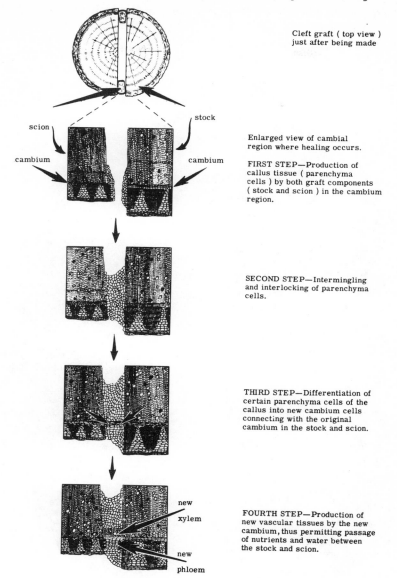

Cleft graft (top view)
just after being made

scion

stock

cambium

cambium

Enlarged view of cambial
region where healing occurs.

FIRST STEP—Production of
callus tissue (parenchyma
cells) by both graft components
(stock and scion) in the cambium
region.

SECOND STEP—Intermingling
and interlocking of parenchyma
cells.

THIRD STEP—Differentiation of
certain parenchyma cells of the
callus into new cambium cells
connecting with the original
cambium in the stock and scion.

new
xylem

new
phloem

FOURTH STEP—Production of
new vascular tissues by the new
cambium, thus permitting passage
of nutrients and water between
the stock and scion.

Figure 11–2. Diagrammatic developmental sequence during the healing of a
graft union as illustrated by the cleft graft.

This added piece of tissue, the scion, will not resume its growth successfully, however, unless vascular connection has been established so that
it may obtain water and mineral nutrients. In addition, the scion must have
a terminal meristematic region—a bud—so that it can resume shoot growth.

In the healing of a graft union, the parts of the graft that are originally prepared and placed in close contact do not themselves move about or grow together. The union is accomplished entirely by cells which develop *after* the actual graft union has been made.

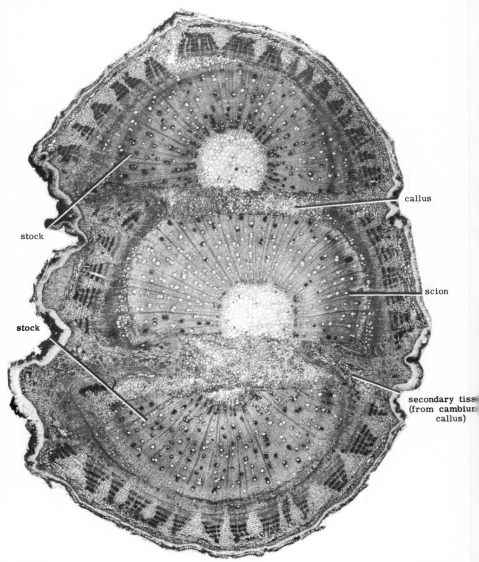

callus

stock

scion

stock

secondary tiss (from cambiur callus)

Figure 11–3. Cross-section of an **Hibiscus** wedge graft showing the importance of callus development in the healing of a graft union. Cambial activity in the callus has resulted in the production of secondary tissues which have joined the vascular tissues of stock and scion. x 10. Reprinted with permission from K. Esau, **Plant Anatomy,** 1953. John Wiley & Sons, Inc.

In addition, it should be stressed that in a graft union *there is no fusion of cells or cell contents.* Cells produced by the stock and by the scion each maintain their own distinct identity.

Considering in more detail the steps involved in the healing of a graft union, the first one listed below may be said to be a preliminary step, but nevertheless it is essential and one over which the propagator has control.

(a) *Establishment of intimate contact of a considerable amount of the cambial region of both stock and scion under favorable environmental conditions.*

Temperature conditions that will cause high cell activity are necessary. Usually, temperatures in the range of 45° to 90°F., depending upon the species, would be conducive to rapid cell growth. The grafting operation should thus take place at a time of year when such favorable temperatures can be expected and when the plant tissues, especially the cambium, are in a naturally active state. These conditions generally occur during the spring months.

The new callus tissue arising from the cambial region is composed of thin-walled, turgid cells which could easily become desiccated and die. It is important for the production of these parenchyma cells that the humidity in the vicinity of the cambial region of the graft union be kept at a high level. This explains the necessity of thoroughly waxing the graft union or using some other method to prevent desiccation of the callus tissue.

It is important, too, that the region of the graft union be kept as free as possible from invading disease organisms. The thin-walled parenchyma cells, under relatively high humidity and temperature conditions, provide a favorable foothold for growth of fungi and bacteria which, of course, are exceedingly detrimental to the successful healing of the graft union. Prompt waxing of the graft is the best prevention against disease infections.

Figure 11–4. Natural graft. These sometimes occur after two branches have been pressing tightly against each other for a long time.

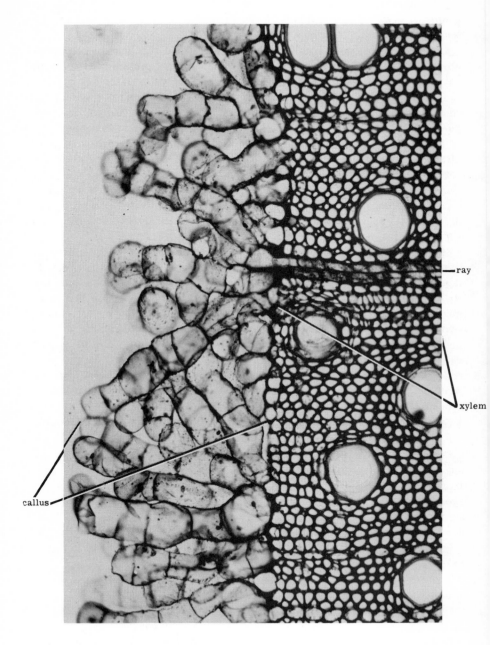

Figure 11–5. Callus production from incompletely differentiated xylem, exposed by excision of a strip of bark. x 120. Reprinted with permission from K. Esau, **Plant Anatomy,** 1953. John Wiley & Sons, Inc.

It is essential that the two original graft components be held together firmly by some means, such as wrapping, tying, or nailing, or better yet, by wedging (as in the cleft or saw kerf grafts) so that the parts will not move about and dislodge the interlocking parenchyma cells after proliferation has started.

The statement is often made that for successful grafting, the cambium layers of stock and scion must be "matched." Although this is desirable, of course, it is unlikely that complete matching of the two cambium layers is, or ever can be, attained. In fact, it is unnecessary. It is only essential that the cambial regions be close enough together so that the parenchyma cells from both stock and scion produced in this region can become interlocked. Two badly matched cambial layers may delay union, or, if extremely mismatched, prevent union.

(b) *Production and interlocking of parenchyma cells* (*callus tissue*) *by both the stock and scion.*

These new parenchyma cells arise from both stock and scion, coming mainly from the parenchyma of the phloem rays and perhaps the immature parts of the xylem rays. The actual cambial layer itself seems to take little or no part in this first development of the callus *(68, 105, 113)*. In grafting scions on established stocks, the stock produces most of the callus, taking the major part in filling the gaps between the components. These parenchyma cells, composing the spongy callus tissue, fill the space between the two original components of the graft (the scion and the stock), becoming intimately interlocked and providing some mechanical support as well as allowing for some passage of water and nutrients from the stock into the scion. At the final stages of this process, the cells of the outer layer of callus become suberized.

(c) *Production of a new cambium across the callus "bridge."*

Along the edges of the original cambium, adjacent cells in the newly formed callus differentiate into new cambium cells. This proceeds further and further inward away from the original cambium layers of stock and scion and on through the callus bridge until the newly formed cambium layers meet, thus providing a new continuous cambium ring. It is only in the callus cells adjacent to the pre-existing cambium cells that the new cambial elements appear.

(d) *Formation of new xylem and phloem from the new vascular cambium in the callus bridge.*

The newly formed cambial sheath in the callus bridge begins typical cambial activity, laying down new xylem and phloem along with the original vascular cambium of the stock and scion, on through the life of the plant.

In the formation of new vascular tissues following cambial continuity, it appears that the type of cells formed by the cambium may be influenced by the cells of the stock adjacent to the cambium. For example, xylem ray cells are formed where the cambium is in contact with xylem rays of the stock, and xylem elements where they were in contact with xylem elements (96).

The new xylem tissue originates from the scion rather than from the stock. This is shown by "ring grafting" (where a ring of bark from a young tree is removed and replaced by a ring of bark from another tree) (103). Using bark rings of the Scugog apple variety, which has purple xylem, subsequent xylem growth of the tree following grafting was entirely purple in color just under the Scugog ring of bark, whereas in the remainder of the tree the xylem remained white (153).

This new production of xylem and phloem then establishes vascular connection between the scion and the stock. It must occur before much new shoot growth takes place from buds on the scion; otherwise, the enlarging leaf surfaces on the scion shoots will have little or no water supply to offset that lost by transpiration, and the scion will quickly become desiccated and die.

A somewhat different developmental sequence has been reported to occur in tobacco (21). Here, xylem tracheary elements and phloem sieve-tubes form directly by differentiation of callus into these vascular elements. A cambium layer subsequently differentiates between the two vascular elements.

THE HEALING PROCESS IN T-BUDDING

In T-budding, the bud piece usually consists of the periderm, cortex, phloem, and often some xylem tissue to which is attached a lateral bud. In budding, this bark piece is laid against the exposed xylem of the stock.

A detailed study of the healing process in this type of budding has been made for the rose (*Rosa multiflora*) (14) and for citrus (80).

When the bud piece is removed from the budstick and when the flaps of bark on either side of the "T" incision on the stock are raised, the cambium and newly formed cambial derivatives in these tissues are usually destroyed due to their very tender, succulent nature. In the rose, about 3 days after budding, the terminal cells of the broken xylem rays and adjacent cambial derivatives on the exposed surface of the stock begin to enlarge and divide, leading to the production of callus strands. In the same manner, formation of callus strands develops from terminal cells of broken phloem rays and adjacent young secondary phloem cells on the cut surface of the inner side of the bud piece.

Within 14 days the space between the stock and bud piece is completely filled with callus, which has developed mainly from the proliferating im-

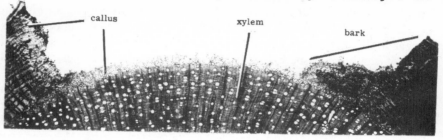

callus xylem bark

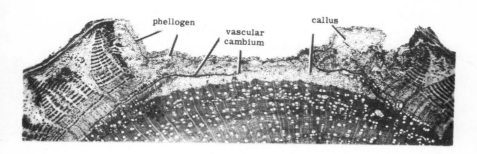

phellogen vascular cambium callus

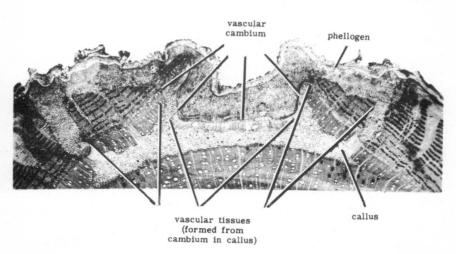

vascular cambium phellogen

vascular tissues
(formed from
cambium in callus)

callus

Figure 11–6. Successive stages **(top** to **bottom)** in the healing of a surface wound, showing the importance of callus production in the regeneration of the missing tissues. **(top)** Callus is formed on the exposed surfaces of the wood and bark. **(center)** A callus cushion covers the entire exposed surface. Some vascular cambium has differentiated in the callus, connecting with the cambium of the uninjured part of the stem. It has produced some vascular tissues (xylem and phloem) near the edges of the wound. A phellogen layer, producing cork cells, has appeared beneath the surface of the callus cushion. **(bottom)** Complete regeneration of the missing portion of the stem. The vascular cambium is continuous across the callus and has formed secondary xylem and phloem. Some callus tissue has been embedded beneath the new xylem. Cross-sections of **Hibiscus rosasinensis** x 9.5. Reprinted with permission from K. Esau, **Plant Anatomy,** 1953. John Wiley & Sons, Inc.

mature secondary xylem of the stock and the immature secondary phloem of the bud piece. During the second week, short areas of cambium cells appear in this newly developed callus tissue. By the tenth day, a completed band of cambium tissue extends over the face of the stock and is joined to the uninjured cambium on either side of the bud piece.

After cambial continuity is completed, continuity of vascular tissues soon becomes established between the bud and stock. In T-budding, then, the primary union is between the surface of the phloem on the inner face of the shield and the meristematic xylem surface of the stock. A secondary type of union may occur, however, at the edges of the shield piece, as it would in chip budding (see p. 393) *(11)*.

The various stages in the healing process of the union in T-budding of citrus have been determined as follows *(80):*

Stage of Development	*Approximate Time After Budding*
1. First cell divisions	24 hours
2. First callus bridges	5 days
3. Differentiation:	
(a) in the callus of the bark flaps	10 days
(b) in the callus of the shield	15 days
4. First occurrence of xylem tracheids:	
(a) in the callus of the bark flaps	15 days
(b) in the callus of the shield	20 days
5. Lignification of the callus completed:	
(a) in the bark flaps	25 to 30 days
(b) under the shield	30 to 45 days
6. First occurrence of meristematic layers in the callus between shield and bark flaps	15 days

FACTORS INFLUENCING THE HEALING OF THE GRAFT OR BUD UNION

As anyone experienced in grafting or budding knows, the results obtained in grafting are often inconsistent, an excellent percentage of "takes" occurring in some operations, whereas in others the results are very discouraging. There are a number of factors which influence the healing of graft unions.

Incompatibility (see p. 290)

One of the symptoms of incompatibility is a complete lack or a very low percentage of successful unions. Obviously, before using a certain graft combination, it is necessary to determine whether or not the components are capable of uniting properly. It is useless to attempt to graft combinations that are distantly related and known to be incompatible.

Kind of Plant

Some plants are much more difficult to graft than others even when no incompatibility is involved. Difficult ones, for example, are the hickories, oaks, and beeches. Such plants, once grafted, though, grow very well with a perfect graft union. In top-grafting apples and pears, even the simplest techniques usually give a good percentage of successful unions, but in top-grafting certain of the stone fruits, such as peaches and apricots, much more care and attention to details are necessary. Strangely enough, top-grafting peaches to some other compatible species, such as plums or almonds, is more successfully done than reworking them back to peaches. Many times one method of grafting will give better results than another or, perhaps, budding may be more successful than grafting, or vice versa. For example, in top-working the native black walnut (*Juglans hindsii*) to the Persian walnut (*Juglans regia*) in California, it has consistently been noted, where comparisons have been made, that the bark graft method is more successful than the cleft graft.

Some species, such as the Muscadine grape (*Vitis rotundifolia*), mango (*Mangifera indica*), and *Camellia reticulata,* are so difficult to propagate by the usual grafting or budding methods that "approach grafting," where both partners of the graft are maintained for a time on their own roots, is often used. This variation among plant species and varieties in their grafting ability is probably related to their production of callus, which is essential for a successful graft union. *Camellia reticulata,* for example, is difficult to graft and is a very poor callus producer.

Temperature and Humidity Conditions During and Following Grafting

There are certain environmental conditions which must be met for callus tissue to develop.

Temperature has a pronounced effect on the production of callus tissue. In apple grafts little, if any, callus is formed below 32°F. or above about

104°F. Even around 40°F., callus development is slow and meager, and at 90°F. and higher, callus production is retarded with cell injury becoming more apparent as the temperature increases, until death of the cells occurs at 104°F. Between 40° and 90°F., the rate of callus formation increases directly with the temperature (118). For such operations as bench grafting, callusing may be allowed to proceed slowly for several months by storing the grafts at relatively low temperatures (45° to 50°F.), or if rapid callusing is desired, they may be kept at higher temperatures for a shorter time. Since excessive callusing of root graft unions may result in the formation of undesirable "callus knots" (sometimes mistaken by plant inspectors for crown gall tumors), it can be controlled by storing well-callused grafts at reduced temperatures to prevent further callus development.

Temperature during the healing period following grafting was found to have a pronounced effect upon the degree of successful unions obtained in whip grafting black walnuts. Studies (121) show clearly that a temperature in the range of 77° to 86°F. during the callusing period gives much better results than either higher or lower temperatures. This was confirmed in later studies (12) when black walnut root grafts placed in a cool nursery cellar at 41° to 56°F. for callusing failed completely to unite. Another group of grafts planted in the nursery row immediately after grafting (air temperature 41° to 72°F.) resulted in only about 3 per cent growing. In

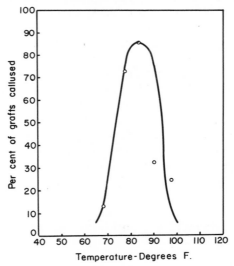

Figure 11–7. Influence of temperature on the callusing of walnut (**Juglans**) grafts. Callus formation is essential for the healing of the graft union. Maintaining an optimum temperature following grafting is very important for successful healing of walnut grafts. Adapted from data of Sitton (121).

a third group which were allowed to callus in a warm greenhouse (air temperature 65° to 80°F.), an average of 88 per cent grew.

Following bench grafting of grapes, a temperature of 70° to 75°F. is about optimum; 85°F. or higher results in profuse formation of a soft type of callus tissue which is easily injured during the planting operations. Below 70°F. callus formation is slow, and below 60°F. it almost ceases.

Grafting operations performed late in the season, when high temperatures can be expected, often result in failure. Tests *(50)* of walnut topgrafting in California during very hot weather in May showed that whitewashing the area of the completed graft union definitely promoted healing of the union. Whitewash would reflect a considerable portion of the radiant energy of the sun rather than allow it to be absorbed, thus resulting in lower bark temperatures. In addition, in these tests, scions placed on the north and east sides of the stub survived much better than those on the south and west. Undoubtedly, this was due to the lower temperatures resulting from their shaded position.

Since the parenchyma cells comprising the important callus tissue are thin-walled and tender with no provision for resisting desiccation, it is obvious that if they are exposed to drying air for very long they will be killed. This was found *(118)* to be the case in studies of the effect of humidity on healing of apple grafts. Air moisture levels below the saturation point inhibited callus formation, the rate of desiccation of the cells increasing as the humidity dropped. In fact, the presence of a film of water against the callusing surface was much more conducive to abundant callus formation than just maintaining the air at 100 per cent relative humidity. Unless a completed graft union is kept by some means at a very high humidity level, the chances of successful healing are rather remote. With most plants, thoroughly waxing the graft union and thereby retaining the natural moisture of the tissues is all that is required to provide the necessary humidity level.

Polyethylene plastic films can be used for supplying a water-saturated air environment to the healing graft union. The completed graft union is enclosed in a ball of moist sphagnum moss which is tightly wrapped with a covering of the polyethylene film. This film allows some passage of such gases as carbon dioxide and oxygen but greatly reduces loss of water vapor. Sometimes the plastic film is used successfully alone, without moss *(93, 151)*.

Root grafts are often not waxed but stored in a moist packing material during the callusing period. Peat moss, to which an amount of water equal to its dry weight has been added, is an excellent packing material for callusing, because it provides the proper moisture and oxygen conditions.

It has been shown *(118)* that the presence of oxygen at the graft union is necessary for the production of callus tissue. This would be expected, since such rapid cell division and growth would be accompanied by high respiration rates, which would utilize oxygen. For some plants, a lower percentage of oxygen than is found naturally in air is sufficient, but for others, healing of the graft union is better if the union is left unwaxed and placed in an enclosure of water-saturated air. This may indicate that the latter have a high oxygen requirement for callus formation. Waxing restricts air movement to such an extent that oxygen may become limiting, and callus tissue fails to form. This situation apparently exists in grafting the grape. For successful healing, the union must not be covered with wax or any other air-excluding material.

Growth Activity of the Stock Plant

In propagating certain species, especially by budding, it is usually quite important that the stock plant be in an active stage of growth, with the bark separating from the wood, i.e., slipping easily. For example, in top-budding fruit trees in the spring, using dormant budwood of the previous season's growth, the percentage of "takes" is much higher if the buds are inserted into vigorous, one-year-old, water sprout shoots than if they are budded into older, slow-growing fruiting twigs.

In budding seedlings in the nursery row, it is important that they have an ample supply of soil moisture just before, during, and following the budding operation. If they should lack water during this period, active growth is checked, the cambium tightens up and the chances of getting the buds to unite are lessened.

Propagation Techniques

Even in using the standard grafting or budding methods, there are numerous possible variables which may or may not affect the success of the operation. There are many opinions, often conflicting, as to the proper techniques to use. For example, in root grafts made by the whip graft method, some (98, 99) believe it important that the graft be made so that the top bud on the scion will be in line with the interlocking tongues on the matched side of the graft, whereas other evidence (5) indicates that it makes no difference where the top bud on the scion is in relation to the graft union.

Sometimes the grafting technique is so poor that only a small portion of the cambial regions of the stock and scion are brought together. Although healing occurs in this region and growth of the scion may start, when a large leaf area develops and high temperatures and high transpiration rates occur sufficient movement of water through the limited conducting area cannot take place, and the scion subsequently dies.

Poor grafting techniques, although they may delay adequate healing for some time—weeks, or even years—do not in themselves cause any permanent incompatibility. Once the union is adequately healed, growth can be normal from then on. This is well illustrated by grafting experiments *(57)* with pea stems. Stems were cut and regrafted with certain of the unions made with as good approximation of the vascular bundles as possible. Others were regrafted with the poorest possible alignment of the vascular bundles of stock and scion, and in still others the unions were intermediate. The final maximum growth rate and the percentage of successful grafts was the same whether the vascular connections in the graft union were good or poor. Only the initial growth rate and the period at which the scion reached its maximum growth were delayed when the vascular connections at the graft union were poor.

Virus Contamination, Insect Pests, and Diseases

The presence of viruses in propagating material may interfere with healing of the union. In sweet cherry propagation, for example, the use of virus-free budwood rather than virus-infected buds has consistently increased the percentage of successful "takes" in T-budding from about 60 to over 90 per cent.

Top-grafting olives in California is seriously hindered in some years due to attacks of the American plum borer (*Euzophera semifuneralis*) that feeds on the soft callus tissue around the graft union, resulting in the death of the scion. In England, nurserymen are often plagued with the red bud borer (*Thomasiniana oculiperda*) that eats the healing callus beneath the bud-shield in newly inserted T-buds *(41)*.

Sometimes bacteria or fungi gain entrance at the wounds made in preparing the graft or bud unions. Chemical control of such infections materially aids in promoting healing of such unions *(48, 78)*. To reduce crown gall infections in fruit tree root grafts, a grafting tape is available containing mercuric chloride.

In South and Central America, rubber (*Hevea*) trees are propagated by a modification of the patch bud. A major cause of budding failures in these countries has been due to infection of the cut surfaces by a fungus, *Diplodia theobromae*. Control of this infection has been obtained by fungicidal treatments *(73)*.

In top-grafting mangos in Florida, control of the fungus diseases, anthracnose and scab, has been found to be essential for success. This is done by spraying the rootstock trees and the source of scionwood regularly with copper fungicides before grafting is attempted *(90)*.

Relation of Growth Substances and Other Chemicals to Healing of the Graft Union

The evidence that the application of growth substances to tree wounds may stimulate callus development is conflicting. In one instance *(117)*, the use of pure lanolin on apple pruning wounds gave slightly faster callusing than occurred in untreated wounds, but the addition of indoleacetic acid did not increase the callusing rate. In other tests *(67)*, a lanolin paste containing indoleacetic acid applied to wounds on the terminal shoots of peach, apple, plum, and pear was reported to have stimulated callusing at the edges of the cut bark and in other areas over the wounded surface.

Extensive studies *(79)* of callusing and wound healing in a number of forest tree species failed to show that any of five growth regulators applied in wound coatings were effective in stimulating wound healing.

A similar conflicting situation exists where growth regulators were applied to graft unions in attempts to promote more rapid callusing and healing. There are a few reported instances of success *(87, 88)*, but there are also reports where no benefits were noted.

In deciduous fruit trees, the use of growth substances has been found *(37)* to be of value in healing grafts of the apple but not those of cherry or pear. In budding plums, the use of indoleacetic acid was helpful in promoting healing, but this same treatment was ineffective in spring grafting plums *(69)*.

Seven different growth regulators were applied *(50)* to Persian walnut scions just before they were grafted on *Juglans hindsii* seedling trees. None of the treatments resulted in any stimulation of callusing or hastening of healing of the union, and some of the higher concentrations used were toxic to the scion.

Treatments of black walnut root grafts with indolebutyric acid in talc failed to result in an increased percentage of successful unions, although it did cause more profuse callus growth and the development of more rootlets *(12)*.

As seen from this evidence, although there are a few reported cases of benefits from the use of growth regulators in stimulating healing of the graft union, the response in general has been so unfavorable that it has failed to encourage much research into this field.

POLARITY IN GRAFTING

As a general rule, in grafting two pieces of stem tissue together, the morphologically proximal end of the scion should be inserted into the morphologically distal end of the stock. But when grafting a piece of stem tissue on a piece of root, as is done in root grafting, the proximal end of the scion should be inserted into the proximal end of the root piece.

The *proximal* end of either the shoot or the root is that nearest the stem-root junction of the plant.

The *distal* end of either the shoot or the root is that furthest from the stem-root junction of the plant and nearest the tip of the shoot or root.

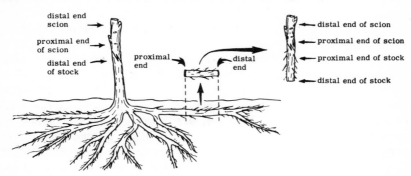

Figure 11–8. Polarity in grafting. In top grafting, the proximal end of the scion is attached to the distal end of the stock. In root grafting, however, the proximal end of the scion is joined to the proximal end of the stock.

This attention to proper polarity is very important if the graft union is to be permanently successful. In all commercial grafting or budding, this rule is strictly observed.

Should a scion be inserted with reversed polarity—"upside down"—in bridge-grafting, for example, it is possible for the two graft unions to be temporarily successful and the scion to stay alive for a time. But as seen

Figure 11–9. Bridge graft on a pear tree five months after grafting. Center scion was inserted with reversed polarity. Although the scion is alive it has not increased from its original size. The two scions on either side have grown rapidly.

in Figure 11–9, the reversed scion does not increase from its original size, whereas the scion with correct polarity enlarges normally.

As described in Chapter 12, in nurse-root grafting, the rootstock may be purposely grafted to the scion with reversed polarity. Union will occur and the root will supply water and mineral nutrients to the scion. Since the scion is unable to supply food materials, and possibly growth-promoting hormones, to the rootstock, the stock eventually dies. In this case, the graft union is purposely set well below the ground level, and the scion itself produces adventitious roots which ultimately become the entire root system of the plant.

In T-budding or patch budding, the rule for observance of correct polarity is not as exacting. Buds can be inserted with reversed polarity and still make permanently successful unions. The buds start growing downward, then the shoots recurve and start upward (106). In the inverted bud piece, the cambium seems to be quite capable of continued functioning and growth. However, in the vessels as well as the fibers formed from cambial activity, there is a twisting tendency which apparently keeps translocation and water conduction oriented in the same manner as it was in the original position (20).

Figure 11–10. Two-year-old Stayman Winesap apple budded on McIntosh seedling by inverted T-buds. Note development of wide angle crotches. Courtesy Arnold Arboretum, Jamaica Plain, Mass.

If a complete ring of bark is removed from the trunk of a young tree, reversed, and regrafted into place, it will markedly retard the growth of the tree. Growth-promoting hormones and carbohydrates that stimulate growth of the roots move downward through the phloem. Reaching the in-

Figure 11-11. Inverted ring of bark after five months. Note swelling at upper edge of ring indicating blocking in the downward movement of food materials.

Figure 11-12. Dwarfing effect in one season by inversion of ring of bark. Two-year-old Baldwin apple tree on left had ring of bark removed and replaced with normal polarity. Similar tree on right had ring of bark replaced upside down. Note production of flower buds on this tree. Suckers produced below inverted ring indicate a checking of auxin movement downward. Courtesy Arnold Arboretum, Jamaica Plain, Mass.

verted bark piece they are possibly blocked, and presumably, without these materials root growth is depressed, subsequently dwarfing the entire tree *(106).*

LIMITS OF GRAFTING

Since one of the requirements for a successful graft union is the close matching of the callus-producing tissues near the cambium layers, grafting is generally confined to the dicotyledons in the angiosperms, and to the gymnosperms, the cone-bearing plants. Both have a vascular cambium layer existing as a continuous tissue between the xylem and the phloem. In the monocotyledonous plants of the Angiospermae, which do not have such a vascular cambium, grafting is usually considered to be impossible. There are cases on record, however, of successful graft unions between the stem parts of monocots. By making use of the meristematic properties found in the intercalary tissues (located at the base of internodes) of certain monocots, some successful grafts have been obtained, although in low percentages *(89).*

Before a grafting operation is started, it should be determined that the plants to be combined are capable of uniting. Unfortunately, there is no definite rule that can be followed exactly which will give this information. *Generally, the more closely the plants to be grafted are related botanically, the more favorable are the chances of the graft union being successful.* This will not hold true consistently, however, since botanical classifications are based on reproductive characters, whereas grafting is concerned primarily with the vegetative properties of plants.

Grafting within a variety. A scion can be grafted back on the plant from which it came, and a scion from a plant of a given clone can be grafted to any other plant of the same clone. For example, a scion taken from an Elberta peach tree could be grafted successfully to any other Elberta peach tree in the world.

Grafting between varieties. Usually, different varieties within a species can be grafted without difficulty. For example, the Elberta peach could be grafted to a J. H. Hale, Lovell, Crawford, or any other variety in the species *Prunus persica.*

Grafting between species. When plants are in different species, but in the same genus, the situation becomes confused. In some cases grafting can be done successfully, in others it cannot. Grafting between most species in the genus *Citrus,* for example, is successfully and widely used commercially. Varieties of the almond (*Prunus amygdalus*), the apricot (*Prunus armeniaca*), the European plum (*Prunus domestica*), and the Japanese plum (*Prunus salicina*)—all different species—are grafted commercially on the peach (*Prunus persica*) as a rootstock, a still different species. On the other hand, the almond and the apricot, both in the same genus, cannot be intergrafted successfully. The complexity of the situation is further illustrated by the fact that the Beauty variety of Japanese plum (*Prunus salicina*) makes a good union when grafted on the almond, but another variety of *P. salicina*, Santa Rosa, cannot be successfully grafted on the almond.

Compatibility with a given scion variety may be associated with seedling variability. Seedlings selected from the St. Julien plum (*Prunus insititia*), propagated vegetatively as rootstocks, and budded with the same variety of peach, have behaved very differently. For example, seedling selections A and C made good trees with no signs of incompatibility, whereas trees on selection B died within 5 years and those on selection D died after 1 year *(152)*.

There are some cases where a given interspecies graft is successful, but the reciprocal graft is not. For instance, the Marianna plum (*Prunus cerasifera* × *P. munsoniana?*) on the peach (*Prunus persica*) makes an excellent graft combination, but grafts of the peach on Marianna plum either soon die *(77)*, or fail to develop normally *(1)*. Although many varieties of Japanese plums (*Prunus salicina*) can be successfully grafted on the European plum *(P. domestica),* most varieties of the European plum are unsuccessful on the Japanese *(61)*.

Grafting between genera. When the plants to be grafted together are in different genera but in the same family—the chances of the union being successful become more remote. Cases can be found where such grafts are highly successful and used commercially, but in most instances, such grafts result in failure.

Trifoliate orange *(Poncirus trifoliata)* is used commercially as a dwarfing stock for the various species in the genus *Citrus*. The quince *(Cydonia oblonga)* has long been used as a dwarfing rootstock for certain varieties of the pear *(Pyrus communis)*. The reverse combination, quince on pear, though, is unsuccessful. Tests *(150)* of the Chinese wingnut *(Pterocarya stenoptera)* as a possible rootstock for the Persian walnut *(Juglans regia)* indicate an apparently compatible combination, at least for some varieties. Intergeneric grafts in the nightshade family, Solanaceae, are quite common. Tomato *(Lycopersicon esculentum)* can be grafted successfully on Jimson weed *(Datura stramonium)*, tobacco *(Nicotiana tabacum)*, Irish potato *(Solanum tuberosum),* and black nightshade *(Solanum nigrum)*.

Grafting between families. Grafting such plants together is usually considered impossible, but there are reported instances *(72, 155)* where it has been accomplished. These are mostly short-lived, herbaceous types, though, where the time involved is relatively short. Grafts, with vascular connections between the scion and stock, were successfully made *(91)* using white sweet clover, *Melilotus alba* (Leguminosae), as the scion and sunflower, *Helianthus annuus* (Compositae), as the stock. Cleft grafting was used, with the scion inserted into the pith parenchyma of the stock. The scions continued growth with normal vigor for over 5 months. As far as is known, however, there are no instances where woody perennial plants belonging to different families have been successfully and permanently grafted together.

INCOMPATIBILITY

When most closely related plants are grafted together, they unite readily and continue their growth as one plant. When entirely unrelated plants are grafted together, the usual result is the complete failure of the graft union. In between these two extremes, all sorts of results are experienced that are entirely unpredictable. Some scion-stock combinations may grow very well, but the reciprocal graft is a failure. Certain combinations will grow in a normal manner for a few weeks or perhaps a few years only to have the scion die or break off at the graft union. Other combinations may grow well for many years, even until the tree is mature, then during a windstorm the tree will break off cleanly at the graft union.

Some combinations unite, but abnormal symptoms, such as dwarfed or stunted growth, yellow foliage, or perhaps a conspicuous overgrowth of the scion just above the graft union, soon become apparent. Such combinations usually last for a time, then die. And, strangely, some fairly closely related plants, which would be expected to graft together readily, show complete failure to form a union or else unite only in very low percentages.

The inability of two plants to produce a successful graft union and the resulting single plant to develop satisfactorily is termed *incompatibility,* or sometimes *uncongeniality.* The opposite, of course, would be *compatibility* or *congeniality.*

It has been suggested *(115)* that the term *incompatibility* be reserved for situations where the stock or scion, or both, fails, and the graft dies rather quickly. *Uncongeniality* should then include cases where the combination lives, but some modification of stock or scion or both occurs. This would include such effects as swelling at the union or dwarfing. Incompatibility would then be considered as an extreme form of uncongeniality.

Figure 11–13. Apple grafts (right-hand portion of tree) five months after being grafted on a pear tree. This is an incompatible combination although it initially makes a strong growth.

Argles suggests *(2)* that "the term *incompatibility* be applied only to such combinations as show distinct failure, i.e., failure to unite, failure to grow in a healthy manner, or premature death, and only where such failure can be attributed with a reasonable degree of certainty to differences between stock and scion." This concept does not include failure of the graft due to environmental conditions or where abnormalities, such as union overgrowths not accompanied by tree failure, occur.

The compatibility relationships between stock and scion may be conveniently classed as follows *(2):*

(a) Combinations in which the physiological and structural differences between stock and scion are so slight that most or all of the graft combinations unite satisfactorily and the tree grows normally for its expected life. Slight dwarfing or such abnormalities as overgrowths at or above the graft union are not considered due to incompatibility if the tree's growth and fruitfulness is normal otherwise.

(b) At the other extreme are combinations in which the physiological and structural differences between the stock and scion are so great that a satisfactory graft union is impossible in all individuals. Sometimes this failure is delayed for a time, even for many years, and has been termed *delayed incompatibility*. It would be better to describe it as "delayed symptoms" of incompatibility, since it is the symptoms and not the incompatibility which are delayed.

(c) Between these two groups are many combinations in which differences—physiological and structural—do exist between stock and scion, but such differences are sufficiently small to allow some degree of grafting success. The success may be influenced by environmental conditions which accentuate or diminish the incompatibility.

Symptoms of Incompatibility

If the following symptoms are consistently noted in a given stock-scion combination under a wide variety of environmental conditions, it is likely that they have resulted from incompatibility. An isolated case of one or more of these symptoms does not necessarily mean that the combination is incompatible, because these symptoms can also result from such environmental conditions as the lack of some essential nutrient, attacks by insects or diseases, or poor grafting or budding techniques *(2)*.

(a) *Failure to form a successful graft or bud union in a high percentage of cases.*

(b) *Premature death of the trees; they may live a year or two in the nursery row, then die.*

(c) *Obvious poor health of the trees; growth may be weak, with yellowish foliage and early leaf drop in the fall.*

(d) *Marked differences in growth rate or vigor of scion and stock.*

(e) *Differences between scion and stock in the time vegetative growth for the season begins or ends.*

(f) *Overgrowths, at, above, or below the graft union.*

The two symptoms below, however, are the most reliable indications of incompatibility, and their occurrence in a single instance provides justification for stating that the particular combination is incompatible.

(a) *The breaking off of trees at the point of union, particularly when they have been growing for some years and the break is clean and smooth, rather than rough or jagged.* This may occur within a year or two after the union is made, for instance, in the apricot on almond roots; but in other instances, such as some apricot trees on myrobalan plum roots, it may not occur until the trees are full grown and bearing crops *(32, 36, 95)*.

(b) *The presence of masses or sheets of parenchymatous and/or bark tissue at the union, rather than normal differentiated tissue (16).*

It was pointed out *(96, 143)* many years ago that one, and perhaps the most common, symptom in incompatible combinations was the deposition of considerable amounts of loose, soft, parenchyma cells at the graft union. This interrupts the normal vascular connection between stock and scion. Sometimes, isolated masses of parenchyma cells occur with the conducting vessels making fairly good connections around them, whereas in other cases the ends of the vessels are almost entirely separated by the masses of parenchyma. In extreme cases the vascular tissue becomes distorted, but the parenchyma layer between stock and scion is continuous. Apparently, the cambial region of either scion or stock or both has produced only parenchyma cells at the line of union, resulting in a continuous sheet of such cells between scion and stock.

Figure 11–14. A case of delayed symptoms of incompatibility. A fifteen-year-old almond tree on a seedling apricot rootstock which broke off cleanly at the graft union.

Swellings at the graft union are often believed to be a certain indication of incompatibility. There does not seem to be justification for this belief if this is the *only* symptom that is present. In studies *(11)* of incompatible graft unions in the apple and pear, there was no correlation between incompatible combinations and swelling at the union. The most incompatible combination (pear on apple) produced no swelling, whereas the greatest swelling occurred in combinations which were compatible. Also, over a 20-year period in England in studies (1) involving various scion and rootstock combinations of plums, peaches, pears, cherries, and apples, it was concluded that the presence of a prominent bulge cannot be considered as evidence of incompatibility. In most of the definitely incompatible combinations, swellings were entirely absent, but in many entirely compatible combinations, swellings were frequently present.

In a study (11) of defective graft unions, it was concluded that incompatible combinations, such as the pear on apple, differ from compatible combinations principally in the failure to maintain cambium continuity. A break in the cambium appears at the end of the growing season. "Regrafting" often occurs naturally but becomes less common as the tree grows older. Then, as the stock and scion expand, the cambium failure leaves a zone of parenchymatous, sometimes suberized, tissue between them, resulting finally in interruption of the vascular system and the development of a mechanically weak structure.

Rather than the accumulation of masses of parenchyma cells, inclusions of bark tissue may develop. This was shown to occur in newly grafted or

Figure 11–15. Radial section through a compatible graft union of a twenty-five-year-old almond tree on peach rootstock. Although a distinct line appears between both components, the tissues are strongly knit together.

budded trees of the incompatible combinations of apple on pear (95) and plum on cherry (96). A layer of bark was found to extend almost to the point at which the cambium layers of stock and scion were placed when

Figure 11–16. Overgrowth of the stock by the scion does not necessarily indicate an incompatible union. Comice pears 18 years after being grafted on Surprise interstock on **Pyrus pyrifolia** roots show considerable overgrowth yet are strong and healthy and produce satisfactory commercial crops. Courtesy W. H. Griggs.

the graft was made. A small amount of continuous new tissue allowed enough movement of water and nutrients to enable the tree to start growth. But the layer of bark laid down by the cambiums of both scion and stock and pinched between the xylem on either side formed a layer of mechanical weakness. Thus, by the second season, with a larger top and greater resistance to wind movement, a break could easily occur at the graft union.

However, there are factors other than just a mechanically poor union that produce incompatibility symptoms. In a comparison (84) of 3-year-old double-worked trees of the combination of (a) Conference pear on C8 pear on Quince A roots with the combination (b) of Conference pear on Quince A on C8 pear, the lower unions in both cases—C8 pear on Quince A and Quince A on C8 pear—were very poor, the woody tissues of stock and scion separated in numerous places by masses of nonlignified, living parenchyma cells. In the last annual ring, a complete layer of parenchymatous tissue was beginning to form between stock and scion. The bark tissues of the stock and scion were separated by dark brown corky layers. Such badly connected and discontinuous unions would be expected to result in incompatibility symptoms due to the restriction of the passage of food substances between stock and scion. The combination of Conference pear on Quince A on C8 pear did show such symptoms (sparse new growth with few leaves, which were yellowish-brown in color), obviously being very incompatible. On the other hand, the combination of Conference pear on C8 pear on Quince A, with just as bad a mechanical union as the other combination, made an entirely satisfactory growth. This indicates, then, in this case at least, that the incompatibility symptoms are due to some factor other than a simple obstruction at the union.

Translocation difficulties due to incompatibility sometimes are found only in the phloem. This is illustrated by peach on Marianna plum, a combination which, in some instances, forms an incompatible union. Although peach buds unite readily with this plum stock and their early growth is satisfactory, later, during the second season, an enlargement appears just above the graft union, followed by wilting of the peach leaves and death of the tree. Anatomical studies (77) showed this to be a case of incompatibility in which good xylem connections developed at the graft union, but the phloem tissues failed to unite. Starvation of the stock tissues and death of the roots resulted, causing subsequent wilting and death of the peach scion. If leafy shoot growth was retained on the Marianna plum stock to nourish the roots, the trees could be kept alive indefinitely.

Causes of Incompatibility

As yet there is no answer to the question of what is the fundamental cause or causes of incompatibility. There is also no way of determining in advance of actual tests whether a particular combination will or will not be compatible or what degree of severity the symptoms of incompatibility may be. Several theories have been advanced in attempts to explain incompatibility, but the evidence supporting most of them is generally inadequate and conflicting.

One of the theories asserts that *different growth characteristics of the stock and scion are associated with incompatibility (16, 45, 145);* that is, if marked differences occur in vigor or in the time of starting or completing vegetative growth for the season, incompatibility may be expected. This theory holds that the stock and scion should exhibit an equal growth rate and a similar seasonal growth pattern for the union to be completely compatible. It is difficult to reconcile this theory with the existing facts, however. Completely compatible combinations can be found that have growth differences between stock and scion that are as great as the differences found in stock and scion combinations whose incompatibility is attributed to those differences. Also, unmistakable incompatibility exists between some combinations which show little, if any, difference in growth rate or time of starting growth *(63)*. Although differences in growth rate may influence the severity of the symptoms, it is unlikely that this is the basic cause of incompatibility.

Another theory attributes incompatibility to *physiological and biochemical differences between stock and scion*. In one example of this theory, the incompatibility has been attributed to nutritional causes. Muskmelon (*Cucumis melo*) grafted on the figleaf gourd (*Cucurbita ficifolia*), an intergeneric combination, is successful and grows for a time, but then the plant suddenly wilts and dies. The reciprocal combination, *C. ficifolia* on muskmelon, is quite successful, however. The incompatibility of muskmelon on *C. ficifolia* can be prevented by retaining some foliage on the stock—as little as four or five leaves. It is believed that the incompatibility is due to the lack of some essential nutrient or growth substance from the muskmelon, which is, however, supplied when leaves of the stock are retained *(149)*. This situation is similar to the incompatibility found when the peach is grafted on Marianna plum; xylem union is successful but no phloem union occurs, and the tree behaves as if it were girdled *(77)*.

This biochemical theory is supported in studies *(63, 86)* on incompatibility between Hale's Early peach grafted on Myrobalan B plum. Various abnormalities in growth and in the distribution of food reserves were observed, but more pronounced than could be ascribed to just a girdling effect at the graft union. This led to the belief that some additional cause was chiefly responsible for these disorders. The rootstock was affected more seriously in rate of growth, phloem development, and starch content than was the scion, indicating that the stock was affected primarily, with the scion disorders a secondary reaction. This view was supported by the fact that upon removal of the scion the stock rapidly returned to normal growth, which suggests that the scion was introducing into the stock some toxic substance.

When either of the plum varieties, President or Victoria, are grafted on the rootstock Myrobalan B, they develop into healthy, vigorous trees with no signs of incompatibility. But if trees of President on Myrobalan B roots are topworked with the Victoria plum, incompatibility symptoms soon appear at the President-Myrobalan B union several feet away, even though Victoria directly on Myrobalan B is a perfectly compatible combination. Again, it may be that some toxin is present that is detrimental to the graft union *(85)*.

In some cases, it is believed that one of the partners of the graft produces some form of toxin which either inhibits the growth or actually kills the other. The idea has also been advanced *(22, 24)* that abnormalities in incompatible graft combinations may result from *viruses* which have arisen directly as a result of the grafting; that is, by the invasion of the cells of one of the graft partners by proteins of the other. It is well known *(81)* that latent viruses or virus complexes do occur, and in particular graft combinations where a susceptible variety is introduced to a latent virus in its graft partner, rapid decline of the entire plant takes place.

In some of the incompatible combinations forming the basis for this theory, it has later developed that the toxic influence was a virus disease. For example, incompatibility was blamed for the difficulty encountered in working sweet orange (*Citrus sinensis*) on sour orange (*C. aurantium*) roots in South Africa about 1910 and in Java in 1928, even though this combination was a success commercially in other parts of the world *(6, 128)*. The incompatibility was believed to be due to the production of some substance by the scion which was toxic to the stock *(128)*. However, in the light of subsequent work stimulated by the development of the orange "quick decline" problem in California and in other parts of the world, it is now known that the toxic substance being produced by the sweet orange scions was a virus, tolerated by the sweet orange, but lethal to the sour orange stocks *(9, 38, 92, 126, 147)*.

A similar situation was found with a clonal apple rootstock, a vegetatively propagated seedling of the Northern Spy apple, designated as USDA 227. It was soon discovered that many scion varieties failed to grow on it, and incompatibility was suggested *(116, 131)*. It was even found that some "strains" of certain varieties such as McIntosh and Winesap grew normally on this stock, whereas others died *(115, 154)*. It was observed that the rootstock first showed injury symptoms with the subsequent death of both the stock and scion. The possibility of a virus was soon suspected *(39, 134)* and later shown *(148)* to be the cause of the trouble. This latent virus apparently occurred in all trees of some apple varieties, only in certain "strains" of other varieties, and not at all in still other varieties. The virus was nonlethal to these varieties, however. On the contrary, USDA 227 was highly susceptible to the virus, and when any scion carrying the virus, regardless of variety, was grafted or budded on this rootstock, the virus quickly caused its death and, of course, the death of the scion.

Correcting Incompatible Combinations

If the fact that an incompatible combination has been made is discovered before the tree dies or breaks off at the graft union, it is possible to correct the condition by bridge grafting (see p. 346) with a mutually compatible variety, if such exists. If a tree has been mistakenly propagated on a rootstock known to show delayed symptoms of incompatibility with the scion variety, and with the probability that the tree will eventually break off at the graft union, it is also possible to correct this condition by inarching (see p. 344). If breakage does not occur until the inarches are strong enough to support the tree, it may thus be possible to save it, the seedlings eventually taking over the functions of the original roots.

STOCK-SCION RELATIONSHIPS

Aside from situations where the stock and scion exhibit incompatibility to such a degree that the combinations have no value, there are many compatible combinations in which unusual effects are produced due to the interaction of stock and scion. Some of these have great value and are utilized commercially, but others are detrimental and are to be avoided. In some cases, the stock has a profound effect on one or more of the growth characteristics of the scion variety and, in the same manner, the scion can alter certain characteristics of the stock.

Effects of the Rootstock on the Scion Variety

Effect on the size and growth habit of the tree. This is probably the most pronounced and definite rootstock influence; some of the other effects noted are possibly a result of the altered vigor. The effect of a rootstock on vigor, as well as some of the other characteristics, can be, of course, modified by other environmental factors such as the scion variety, soil type, and so forth. Many examples of the effect of the rootstock on vigor of the plant can be cited, one of the most notable being the series of sixteen vegetatively propagated apple rootstocks investigated at the East Malling Research Station in England. They were separated into four groups based primarily on the degree of vigor induced in the scion variety and designated as *very dwarfing, semi-dwarfing, vigorous,* and *very vigorous (53, 54, 55, 94).* (These and other apple rootstocks are discussed in detail in Chapter 16.)

Growth of sweet cherry (*Prunus avium*) trees is definitely affected by the rootstock used. Mazzard (*P. avium*) roots produce large, vigorous trees, whereas Stockton Morello (a vegetatively propagated variety of *P. cerasus*) roots produce somewhat dwarfed trees. If *P. mahaleb* is used as the rootstock, the trees are generally intermediate in size *(31).*

In citrus, too, the rootstock has a marked effect on the ultimate size of the scion variety. Studies *(13)* in India showed that after 4 years trees of the Malta sweet orange variety were over three times as large if budded on the rough lemon (*Citrus limon*) than if they were budded on the citron (*C. medica*). Rootstock studies (8) with two varieties of the sweet orange in California showed that the rootstock used markedly affected tree size as well as the fruit size and yield. Various rootstock-scion combinations produced dwarfed trees (7).

Often, alterations in the normal shape of the tree are associated with the dwarfing effect due to certain rootstocks. Rather than being upright, a low and spreading form may develop. This is shown in grafts of the McIntosh apple on the semi-dwarfing rootstock, *Malus sikkimensis (106)*.

The behavior of one scion variety on a given rootstock in regard to vigor or other characteristics cannot be extended to other varieties with certainty. It is often necessary to actually test each combination of variety and rootstock before any conclusions concerning the behavior of the combination can be given (17, 124).

The fact should not be overlooked that symptomless (latent) viruses are known to occur in plants which, in themselves, may exert a dwarfing influence. Dwarfing effects could thus conceivably be due to the presence of a virus, which would be perpetuated in clonal stocks.

Effect of rootstock on early bearing, fruit-bud formation, fruit set, and yield. There is some indication that the mere presence of a graft or bud union tends to stimulate earlier and perhaps, heavier bearing. In an imperfect graft union, there is probably a partial blocking effect on the movement of nutrients, acting somewhat as a girdle, which would lead to increased fruitfulness. This is shown in rootstock studies (64) with citrus, where five rootstocks—sour orange, sweet orange, trifoliate orange, grapefruit, and rough lemon—all came into bearing two seasons earlier when budded to themselves than when unbudded, although in each case the trees were about the same size.

In the Oriental persimmon (*Diospyros kaki*), there seems to be a direct influence of the rootstock on flower production and fruit set. In tests (110) with the Hachiya variety grafted on three rootstocks, *D. kaki, D. lotus,* and *D. virginiana,* the influence of the rootstock on the number of blossoms produced and the percentage maturing as fruit was quite pronounced. Trees on *D. lotus* produced more blossoms but matured less fruit than those on *D. kaki.* Trees on *D. virginiana* produced so few blossoms that crops were unsatisfactory.

Dwarfing stocks, of course, soon limit the general vigor and vegetative growth of the scion variety. This is followed by carbohydrate accumulation and the resultant tendency toward fruit bud formation and early fruitfulness. Usually, the more dwarfing the rootstock, the greater is the tendency for early bearing. Conversely, strong, vigorous stocks tend to stimulate vegetative growth in the scion variety and maintain vigorous tree growth, thus delaying the age of bearing.

A pronounced rootstock effect is shown by studies *(135)* in which six apple varieties were grown for 5 years on eight of the Malling rootstocks. The largest trees were produced in this time on Malling XII, a very vigorous stock, followed in decreasing order by trees on Malling XIII and then by trees on Malling numbers V, IV, I, and II, with trees on Malling VII, a semi-dwarfing stock, the smallest. Blooming and fruiting precocity was just the reverse order; the earliest bearing was from trees on Malling VII, followed by those on Malling I and II, then by trees on Malling IV, V and XIII, with trees on Malling XII the last to start bearing.

Tests *(59)* in the eastern United States of the influence of various plum rootstocks on the behavior of fifteen varieties of plums, showed a marked effect on both vigor and yield of the trees. Of the rootstocks tested—*Prunus americana, P. cerasifera* (myrobalan plum), Marianna plum, St. Julien plum, and peach—the myrobalan plum roots in most instances produced both larger trees and higher yields than other rootstocks. This is probably due to the adaptability of myrobalan roots to the somewhat wet, poorly aerated soils used in this test. Trees on peach roots were winter killed. The effects on vigor and yield were the outstanding influences. No effect was observed on time of maturity of the wood or the fruit, and there was no appreciable effect on color, quality, or size of the fruit. On the other hand, in the milder winter climate of California and on good, well-drained orchard soils, it has frequently been observed *(32)* that the prune—certain *Prunus domestica* varieties—grows faster, comes into bearing earlier, and sets heavier crops on peach roots than it does on myrobalan plum roots.

Grape varieties are definitely influenced by the type of rootstock on which they are grafted *(51)*. Large increases in yield of certain varieties of the American type (*Vitis labrusca*) grape were obtained *(137)* when they were grafted on vigorous rootstocks in comparison with own-rooted plants. Over a 6-year period, the yield of Concord vines was increased from 30 to 150 per cent, depending upon the variety of rootstock used.

The use of vigorous, strongly growing rootstocks in some cases results in a larger and more vigorous plant which produces greater crops over a period of years. On the other hand, trees on dwarfing stocks may be more fruitful, and if closely planted, produce higher yields per acre.

Effect of rootstock on size, quality, color, and maturity of the fruit. There is considerable variation among plant species in regard to the effect of the rootstock on the fruit characteristics of the scion variety. In deciduous fruit species, situations in which the rootstock directly affects the size or quality of the fruit are rather rare, although secondary effects due to dwarfing do occur, such as increased fruit size caused by the checking of the vegetative growth and accumulation of carbohydrates which become available for fruit growth.

No carry-over of characteristics of the fruit of the stock is encountered in fruit of the scion variety. For example, the quince, commonly used as a pear rootstock, has a pronounced tart and astringent flavor, yet this flavor does not appear in the pear fruits. The peach is often used as a rootstock for the almond, yet there is no indication that the fruits of the almond have taken on any characteristics of the peach.

Although there is no intermingling of fruit characteristics between the stock and the scion, certain rootstocks can definitely affect the fruit quality of the scion variety. An outstanding example of this is found in the so-called "black-end" disease of pears. The Bartlett, Anjou, and some other pear varieties on several rootstocks often produce fruits which are abnormal at the calyx end. The injury usually consists of blackened flesh, which in severe cases cracks open. Sometimes the calyx end of the fruit is hard and protruding. Such fruit is worthless commercially. It has been shown *(25, 26, 62)* that this trouble develops when the trees are propagated on certain rootstocks, such as *Pyrus pyrifolia,* but only rarely when the French pear, *P. communis,* is used. This trouble affects only the fruit; no symptoms of adverse tree growth appear.

The development of black-end fruits disappears if trees on *P. pyrifolia* rootstock are inarched with *P. communis* seedlings and—after the inarches are able to support the tree—the original *P. pyrifolia* roots are cut away. Black-end fruits continue to appear unless the original connection of the Bartlett top with the *P. pyrifolia* roots is broken. Whether the *P. pyrifolia* roots fail to supply the developing fruits with needed materials from the soil or whether they are producing substances toxic to the fruit or whether some other interaction is in effect, has not been established.

In citrus, striking effects of the rootstock appear in the fruit of the scion variety *(3, 46, 66, 97, 120, 122).* If sour orange (*Citrus aurantium*) is used as the rootstock, fruits of the sweet orange, tangerine, and grapefruit are smooth, thin-skinned, juicy, with excellent quality, and store well without deterioration. Sweet orange (*C. sinensis*) rootstocks also result in thin-skinned, juicy, high quality fruits. Citrus fruits on grapefruit (*C. paradisi*) stocks are usually excellent size, grade and quality, if heavy fertilization is provided. But when the rough lemon (*C. limon*) is used as the stock, the fruits are often thick-skinned, somewhat large and coarse, inferior in quality, and low in both sugar and acid.

Fruit size of both the Washington Navel orange and the Valencia orange is strongly influenced by the rootstock. In tests *(8),* the largest Navel orange fruits were produced on sour orange stocks and the smallest on the Palestine sweet lime. The largest Valencia oranges are found on the dwarfing trifoliate orange stock, whereas the sweet orange rootstocks produce the smallest fruits.

An interesting example of the effect of the stock on the fruit of the scion is the tomato (*Lycopersicon esculentum*) grafted on the Jimson weed (*Datura stramonium*). This combination had been used commercially to some extent in the southern part of the United States, due to the resistance of *D. stramonium* roots to nematodes. As it is known that Jimson weed contains poisonous alkaloids, concern was felt as to whether such alkaloids might not be translocated from the rootstock to the fruit of the tomato. Tests showed that this actually was the case. The alkaloid content of tomato fruits from grafted plants ranged from 1.77 to 13.00 mgs. per pound of fresh fruit, whereas ungrafted control plants had no alkaloid content (76).

There are other examples similar to this of translocation of compounds between stock and scion in intergeneric grafts in Solanaceae. In a series of reciprocal grafts between tomato and tobacco, nicotine was present in tomato scions when they were grown on tobacco rootstocks, but when tobacco scions were grown on tomato rootstocks, none of the three major tobacco alkaloids were found, either in the tobacco scions or tomato rootstocks. This is because the sole origin of nicotine is in the roots of tobacco (27, 28).

Miscellaneous effects of the rootstock on the scion variety—winter hardiness, disease resistance, and time of fruit maturity. In citrus, there appears to be a definite effect of the rootstock on the cold hardiness of the scion. During killing freezes in the winter of 1950–51 in the Rio Grande Valley, young grapefruit trees on Rangpur lime rootstocks survived much better than those on rough lemon or sour orange, whereas trees on Cleopatra mandarin were the most severely damaged (19). In the apple, on the other hand, the type of rootstock used—relatively winter hardy or tender—appears to have no effect on the cold hardiness of the scion variety (35, 123).

Reports arise occasionally of fruits maturing abnormally early, resulting supposedly from the scion variety being grafted on a rootstock variety whose fruits mature early. An investigation (29) of this situation, involving observations of the Grand Duke plum variety grafted on eleven different types of rootstocks, showed that every reported instance of early fruit ripening was associated with some difficulty at the graft union, such as an incompatible combination, abnormal union, or partial girdling.

Different rootstocks respond differently to certain soil conditions, thus resulting in an altered effect on the behavior of the scion variety (75). This is illustrated in Figure 11–17. Almond and myrobalan plum roots are apparently much more tolerant of excess boron in the soil than Marianna plum roots. Thus, in this case, fairly good growth of the French prune occurred on almond and myrobalan plum roots under conditions in which it was severely injured when worked on Marianna plum or apricot roots (49).

Comparing the four rootstocks commonly used for stone fruits—plum, peach, apricot, and almond—it is well known (32) that they differ markedly

Figure 11-17. The tolerance of fruit trees to toxic amounts of certain elements may be influenced by the rootstock used. This is illustrated here by French prune trees on four different rootstocks which were irrigated with water containing different levels of boron. Rootstocks were: **(A)** almond seedlings; **(B)** myrobalan plum seedlings; **(C)** apricot seedlings; **(D)** Marianna plum cuttings. Irrigation water containing the following five concentrations of boron were used for each rootstock: **(left to right)** 1/2 ppm (tap water); 2 ppm; 3 ppm; 5 ppm; 10 ppm. Courtesy C. J. Hansen.

in their response to adverse soil conditions. The growth of the scion variety under such conditions would, of course, depend upon the particular rootstock on which it was propagated. For example, trees with myrobalan plum as the rootstock would be the most tolerant of excessive soil moisture, followed by peach or apricot roots, with almond being most susceptible to injury from such conditions.

The severity of lime-induced chlorosis symptoms in citrus on calcareous soils is greatly influenced by the rootstock used. Tests of grapefruit on thirty-six different rootstocks showed that with four of the stocks no chlorosis appeared, but severe chlorosis developed when thirteen of the rootstocks were used *(18)*.

These examples illustrate cases where the growth of the scion variety was definitely affected by the rootstock used. This was, in turn, traced to reactions of the rootstock to certain unfavorable soil conditions. This can be extended further, of course. It is known that some rootstocks are more tolerant than others to adverse soil situations caused by organisms such as nematodes (*Meloidogyne* sp.) or oak root fungus (*Armillaria mellea*). The growth of the scion variety would subsequently be influenced by the rootstock through the latter's relative ability to withstand such conditions.

Cases where the use of a certain rootstock imparts disease resistance to the scion variety are not common. One example is furnished in the case of infections of stone fruits in California by bacterial canker (*Pseudomonas syringae*). It was noted *(30)* in a number of instances that both apricots and plums, when grafted on myrobalan plum roots, became much more seriously infected than when they were worked on peach roots. Another example of this situation is the increased resistance to apple scab (*Venturia inaequalis*) observed in scion varieties worked on the rootstock, Malling XVI *(83)*.

There is evidence *(33)* that the time of seed germination of the tomato and the size and vigor of the resulting seedlings are influenced by the rootstock (various species of Solanaceae) upon which tomato scions were grafted. This is an unusual case where the effect of the stock reached beyond the vegetative tissues to the reproductive structure.

Effects of the Scion Variety on the Rootstock

Although there is a tendency to attribute all cases of dwarfing or invigoration of a grafted plant to the rootstock, the effect of the scion on the behavior of the complete plant may be fully as important as that of the rootstock. Unquestionably, however, the effect of the scion, the rootstock, and the graft union itself, all interact to influence each other and determine the over-all behavior of the plant. In some combinations, on the other hand, a particular member of the combination may have a marked influence no matter what part of the plant it becomes. For instance, a dwarfing stock will exert a dwarfing influence on the entire plant whether used as the rootstock, intermediate stock, or scion.

Effect of the scion variety on the vigor of the rootstock. This seems to be the major influence of the scion on the stock, just as it was in the case of the effect of rootstock on the scion variety. If a strongly growing scion variety is grafted on a weak rootstock, the growth of the rootstock will be stimulated so as to become larger than it would have been if left ungrafted. Conversely, if a weakly growing scion variety is grafted on a vigorous rootstock, the growth of the rootstock will be lessened from what it might have been if left ungrafted. In citrus, for example, when the scion variety is less vigorous than the rootstock variety, it is the scion variety rather than the rootstock which determines the rate of growth and ultimate size of the tree (65).

That the scion influences the growth of the rootstock was recognized at least as early as the middle of the nineteenth century (43). It has long been known, particularly with apples, that the size, nature, and form of the root system which develops from the seedling rootstocks of grafted trees can be affected by the variety of the scion (100, 114, 130). Different scion varieties may cause a typical root growth pattern to develop in the rootstock. For example, if apple seedlings are budded or grafted with the Red Astrachan apple variety, a very fibrous root system with few taproots develops. If other similar seedlings are budded or grafted with the Oldenburg or Fameuse variety, the subsequent root system is not fibrous but has a two- or three-pronged deep taproot system (60). In fact, nurserymen propagating apple varieties can often identify many of the scion varieties by the appearance of the root system of the grafted rootstock. Nurserymen have also experienced striking differences when digging nursery trees of different scion varieties. Additional power must be used on their digging machines when, for example, the Oldenberg apple, with the deep taproot system developed by the seedling stock is dug.

This effect of the scion variety on the type of root system developed by the stock has been noted principally with seedling stocks. The vegetatively propagated clonal stocks have not usually shown such an effect (100, 125). For instance, the root systems of a rootstock variety, such as Malling IX or XII, grafted with different scion varieties seem to retain their own distinct morphological characters regardless of the scion variety used, although the scion variety may have a marked influence on the quantity of roots (138).

Effect of the scion variety on cold hardiness of the rootstock. In some species at least, the cold hardiness of a particular rootstock can be influenced by the particular scion variety which is grafted to it. This effect is not due necessarily to a winter hardy scion imparting hardiness to the rootstock. Rather, it is probably related to the degree of maturity attained by the rootstock, certain scion varieties tending to prolong growth of the roots long into the fall so that insufficient maturity of the root tissues is reached by the time killing low temperatures occur in the winter. The rootstock, if left ungrafted or grafted to a scion variety which stops growth in early fall, may mature its tissues sufficiently early so as to develop adequate winter hardiness.

In the Northern Great Plains states in the United States, the Malling apple rootstocks have not been winter hardy even when the hardy Wealthy variety was used as the scion. But when the winter hardy Dolgo crabapple was used as the scion, young trees on eight of the Malling stocks lived through four winters in North Dakota and when dug for examination were entirely healthy and free from winter injury. The Dolgo crabapple ripens its fruit in late August, and the tree ceases growth and matures its wood early in the season in comparison with the Wealthy variety. In this case, the hardy Dolgo crabapple apparently did increase the hardiness of the Malling stocks used, an effect probably due to its early maturing growth habit rather than its inherent hardiness *(111)*.

Cold hardiness of citrus roots is also affected by the scion variety. Sour orange seedlings budded to Eureka lemon suffered much more from winter injury than unbudded seedlings. The lemon tops were killed, as well as several inches down into the sour orange stock, but unbudded sour orange seedlings suffered only slight foliage injury *(144, 145)*.

Effects of an Intermediate Stock on Scion and Rootstock

When trees are topworked to change varieties, the original scion variety then becomes an intermediate stock. It is important to know whether such interstocks exert an influence on the growth of the rootstock or scion and subsequently the entire plant. Several studies have shown that there can be a decided effect *(42)*. Tests *(127)* to determine if intermediate stocks of various apple varieties inserted between the apple rootstock Malling II and the scion variety Jonathan or Delicious had any effect on the behavior of the scion, showed that in every case a depression of growth occurred in comparison with cases where the scion variety itself was used as the interstock.

If the intermediate stem piece is of a dwarfing nature, such as the Malling IX, it will dwarf the entire tree to some extent. Repeated comparisons of the influence exerted on the scion variety by both the rootstock and an intermediate stock have shown that they both have an influence but that of the rootstock is greater *(71, 133, 140)*.

This interstock effect could be due to the introduction of an additional graft union with the possibility of restrictions in the upward flow of water and nutrients or the downward movement of sugars and other organic compounds to the roots. The fact that graft unions in the apple with the dwarfing Malling IX as rootstocks, although strong and well-knit, are often gnarled and rough rather than smooth as when vigorous stocks are used, supports the belief that the dwarfing effect could be due to a certain amount of blocking of the graft union.

Imperfect graft unions are also indicated as the cause of the dwarfing exerted on orange trees by a lemon interstock. Unlike the dwarfing situation in apples with a Malling IX interstock, the lemon itself is strong-growing.

On the other hand, there is evidence that the observed effects of the interstock are due directly to an influence of the interstock piece rather than to abnormalities at the graft union. The dwarfing effect of the Malling IX stock would seem to be due to something more than restrictions at the graft union, since this variety is an early bearing, dwarf tree itself. The belief that the influence of intermediate stocks may be due to a direct scion-stock interaction, rather than just a poor graft union, is further supported by studies *(108)* with the Baldwin and Stayman apple varieties. When they were worked directly on an apomictic (see p. 43) seedling rootstock, Hybrid 33340 (*Malus sargentii* $\times$ *M. astracanica*), they either died or made very poor growth. But if either of these two varieties were worked on Hybrid 33340 as an interstock, with *Malus sikkimensis* as the rootstock, the trees made excellent, normal growth. In both cases the Baldwin (or Stayman)—Hybrid 33340 graft union was present, but it was only when the 33340 was actually used as the rootstock that the trees failed to grow.

Further evidence that the interstock effect is due to a direct influence of the stock itself comes from the fact that increasing the length of the interstock has intensified its effect *(44)*.

Kemmer in Germany points out *(70)* that the rootstock should be considered as one of the environmental factors acting upon the scion variety. He has stated the idea of stock influence on tree vigor as follows: If two or more stocks act upon a tree, vegetative growth is determined (a) in a *vertical* arrangement (when one or more of the stocks is used as an interstock) by that stock which induces the weakest growth performance; and (b) in a *horizontal* arrangement (when the stocks are used as inarches) by that stock which induces the strongest growth performance.

Possible Explanations for the Effects of Stock on Scion and Scion on Stock

The fundamental causes of reciprocal stock-scion influences have yet to be fully determined. The explanations offered for the observed effects are often conflicting and not well substantiated. Several theories have been advanced as possible explanations for the interactions between stock and scion.

Roberts and Swarbrick *(100, 104, 125),* considering the apple in particular, hold that the effects of the rootstock are localized in the *stem* portion of the stock rather than in the *absorbing root system*. They explain that a scion variety may behave quite differently if it is grafted on a root piece (as in root grafting) than if it is grafted (or budded) high up on the stem portion of the rootstock. It is believed by this theory that the rootstock influences are the result of *translocation effects* rather than the *absorbing ability* of the root system. That the stem portion of the tree has, to some extent at least, a definite influence is shown by experiments *(10)* in which rootstock varieties are used as intermediate stocks between a vigorous root system and the scion variety. The expected rootstock effects are still present, although to a lesser degree, even though the stocks are used as interstocks rather than as the entire root-absorbing system. This same stock influence is noted in the scion variety if the intermediate stock tissue is reduced to just a ring of bark *(101, 102, 103)*.

By this theory, the uniformity of trees which are produced on vegetatively propagated rootstocks is due to the uniformity of the *stems* of such stocks, whereas the variable stems of seedlings are responsible for the variation encountered in the growth of the scion variety. This is especially so if they are grafted or budded high on the stem so that there is more opportunity for stem influence to be exerted. But if the grafting is done on the roots of the seedlings—as is done in root grafting—this variability would not appear due to the absence of the influencing stem section. Therefore, a fairly uniform group of trees could be produced even though they were on seedling rootstocks.

This theory also attempts to explain the influence of the scion variety on the nature of the growth of the rootstock as being due to the presence or absence of the *stem* portion of the rootstock. If an apple scion variety is budded or grafted high on the stem of the rootstock—either a seedling or a clonal stock—there is little or no scion influence on the development of the root system of the stock. In other words, the presence of the stem of the rootstock is dominating in its influence. But if the scion variety is grafted directly on a *root* piece of the rootstock, with no rootstock stem present, then the scion exerts a strong influence on the character of growth of the rootstock.

Some of the evidence for support of this theory was obtained in comparisons between piece root grafts (rootstock stem absent) and budded trees (rootstock stem present). In the former case, the scion has an opportunity to influence root growth and distribution from the start. In the latter, the seedling would have grown a year at least and have had its roots well established before the bud would have had an opportunity to influence root development. It would thus be expected in root grafts that the scion would have greater influence on root growth than would be found in budded trees.

Some workers in England conclude from their experiments *(56, 71, 138, 140)* that the *root system* itself rather than the *stem* of the rootstock plays the major role in rootstock effects on the scion, although they agree that the stem section does have some influence.

While Swarbrick and Roberts believe *(125)* that the scion variety definitely influences root anatomy when the graft is placed directly on the root piece, Vyvyan's experiments *(138)* in England, although with different scion varieties and trees of a different age, failed to support this conclusion. In fact, the root system of two clonal apple stocks retained their distinct characteristics whether worked with either of two scion varieties, scions of their own variety, or unworked. When worked with the two scion varieties, it made no difference in root characteristics whether they were root-grafted on piece roots or grafted on the stem of the rootstock. In the same manner, seedling rootstocks failed to assume any distinct morphological characteristics when worked with either of two scion varieties, regardless of whether a piece of the rootstock stem was left below the graft union.

Chandler *(15)* and Gardner, Bradford, and Hooker *(40)*, discussing the subject in more general terms, believe that the effects of stock on scion and scion on stock can be explained by *physiological factors,* chiefly the influences due to *changes in vigor.* Chandler points out that when the scion is the more vigorous part of the combination, the carbohydrate supply to the roots should be greater. And since certain roots supply and are supplied by certain branches, it would be expected that the branching habit of the top would influence the branching habit of the roots, thus explaining the different roots types obtained in using different scion varieties. If trees of different varieties were pruned to exactly the same number and distribution of branches, then the difference in rootstock growth associated with the different scion varieties might not occur. Chandler concludes that "there is little experimental evidence indicating any influence of stock on scion other than an increase or decrease of water and mineral nutrient supply as determined by the growth habits of the stock." A weakly growing rootstock would reduce the water and nutrient supply to the top, thereby inducing earlier maturity of the fruit. Increased fruit size could be the result of a larger than normal supply of organic foods due to the restriction at the graft union, in the same manner as girdling grapes causes larger sized fruits.

The fruitful condition existing in young apple trees worked on the dwarfing Malling IX roots was found to be associated with accumulation of starch in the shoots early in the season *(17)*. Such an early starch storage would be expected to be favorable for the initiation of flower bud primordia. Nonfruitful trees on the vigorous Malling XII roots failed to show such a starch accumulation. The increased supply of water and nutrients from the vigorous roots would be expected to stimulate the production of new growth rather than retard growth and allow for the accumulation of carbohydrates, as would be the case with the weaker, dwarfing rootstocks.

Differences in growth rate was suggested by Vyvyan *(139, 141)* as a possible explanation of some of the observed reciprocal effects of stock and scion, especially vigor. He points out that for a given scion variety on a given soil, the stem/root ratio in any given scion-stock combination is remarkably constant, regardless of tree size or age. This constant ratio between stem and root means that both grow at the same rate. If two different varieties with markedly different growth rates are combined as stem and root by grafting into one plant which would subsequently have a constant growth rate, there must be some alteration in the growth rate of the components. Either the slowly growing variety must speed up or the faster· growing one must decrease its rate. Thus, the stock and the scion would be expected to mutually affect each other's growth rate.

Rootstock effects are not invariably related to vigor. Such things as fruit setting, fruit size, and fruit color or quality may be affected by the rootstock used even on trees showing an equal amount of vigor. For example, the marked effect of the rootstock on the development of black-end in pears (see p. 302) is certainly not due to an alteration in vigor.

A theory sometimes given for explaining the altered growth of scion varieties on different rootstocks is the different *mineral absorption* by the various rootstocks which is made available for use by the scion variety. For example, the very vigorous Shalil peach root system grown at low nutrient levels was able to pick up and furnish the scion variety with a greater supply of nutrients and water than the less vigorous Lovell rootstock. Under these conditions, the scion variety showed better growth on Shalil than on Lovell roots. But when the salt level was higher and included toxic chloride ions, the greater accumulation of such salts, subsequently translocated to the scion variety, caused injury and growth depression. In this case, then, the difference in vigor of two rootstocks caused opposite effects under two different soil conditions—a low salt and a high salt condition *(58)*.

A possible explanation for the dwarfing effect of certain rootstocks is supplied by studies *(142)* concerning the *efficiency of water conductivity* of the graft union. There are indications that the graft union does introduce an additional resistance to the flow of water. This resistance was greater in unions where the Malling IX stock was one of the components. Certain of the growth characteristics of trees on Malling IX roots, such as small leaves, short internodes, and the early cessation of seasonal shoot growth, are those generally associated with a slight water deficit in the tree. As mentioned before, however, although a restricted graft union may contribute to the dwarfing influence of certain rootstocks, the primary influence probably lies in the nature of the growth characteristics of such stocks.

It is possible that a certain *anatomical structure* of the rootstock may be associated with an observed effect of the rootstock. Studies *(4)* in England showed that dwarfing apple rootstocks have a high proportion of bark (all tissues outside the cambium) to wood in the lateral roots, whereas rootstocks causing increased vegetative vigor in the scion have, in the lateral roots, a lower proportion of bark to wood. Also much of the functional wood tissue of the roots of dwarfing apple sticks is composed of living cells, whereas in nondwarfing, vigorous rootstocks, the wood consists of a relatively large amount of lignified tissue without living cell contents. Such marked differences in internal structure between dwarfing and invigorating rootstocks could lead to important physiological differences, such as metabolic requirements and water and food conducting ability, thus accounting, possibly, for the observed differences in influence on the scion.

The idea has been advanced by Sax *(108, 109)* that some of the growth alterations noted when certain intermediate stocks are used, or when a ring of bark in the trunk of young trees is inverted, may be due to interference with the normal downward flow of *natural hormones* and nutrients from the leaves to the roots. It is known that such hormones do exist (e.g., vitamin B_1), which are necessary for root growth. Anything that would stop or reduce the flow of such substances would, of course, limit growth of the rootstock, subsequently dwarfing the entire tree. Dwarfing rootstocks may show their characteristic effect due to their inability to conduct or utilize root growth-promoting hormones manufactured by the scion. Often trees on dwarfing stocks will make vigorous growth for a year or two in the nursery *(132)* when such hormones would still be present in ample amounts. Several years later, however, the dwarfing effect may be initiated by the increasing lack of sufficient hormones to result in normal root growth.

The belief that the reciprocal stock-scion influences could be due to alterations in the normal movement of growth-regulating hormones is supported by the fact that some natural growth-regulating substances do pass from one graft partner to another. In one case *(34)* when the juvenile form of ivy (*Hedera helix*) was grafted to the adult form, the capacity to flower was lost by the adult form and its new growth showed juvenile characters.

It has also been demonstrated by photoperiodism experiments *(47)* that when plants in the reproductive stage are grafted to plants in the vegetative stage, flowering is induced in the latter type plant. Passage of hormones may be involved in the situation where nonflowering varieties of the sweet potato (*Ipomoea batatas*) are induced to flower by grafting them on related flowering plants, such as the morning glory (*Ipomoea purpurea*) *(119, 156)*.

REFERENCES

1. Amos, J., et al., Studies in incompatibility of stock and scion. I. Information accumulated during twenty years of testing fruit tree rootstocks with various scion varieties at East Malling, *Ann. Rpt. East Malling Res. Sta. for 1935*, A–19:81–99. 1936.
2. Argles, G. K., A review of the literature on stock-scion incompatibility in fruit trees, with particular reference to pome and stone fruits, *Imp. Bur. of Fruit Prod., Tech. Comm. No. 9,* 1937.

3. Batchelor, L. D., and H. J. Webber, Production of the crop, *The Citrus Industry.* Berkeley: Univ. of Calif. Press, 1948. Vol. II.

4. Beakbane, A. B., Anatomical structure in relation to rootstock behavior, *Rpt. 13th Int. Hort. Cong.,* Vol. 1:152–158. 1953.

5. Bennett, H. D., An account of an experiment with piece root grafts in the apple and pear and of the influence on growth of the position of the top bud of the scion relative to the graft union, *Proc. Amer. Soc. Hort. Sci.,* 23:255–259. 1927.

6. Bioletti, F. T., et al., Citrus culture in Cape Colony. Rpt. Comm. of Inquiry into the Causes of the Failure of Citrus Trees in Cape Colony. *Cape of Good Hope Dept. of Agr.,* 21:1–20. 1904.

7. Bitters, W. P., Citrus rootstocks for dwarfing, *Calif. Agr.,* 4(2):5–14. 1950.

8. Bitters, W. P., and L. D. Batchelor, Rootstocks affect orange sizes, *Calif. Agr.,* 5:4–16. 1951.

9. Bitters, W. P., and E. R. Parker, Quick decline of citrus as influenced by top-root relationships, *Calif. Agr. Exp. Sta. Bul. 733,* 1953.

10. Blair, D. S., Rootstock and scion relationship in apple trees, *Sci. Agr.,* 19:85–94. 1938.

11. Bradford, F. C., and B. G. Sitton, Defective graft unions in the apple and pear, *Mich. Agr. Exp. Sta. Tech. Bul. 99,* 1929.

12. Brierley, W. G., Effects of hormone and warm temperature treatments upon growth of black walnut root grafts, *The Nutshell,* Vol. 7, No. 2. Jan., 1955.

13. Brown, W. R., The orange: a trial of stocks at Peshawar, *Pusa Agr. Res. Inst. Bul. 93,* 1920.

14. Buck, G. J., The histological development of the bud graft union in roses, *Proc. Amer. Soc. Hort. Sci.,* 62:497–502. 1953.

15. Chandler, W. H., *Fruit Growing.* Boston: Houghton Mifflin, 1925.

16. Chang, Wen-Tsai, Studies in incompatibility between stock and scion, with special reference to certain deciduous fruit trees, *Jour. Pom. and Hort. Sci.,* 15:267–325. 1938.

17. Colby, H. L., Stock-scion chemistry and the fruiting relationships in apple trees, *Plant Phys.,* 10:483–498. 1935.

18. Cooper, W. C., and E. O. Olson, Influence of rootstock on chlorosis of young Red Blush grapefruit trees, *Proc. Amer. Soc. Hort. Sci.,* 57:125–132. 1951.

19. Cooper, W. C., Influence of rootstock on injury and recovery of young citrus trees exposed to the freezes of 1950–51 in the Rio Grande Valley, *Proc. 6th Ann. Rio Grande Valley Hort. Inst.,* pp. 16–24. 1952.

20. Colquhoun, T. T., Polarity in *Casuarina paludosa, Trans. and Proc. Roy. Soc. South Australia,* 53:353–358. 1929.

21. Crafts, A. S., Phloem anatomy in two species of *Nicotiana,* with notes on the interspecific graft union, *Bot. Gaz.,* 95:592–608. 1934.

22. Crane, M. B., Origin of viruses, *Nature,* 155:115–116. 1945.

23. Crane, M. B., and E. Marks, Pear-apple hybrids, *Nature,* 170:1017. 1952.

24. Darlington, C. D., Heredity, development, and infection, *Nature,* 154:164–169. 1944.

25. Davis, L. D., and W. P. Tufts, Black end of pears III, *Proc. Amer. Soc. Hort. Sci.,* 33:304–315. 1936.

26. ———, Pear growing in California, *Calif. Agr. Ext. Cir. 122,* 1941.

27. Dawson, R. F., Accumulation of nicotine in reciprocal grafts of tomato and tobacco, *Amer. Jour. Bot.,* 29:66–71. 1942.

28. ———, An experimental analysis of alkaloid production in *Nicotiana:* the origin of nornicotine, *Amer. Jour. Bot.,* 32:416–423. 1945.

29. Day, L. H., Ripening dates of Grand Duke plums on various understocks, *Proc. Amer. Soc. Hort. Sci.,* 30:357–360. 1933.

30. ————, The influence of rootstocks on the occurrence and severity of bacterial canker, *Pseudomonas cerasi,* of stone fruits, *Proc. Amer. Soc. Hort. Sci.,* 50:100–102. 1947.

31. ————, Cherry rootstocks in California, *Calif. Agr. Exp. Sta. Bul. 725,* 1951.

32. ————, Rootstocks for stone fruits, *Calif. Agr. Exp. Sta. Bul. 736,* 1953.

33. Detjen, L. R., The influence of the rootstock on seeds and seedling progenies of tomato grafts, *Proc. Amer. Soc. Hort. Sci.,* 43:147–148. 1943.

34. Doorenbos, J., "Rejuvenation" of *Hedera helix* in graft combinations, Proc. Kon. Akad. Wetensch., (Series C.) 57:99–102. 1954. (Abst. in *Hort. Abst.* 2174. Vol. 24, No. 3. 1954.)

35. Dorsey, M. J., Hardiness in top-worked varieties of the apple, *Proc. Amer. Soc. Hort. Sci.,* 15:38–45. 1918.

36. Eames, A. J., and L. G. Cox, A remarkable tree-fall and an unusual type of graft union failure, *Amer. Jour. Bot.,* 32:331–335. 1945.

37. Evenari, N., and E. Konis, The effect of hetero-auxin on root formation by cuttings and on grafting, *Palest. Jour. Bot.,* (J), 1:13–26. 1938.

38. Fawcett, H. S., and J. M. Wallace, Evidence of the virus nature of citrus quick decline, *Calif. Citrogr.,* 32:2, 50, 88–89. 1946.

39. Gardner, F. E., P. C. Marth, and J. R. Magness, Lethal effects of certain apple scions on Spy 227 stock, *Proc. Amer. Soc. Hort. Sci.,* 48:195–199. 1946.

40. Gardner, V. R., F. C. Bradford, H. D. Hooker, Jr., *Fundamentals of Fruit Production,* 2nd ed., New York: McGraw-Hill, 1939.

41. Garner, R. J., and D. H. Hammond, Studies in nursery technique. Shield budding. Treatment of inserted buds with petroleum jelly, *Ann. Rpt. East Malling Res. Sta. for 1938,* pp. 115–117. 1939.

42. Garner, R. J., *The Grafter's Handbook.* London: Faber and Faber, 1947.

43. Goodale, S. L., Influence of the scion upon the stock, *Hort.,* 1:290. 1846.

44. Grubb, N. H., East Malling Ann. Rpt., 17:35. 1929.

45. Haas, A. R. C., and F. F. Halma, Chemical relationship between scion and stock in citrus, *Plant Phys.,* 4:113–121. 1929.

46. Haas, A. R. C., Effect of the rootstock on the composition of citrus trees and fruit, *Plant Phys.,* 23:309–330. 1948.

47. Hamner, K., and J. Bonner, Photoperiodism in relation to hormones as factors in floral initiation and development, *Bot. Gaz.,* 100:388–431. 1938.

48. Hamond, J. B., The morphology, physiology and mode of parasitism of a species of *Chalaropsis* infecting nursery walnut trees, *Jour. Pom. and Hort. Sci.,* 13:81–107. 1935.

49. Hansen, C. J., Influence of the rootstock on injury from excess boron in French (Agen) prune and President plum, *Proc. Amer. Soc. Hort. Sci.,* 51:239–244. 1948.

50. Hansen, C. J., and H. T. Hartmann, Influence of various treatments given to walnut grafts on the percentage of scions growing, *Proc. Amer. Soc. Hort. Sci.,* 57:193–197. 1951.

51. Harmon, F. N., Comparative value of thirteen rootstocks for ten vinifera grape varieties in the Napa Valley in California, *Proc. Amer. Soc. Hort. Sci.,* 54:157–162. 1949.

52. Harris, R. V., Grafting as a method for investigating a possible virus disease of the strawberry, *Jour. Pom. and Hort. Sci.,* 10:35–41. 1932.

53. Hatton, R. G., The influence of different rootstocks upon the vigor and productivity of the variety budded or grafted thereon, *Jour. Pom. and Hort. Sci.,* 6:1–28. 1927.

54. ————, Results of researches on fruit tree stocks, *Jour. Pom. and Hort. Sci.,* 2:1–10. 1930.

55. ———, The relationship between scion and rootstock with special reference to the tree fruits, *Jour. Roy. Hort. Soc.*, 55:169–211. 1930.

56. ———, The influence of vegetatively raised rootstocks upon the apple, with special reference to the parts played by the stem and root portions in affecting the scion, *Jour. Pom. and Hort. Sci.*, 9:265–277. 1931.

57. Hayward, H. E., and F. W. Went, Transplantation experiments with peas. II. *Bot. Gaz.*, 100:788–801. 1939.

58. Hayward, H. E., and E. M. Long, Vegetative responses of the Elberta peach on Lovell and Shalil rootstocks to high chloride and sulfate solutions, *Proc. Amer. Soc. Hort. Sci.*, 41:149–155. 1942.

59. Hedrick, U. P., Stocks for plums, *N.Y. (Geneva) Agr. Exp. Sta. Bul. 498,* 1923.

60. ———, Stocks for fruits, *Rpt. N.Y. State Fruit Growers' Assoc.*, pp. 84–94. 1915.

61. Heppner, M. J., and R. D. McCallum, Grafting affinities with special reference to plums, *Calif. Agr. Exp. Sta. Bul. 438,* 1927.

62. Heppner, M. J., Pear black-end and its relation to different rootstocks, *Proc. Amer. Soc. Hort. Sci.*, 24:139. 1927.

63. Herrero, J., Studies of compatible and incompatible graft combinations with special reference to hardy fruit trees, *Jour. Hort. Sci.*, 26:186–237. 1951.

64. Hodgson, R. W., and S. H. Cameron, On bud union effect in citrus, *Calif. Citrog.*, 20(12):370. 1935.

65. ———, Some instances of scion domination in citrus, *Proc. Amer. Soc. Hort. Sci.*, 43:131–138. 1943.

66. Hodgson, R. W., and E. R. Eggers, Rootstock influence on the composition of citrus fruits, *Calif. Citrog.*, 23:499, 531. 1938.

67. Jakes, E., and H. Hexnerova, Über den Einfluss der Wuchsstoffe auf Wundgewebebildung bei Obstbäumen, *Gartenbauwiss.*, 13:83–93. 1939.

68. Juliano, J. B., Callus development in graft union, *Philippine Jour. Sci.*, 75:245–251. 1941.

69. Kawakami, S., and T. Isimaru, Mume and apricot growing in cold districts II. The effect of growth substances on grafting and budding, *Jour. Hort. Assoc. Jap.*, 12:123–142. 1941.

70. Kemmer, E., Die Unterlage als Standortfaktor, *Land Wald und Garten*, Heft 11. 1947.

71. Knight, R. C., Further observations on the parts played by root and stem in stock influence, *Ann. Rpt. East Malling Res. Sta. for 1933*, pp. 114–116. 1934.

72. Kunkel, L. O., Contact periods in graft transmission of peach viruses, *Phytopath.*, 28:491–497. 1938.

73. Langford, M. H., et al., *Hevea* diseases of the Western Hemisphere, *Plant Disease Rpt. Suppl. 225*, May 15, 1954.

74. Langford, M. H., and C. H. T. Townsend, Jr., Control of South American leaf blight of *Hevea* rubber trees, *Plant Disease Rpt. Suppl. 225*, May 15, 1954.

75. Lilleland, O., The present status of leaf analysis in relation to fruit tree nutrition, *Blue Anchor* (Calif. Fruit Exchange, Sacramento), 23(1). 1946.

76. Lowman, M. S., and J. W. Kelley, The presence of mydriatic alkaloids in tomato fruit from scions grown on *Datura stramonium* rootstock, *Proc. Amer. Soc. Hort. Sci.*, 48:249–259. 1946.

77. McClintock, J. A., A study of uncongeniality between peaches as scions and the Marianna plum as a stock, *Jour. Agr. Res.*, 77:253–260. 1948.

78. McDaniel, J. C., Practices that improve bud propagation. III. *Orchard Topics,* Univ. of Illinois. Aug., 1954.

79. McQuilkin, W. E., Effects of some growth regulators and dressings on the healing of tree wounds, *Jour. Forest.*, 48(9):423–428. 1950.

80. Mendel, K., The anatomy and histology of the bud-union in citrus, *Palest. Jour. Bot.*, (R), 1(2):13–46. 1936.

81. Milbraith, J. A., and S. M. Zeller, Latent viruses in stone fruits, *Science*, 101:114–115. 1945.

82. Miller, P. W., Technique for indexing strawberries for viruses by grafting to *Fragaria vesca*, *Plant Disease Rpt.* 36:94–96. 1952.

83. Moore, M. H., The incidence and control of apple scab and apple mildew at East Malling, *Jour. Pom. and Hort. Sci.*, 8:229–304. 1930.

84. Mosse, B., and J. Herrero, Studies on incompatibility between some pear and quince grafts. *Jour. Hort. Sci.*, 26:238–245. 1951.

85. Mosse, B., and R. J. Garner, Growth and structural changes induced in plum by an additional scion, *Jour. Hort. Sci.*, 29:12–19. 1954.

86. Mosse, B., Symptoms of incompatibility induced in a peach by ring grafting with an incompatible rootstock variety, *Ann. Rpt. East Malling Res. Sta. for 1954*, pp. 76–77. 1955.

87. Müller-Stoll, W. R., Indoleacetic acid as a material promoting the formation of callus in grafts of grapes, *Angew. Bot.*, 20:218–238. 1938.

88. ———, Further experiments on the use of growth substances for vine grafting, *Gartenbauwiss.*, 14:151–168. 1940.

89. Muzik, T. J., and C. D. LaRue, The grafting of large monocotyledonous plants, *Science*, 116:589–591. 1952.

90. Nelson, R., S. Goldweber, and F. J. Fuchs, Top-working for mangos, *Fla. Grower and Rancher*, p. 45. Jan., 1955.

91. Nickell, L. G., Heteroplastic grafts, *Science*, 108:389. 1948.

92. Oberholzer, P. C. J., The Bitter Seville rootstock problem, *Fmg. South Africa*, 22:255, 489–495. 1947.

93. Palmer, C. S., The use of plastic film in grafting, *Gdnrs.' Chron.*, 135:111. 1954.

94. Pearl, R. T., Apple rootstocks, I–XVI, *Jour. South-Eastern Agr. College*, Wye, Eng., 30:194–214. 1932.

95. Proebsting, E. L., Structural weaknesses in interspecific grafts of *Pyrus*, *Bot. Gaz.*, 82:336–338. 1926.

96. ———, Further observations on structural defects of the graft union, *Bot. Gaz.*, 86:82–92. 1928.

97. Richards, A. V., Influence of rootstocks on quality of fruit, *Proc. Amer. Soc. Hort. Sci.*, 37:298. 1940.

98. Roberts, R. H., Variation in growth of nursery grafts, *Science*, 62:356. 1925.

99. ———, Factors affecting the variable growth of apple grafts in the nursery row, *Wis. Agr. Exp. Sta. Res. Bul. 77*, 1927.

100. ———, Some stock and scion observations on apple trees, *Wis. Agr. Exp. Sta. Res. Bul. 94*, 1929.

101. ———, Ring grafting and stock effect, *Proc. Amer. Soc. Hort. Sci.*, 32:328–329. 1934.

102. ———, A further trial of ring grafting to produce stock effects, *Proc. Amer. Soc. Hort. Sci.*, 33:358–359. 1935.

103. ———, A third experience in producing stock effects with ring grafts, *Proc. Amer. Soc. Hort. Sci.*, 34:296–297. 1936.

104. ———, Theoretical aspects of graftage, *Bot. Rev.*, 15:423–463. 1949.

105. Sass, J. E., Formation of callus knots on apple grafts as related to the histology of the graft union, *Bot. Gaz.*, 94:364–380. 1932.

106. Sax, Karl, Dwarf trees, *Arnoldia*, 10:73–79. 1950.

107. ———, The effect of the rootstock on the growth of seedling trees and shrubs, *Proc. Amer. Soc. Hort. Sci.,* 56:166–168. 1950.

108. ———, Interstock effects in dwarfing fruit trees, *Proc. Amer. Soc. Hort. Sci.,* 62:201–204. 1953.

109. ———, The control of tree growth by phloem blocks, *Jour. Arn. Arb.,* 35:251–258. 1954.

110. Schroeder, C. A., Rootstock influence on fruit set in the Hachiya persimmon, *Proc. Amer. Soc. Hort. Sci.,* 50:149–150. 1947.

111. Schultz, J. H., and H. A. Graves, The effect of Dolgo crabapple upon hardiness of Malling apple stocks, *Proc. Amer. Soc. Hort. Sci.,* 57:142–144. 1951.

112. Schwartze, C. D., and A. D. Myhre, Results of grafting Northwest and Marshall strawberry plants to a virus indicator, *Proc. Amer. Soc. Hort. Sci.,* 58:80–90. 1951.

113. Sharples, A., and H. Gunnery, Callus formation in *Hibiscus rosasinensis L.* and *Hevea brasiliensis* Mull. Arg., *Ann. Bot.,* 47:827–839. 1933.

114. Shaw, J. K., The root systems of nursery apple trees, *Proc. Amer. Soc. Hort. Sci.,* 12:68–72. 1915.

115. Shaw, J. K., and L. Southwick, Certain stock-scion incompatibilities and uncongenialities in the apple, *Proc. Amer. Soc. Hort. Sci.,* 44:239–246. 1944.

116. ———, A second report on some lethal rootstock-scion combinations, *Proc. Amer. Soc. Hort. Sci.,* 45:198–202. 1944.

117. Shear, G. M., Lanolin as a wound dressing for trees, *Proc. Amer. Soc. Hort. Sci.,* 34:286–288. 1936.

118. Shippy, W. B., Influence of environment on the callusing of apple cuttings and grafts, *Amer. Jour. Bot.,* 17:290–327. 1930.

119. Shue-lock, Lam, and H. B. Cordner, Flowering hormone in relation to blooming in sweet potatoes, *Science,* 121:140–141. 1954.

120. Sinclair, W. B., and E. T. Bartholomew, Effects of rootstock and environment on the composition of oranges and grapefruit, *Hilgardia,* 16:125–176. 1944.

121. Sitton, B. G., Vegetative propagation of the black walnut, *Mich. Agr. Exp. Sta. Tech. Bul. 119,* 1931.

122. Smith, P. F., W. Reuther, and A. W. Specht, The influence of rootstock on the mineral composition of Valencia orange leaves, *Plant Phys.,* 24:455–460. 1949.

123. Stuart, N. W., Cold hardiness of some apple understocks and the reciprocal influence of stock and scion on hardiness, *Proc. Amer. Soc. Hort. Sci.,* 35:386–389. 1937.

124. Sudds, R. H., Sixteen years' results of orchard tests with apple trees on selected rootstocks. Kearneysville, W. Va. *Proc. Amer. Soc. Hort. Sci.,* 54:144–148. 1949.

125. Swarbrick, T., and R. H. Roberts, The relation of scion variety to character of root growth in apple trees, *Wis. Agr. Exp. Sta. Res. Bul. 78,* 1927.

126. Tena, G. J. A., A virus disease as the cause of incompatibility of citrus rootstocks in Java, *Indones. Jour. Nat. Sci.,* 107:17–24. 1951.

127. Thomas, L. A., Stock and scion investigations. X. Influence of an intermediate stem-piece upon the scion in apple trees. *Jour. Hort. Sci.,* 29:150–152. 1954.

128. Toxopeus, H. J., Stock-scion incompatibility in citrus and its cause, *Jour. Pom. and Hort. Sci.,* 14:360–364. 1936.

129. Tukey, H. B., Stock and scion terminology, *Proc. Amer. Soc. Hort. Sci.,* 35:378–392. 1937.

130. Tukey, H. B., and K. D. Brase, Influence of the scion and of an intermediate stem-piece upon the character and development of roots of young apple trees, *N.Y. (Geneva) Agr. Exp. Sta. Tech. Bul. 218,* 1933.

131. ———, Random notes on fruit tree rootstocks and plant propagation, *N.Y. (Geneva) Agr. Exp. Sta. Bul. 649,* 1934.

132. ———, Similarity in the nursery of several Malling apple stock and scion combinations which differ widely in the orchard, *Proc. Amer. Soc. Hort. Sci.,* 39:245–246. 1941.

133. ———, The dwarfing effect of an intermediate stem-piece of Malling IX apple, *Proc. Amer. Soc. Hort. Sci.,* 42:357–364. 1943.

134. ———, Differences in congeniality of two sources of McIntosh apple budwood propagated on Rootstock USDA 227, *Proc. Amer. Soc. Hort. Sci.,* 45:190–194. 1944.

135. Tukey, H. B., and R. F. Carlson, Five-year performance of several apple varieties on Malling rootstocks in Michigan, *Proc. Amer. Soc. Hort. Sci.,* 54:137–143. 1949.

136. Tydeman, H. M., Experiments hastening the fruiting of seedling apples, *Ann. Rpt. East Malling Res. Sta. for 1936,* pp. 92–99. 1937.

137. Vaile, J. E., The influence of rootstocks on the yield and vigor of American grapes, *Proc. Amer. Soc. Hort. Sci.,* 35:471–474. 1938.

138. Vyvyan, M. C., The effect of scion on root. III. Comparison of stem and root worked trees. *Jour. Pom. and Hort. Sci.,* 8:259–282. 1930.

139. ———, The distribution of growth between roots, stems and leaves in a young apple tree and its possible bearing on the problem of stock effect on tree vigor, *Ann. Rpt. East Malling Res. Sta. for 1933,* pp. 122–131. 1934.

140. ———, The relative influence of rootstock and of an intermediate piece of stock stem in some double-grafted apple trees, *Jour. Pom. and Hort. Sci.,* 16:251–273. 1938.

141. Vyvyan, M. C., and D. H. Maggs, Progress in the study of rootstock-scion interaction, *Ann. Rpt. East Malling Res. Sta. for 1953,* pp. 141–144. 1954.

142. Warne, L. G. G., and Joan Raby, The water conductivity of the graft union in apple trees, with special reference to Malling rootstock No. IX, *Jour. Pom. and Hort. Sci.,* 16:389–399. 1939.

143. Waugh, F. A., The graft union, *Mass. (Hatch) Agr. Exp. Sta. Tech. Bul. 2,* 1904.

144. Webber, H. J., et al., A study of the effects of freezes on citrus in California, *Calif. Agr. Exp. Sta. Bul. 304,* 1919.

145. Webber, H. J., Rootstock reactions as indicating the degree of congeniality, *Proc. Amer. Soc. Hort. Sci.,* 23:30–36. 1926.

146. ———, Variations in citrus seedlings and their relation to rootstock selection, *Hilgardia,* 7:1–79. 1932.

147. ———, The "Tristeza" disease of sour orange rootstock, *Proc. Amer. Soc. Hort. Sci.,* 43:160–168. 1943.

148. Weeks, W. D., Further scion and stock combinations with Spy 227, *Proc. Amer. Soc. Hort. Sci.,* 52:137–140. 1948.

149. Wellensiek, S. J., Het voorkomen van entings incompatibiliteit door eigen bladann de onderstam. *Meded. Landbouwhoogesch. Wageningen.,* 49(9):257–272. 1949. (*Biol. Abst.* 25:585. 1951.)

150. Whitehouse, W. E., and L. E. Joley, Notes on the growth of Persian walnut propagated on rootstocks of the Chinese wingnut, *Pterocarya stenoptera, Proc. Amer. Soc. Hort. Sci.,* 52:103–106. 1948.

151. Whitehouse, W. E., Budding and grafting, *Nat. Hort. Mag.,* 33:25–36. 1954.

152. Witt, A. W., and R. J. Garner, Peach stock trials, a progress report, *Ann. Rpt. East Malling Res. Sta. for 1928–29–30.* II. Suppl. 1931.

153. Yeager, A. F., Xylem formation from ring grafts, *Proc. Amer. Soc. Hort. Sci.,* 44:221–222. 1944.

154. Yerkes, G. E., and W. W. Aldrich, Behavior of apple varieties on certain clonal stocks, *Proc. Amer. Soc. Hort. Sci.,* 48:227–235. 1946.

155. Zebrak, A. R., Intergeneric and interfamily grafting of herbaceous plants, *Timirjazey Seljskohoz Akad.,* 2:115–133. 1937. (*Herb. Abst. 9:*675. 1939).

156. Zobel, M. P., and G. C. Hanna, Sweet potato flowering induced by grafting scion on ornamental stock, *Calif. Agr.,* 7(7):13. 1953.

• **Supplementary Reading**

Argles, G. K., "A Review of the Literature on Stock-Scion Incompatibility in Fruit Trees with Particular Reference to Pome and Stone Fruits," *Imperial Bureau of Fruit Production, Technical Communication No. 9* (1937).

Beakbane, A. B., "Possible Mechanisms of Rootstock Effect," *Annals of Applied Biology,* Vol. 44 (1956), pp. 517–521.

Chang, Wen-Tsai, "Studies in Incompatibility Between Stock and Scion with Special Reference to Certain Deciduous Fruit Trees," *Journal of Pomology and Horticultural Science,* Vol. 15 (1938), pp. 267–325.

Daniel, L., *Etudes sur la Greffe.* Rennes, France: Imprimerie Oberthur, 1927, 1929. Vols. I and II.

Gardner, V. R., F. C. Bradford, and H. D. Hooker, *Fundamentals of Fruit Production,* 2nd ed., Sect. VI, *Propagation.* New York: McGraw-Hill, 1939.

Hatton, R. G., "The Relationship Between Scion and Rootstock with Special Reference to the Tree Fruits," *Journal Royal Horticultural Society,* Vol. 55 (1930), pp. 169–211.

Roberts, R. H., "Theoretical Aspects of Graftage," *Botanical Review,* Vol. 15 (1949), pp. 423–463.

Rogers, W. S., and A. B. Beakbane, "Stock and Scion Relations," *Annual Review of Plant Physiology.* Vol. 8 (1957), pp. 217–236.

12 Techniques of Grafting

In constructing a successful graft, the goal is to connect or fit two pieces of living plant tissue together in such a way that they will unite and subsequently behave as one plant. As any technique that will accomplish this could be considered a method of grafting, it is not surprising that there are innumerable procedures for grafting described in the literature on this subject. Through the years there have become established several distinct methods, the use of which enables the propagator to cope with almost any grafting problem at hand. These are described with the realization that there are many variations of each and that there are other, somewhat different, forms which could give the same results as the methods described.

DEFINITION OF TERMS

Scion (*Cion*) is the short piece of detached shoot containing several dormant buds, which, when united with the stock, comprises the upper portion of the graft and from which will grow the stem and/or branches of the new, grafted plant. It should be of the desired variety and free from disease. (See page 356 for information on the selection of the proper type of scion wood.)

Stock (*Rootstock, Understock*) is the lower portion of the graft which develops into the root system of the grafted plant. It may be a seedling, a rooted cutting, or a layered plant. If the grafting is done high in a tree, such as in top-working, the stock may consist of the roots, trunk, and scaffold branches.

Cambium is a thin tissue of the plant located between the bark (phloem) and the wood (xylem). Its cells are meristematic: they are capable of dividing and forming new cells. For a successful graft union, it is essential that the cambium of the scion be placed in close contact with the cambium of the stock.

Callus is a term applied to the mass of parenchyma cells that develops from and around wounded plant tissues. It occurs at the junction of a graft union,

320

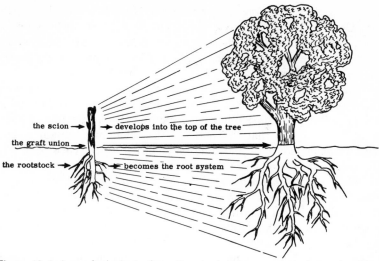

the scion → develops into the top of the tree

the graft union

the rootstock → becomes the root system

Figure 12–1. In grafted plants the entire shoot system consists of growth arising from one (or more) buds on the scion. The root system consists of an extension of the original rootstock. The graft union remains at the junction of the two parts throughout the life of the plant.

arising from the living cells of both scion and stock. The production and interlocking of these parenchyma (or callus) cells is one of the important steps in the healing process of a successful graft.

For any grafting operation to be successful there are five important factors to consider:

Figure 12–2. (left) Graft union between a Northern California black walnut (Juglans hindsii) rootstock and a Persian walnut (J. regia) top. (right) The bark characteristics of these two species remain distinctly different after grafting.

(a) *The stock and scion must be compatible.* They must be capable of uniting. Usually, but not always, plants closely related, such as two apple varieties, can be grafted together. Distantly related plants, such as an oak tree and an apple tree, cannot be grafted. (See Chapter 11 for a detailed discussion of this factor.)

(b) *The cambium of the scion must be in intimate contact with the cambium of the stock.* The cut surfaces should be held together tightly by wrapping, nailing, or some other such method. Rapid healing of the graft union is necessary so that the buds of the scion may obtain water and nutrients from the stock by the time they start to open. (See page 270 for details on how the two parts of the graft unite.)

(c) *The grafting operation must be done at the proper time of year, and the buds on the scions should be in a dormant condition at the time the grafting is done.* Most grafting work takes place just as growth starts in early spring. For deciduous plants, dormant scion wood is often collected during the winter and kept inactive by storing at cool temperatures. (See page 356 for the proper method of collecting and storing scion wood.)

(d) *Immediately after the grafting operation is finished, all cut surfaces must be thoroughly covered with some type of grafting wax or otherwise prevented from drying out.* (See page 351 for a discussion of types of grafting wax).

(e) *Proper care must be given the grafts for a period of time after grafting.* Shoots coming from the stock below the graft will often choke out the desired growth from the scion. Or, in some cases, shoots from the scion will grow so vigorously that they will break off unless staked and tied or cut back. (See page 368 for details on how to care for grafted trees.)

METHODS OF GRAFTING

Whip or Tongue Grafting

This method is particularly useful for grafting relatively small material, ¼ to ½ inch in diameter. It is highly successful if properly done, because there is a considerable region of cambial contact. It heals quickly and makes a strong union. Preferably, the scion and stock should be of equal diameter. The scion should contain two or three buds with the graft made in the smooth internode area below the lower bud.

The cuts made at the top of the stock should be exactly the same as those made at the bottom of the scion. First a long, smooth, sloping cut is made, 1 to 2½ inches long. The longer cuts are made when working·with larger material. This first cut should be made, preferably with one single stroke of the knife, so as to leave a very smooth surface. To do this, the knife must be sharp. Wavy, uneven cuts will not result in a satisfactory union.

On each of these cut surfaces, a reverse cut is made. It is started downward at a point about one-fourth of the distance from the tip and should

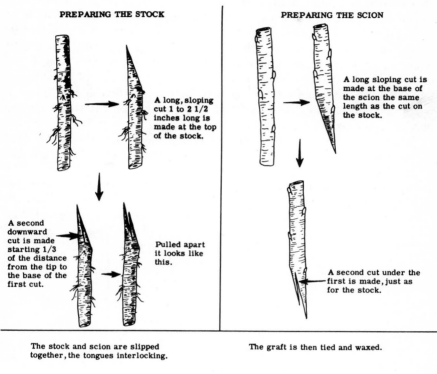

PREPARING THE STOCK

A long, sloping cut 1 to 2 1/2 inches long is made at the top of the stock.

A second downward cut is made starting 1/3 of the distance from the tip to the base of the first cut.

Pulled apart it looks like this.

PREPARING THE SCION

A long sloping cut is made at the base of the scion the same length as the cut on the stock.

A second cut under the first is made, just as for the stock.

The stock and scion are slipped together, the tongues interlocking.

The graft is then tied and waxed.

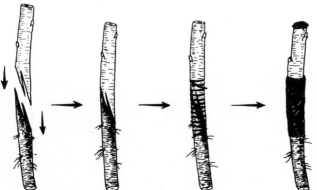

Figure 12–3. The whip or tongue (whip) graft. This method is widely used in grafting small plant material and is especially valuable in making root grafts as is illustrated here.

be about one-half the length of the first cut. To obtain a smooth-fitting graft, this second cut should not just split the grain of the wood but should follow along under the first cut, tending to parallel it.

The stock and scion are then inserted into each other, with the tongues interlocking. It is extremely important that the cambium layers match along at least one side, preferably along both sides. The lower tip of the scion should not overhang the stock, as there is a likelihood of the formation of large callus knots. In some species, such callus overgrowths are often mistaken for crown gall knots, which are caused by bacteria. The use of scions larger than the stock should be avoided for the same reason. If the scion is smaller than the stock, it should be set at one side of the stock so that the cambium layers will be certain to match along that side. If the scion is considerably smaller than the stock, the first cut on the stock consists only of a slice taken off one corner.

After the scion and stock are fitted together, they should be held securely in some manner until the pieces have united. There are a number of possible ways of doing this.

(a) If the unions are very well made with a tight, snug fit, it is possible that no additional wrapping or tying is needed, but it is safer to provide some type of wrapping. If not wrapped, the grafts must be protected from

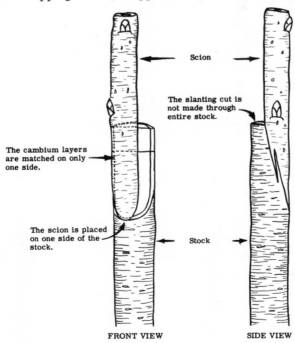

The cambium layers are matched on only one side.

Scion

The slanting cut is not made through entire stock.

The scion is placed on one side of the stock.

Stock

FRONT VIEW   SIDE VIEW

Figure 12–4. Method of making a whip or tongue graft in cases where the scion is considerably smaller than the stock.

drying out by burying in moist sand, peat moss, or sawdust until the union has healed. Or they may be planted directly in the nursery with the union below the soil level. If the whip graft is used in topworking, the exposed union must be protected in some manner.

(b) With a good secure fit it may be sufficient to omit tying and merely cover the union with hot grafting wax, which will secure the pieces to some extent and give good protection against drying. This is not recommended for inexperienced grafters.

(c) A common method is to wrap the union with budding rubbers or possibly raffia or waxed string, such as No. 18 knitting cotton. After wrapping, the whole union can be covered with grafting wax. Waxing may be omitted if the grafts are to be protected from drying out by burying in moist sand or peat moss, or if the grafts are planted immediately with the union below the soil surface.

(d) A practice widely used is to wrap the grafts with some type of adhesive tape. A special nurseryman's tape is available. The tape is drawn tightly around the graft union with the edges slightly overlapping. This holds the parts together very well and prevents drying, thus eliminating the need for waxing. If just one thickness of tape is used, it will rot away sufficiently fast (if the union is below ground) so that no constriction of growth will develop. If used above ground the tape should be cut after the graft is well united. The use of tight wrapping material such as this is especially recommended when difficulty is encountered with the formation of excessive callus.

(e) A plastic resin tape is available which is quite useful in wrapping grafts. It is used just as adhesive tape, although it is not adhesive. The final turn of the tape is secured by slipping it under the previous turn. This tape has some elasticity and will rot if placed below ground.

(f) A method that can be used when the whip graft (or any other method), is to be used in topworking is to cover the union with a wrapping of polyethylene plastic sheeting to prevent drying, and tying at the top and the bottom. This covering can be removed after the union has healed.

(g) If the stock plant being grafted is growing in a small container, the graft union may be wrapped with budding rubber or tape. Then, without being waxed, the entire plant can be set under a bell jar or some other tight enclosure such as a cold frame or a grafting case in the greenhouse. Here, the humidity is maintained at a high level, thus preventing the cut surfaces of the graft from drying out. *Plants in such closed containers should never be set in the direct sun or excessively high temperatures will build up.*

The whip graft can also be used in topworking young trees. The stocks in this case would be small, pencil-sized branches, well distributed around the tree. The grafts are usually tied with nurseryman's adhesive tape or with string, the latter covered with a coat of grafting wax. After the parts of

Figure 12–5. Whole root apple grafts made by the whip or tongue method and wrapped with adhesive nursery tape.

the graft have united, the tying material needs to be cut; otherwise, the branch may be constricted as growth commences.

Side Grafting

There are numerous variations of the side graft; three of the most useful are described. As the name suggests, the scion is inserted into the side of the stock, which is generally larger in diameter than the scion.

Stub graft. This method is useful in grafting branches of trees that are too large for the whip graft yet not large enough for other methods such as the cleft or bark graft. For this type of side graft, the best size stocks are branches about 1 inch in diameter. An oblique cut is made into the stock branch with a chisel or heavy knife at an angle of 20 to 30 degrees. The cut should be about 1 inch deep, and at such an angle and depth that when the branch is pulled back the cut will open slightly but will close when the pull is released.

The scion should contain two or three buds and be about 3 inches long. At the basal end of the scion, a wedge about 1 inch long is made. The cuts on both sides of the scion should be very smooth, each made by one single cut with a sharp knife. The scion is best inserted into the stock at an angle as shown in Figure 12–6 so as to obtain maximum contact of the cambium layers. The scion is inserted into the cut while the upper part of

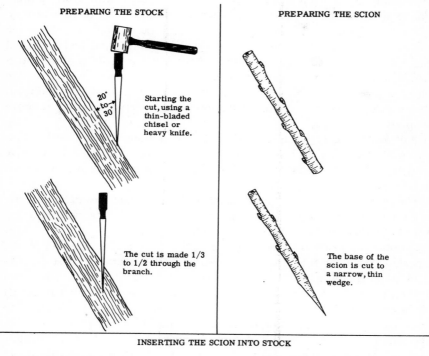

PREPARING THE STOCK

20° to 30°

Starting the cut, using a thin-bladed chisel or heavy knife.

The cut is made 1/3 to 1/2 through the branch.

PREPARING THE SCION

The base of the scion is cut to a narrow, thin wedge.

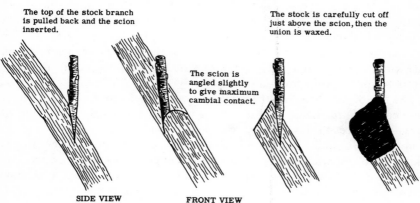

INSERTING THE SCION INTO STOCK

The top of the stock branch is pulled back and the scion inserted.

The stock is carefully cut off just above the scion, then the union is waxed.

The scion is angled slightly to give maximum cambial contact.

SIDE VIEW   **FRONT VIEW**

Figure 12–6. Steps in preparing the side, or stub graft. A thin-bladed chisel as illustrated here is ideal for making the cut, but a heavy butcher knife could be used satisfactorily.

the stock is pulled backward, using care to obtain the best cambium contact. Then the stock is released. The pressure of the stock should grip the scion tightly, making tying unnecessary, but if it is desired, the scion can be further secured by driving two small flat-headed wire nails (No. 20 gauge, ⅝ inch long) into the stock through the scion. Wrapping the stock and scion at the point of union with nurseryman's tape may also be helpful. The entire graft union must be thoroughly covered with grafting wax, sealing all openings. The end of the scion should also be covered with wax.

After the graft is completed, the stock may be cut off just above the union. Under some conditions, healing will be more rapid and certain if the stock is left intact and cut off above the scion later. In grafting citrus seedlings by use of side grafting methods, it is a common practice to lop over the top of the stock about 6 inches above the graft. Some time later, after growth starts from the scion, the top is completely removed just above the graft.

This method may be used to provide a new branch at a position in a tree where it is particularly needed. To force the new scion into active growth, it may be necessary to prune back rather severely the top of the stock branch above the graft.

This grafting method is recommended *(16)* as being particularly useful in the nursery for the purpose of spring grafting young nursery trees which were fall-budded but in which the bud failed to grow.

Side-tongue graft. This type of side graft is very useful for small plants, especially some of the broad- and narrow-leaved evergreen species. The stock plant should have a smooth section in the stem just above the crown of the plant. The diameter of the scion should be slightly smaller than that of the stock. The cuts at the base of the scion are made just as for the whip graft. Along a smooth portion of the stem of the stock, a thin piece of bark and wood, the same length as the cut surface of the scion, is completely removed. Then a reverse cut is made downward in the cut on the stock, starting one-third of the distance from the top of the cut. This second cut in the stock should be the same length as the reverse cut in the scion. The scion is then inserted into the cut in the stock, the two tongues interlocking. The graft is wrapped tightly, using one of the methods (c, d, e, or g) described for the whip graft on page 325.

The top of the stock is left intact for several weeks until the graft union has healed. Then it may be cut back above the scion gradually or all at once. This forces the buds on the scion into active growth.

Veneer side graft (spliced side graft). This variation of side grafting is widely used, especially for grafting small potted plants, such as seedling evergreens. The method of making this graft is very simple. A shallow downward and inward cut from 1 to 1½ inches long is made in a smooth area just above the crown of the stock plant. At the base of this cut, a second short inward and downward cut is made, intersecting the first cut,

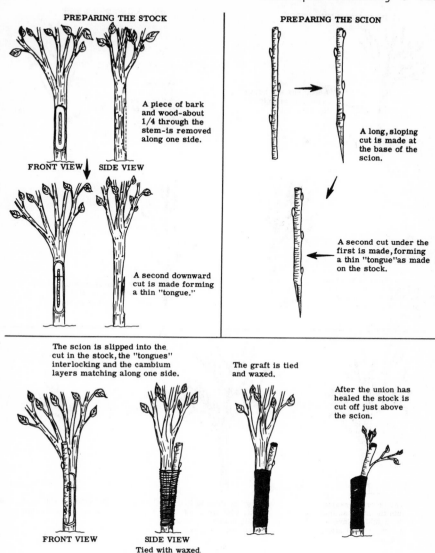

PREPARING THE STOCK

A piece of bark and wood-about 1/4 through the stem-is removed along one side.

FRONT VIEW   SIDE VIEW

A second downward cut is made forming a thin "tongue."

PREPARING THE SCION

A long, sloping cut is made at the base of the scion.

A second cut under the first is made, forming a thin "tongue"as made on the stock.

The scion is slipped into the cut in the stock, the "tongues" interlocking and the cambium layers matching along one side.

The graft is tied and waxed.

After the union has healed the stock is cut off just above the scion.

FRONT VIEW   SIDE VIEW
Tied with waxed string.

Figure 12–7. The side-tongue graft. This method is very useful for grafting broad-leaved evergreen plants.

so as to remove the piece of wood and bark. The scion is prepared with a long cut along one side and a very short one at the base of the scion on the opposite side. These scion cuts should be the same length and width as those made in the stock so that the cambium layers can be matched as closely as possible.

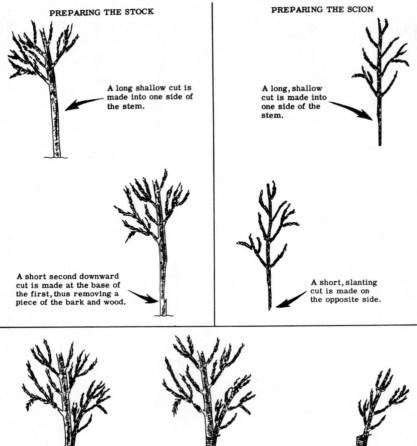

PREPARING THE STOCK

A long shallow cut is made into one side of the stem.

A short second downward cut is made at the base of the first, thus removing a piece of the bark and wood.

PREPARING THE SCION

A long, shallow cut is made into one side of the stem.

A short, slanting cut is made on the opposite side.

The scion is inserted into the stock so that the cambium layers match, at least along one side.

The graft union is tied tightly with string-and, if leafy scions are used, placed under a glass cover. It may, or may not, be waxed.

The stock is cut back in stages, to the scion.

Figure 12–8. Steps in making the side-veneer graft. This is widely used in propagating narrow-leaved evergreen species that are difficult to start by cuttings.

After inserting the scion, the graft is tightly wrapped with waxed or paraffined string or ordinary budding rubbers. The graft may or may not be covered with wax, depending upon the species. A common practice in side grafting small potted plants of some of the woody ornamental species is to plunge the grafted plants in a damp medium, such as peat moss, just covering the graft union. The newly grafted plants may be placed for healing in a mist propagating house or set in grafting cases. The latter are closed boxes with a greenhouse sash cover which permits retention of a high humidity around the grafted plant until the graft union has healed. The grafting cases are usually kept closed for a week or so after the grafts are put in, then are gradually opened over a period of several weeks until the covering sash is taken off completely.

After the union has healed, the stock can be cut back above the scion either in gradual steps or all at once.

Cleft Grafting

This is one of the oldest and most widely used methods of grafting, being especially adapted to topworking trees, either in the trunk of small trees or in the scaffold branches of larger trees. Cleft grafting is also useful for smaller plants, such as crown grafting established grape vines or camellias. In topworking trees, the use of this method should be limited to stock branches of about 1 to 4 inches in diameter and to species with fairly straight-grained wood which will split evenly. Although cleft grafting can be done any time during the dormant season, the chances for successful healing of the graft union are best if the work is done in early spring just when the buds of the stock are beginning to swell but before active growth has started. If cleft grafting is done after the tree is in active growth, it is likely that the bark of the stock will separate from the wood, causing difficulties in obtaining a good union. When this occurs, the loosened bark must be firmly nailed back in place. The scions should be made from dormant, 1-year-old wood. Unless the grafting is done early in the season (when the dormant scions can be collected and used immediately), the scion wood should be held under refrigeration until time for use. (See page 356 for details on collecting and storing scion wood.)

In sawing off the branch for this and other topworking methods, the cut should be made at right angles to the main axis of the branch. The proper method of sawing the branches is shown in Figure 12-32.

In making the cleft graft, a heavy knife, such as a butcher knife, or one of several special cleft grafting tools is used to make a vertical split for a distance of 2 to 3 inches down the center of the stub to be grafted. This is done by pounding the knife in with a hammer or mallet. It is very important to have the branch sawed off in such a position that the end of the stub which is left is smooth, straight-grained, and free of knots for at least 6 inches; otherwise, when the split is made it may not be straight or the wood may split one way and the bark another. The split should be in tangential rather than radial direction in relation to the center of the tree. This permits better placement of the scions for their subsequent growth.

PREPARING THE STOCK

PREPARING THE SCION

The stub is split for a distance of several inches.

The scion is made by cutting a long, gradually tapering wedge.

A smooth straight-grained section should be used so the split will be even.

The outside edge of the wedge should be slightly thicker than the inside.

INSERTING THE SCIONS INTO THE STOCK

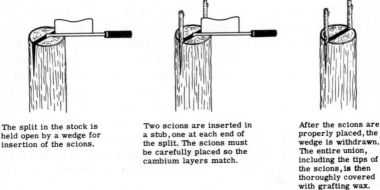

The split in the stock is held open by a wedge for insertion of the scions.

Two scions are inserted in a stub, one at each end of the split. The scions must be carefully placed so the cambium layers match.

After the scions are properly placed, the wedge is withdrawn. The entire union, including the tips of the scions, is then thoroughly covered with grafting wax.

Figure 12–9. Steps in making the cleft graft. This method of grafting is very widely used and is quite successful if the scions are inserted so that the cambium layers of stock and scion match properly.

After a good, straight split is made, a screwdriver, chisel, or the wedge part of the cleft-grafting tool is driven into the top of the split to hold it open.

Two scions are usually inserted, one at each side of the stock where the cambium layer is located, although in large branches, two splits are sometimes made at right angles to each other and four scions inserted. The scions should be 3 or 4 inches long and have two or three buds. The basal end of each scion should be cut into a long, gently sloping wedge—about 2 inches long. It is not necessary that the end of the wedge come to a point. The side of the wedge which is to go to the outer side of the stock should be slightly wider than the inside edge. Thus, when the scion is inserted and the tool is removed, the full pressure of the split stock will come to bear on the scions at the position where the cambium of the stock touches the cambium layer on the outer edge of the scion. Since the bark of the stock is almost always thicker than the bark of the scion, it is usually necessary for the outer surface of the scion to set slightly in from the outer surface of the stock in order to match the cambium layers.

In all types of grafting the scion must be inserted right side up. That is, the points of the buds on the scion should be pointing away from the stock. Failure to observe this means ultimate failure of the graft to grow.

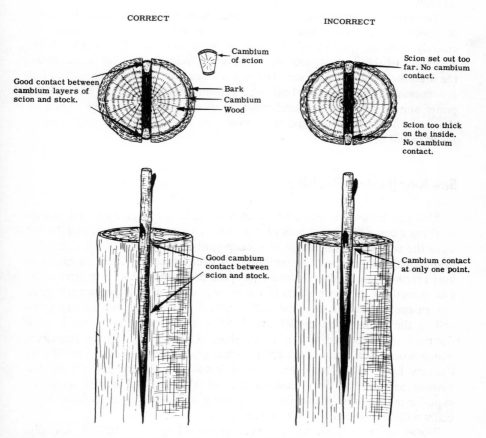

Figure 12–10. In making the cleft graft, the proper placement of the scions is very important. The correct way of doing this is shown on the left. Scions inserted as shown on the right probably would not grow.

The long sloping wedge cuts at the base of the scion should be smooth, made by a single cut on each side with a very sharp knife. Both sides of the scion wedge should press firmly against the stock for their entire length. A common mistake in cutting scions for this type of graft is to make the cut on the scion too short with too abrupt a slope, so that the only point of contact is just at the top. Shaving slightly the sides of the split in the stock will often permit a smoother contact.

After the scions are properly made and inserted, the tool should be carefully withdrawn, using care not to disturb the scions. They will be held very tightly by the pressure of the stock and should not be able to be pulled loose by hand. No further tying or nailing is needed unless very small stock branches have been used, in which case wrapping around the top of the stock tightly with string or waxed cloth will hold the scions securely.

Thorough waxing of the completed graft is essential. (See page 351 for a discussion of grafting waxes.) The top surface of the stub should be entirely covered, permitting the wax to work into the split in the stock. The sides of the grafted stub should be well covered with wax as far down the stub as the split has gone. The tops of the scions should be waxed but not necessarily the bark or buds of the scion. Two or 3 days later all the grafts should be inspected and rewaxed where openings appear. Lack of thorough and complete waxing in this type of graft is almost certain to result in failure.

Saw Kerf (Notch) Grafting

This can be used in place of the cleft graft. It is especially useful in top-working trees with branches 3 to 4 inches or more in diameter. It does not have the serious disadvantage of a deep split in the stock, as does the cleft graft which may permit the entrance of decay-producing organisms. Saw kerf grafting can be done over a long period of time—2 to 3 months—before growth of the stock starts in the spring. If the work is to be performed late in the season, at the time active growth is starting, it is necessary to collect the scion wood earlier and hold it under refrigeration to keep it dormant until the grafting is to be done. Curly-grained stock branches, which would not split evenly for the cleft graft, can be worked readily by the saw kerf graft. The latter method is somewhat more difficult for beginners to perform than most of the other types, but in the hands of experienced workers it can be done rapidly and is highly successful, especially with certain hard-to-graft species, such as the peach.

There are two types of saw kerf grafts—deep and shallow. Usually, three scions are inserted in each stock branch. A cut with a thin-bladed, fine-toothed saw is made into the stub for each scion. This cut should extend 1 to 1½ inches toward the center of the stub and about 4 inches down the side of the stub. Then, using a very sharp "round knife," this saw cut is widened to fit the scion. The knife should be placed at the bottom of the saw cut and brought upward and inward to cut out thin slices of wood. Care should be taken not to get the cut in the stock too wide for use with the available scions.

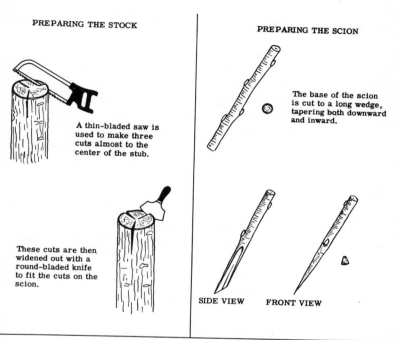

PREPARING THE STOCK

A thin-bladed saw is used to make three cuts almost to the center of the stub.

These cuts are then widened out with a round-bladed knife to fit the cuts on the scion.

PREPARING THE SCION

The base of the scion is cut to a long wedge, tapering both downward and inward.

SIDE VIEW   FRONT VIEW

INSERTING THE SCIONS INTO THE STOCK

If the scions match the cuts in stock they will be held securely just by tapping into place. No nailing or tying is necessary.

Three scions are usually put into each stub. The cambium layers of the scion and stock must match.

The graft union and the ends of the scion are finally covered with grafting wax.

Figure 12–11. Steps in making the saw kerf (notch) graft.

The scions should be 4 or 5 inches long and contain two or three buds. The basal end of the scion is cut to a wedge shape with the outside edge of the wedge somewhat thicker than the inside edge so as to conform to the general shape of the widened saw cut as made in the stock. The wedge cut on the scions should be 1½ to 2 inches long and, as in all grafting, the cut areas should be perfectly smooth, with no wavy surfaces. The scion should be tried for a good fit as the groove in the stock is widened to the right size. It is usually easier to enlarge the cut in the stock so as to fit the scion rather than trying to fit the scion to the cut in the stock. After the cuts on the scion and stock are completed, the scion is tapped firmly into place. The cambium layers should cross to insure contact. Since the bark of the scion is usually thinner than that of the stock, at the correct position the scion will set slightly in from the outside of the stock. If this graft is properly made, the scion should be held very securely by tapping it into place. No further nailing or tying is necessary but, of course, as with all exposed grafts, the cut surfaces must be thoroughly waxed.

The round knife is a very useful tool in making this graft. It may be adapted from a leather-worker's knife or a cook's mincing knife. The edge of the knife should be sharpened so that it is flat on one side and beveled on the other, being used so that the flat side is held against the wood in widening out the saw cut made in the stock. If a round knife of this type is not available, a large-bladed grafting knife may be substituted.

The shallow type of saw kerf graft is made in essentially the same manner, except that the cut into the stock is quite shallow. The outer edge of the scion is considerably thicker than the inner edge. It should be cut to just fit into the opening in the stock. Care must be taken to see that the cambium layers match exactly. The scions, in this case, are held in place by nailing with flat-headed wire nails (⅝ inch, 20 gauge). Finally, of course, the exposed cut surfaces and the end of the scions are thoroughly covered with wax.

Bark Grafting

This method is rapid, simple, readily performed by amateurs and, if properly done, gives a high percentage of "takes." It requires no special equipment and can be performed on branches ranging from 1 inch up to a foot or more in diameter. The latter size is not recommended as it is difficult to heal over such large stubs before decay-producing organisms get started. The bark graft, since it depends on the bark separating readily from the wood, can only be done after active growth of the stock has started in the spring. As dormant scions must be used, it is necessary to gather the scion wood for deciduous species during the dormant season and hold it under refrigeration until the grafting operation is done. (See page 357 for instructions on storing scion wood.) For evergreen species, freshly collected scion wood can be used. Bark grafted scions are not as securely attached to the stock as in some of the other methods and are more susceptible to wind breakage during the first year even though the healing has been satisfactory. Therefore, the new shoots probably should be staked during the first year, especially in windy areas. After a few years' growth, the bark graft union is as strong as the unions formed by other methods.

There are several modifications of the bark graft. Three of the important types are described.

Bark graft (method No. 1). Several scions are inserted in each stub. For each scion, a vertical knife cut about 2 inches long is made at the top end of the stub through the bark to the wood. The bark is then lifted slightly along both sides of this cut, ready for the insertion of the scion. The scion should be of dormant wood, 4 or 5 inches long, containing two or three buds, and be $\frac{1}{4}$ to $\frac{1}{2}$ inch in thickness. One cut about 2 inches long is made along one side at the base of the scion. With large scions, this cut extends about one-third of the way into the scion, leaving a "shoulder" at the top. The purpose of this shoulder is to reduce the thickness of the scion to minimize the separation of bark and wood after insertion in the stock. The scion should not be cut too thin, however, or it will be mechanically weak and break off at the point of attachment to the stock. If small scions are used, no shoulder is necessary. On the side of the scion opposite the first long cut, a second shorter cut is made, as shown in Figure 12-12, thereby bringing the basal end of the scion to a wedge shape. The scion is then inserted between the bark and the wood of the stock, centered directly under the vertical cut through the bark. The longer cut on the scion is placed against the wood, and the shoulder on the scion is brought down until it rests on top of the stub. The scion is then ready to be fastened in place. A satisfactory method is to nail the scion into the wood, using two nails per scion. Flat-headed nails $\frac{5}{8}$ to 1 inch long, of No. 19 or 20 gauge wire, depending on the size of the scions, are very satisfactory. The bark on both sides of the scion should also be securely nailed down, or it will tend to peel back from the wood. Another method commonly used is to insert all the scions in the stub and then hold them in place by wrapping with string, adhesive tape, or waxed cloth around the stub. This is better than nailing in preventing the scions from blowing out but probably does not give as tight a fit as is obtained by nailing. Both nailing and wrapping are advisable for maximum strength. If a wrapping material is used, it may be necessary to cut this later to prevent constriction.

In cases where the bark of the stock is quite thick and small scions are used, it may not be necessary to make the vertical slit cut in the bark. The scions, cut as described before, can be pushed into place between the

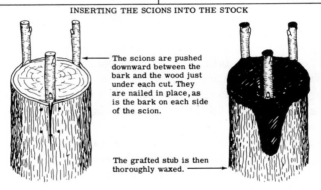

PREPARING THE STOCK

A vertical cut 1 to 2 inches long is made through the bark to the wood.

The bark on both sides of the cut is slightly separated from the wood.

PREPARING THE SCION

The scion is cut as shown below, a long cut with a shoulder on one side, and a shorter cut on the opposite side.

SIDE VIEW   BACK VIEW   FRONT VIEW

(This side is placed next to the wood of the stock.)

INSERTING THE SCIONS INTO THE STOCK

The scions are pushed downward between the bark and the wood just under each cut. They are nailed in place, as is the bark on each side of the scion.

The grafted stub is then thoroughly waxed.

Figure 12–12. Steps in preparing the bark graft (Method No. 1). In grafting some thick-barked plants the vertical cut in the bark is unnecessary, the scion being inserted between the bark and wood of the stock.

bark and the wood. They can then be nailed or tied securely with string or waxed cloth.

After the stub has been grafted and the scions fastened by nailing or tying, all cut surfaces, including the end of the scions, should be thoroughly covered with grafting wax.

Bark graft (method No. 2). This type of graft is similar to method No. 1, except that the scion is not inserted centered on the vertical cut in the bark of the stock. The bark is lifted only along one side of the vertical cut. The bark on the other side is not disturbed. The scion is inserted under the raised bark and held in place with two nails driven through the bark of the stock, through the scion, and into the wood of the stock. The scion is cut with a shoulder, just as described for method No. 1. However, the short cut on the back of the scion, rather than being parallel with the first longer cut, is slanted to one side slightly so as to conform to the slope of the bark under which the scion is inserted. As in method No. 1, the raised bark near

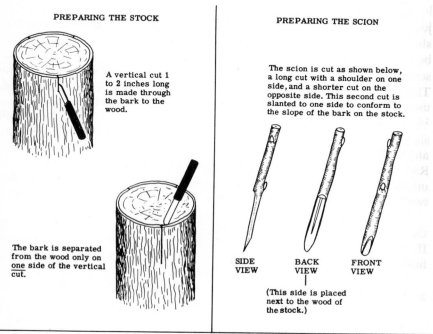

PREPARING THE STOCK

A vertical cut 1 to 2 inches long is made through the bark to the wood.

The bark is separated from the wood only on one side of the vertical cut.

PREPARING THE SCION

The scion is cut as shown below, a long cut with a shoulder on one side, and a shorter cut on the opposite side. This second cut is slanted to one side to conform to the slope of the bark on the stock.

SIDE VIEW   BACK VIEW   FRONT VIEW

(This side is placed next to the wood of the stock.)

INSERTING THE SCIONS INTO THE STOCK

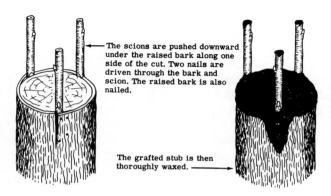

The scions are pushed downward under the raised bark along one side of the cut. Two nails are driven through the bark and scion. The raised bark is also nailed.

The grafted stub is then thoroughly waxed. ──────▶

Figure 12–13. Steps in making the bark graft (Method No. 2).

the scion should be fastened securely in place with two or more nails to prevent it from peeling back. This modification of the bark graft has been widely used with good results. It has an advantage over method No. 1, in that one of the edges of the scion is placed against undisturbed bark with its intact cambium cells. This tends to promote more rapid healing of the union. In method No. 1 where the bark is lifted away from the scion on both sides, intact cambium cells are some distance from the scion and healing is usually slower.

Bark graft (method No. 3). In this method, two knife cuts about 2 inches long are made through the bark of the stock down to the wood, rather than just one as in the other two methods. The distance between these two cuts should be exactly the same as the width of the scion. The piece of bark between the cuts should be lifted and the terminal two-thirds cut off. The scion is prepared with a smooth slanting cut along one side at the basal end. This cut should be about 2 inches long but made without the shoulder, as used in the other two methods. On the opposite side of the scion, a cut about ½ inch long is made, forming a wedge at the base of the scion. The scion should fit snugly into the opening in the bark with the longer cut inward and with the wedge at the base slipped under the flap of remaining bark. Rapid healing can be expected because both sides of the scion are touching undisturbed bark and cambium cells, which is not the case in the other two types of the bark graft.

The scion should be nailed into place with two nails, the lower nail going through the flap of bark covering the short cut on the back of the scion. If the bark along the sides of the scion should accidentally become disturbed, it must be nailed back into place.

This third method is well adapted for use with thick-barked trees, such as walnuts, where it is not feasible to insert the scion under the bark.

Approach Grafting

The distinguishing feature of approach grafting is that two independent, self-sustaining plants are grafted together. After a union has occurred, the top of the stock plant is removed above the graft and the base of the scion plant is removed below the graft. Sometimes it is necessary to sever these parts gradually rather than all at once. Approach grafting provides a means of establishing a successful union between certain plants which are difficult to graft together otherwise. It is usually performed with one or both of the plants to be grafted growing in a pot or container. Use is often made of this method by placing seedling plants growing in containers under an established plant which is to furnish the scion part of the new, grafted plant.

This type of grafting can be done at any time of the year, but healing of the union is more rapid if it is performed at a season of the year when

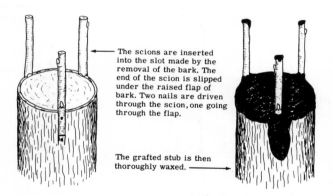

PREPARING THE STOCK

Two parallel vertical cuts 1 to 2 inches long are made through the bark to the wood. The distance between the cuts should equal the width of the scion.

A horizontal cut is made between the two vertical cuts and most of the piece of bark is removed. A small flap is left at the bottom.

PREPARING THE SCION

The scions are made with a long sloping cut on one side and a shorter cut on the opposite side.

SIDE
VIEW

BACK
VIEW

FRONT
VIEW

(This side is placed next to the wood of the stock.)

INSERTING THE SCION INTO THE STOCK

The scions are inserted into the slot made by the removal of the bark. The end of the scion is slipped under the raised flap of bark. Two nails are driven through the scion, one going through the flap.

The grafted stub is then thoroughly waxed. ⟶

Figure 12–14. Steps in making the bark graft (Method No. 3).

growth is active. As in other methods of grafting, the cut surfaces should be securely fastened together, then covered with grafting wax to prevent drying of the tissues.

Three useful methods of making approach grafts are described below.

Spliced approach graft. Preferably the two stems should be approximately the same size. At the point where the union is to occur, a slice of

SPLICED APPROACH GRAFT

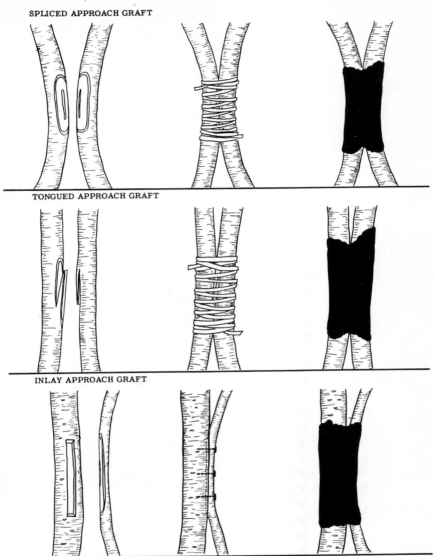

TONGUED APPROACH GRAFT

INLAY APPROACH GRAFT

Figure 12–15. Three methods of making an approach graft.

bark and wood 1 to 2 inches long is cut from both stems. This cut should be the same size on each so that identical cambium patterns will be made. The cuts must be perfectly smooth and as nearly flat as possible so that when they are pressed together there will be close contact of the cambium layers. The two cut surfaces are then bound tightly together with string, raffia, or nurseryman's tape. The whole union should then be covered with grafting wax. After the parts are well united, which may require considerable time in some cases, the stock above the union and the scion below the union are cut and the graft is then completed. It may be necessary to reduce the leaf area of the scion if it is more than the root system of the stock can sustain.

Tongued approach graft. This is the same as the spliced approach graft except that after the first cut is made in each stem to be joined, a second cut—downward on the stock and upward on the scion—is made, thus providing a thin tongue on each piece. By interlocking these tongues a very tight, closely fitting graft union can be obtained.

Inlay approach graft. This method may be used if the bark of the stock plant is considerably thicker than that of the scion plant. A narrow slot, 3 or 4 inches long, is made in the bark of the stock plant by making two parallel knife cuts and removing the strip of bark between. This can only be done when the stock plant is actively growing and the bark "slipping." The slot should be exactly as wide as the scion to be inserted. The stem of the scion plant, at the point of union, should be given a long, shallow cut along one side, the same length as the slot in the stock plant and deep enough to go through the bark and slightly into the wood. This

Figure 12–16. Approach grafting used in obtaining a desirable scion variety on a seedling camellia. **(top)** Seedling plant in container is set close to a large plant of the desired variety. The graft union is made and tightly wrapped with adhesive tape. **(below)** After the graft union has healed, which may take several weeks or longer, the stock plant is cut off **above** the graft union and the scion is severed from the parent plant just **below** the graft union. Approach grafting is sometimes necessary for plants very difficult to graft by other methods.

cut surface of the scion branch should be laid into the slot cut in the stock plant and held there by nailing with two or more small, flat-headed wire nails. The entire union must then be thoroughly covered with grafting wax. After the union has healed, the stock can be cut off above the graft and the scion below the graft.

Inarching

This method, although similar to approach grafting in that both stock and scion plants are on their own roots at the time of grafting, differs in that the top of the new rootstock plant usually does not extend above the point of the graft union as it does in approach grafting. Inarching is generally considered to be a form of "repair grafting," being used in cases where the roots of an established tree have been damaged by such things as cultivation implements, rodents, or disease. It can be used to very good advantage in saving a valuable tree.

Seedlings (or rooted cuttings) planted beside the older, damaged tree, or suckers arising near its base, are grafted into the trunk of the tree for the purpose of providing a new root system to supplant the damaged roots. The seedlings to be inarched into the tree should be spaced about 5 or 6 inches apart around the circumference of the tree if the damage is extensive. The tree will usually stay alive for some time after the injury occurs unless it is very severe. A satisfactory procedure for inarching is to plant seedlings of a compatible species or variety (see p. 290) around the tree during the dormant season. Then, as active growth commences in early spring, the grafting operation can be done.

Inarching old, weakly growing trees with strong, vigorous seedling rootstocks has on some occasions (7) proven very beneficial after several seasons in promoting renewed active growth of the old trees.

The seedling plants to provide the new root system are usually considerably smaller than the tree to be repaired. The graft union is made in a manner similar to that described for method No. 3 of the bark graft. The upper end of the seedling, which should be ¼ to ½ inch thick, is given a long shallow cut along the side for 4 to 6 inches. This cut should be on the side next to the trunk of the tree and made deep enough to remove some of the wood, thus exposing two strips of cambium tissue. At the end of the seedling, another shorter cut, about ½ inch long, is made on the side opposite the long cut; this makes a sharp, wedge-shaped end on the seedling stem. A long slot is made in the trunk of the older tree by removing a piece of bark the exact width of the seedling and just as long as the cut surface made on the seedling. A small flap of bark is left at the upper end of the slot under which the wedge end of the seedling is inserted. Then

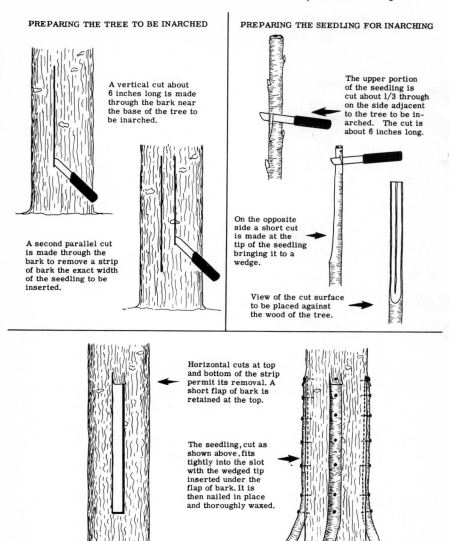

PREPARING THE TREE TO BE INARCHED

A vertical cut about 6 inches long is made through the bark near the base of the tree to be inarched.

A second parallel cut is made through the bark to remove a strip of bark the exact width of the seedling to be inserted.

PREPARING THE SEEDLING FOR INARCHING

The upper portion of the seedling is cut about 1/3 through on the side adjacent to the tree to be inarched. The cut is about 6 inches long.

On the opposite side a short cut is made at the tip of the seedling bringing it to a wedge.

View of the cut surface to be placed against the wood of the tree.

Horizontal cuts at top and bottom of the strip permit its removal. A short flap of bark is retained at the top.

The seedling, cut as shown above, fits tightly into the slot with the wedged tip inserted under the flap of bark. It is then nailed in place and thoroughly waxed.

Figure 12–17. Steps in inarching a large plant with smaller ones planted around its base.

the seedling is nailed into the slot with four or five small, flat-headed wire nails. The nail at the top of the slot should go through the flap of bark and through the end of the seedling. If any of the bark of the tree along the sides of the seedling should accidentally be pulled loose, it is necessary to nail it back in place. After nailing, the entire area of the graft union should be thoroughly waxed.

Figure 12–18. Inarching can be used for invigorating existing trees by replacing a weak, disease-susceptible rootstock with a more vigorous disease-resistant one. Here a Persian walnut tree has been inarched with vigorous Paradox Hybrid **(J. hindsii x J. regia)** seedlings.

Due to the food materials translocated into the seedlings from the larger tree, they grow very rapidly and soon provide a considerable amount of new roots for the grafted tree. If shoots arise from the inarches, they should be suppressed by cutting off their tips. The shoots should finally be removed entirely as the union becomes well established.

Bridge Grafting

This is a form of repair grafting, and is used in cases where the root system of the tree has not been damaged but where there is injury to the bark of the trunk. Sometimes cultivation implements, rodents, disease, or winter injury will damage a considerable trunk area, often girdling the tree completely. If the damage to the bark is extensive, the tree is almost certain to die, because the roots will be deprived of their food supply from the top of the tree. Trees of some species, such as the elm, cherry, and pecan, can heal over extensively injured areas by the development of callus tissue. Trees of most species, however, which have had the bark of the trunk severely damaged should be bridge grafted if they are to be saved.

The bridge grafting operation is best performed in early spring just as active growth of the tree is beginning and the bark is slipping easily. The scions to be used should be taken when dormant from 1-year-old growth, ¼ to ½ inches in diameter, of the same or a compatible species, and held under refrigeration until the grafting work is to be done. (See page 356 for information on collecting and storing scion wood.) In an emergency, bridge grafting may be successfully performed late in the spring using scion

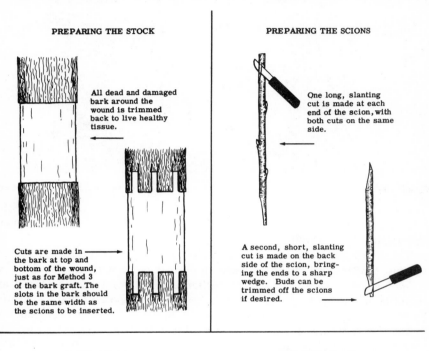

PREPARING THE STOCK

All dead and damaged bark around the wound is trimmed back to live healthy tissue.

Cuts are made in the bark at top and bottom of the wound, just as for Method 3 of the bark graft. The slots in the bark should be the same width as the scions to be inserted.

PREPARING THE SCIONS

One long, slanting cut is made at each end of the scion, with both cuts on the same side.

A second, short, slanting cut is made on the back side of the scion, bringing the ends to a sharp wedge. Buds can be trimmed off the scions if desired.

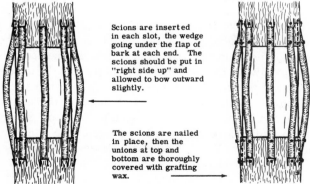

Scions are inserted in each slot, the wedge going under the flap of bark at each end. The scions should be put in "right side up" and allowed to bow outward slightly.

The scions are nailed in place, then the unions at top and bottom are thoroughly covered with grafting wax.

Figure 12–19. A satisfactory method of making a bridge graft, using a modification of Method No. 3 of the bark graft.

Figure 12–20. Injured trunk of a cherry tree successfully bridge-grafted by a modification of the bark graft.

wood whose buds have already started to grow. The developing buds or new shoots must be removed.

The first step in bridge grafting is to trim the wounded area back to healthy, undamaged tissue by removing dead or torn bark. Then every 2 or 3 inches around the injured section a scion is inserted, attached at both the upper and lower ends into live bark. It is important that the scions be inserted right side up. If they are put in reversed, they may make a union and stay alive for a year or two, but the scions will not grow and enlarge in diameter as they would if inserted correctly (see Figure 11–9).

Figure 12–19 shows the details of making a satisfactory type of bridge graft. It is essentially the same as method No. 3 of the bark graft. Just above and below the injured area, a slot 2 to 3 inches long and exactly the width of the scion is cut in the bark of the trunk for each scion. The piece of bark is removed with the exception of a flap about ½ inch long which is left at the end of the slot. The scions are cut to the proper length so that they will fit into these slots at each end of the wound, being made long enough so they can be bowed outward slightly. This bow allows for good contact at each end and permits some swaying of the trunk in the wind without tearing the scions loose. To prepare the scions, a cut is made along both ends on the side which is to fit into the slot. The cut should be the same length as the slot and deep enough to remove some bark and wood and expose two strips of cambium tissue. Then, on the opposite side of the scion, at each end, another shorter cut, about ½ inch long, is made so as to bring the ends of the scion to a wedge shape. The ends of the scion should be inserted under the flaps of bark and nailed in place, using ¾ inch, No. 20 flat-headed wire nails. One nail should go through the flap of bark at each end of the scion with enough additional nails to hold the scion securely.

After all the scions have been inserted, the cut surfaces must be thoroughly covered with grafting wax, taking particular care to work the wax around the scions especially at the graft unions. The exposed wood of the injured section may also be covered with grafting wax to prevent the entrance of decay organism and to prevent excessive drying out of the wood, which is important as the path for upward movement of water and nutrients in the tree.

The buds on the scions will often push into growth if the grafts are successful. These shoots should be broken off, because no branches would be desired in this position. The scions will rapidly enlarge in size and completely heal over the wound in a few years.

Bracing

The same type of graft union practiced in inarching and bridge grafting can often be used to establish a "natural" brace in young trees. This method is useful in supporting branches that may be in danger of breaking off or where there is a weak crotch. A small branch, about pencil size or a little larger, coming a foot or so above the weak crotch is grafted into the adjacent branch to be supported. It should be wrapped spirally and upward partly around the branch. In the region where the graft union is to be, the bark on the large branch is cut just under the small branch to its exact

Figure 12–21. Brace graft after two seasons' growth.

width. This should extend for a length of 6 inches or more and the spiral piece of bark removed. Grafting such as this could only be done at a time of year when there is active growth and the bark is slipping easily. Early spring, just as the new growth is starting, would be the preferable time.

After the slot in the bark is ready, the "scion"—the small branch— should be smoothly cut on the lower side through about a third of its thickness and for the length of the slot—6 inches or more. If the cuts are well made, the small branch should fit snugly into the slot. It is helpful to trim the end of the small branch, the "scion," to a wedge point by cutting it on the top side so that it can be inserted under the bark at the top end of the slot.

The next step is to nail the branch in place in the slot with small, flat-headed wire nails (⅝ or ¾ inch, No. 20) placed at 1 or 2 inch intervals. The graft union should then be thoroughly waxed to prevent drying out. It is also advisable to tie the two branches together temporarily with a strong cord to prevent whipping by the wind which might pull the graft union loose.

TOOLS AND ACCESSORIES FOR GRAFTING

Special equipment needed for any particular method of grafting has been illustrated along with the description of the method. There are some pieces of equipment, however, which are used in all types of grafting.

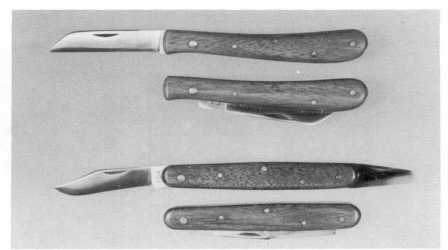

Figure 12–22. Types of folding knives used in plant propagation. (above) Grafting knife. (below) Budding knife. The blunt part on the right of this knife is used in T-budding to open the bark flaps for insertion of the shield bud piece.

Knives

For propagation work, the two general types used are the budding knife and the grafting knife. Where a limited amount of either budding or grafting is done, the budding knife can be used satisfactorily for both operations. The knives have either a folding or a fixed blade. The fixed-bladed type is stronger, and if a holder of some kind is used to protect the cutting edge, it is probably the most desirable. A well-built, sturdy knife of high quality steel is essential if very much grafting work is to be done. The knife must be kept very sharp in order to do good work.

HOW TO SHARPEN A KNIFE PROPERLY

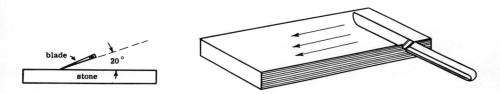

The initial grinding may be done with a fairly coarse stone, but a hard, fine-grained stone should be used for the final grinding. Do not use a carborundum stone, because it is too abrasive and will grind off too much metal. Some prefer to use knives beveled on both sides, whereas others prefer a knife beveled on one side only, the back side being flat. In sharpening the knife, hold it so that only the edge of the blade touches the stone in order that a stiff edge for cutting can be obtained. Use the whole width of the stone so that its surface will remain flat. A correctly sharpened knife of high-quality steel should retain a good edge for several days work, with only occasional stropping on a piece of leather needed to maintain a perfect cutting edge.

Grafting Waxes

It is best to use only materials that have been especially developed for grafting rather than some similar appearing preparation, such as a roofing compound, which may contain components very toxic to plant tissues.

The chief purposes of grafting wax are: (a) To seal over the graft union thereby preventing the loss of moisture and death of the tender, exposed cells of the cut surfaces of the scion and stock. These cells are essential for callus production and healing of the graft union. (b) To prevent the entrance of various decay producing organisms which may lead to wood rotting.

A good grafting wax should adhere well to the plant surfaces, not be washed off by rains, not be so brittle as to crack and chip during cold weather, not be so soft that it will melt and run off during hot days, but still be pliable enough to allow for swelling of the scion and growth enlargement of the stock.

Although a great many different materials have been used as grafting waxes, in recent years various formulations of the so-called *hot waxes* or the *cold waxes* are generally preferred.

Hot waxes. The ingredients used in this type of wax are resin, beeswax, either raw linseed oil or tallow, and lampblack or powdered charcoal. The proportions of each ingredient may vary considerably without affecting the results appreciably. The purpose of the lampblack is to give some color to the otherwise colorless wax so as to be able to determine more readily when the grafts have been well covered. Lampblack also imparts a more workable consistency to the wax, eliminating some of the stickiness and stringiness. After application, the dark colored wax may absorb more heat so that it remains soft and pliable. During hot weather, however, this could be undesirable, because the wax may become too soft.

Directions for Making Hot Grafting Wax (Hard Type)

Ingredients:

Resin .... 5 lbs.
Beeswax .... ¾ lb.
Raw linseed oil .... ½ pt.
Lampblack .... 1 oz.
Fish glue .... 1½ oz.

Heat the glue in a double boiler with just enough water to dissolve it. Melt the other ingredients in another container and allow the mixture to cool but still remain fluid. Add the glue slowly to the partly cooled mixture, stirring continually. Pour out into shallow greased pans or wooden boxes lined with greased paper. Allow to harden. To use, chip or break into small lumps. Reheat in a grafting wax melter and apply with a small paint brush.

The hard type of hot grafting wax solidifies upon cooling and must be reheated just before applying to the graft union. It is important that this wax be at the right temperature when it is used. If heated until the wax is bubbling and boiling, it will probably injure the plant tissues. At the other extreme, if the wax is too cool it will not flow easily into all the crevices in the bark, thus leaving openings for the entrance of air. *The wax should be hot enough to flow easily yet not be at the bubbling stage.*

For heating the wax, any type of small burner is satisfactory. A brush is used to apply the wax but provision should be made to suspend it from the side, for if the brush rests at the bottom of the burner the heat will burn the bristles. Home made grafting wax melters can easily be constructed *(13)*.

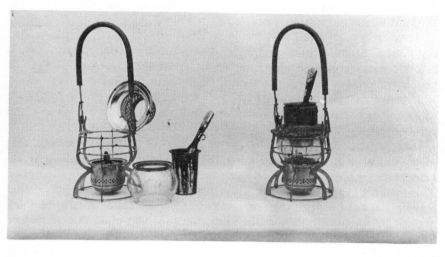

Figure 12–23. Two types of wax pots for melting hot grafting wax. Alcohol is commonly used as the fuel for the burners. **(left)** Units disassembled. **(right)** Burners ready to use.

Hand waxes. Hand wax, which does not require heating, is soft and pliable and is applied to the graft union by pressing in and around the graft with the fingers. It is sticky, though, and unpleasant to use. Hand wax is made by heating together 4 parts of resin, 2 parts of beeswax, and 1 part of tallow. (An alternative formula is 4 parts resin, 1 part beeswax, and 2 parts tallow or linseed oil.) The tallow is melted first, then the beeswax is added, and finally the resin. When the ingredients have melted together, the mixture is poured into a large vessel of cold water. After cooling it is removed, then pulled and worked with the hands until it is light yellow. It is then made into small balls and wrapped in waxed paper for storing.

This soft hand wax is suitable for small operations, but for general use the hard wax is more satisfactory.

Another type of hand wax available is an asbestos base, plastic sealing compound. Manufactured primarily for electrical and laboratory uses, it is quite satisfactory as a grafting wax. It has an advantage in that its plasticity and workability are unaffected by temperature changes over a wide range—from minus 40° to 125°F. These hand waxes are somewhat more difficult and time-consuming to apply than the more fluid hot and cold waxes.

Cold waxes. A commercially prepared type of grafting wax consisting of an emulsion of asphalt and water has become generally available in recent years. It has proven to be quite satisfactory and is widely used *(14).* This material is about 50 per cent water, which evaporates after application leaving a coat of asphalt over the graft. For the remaining wax to be thick enough to adequately protect the graft, the original application should be fairly heavy. Since this material is water soluble until it dries, rains occurring within a day or so after application are likely to wash it off. It would then, of course, be necessary to rewax the grafts immediately. If grafting is done during rainy weather, it would be advisable to use the hot type of wax which is not affected by rains. The emulsions of this type of cold wax are broken down by freezing, so it is very important that the containers be stored in a warm place during cold weather.

Do not confuse this material with roofing compounds which have a similar appearance but are entirely unsuitable for use as a grafting wax.

Tying and Wrapping Materials

Some of the grafting methods, particularly the whip or tongue, require that the graft union be held together by tying until the parts unite. This can be done in several ways—the simplest would be merely tying with ordinary string and covering with grafting wax. For large-scale operations, waxed string is convenient because it will adhere to itself and the plant parts, without tying. It should be strong enough to hold the grafted parts together yet weak enough to be broken by hand.

A good waxed string for this purpose can be prepared by soaking balls of No. 18 knitting cotton for about 10 minutes in a mixture of the following ingredients which have been melted together:

Resin	2 lbs.
Beeswax	1 lb.
Tallow	½ lb.
Linseed oil	½ lb.
Paraffin	¼ lb.

If this mixture is too soft and sticky, smaller amounts of linseed oil and tallow should be used. Hot grafting wax without the lampblack can also be used in preparing waxed string. The balls should be turned several times while they are draining to prevent an accumulation of excess wax on one side.

Strips of waxed cloth about ½ inch wide are quite useful in some instances, such as wrapping whip grafts or holding the scions in bark grafts. They are also useful in wrapping patch and I-buds (see p. 386). Waxed cloth strips not only hold the plant parts together but seal the union against air, thus eliminating the need for waxing. Fairly weak cloth should be used, such as old muslin. It is torn into strips and wrapped around sticks into rolls of convenient size. The rolls are then dipped into the wax mixture described above, or into plain melted beeswax, drained, and allowed to dry. If used on a fairly warm day, the cloth is sticky and adheres well to the graft.

A special nurseryman's adhesive tape is manufactured which is similar to surgical adhesive tape except that it is lighter weight and is not sterilized. It is more convenient to use than the waxed cloth tape. Adhesive tape is very useful for tying and sealing whip grafts. When using any kind of tape or string for wrapping grafts, it is very important not to wrap too many layers or the material may eventually girdle the plant unless it is cut. When this type of wrapping is covered with soil it usually will rot and break before damage can occur, unless it has been wrapped in too many layers.

Grafting Machines

Several machines or devices have been developed to make graft and bud unions, and some offer considerable promise. Bench grafting of grapes has been quite successful with the use of an electrically driven circular saw which cuts square notches in the ends of the stock and scion. This enables them to be pushed together, giving a very tight and secure fit *(1)*.

Figure 12–24. Machine used for making the grape grafts shown in Figure 12–25. The protective cover has been removed from the saw blade.

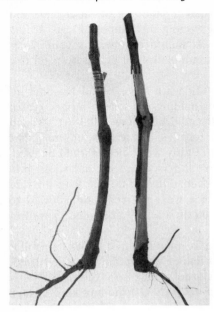 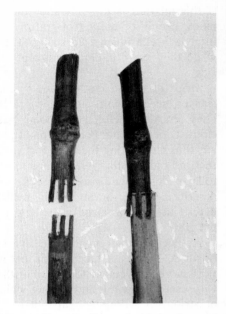

Figure 12–25. Grapes propagated by machine grafting. Small, one-budded scions are grafted on rooted cuttings during the dormant season. The graft union is wrapped with a budding rubber, then allowed to callus before planting.

SELECTION AND STORAGE OF SCION WOOD

Since almost all grafting of deciduous species takes place in late winter or early spring, the use of scion wood consisting of shoots that grew the previous summer is necessary. It is important that suitable scion wood be obtained and cared for properly until used. Storage of scions should not be attempted if succulent, herbaceous plants are being grafted, but scions should be obtained at the time of grafting and used immediately. In grafting certain of the broad-leaved evergreen species, such as olives, it is also unnecessary to collect the scion wood previously and hold it in storage. Grafting of such species is done in the spring before much active growth starts, and the scion wood is taken directly from the tree as needed, using wood on the basal part of the shoots containing dormant, axillary buds. The leaves are removed from such scion wood at the time it is collected.

In selecting the best scion material of woody plants, the following points should be observed.

(a) For most species, the wood should be only 1 year old. Avoid the use of older growth if possible, although in some species, such as the fig or olive, 2-year-old wood is satisfactory or even preferable if it is of the proper size.

(b) Healthy, well-developed vegetative buds should be visible. Avoid wood with flower buds. Usually, vegetative buds are narrow and pointed, whereas flower buds are round and plump (see,Figure 13–1).

(c) Vigorous, but not overly succulent, watersprouts make good scion wood. This type of growth can be produced by cutting the tree back heavily the previous winter. Do not use suckers or watersprouts around the base of the tree, because these may be coming from the rootstock below the graft union.

(d) Good scion wood is from $\frac{1}{4}$ to $\frac{1}{2}$ inch in diameter and taken from growth 2 to 3 feet long. The best scions are obtained from the center portion or from the basal two-thirds of such shoots. The terminal sections are likely to be too succulent and pithy and low in stored carbohydrates. Well-matured wood with short internodes should be selected if possible.

(e) Scion wood should be taken only from healthy, vigorous trees showing good production of the desired variety. It is especially important to avoid trees which may have virus diseases, because these are readily transmitted by propagation. In species such as citrus, where undesirable sports or mutations frequently occur, it is advisable to use single, high-producing trees known to give high quality fruit as the source of scion or bud wood rather than collecting it indiscriminately through an orchard. Trees propagated by scion wood taken from a tree which has been unusually productive does not necessarily mean that they will have the same high productivity. It is better to collect scion wood from a bearing rather than a nonbearing tree so that the variety can be more accurately known and it can be determined whether it is actually what is wanted in the new grafted tree.

(f) For deciduous trees which are to be grafted in late winter or early spring, it is best to collect the scion wood some time during the winter season when the trees are fully dormant. In climates with severe winters, the wood should be gathered at a time when the wood is not frozen. Any wood that shows freezing injury should not be used. Where considerable winter injury is likely, it is best to collect the scion wood and put it in storage after leaf fall but before the onset of the winter season.

Usually, the scion wood is collected several weeks before the grafting is done. For that reason, the proper storage of the wood is important. It should be kept slightly moist and at a temperature which will prevent development of the buds. A common method is to wrap the wood, in bundles of 25 to 100 sticks, in heavy, waterproof paper. Some slightly moist material, such as sawdust, shingle tow, peat moss, or sphagnum moss, should be sprinkled through the bundle. Sand should not be used, because it will adhere to the scion wood and dull the edge of the grafting knife during the grafting operation. It is important that the packing material not be too wet, otherwise various fungi will develop and damage the buds, even at low storage temperatures. The packing should be barely moist; scion wood is more apt to be damaged by being too wet than too dry. If it is to be stored for a prolonged period, the bundle should be examined every few weeks to see that the wood is not becoming dried out or is not too wet. When the buds show signs of swelling, the wood should either be used or moved to a lower storage temperature.

Polyethylene plastic sheeting or polyethylene-coated Kraft paper is a good material for wrapping scion wood. It allows the passage of gases, such as oxygen and carbon dioxide, which are exchanged during the respiration process of the stored wood, but retards the passage of water vapor. Therefore, if this type of wrapping is tightly sealed, no moist packing material is needed; the natural moisture in the wood will be sufficient, since little will be lost. Polyethylene bags are useful for storing small quantities of scion wood. All bundles should be accurately labeled.

The temperature at which the wood is stored is important. If it is to be kept for just a short time before grafting—2 or 3 weeks—the temperature of the home refrigerator—40° to 50°F.—is satisfactory. *Do not store in a home freezer*. If stored for a period of 1 to 3 months, scion wood should be kept about 32°F. This is necessary in order to keep the buds dormant. *Attempting to use scion wood in which the buds are starting active growth is almost certain to result in failure*. In such cases, after grafting, the buds will quickly leaf out before the graft union has occurred; consequently the leaves, by transpiration, will withdraw water from the scions and cause them to die. If cold storage facilities are not available, the scion wood can be kept for a period of time—the length depending upon the soil temperature—by burying the bundles in the ground 12 to 18 inches deep, below frost level, on the north side of a building or tall hedge. Care should be taken to see that drainage is good so that excess water does not remain around the scions and cause the buds to rot.

GRAFTING CLASSIFIED ACCORDING TO PLACEMENT

Grafting may be classified according to the part of the plant on which the scion is placed—a root, the crown (the junction of the stem and root at the ground level), or various places in the top of the plant.

Root Grafting

In this class of grafting the rootstock seedling, rooted cutting, or layered plant is dug up, and the roots are used as the stock for the graft. The entire root system may be used (*whole-root graft*), or the roots may be cut up into small pieces and each piece used as a stock (*piece-root graft*). Both methods give satisfactory results. As the roots used are relatively small

(¼ to ½ inch in diameter), the whip or tongue graft (see p. 322) is generally used. Root grafting is usually performed indoors during the late winter or early spring. The scion wood, collected previously (see p. 356), is held in storage, while the rootstock plants are also dug in the late fall and stored under cool (40° to 50°F.) and moist conditions until the grafting is done.

The term *bench grafting* is sometimes given to this process, because it is often performed at benches by skilled grafters as a large-scale operation. A number of plants are propagated commercially by root grafting—apples, pears, grapes, and such ornamentals as the wistaria and rhododendron.

In making root grafts, the root pieces should be 3 to 6 inches long and the scions about the same length, containing two to four buds. After the grafts are made and properly tied, they are bundled together in groups of fifty to one hundred and stored for callusing in damp sand, peat moss, or other packing material. They may be placed in a cool cellar or under refrigeration at 40° to 45°F. for about 2 months. The callusing period for some plants can be shortened to 10 or 12 days if the grafts are stored at a temperature of about 70°F. This high callusing temperature is especially beneficial for coniferous evergreen grafts *(3)*. The best results are obtained with both apples and pears if the grafts are lined-out in early spring to the nursery row directly from the 45°F. storage conditions. For general callusing purposes, temperatures below 70°F. rather than higher are the most satisfactory. By the proper regulation of temperature, callusing processes may be accelerated by increased temperature or retarded by decreased temperature so that, within reasonable limits, a desired degree of callus formation may be had within a given length of time *(12)*. An excessive amount of callus sometimes develops, especially in apple root grafts. As an aid in controlling this, the stored grafts can be held at low temperatures, just above freezing, with the packing material relatively dry. Provision should be made for adequate aeration of the callusing grafts *(12)*.

As soon as the ground can be prepared in the spring, the grafts are lined out in the nursery row 4 to 6 inches apart. They should be planted before growth of the buds or roots begins. If this starts before the grafts can be planted they should be moved to lower temperatures (30° to 35°F.). The grafts are usually planted deep enough so that just the top bud of the scion is above ground. When the graft union is below the ground level, the scion will probably also produce roots. To have roots arising only from the rootstock, the graft should be set with the scion well above the soil level. It is very important to prevent scion rooting where certain definite influences, such as dwarfing or disease resistance, are expected from the rootstock.

After one summer's growth, the grafts may be large enough to transplant to their permanent location. If not, the scion may be cut back to one or two buds, or headed back somewhat to force out scaffold branches and then allowed to grow a second year. With the older root system a strong, vigorous top is obtained the second year.

Nurse-root grafting. Under certain conditions, it is desired to have a stem cutting of a difficult-to-root species on its own roots. One way this can be done is by making a simple root graft the usual way, using the plant to be grown on its own roots as the scion and a root of a compatible species as the stock. The scion may be made longer than usual and the

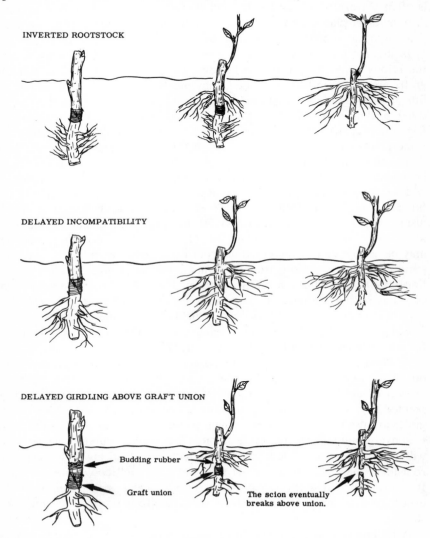

Figure 12–26. The "nurse root" graft is a temporary graft used to induce the scion to develop its own roots. The nurse root sustains the plant until scion roots form; then it dies. Three methods are shown here for preparing a "nurse root" graft.

graft planted deeply with the major portion of the scion below ground. After one or two season's growth, it will be found that many of the scions have produced a considerable number of roots. The temporary nurse rootstock is then cut off and the top reduced proportionately to allow for the reduction in the root system. Then the rooted scion is replanted, ready to complete its growth on its own roots. In some cases scion rooting is stimulated by rubbing a rooting stimulant, such as indolebutyric acid dispersed in talc, on the base of the scion immediately above the graft union. This material may be more effective if rubbed into several vertical cuts made through the bark. This is done just before planting, and the grafts are set deeply so that most of the scion is covered with soil (8, 9). Scion rooting is often much improved if the nurse-root graft is buried deep enough so that a new shoot of the current season's wood, developing from a bud on the scion, will be rooted, rather than trying to root the older, lignified tissue of the original scion. This is essentially a form of layering (see p. 409). As the new scion shoot grows, soil is gradually mounded up around it to a total height of 5 or 6 inches, although the terminal leaves are at no time covered (10).

Several methods of handling make it possible to avoid the necessity of digging up the graft and cutting off the rootstock. To be certain that the rootstock piece will eventually die, it can be grafted onto the scion in an inverted position (3, 10). The inverted stock piece can sustain the scion until scion roots are formed, but the stock fails to receive food from the scion and eventually dies, thus leaving the scion on its own roots. In another method, the rootstock used is one that is known to exhibit delayed incompatibility with the scion to be rooted. Hence, if the graft is planted deeply, so that roots form at the base of the scion, these roots will gradually become more important in sustaining the plant, whereas the incompatible rootstock will finally cease to function.

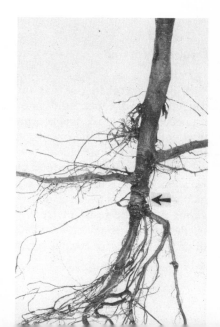

Figure 12–27. Nurse root graft. A Malling IX apple scion was root-grafted to an apple seedling "nurse root." Just above the graft union the scion was wrapped with a budding rubber strip (see arrow). After two years in the nursery, vigorous scion roots were produced. The budding rubber has effectively constricted development of the seedling "nurse root" which can now be broken off and discarded. Courtesy D. S. Brown.

In a third method the base of the scion, just above the graft union, can be bound with some type of wrapping material so as to eventually girdle and cut off the rootstock. Tests (2) have shown that excellent results can be obtained with ordinary budding rubber strips (0.016 gauge). Although budding rubbers disintegrate within a month when exposed to sun and air, when buried in the soil, as they would be in this case, they will last as long as 2 years. Thus, in choking off the nurse root, the action is gradual, allowing sufficient time for the scion to become rooted. Yet, due to the slow deterioration of the rubber below ground, the rootstock is finally girdled and cut off.

Crown Grafting

When a graft union is made at the root-stem transition region—the "crown" of the plant—while the rootstock portion of the graft is still growing undisturbed in the soil, it is termed a "crown graft." Several methods of grafting are commonly used in crown grafting, such as the whip, side, cleft, saw kerf, or bark graft, depending upon the species and size of the rootstock.

Crown grafting of deciduous plants is best done in late winter or early spring, shortly before new growth starts. The scions should be prepared from well matured, dormant wood of the previous season's growth.

Since the operation is performed just below, at, or just above the soil level, it is possible to cover the graft union, or even the entire scion, with soil and thus eliminate the necessity for waxing. The union should be tied securely with string or tape to hold the grafted parts together until healing takes place.

Double-Working

A double-worked tree has three component parts, usually all different genetically—rootstock, the intermediate stock, and the top or fruiting branches. Such a tree has two graft unions, one between the rootstock and intermediate stock, and one between the intermediate stock and the fruiting top. The intermediate stock may be less than an inch in length or extensive enough to include the trunk and secondary scaffold branches. Double-working is used for various purposes, such as (a) overcoming grafting incompatibility between a desired top variety and the rootstock, (b) providing a disease-resistant trunk, (c) obtaining a dwarfing effect imparted by the use of certain intermediate stocks, or (d) obtaining the strong trunk or crotch systems of certain varieties.

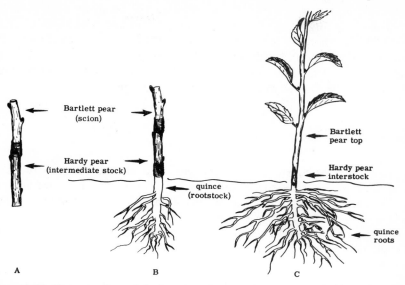

Figure 12–28. There are three distinct parts and two graft unions in a **double-worked** plant, illustrated here by a Bartlett pear grafted on a Hardy pear which is grafted on quince as a rootstock. The Hardy pear, in this case, is the **intermediate stock—or interstock.**

A good example of double-working is the use of the Bartlett pear on dwarfing quince roots. The Bartlett pear will not form a compatible union if grafted directly on quince. Therefore, an intermediate stock must be used to insure a normal tree life. This can be done in several ways. Cuttings of the quince may be rooted during one summer and fall-budded to a compatible stock, such as the Hardy pear. This grows the following summer after which it is again fall-budded to the Bartlett pear, the Bartlett bud being inserted in the intermediate stock. The Bartlett top is developed the next summer, after which the double-worked nursery tree is ready to dig up and set in its permanent location.

A quicker method is illustrated in Figure 12–28. By bench grafting during late winter, using the whip or tongue grafting method, dormant Bartlett pear scions are grafted on dormant Hardy pear stem pieces. These grafts are then placed in damp packing material for several weeks in a cool location until they have become well callused and have united. In early spring, these grafts of the scion variety on the interstock are crown grafted in the nursery row to the rootstock, in this case, rooted quince cuttings. Then after this combination—Bartlett on Hardy on quince—grows for 1 year in the nursery row, the double-worked nursery trees are ready to be dug *(4)*.

Another method of double-working all at one time is by bench grafting, using the whip or tongue grafting method, but making two graft unions rather than one. The subsequent callusing and planting procedure is the same as for a simple root graft *(15)*.

A still simpler method for double-working has been developed and reported both in England *(5)* and Germany *(11)*, termed "double-shield budding." This method is illustrated in Figures 13–15 and 13–16. Essentially, it consists of preparing an ordinary T-bud (see p. 382) but inserting a thin budless shield of the intermediate variety under and below the usual shield piece containing the bud of the variety desired for the top.

Top-Grafting (Topworking)

One of the principal uses of grafting is to change the variety of an established plant—tree, shrub, or vine. Budding, rather than grafting, can also be used to change varieties, in which case the process is termed *top-budding* (see p. 395).

Any of the methods of grafting described earlier in this chapter—whip, side, cleft, saw kerf, or bark—can be used for top-grafting.

Figure 12–29. Topworking a 55-year-old Glou Morceau pear tree to the Comice variety. **(left)** Just after grafting. The scions are well-placed in the proper size branches but they should be shorter. **(center)** The same tree one year later. **(right)** The same tree 6 years later. Courtesy W. P. Tufts, Calif. Agr. Exp. Sta.

Preparation for top-grafting. Top-grafting is usually done in the early spring, shortly before new growth starts. The exact time depends upon the method to be used. The cleft, side, whip, and saw kerf graft can be done early, before the bark is slipping. The bark graft must be done later, when the bark is slipping, preferably just as the buds of the stock tree are starting growth.

It is usually advisable to obtain an ample amount of good quality scion wood prior to grafting and store it under the proper conditions (see p. 356).

In preparing the stock tree for topworking, a decision must be made with each individual tree as to which and how many scaffold branches (usually three to five) should be used. In some cases, especially with top-budding, the work may be done higher in the tree in the smaller, secondary scaffold branches where six to twelve branches are topworked. The latter practice is likely to result in an earlier return to bearing than when fewer and larger limbs are grafted lower in the tree. The branches to be grafted should be well distributed around the tree and up and down the main trunk. Branches with weak, narrow crotches should not be selected. All others can be removed, unless one or more nurse branches are used.

Retaining *nurse branches* is a common practice in topworking deciduous trees in regions where cold winters are experienced. In localities where the winters are mild and damage of succulent growth by winter killing is slight, nurse branches are not used. For broad-leaved evergreens, such as the citrus and the olive species, it is customary to leave nurse branches. The presence of nurse branches, especially if they are on the south and west sides of the tree, is often desirable because they protect the grafted branches from sun scald; otherwise, the branches should be whitewashed to prevent this (see p. 369). Retaining a large scaffold branch as a nurse limb results in less vigorous growth of the scions. They are then less likely to blow out in winds or be winter killed than the more vigorous, succulent shoots which develop from the scions when no nurse branches are retained. Also, fewer suckers and watersprouts (which must be removed) develop when nurse branches are left. The latter should be so pruned as not to interfere with the growth of the young grafts.

A practice which is often recommended, especially for older trees, is to topwork them during a 2-year period, grafting perhaps two main branches on the northeast side of the tree the first year and retaining two branches on the southwest as nurse branches. The second year these are topworked.

Topworking is most successful when done on relatively young trees where the branches to be grafted are not larger than 3 or 4 inches in diameter and are relatively close to the ground. When attempting to topwork large, old trees it is often necessary to go high up in the trees to find branches with a diameter as small as 4 inches. If the grafting is done on such branches, the new top is inconveniently high for the various orchard opera-

Figure 12–30. Proper method of topworking large trees. The scions should be inserted in fairly small branches even though they may be rather high in the tree. Complete healing of the graft unions are more likely than when large branches close to the ground are grafted. Courtesy C. J. Hansen.

Figure 12–31. An improper method of topworking large trees. This walnut tree was cut off close to the ground and a number of scions inserted around its circumference by the bark graft method. Two of the scions grew successfully but the remainder failed. Most of the original tree is dead; healing of such a large cut is almost impossible. A better method of top-grafting large trees is shown in Figure 12–30.

tions, such as thinning and harvesting. The other alternative is cutting off the branches or main trunk low to the ground and inserting the scions into wood one or more feet in diameter. Although many scions can be inserted around the tree between the bark and the wood by the bark graft method and may grow well for several years, it is quite likely that wood rot will develop in the center of the stub before the growth of the scions can heal it over. Also, some scions are not mechanically held in place very securely and may be blown out by strong winds after they reach considerable size.

It is important that the branch to be topworked be cut off in such a location that the region just below the cut is smooth and free from knots or small branches so as to have a satisfactory place for inserting the scions. The branches are best cut off about 9 to 12 inches from the main trunk to keep the tree headed low. The branch should not be cut off more than a few hours before the grafting is to be done.

Figure 12–32. Sawing off a branch to leave a stub for grafting. **(top—left)** The first cut is made starting from the under side of the branch and going about one-third the distance through. **(top—right)** The second cut is made starting from the upper portion of the branch and cutting downward. It should be out an inch or two further on the branch than the first cut. **(below)** After the branch breaks off cleanly, the first cut is then completed, leaving a smooth surface for grafting.

IN PREPARATION FOR TOPWORKING

(a) Do the work in early spring.

(b) Select for grafting three to five well-placed scaffold branches which are not larger than 4 inches in diameter and which are as close to the ground as possible.

(c) Retain nurse branches for broad-leaved evergreen trees and for deciduous trees where winters are severe.

(d) Cut off the branches properly so that the bark is not split down the trunk.

It is best to do the grafting operation on a day which is cool and overcast with no wind blowing. This offers the most protection from drying of the cut surfaces of the scion and stock until they can be covered with grafting wax. Hot, sunny, and windy days should be avoided.

During the actual grafting operation, the scion wood must not be allowed to dry out by letting it be exposed to the sun. The scion wood should be kept moist and cool in some container or by wrapping in moist burlap. (See page 356 for further information on collecting scion wood.)

Immediately after each stub is grafted, it should be thoroughly covered with some type of grafting wax as described on page 351. The need for prompt and thorough coverage of all cuts, including the tip end of the scions, cannot be stressed too strongly. The wax should be worked into the bark of the stock, sealing all small cuts or cracks where air could penetrate in and around the cut surfaces where healing tissue is expected to develop.

Subsequent care of topworked trees. After the actual top-grafting (or top-budding) operation is finished, much important work needs to be done before the topworking is successfully completed. A good grafting job can be ruined by failure to care for the trees properly.

If the grafting has been done late in the season (April or early May) when growth is active, trees of some species, such as the walnut, will "bleed" to a considerable extent from the grafted stub, even though it has been covered with grafting wax. This flow of sap around the scions can be so heavy as to interfere with the normal healing processes at the graft union. If this condition appears, it can often be corrected by making several slanting cuts with a knife through the bark in the trunk of the tree several feet below the grafted stubs. The bleeding will then take place at these cuts rather than around the graft union. This extensive sap flow is not particularly harmful to the tree and will usually stop within a few days.

In 3 to 5 days after grafting, the trees should be carefully inspected and the graft unions rewaxed if cracks or holes appear in the wax.

A problem needing immediate attention is the prevention of sunburn on the portions of the trunk and large branches which may be exposed to the direct rays of the sun by the removal of the protecting top foliage. This is especially important if the grafting has been done late in the season when hot weather can be expected, and when no protecting nurse branches have been retained. The radiant energy from the sun absorbed by the dark-colored bark can raise the temperature of the living cells below the bark to a lethal level.

It is generally advisable to whitewash the trunk, branches and scions of the grafted trees, unless the grafting is done in late winter or early spring when the days are still cold. Various cold water paints, some made especially for this purpose, are available. The white color reflects a considerable portion of the sun's radiant energy, thus keeping the temperature of the living tissues within safe limits.

To Prepare Whitewash for Grafted Trees

A satisfactory whitewash may be made by using the following ingredients: Quicklime, 5 lbs.; Salt, ½ lb.; Sulfur, ¼ lb. Add water to the lime to start it slaking. Then add the salt and sulfur. This mixture should be prepared in a crockery or wood container. Allow to age for several days then dilute to a consistency just thick enough to apply with a paint brush. Dilute to a thinner consistency for spray application.

One way of protecting the scions from the heat of the sun when the grafting has been done late in the season is to cover the end of the grafted stub and the scions with an ordinary large paper bag, the corners of which have been cut to allow for ventilation. The bag is tied securely on the stub with heavy string. In a test (6), however, of various methods of protecting scions of grafted walnut trees, including the use of paper bags, whitewashing proved the best.

Another help in preventing sunburn is to retain some of the water-sprouts which soon start growth along the trunk and branches of the grafted tree. They must be kept under control or they will quickly shade out the developing scions. Rather than remove the watersprouts completely, they can be headed back to several inches in length and will shade the bark underneath. An additional benefit is that the food manufactured by this leaf area will help sustain the tree until the new scions develop sufficient foliage to do so.

It should be emphasized that, especially during the first summer after topworking, the sucker and watersprout growth arising from below the grafted branches must be kept pruned back so as not to interfere with the growth of the scions. If it has been a customary practice to fertilize the trees with nitrogen, this should be withheld for a year or two after grafting, because no stimulation of growth is usually needed. If the trees have been under irrigation, their water requirement will be much less due to the removal of a considerable amount of leaf area when the tops were cut back for grafting.

Two to four scions are generally inserted in each stub. If all the scions grow, they should all be retained during the first year, because they will help heal over the stub. However, just one branch, from the best placed and strongest growing scion, should be retained permanently. Growth from the remaining scions should be retarded by rather severe pruning, keeping them alive to help heal the branch, but allowing the permanent scion to become the dominant one. To keep two, or more, scions for permanent branches at one point would undoubtedly result in a weak crotch which would eventually break. The first year, then, the best practice is to retain all scions to help heal the stub, but by pruning, retard the growth of all but the best one. If two shoots arise from the scion to be retained permanently, select the best one of these and remove the other. After the stub has healed over, the temporary scions can be removed completely. This may be in the second or third year.

Figure 12–33. Graft union showing successful healing. Two scions were inserted in this stub. Both were saved but one was pruned severely to keep it small. The small scion has helped heal over the stub and is about ready to be completely removed. Courtesy C. J. Hansen.

If the permanent scion grows rather vigorously, the problem arises of its becoming top-heavy and breaking off during winds. This may be handled in two ways—either by retarding the growth of the permanent branch by pruning it back or by nailing a lath or other type of stick onto the tree and tying the new branch to this stick. *When tying a cord around a branch, always make a big loop so that there is no chance of the branch being girdled as it grows.*

Should only one scion grow at each stub, the problem of securing adequate healing of the stub on the side opposite the living scion may be serious.

Healing may be helped by sawing off the stub at an angle away from the surviving scion. The cut surface of the stub can be covered with grafting wax to retard wood rotting. It may take a number of years for the single scion to heal over the stub, and it is quite possible that wood rotting may start before it can do so.

When none of the scions grow in a stub, there are still some possibilities for getting it topworked. One is by allowing several well-placed water-sprouts arising just below the cut surface to grow, then top-budding them during the summer. Or the watersprouts may be allowed to grow so as to keep the branch alive and healthy, then the grafting operation repeated the following year, making a fresh cut a foot or so below the original cut.

If nurse branches have been used, they should be watched carefully, cutting them back and away from the scions at intervals throughout the summer so that scion shoots are always fully exposed to the sun and have sufficient space to grow. Nurse branches should be removed entirely or grafted by the second or third year.

When the top of the tree has been finally worked over to the new variety, it will grow vigorously for a few years. Good pruning practices are needed to prevent badly placed branches from developing.

REFERENCES

1. Alley, C. J., Mechanized grape grafting, *Calif. Agr.*, 11(6):3, 12. 1957.
2. Brase, K. D., The nurse-root graft, an aid in rootstock research, *Farm Research*, 17(1):16. 1951.
3. Fillmore, R. H., Major techniques in plant propagation, *Amer. Nurs.*, 97 (10): 13, 34–43. 1953.
4. Garner, R. J., Studies in nursery technique. The production of double worked pear trees. *Ann. Rpt. East Malling Res. Sta. for 1939*, pp. 84–86. 1940.
5. ———, Double working pears at budding time, *Ann. Rpt. East Malling Res. Sta. for 1952*, pp. 174–175. 1953.
6. Hansen, C. J., and H. T. Hartmann, Influence of various treatments given to walnut grafts on the percentage of scions growing, *Proc. Amer. Soc. Hort. Sci.*, 57: 193–197. 1951.
7. Hearman, J., et al., The reinvigoration of apple trees by the inarching of vigorous rootstocks, *Jour. Pom. and Hort. Sci.*, 14:376–390. 1936.
8. Jones, F. D., Hormone on root graft, *Amer. Nurs.*, 72(11): 6–7. 1950.
9. Kerr, W. L., A simple method of obtaining fruit trees on their own roots, *Proc. Amer. Soc. Hort. Sci.*, 33:355–357. 1936.
10. Lincoln, F. B., Layering of root grafts—a ready method for obtaining self-rooted apple trees, *Proc. Amer. Soc. Hort. Sci.*, 35:419–422. 1938.
11. Nicolin, P., Nicolieren, a new method of grafting, *Deutsche Baumschule*, 5:186–187. 1953.
12. Shippy, W. B., Influence of environment on the callusing of apple cuttings and grafts, *Amer. Jour. Bot.*, 17:290–327. 1930.
13. Sitton, B. G., and E. P. Akin, Grafting wax melter, *USDA Leaflet 202*, 1940.

14. Thompson, L. A., and C. O. Hesse, Some factors which may affect the choice of grafting compounds for top-working trees, *Proc. Amer. Soc. Hort. Sci.,* 56:213–216. 1950.
15. Tukey, H. B., and K. D. Brase, The dwarfing effect of an intermediate stem-piece of Malling IX apple, *Proc. Amer. Soc. Hort. Sci.,* 42:357–364. 1943.
16. Upshall, W. H., The stub graft as a supplement to budding in nursery practice, *Proc. Amer. Soc. Hort. Sci.,* 47:187–189. 1946.

• **Supplementary Reading**

Baltet, C., *The Art of Grafting and Budding,* 6th ed. London: Crosby, Lockwood, 1910.

Brase, K. D., "Propagating Fruit Trees," *New York Agricultural Experiment Station Bulletin 773.* (1956).

Chandler, W. H., *Deciduous Orchards,* 3rd ed. Philadelphia: Lea and Febiger, 1957. Chap. 13.

Garner, R. J., *The Grafter's Handbook,* 2nd ed. London: Faber and Faber, 1958.

Hansen, C. J., and H. T. Hartmann, "Propagation of Temperate Zone Fruit Plants," *California Agricultural Experiment Station Circular 471* (1958).

Yerkes, G. E., "Propagation of Trees and Shrubs," *U.S. Department of Agriculture Farmers' Bulletin 1567* (1945).

Techniques
of
Budding

In contrast to grafting where the scion consists of a short detached piece of stem tissue with several buds, budding utilizes only one bud and a small section of bark, with or without wood. Budding is often termed "bud grafting," since the physiological processes involved are the same as in grafting.

The commonly used budding methods depend upon the bark "slipping." This term indicates the condition when the bark can be easily separated from the wood. It denotes the period of year when the plant is in active growth and the cambium cells are soft, succulent, actively dividing, and therefore easily torn as the bark is lifted from the wood. Beginning with new growth in the spring, this period should last until the plant ceases growth in the fall. However, adverse growing conditions, such as lack of water, defoliation, or low temperatures, may lead to a tightening of the bark and can seriously interfere with the budding operation. Getting the stock plants in the proper condition for budding is an important consideration. Of the commonly used methods described here, only one—the chip bud—can be done when the bark is not slipping.

The budding operation, particularly T-budding, can be performed more rapidly than the simplest method of grafting, some rose budders inserting as many as two thousand to three thousand or more T-buds a day if the tying is done by a helper. If performed under the proper conditions, the percentage of successful unions in T-budding is very high—in the range of 90 to 100 per cent. Budding is widely used in producing nursery stock of named varieties of roses and fruit trees, where hundreds of thousands of individual plants are propagated each year. Therefore, for propagation operations involving a large number of plants where speed and low mortality is essential, budding upon selected rootstocks is likely to be chosen.

The use of budding is confined generally to young plants or the smaller branches of large plants where the buds can be inserted into shoots which are from ¼ to 1 inch in diameter. Topworking young trees by top-budding is quite successful. Here the buds are inserted in small, vigorously growing branches in the upper portion of the tree (see p. 395).

Budding may result in a stronger union, particularly during the first few years, than is obtained by some of the grafting methods so that the shoots are not as likely to blow out in strong winds. Budding makes more economical use of propagating wood than grafting, each bud potentially being capable of producing a new plant of the desired variety. This may be quite important if propagating wood is scarce. In addition, the techniques involved in budding are quite simple and can be easily performed by the amateur.

ROOTSTOCKS FOR BUDDING

In propagating nursery stock of the various fruit and ornamental species by budding, a rootstock plant is used. It should have the desired characteristics of vigor, growth habit, and disease resistance, as well as being easily propagated. Such rootstock plants may be a rooted cutting, a rooted layer, or more commonly a seedling. Usually, one year's growth in the nursery row preceding the time the budding is to be done is sufficient to produce a rootstock plant large enough to be budded, but seedlings of slow-growing species often require two seasons. (See Chapters 16 and 17.)

TIME OF BUDDING—FALL, SPRING, OR JUNE

The important budding methods are performed at seasons of the year when the stock plant is in active growth, and the cambial cells are actively dividing so that the bark separates readily from the wood. It is also necessary that well-developed buds of the desired variety be available at the same time. These conditions exist for most plant species at three different times during the year. In the Northern Hemisphere, these periods are late July to early September (*fall budding*), March and April (*spring budding*), and late May and early June (*June budding*).

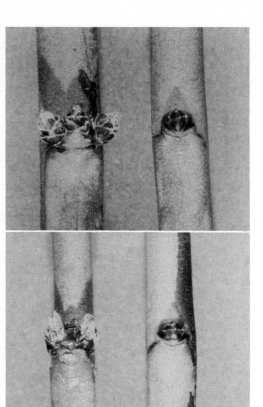

ALMOND. The shoot on the left has two flower buds with a vegetative bud in between. This could be used for budding but the single vegetative bud on the right is more desirable.

PEACH. This is similar to the almond. The shoot on the left has two flower buds with a vegetative bud in between. The single vegetative bud on the shoot at the right is more desirable for budding.

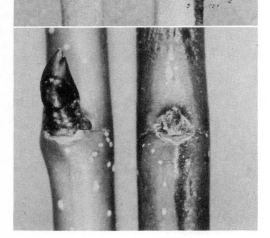

PEAR. The flower bud on the shoot at the left would be entirely unsuitable for budding. The small, pointed vegetative bud on the shoot at the right should be used.

Figure 13–1. In budding it is important that vegetative rather than flower buds be used. Vegetative buds are usually small and pointed while flower buds are larger and more plump. Differences between vegetative and flower buds in three fruit species are illustrated here.

Fall Budding

This is the most important time of budding in the propagation of fruit tree nursery stock, although actually the budding is mostly done in late summer rather than fall. The rootstock plants are usually large enough by late July or August to accommodate the bud, and the plants are still actively growing, with the bark slipping easily. Once growth has stopped and the bark adheres tightly to the wood, budding can no longer be done.

In fall budding, the budsticks, consisting of the current season's shoots, are obtained at the time of budding. They should be vigorous and contain vegetative or leaf buds. Such shoots are sometimes termed *watersprouts,* especially if they are very vigorous. Short, slowly growing shoots on the outer portion of the tree should be avoided, because they may have chiefly flower buds rather than vegetative buds. Flower buds are usually round and plump, whereas leaf buds are smaller and pointed. Some species have mixed buds; the node containing both vegetative and flower buds. These are satisfactory to use in budding.

As the budsticks are selected they should have the leaves removed immediately, leaving only a short piece of the leaf stalk or petiole attached to the bud; this will aid in handling the bud later on. The budsticks should be cared for so as to avoid drying by wrapping in some material, such as moist burlap, and keeping them in a cool, shady location until they are needed. The budsticks should be used promptly after cutting, although they can be stored for a short time if kept cool and moist. It is best, if possible, when a considerable amount of budding is being done, to collect the budsticks as they are being used, a day's supply at a time.

The best buds to use on the stick are usually those in the middle and basal portions. Buds on the succulent terminal portion of the shoot should be discarded. In certain species, such as the sweet cherry, buds on the basal portion of the shoots are flower buds, which of course should not be used.

In fall budding after the buds have been inserted, there is nothing more to be done until the following spring. *Although eventually the rootstock is to be cut off above the bud, in no case should this be done immediately after the bud has been inserted.* Healing of the bud piece to the stock is greatly facilitated by the normal movement of water and nutrients up and down the stem of the rootstock. This would, of course, be stopped if the top of the rootstock was cut off above the bud.

If the budding operation is done properly, the bud piece should unite with the stock in 2 to 3 weeks, depending upon the growing conditions. If the leaf stalk or petiole drops off cleanly next to the bud, it is a good indication that the bud has united, especially if the bark piece remains its normal light brown or green color and the bud stays plump. On the other hand, if the leaf petiole does not drop off cleanly but adheres tightly and starts to shrivel and darken, while the bark piece also commences to turn black, it is likely that the operation has failed. If the bark of the root-stock is still slipping easily and budwood is still available, there may be time for the budding to be repeated.

Even though the bud union has healed, in most deciduous species the bud usually does not grow or "push out" in the fall, since it is in the physiological rest period. It remains just as it is until spring, at which time the chilling winter temperatures have overcome the rest influence and the bud is ready to grow. There are some exceptions to this; for example, in fall budding maples, roses, honey locust, and certain other plants, some of the buds may start growth in the fall. In northern areas, if such fall-forced buds do not start early enough for the shoots to mature before cold weather starts, they are likely to be winter killed.

In the spring, just before new growth begins, the rootstock is cut off immediately above the bud. It is desirable to make a sloping cut, slanting away from the bud. Although this cut may be waxed, it is usually not essential unless the stock is large in diameter. Cutting back the rootstock forces the inserted bud into growth. In citrus budding, it is a frequent practice to only partially cut the stock above the bud and to lop or bend it over away from the bud. The leaves of the stock still furnish the roots with some nutrients, but the partial cutting forces the bud into growth. After the new shoot from the bud is well established, the top is then completely removed.

In northern regions, fall-inserted buds are sometimes covered with soil during the winter until danger of frost has passed and are then uncovered and topped-back in late spring.

Where strong winds occur and in species in which the new shoots grow vigorously, support for the newly developing shoot may be necessary. One practice sometimes followed is to cut off the rootstock several inches above the bud, using this projecting stub as a support on which to tie the tender young shoot arising from the bud. This stub is eventually removed after the shoot has become well established. In another procedure, stakes may be driven into the ground next to the stock to which the developing shoot is tied at intervals during its growth.

Cutting back to force the main bud to grow also forces many latent buds on the rootstock into growth. These must be rubbed off as soon as they appear or they will soon choke out the desired inserted bud. It may be necessary to go over the budded plants several times before these "sprouts" stop appearing.

The shoot arising from the inserted bud becomes the top portion of the plant. After one season's growth in the nursery row, with favorable conditions of soil, water and nutrients, temperature, and insect and disease control, this shoot will have developed sufficiently to enable the plant to be dug and moved to its permanent location during the following dormant season. Such a tree would have a 1-year-old top and a 2- or perhaps 3-year-old root, but it is still considered to be a "yearling" tree. If the top makes insufficient growth the first year, it can be allowed to grow a second year and is then known as a 2-year-old tree.

Spring Budding

This method is similar to fall budding except that the work takes place the following spring as soon as active growth of the rootstock begins and the bark separates easily from the wood. The period for successful spring budding is limited and should be completed before the rootstocks have made much new growth.

Budsticks are chosen from the same type of shoots—in regard to vigor of growth and type of buds—that would have been used in fall budding except that they are not collected until the dormant season the following winter. The leaves would, of course, have fallen by this time, and the buds would have experienced sufficient chilling to overcome their rest period. It is very important that the budwood be collected while it is still dormant —before there is any evidence of the buds swelling. Since the buds must be dormant when they are inserted and the rootstocks must be in active growth, it is necessary in spring budding that the budsticks be gathered some time in advance of the time of budding and stored at temperatures (32° to 40°F.) which will hold the buds dormant. The budsticks should be wrapped in bundles with damp peat moss or some similar material to prevent their drying out.

In spring budding, the actual budding operation should be done just as soon as the bark on the rootstock slips easily. Then, about 2 weeks after budding, when the bud unions have healed, the top of the stocks must be cut off above the bud to force the inserted bud into active growth. At the same time, latent buds on the rootstock begin to grow and should be removed. Sometimes it is helpful to permit such shoots from the rootstock to develop to some extent to prevent sunburn and help nourish the plant. They must be held in check, however, and eventually removed.

Although the new shoot from the inserted bud gets a later start in spring budding than in fall budding, if growing conditions are favorable, spring buds will usually develop rapidly enough to make a satisfactory top by fall. Fall budding, however, is to be preferred for several reasons: the higher temperatures at that time promote more certain healing of the union, the budding season is longer, there is no necessity to store the budsticks, the inserted buds start growth earlier in the spring, and the pressure of other work is usually not as great for nurserymen in the late summer as in the spring. Spring budding is used sometimes on rootstocks which were fall budded but on which the buds failed to take.

June Budding

June budding is used to obtain a "1-year-old" budded tree in a single growing season. Its principal characteristic is that budding is done in the early part of the growing season and the inserted bud forced into growth immediately during the same season. As a method of nursery propagation, June budding is largely confined in the United States to the southern states and California which have a relatively long growing season. In the propagation of fruit trees, June budding is used mostly in producing such stone fruits as peaches, nectarines, apricots, almonds, and plums, which can be budded on peach seedlings as a rootstock. The T-bud method (see p. 382) is generally used. By planting seeds in the fall, or stratified seeds (see p. 127) as early as possible in the spring, the seedlings usually attain sufficient size to be budded by late May or early June. June budded trees are not as large by the end of the growing season as those propagated by fall or spring budding, but they are of sufficient size to be commercially salable.

The budwood used in June budding consists of current season's growth; that is, new shoots which have developed since growth started in the spring. By late May or early June, these shoots will usually have grown sufficiently to have a well-developed bud in the axil of each leaf. At this time of year these buds will not as yet have entered the rest period, so when they are used in budding they continue their growth on through the summer, producing the top portion of the budded seedling.

Handling June budded trees following the actual operation of budding is somewhat more exacting than is the case with fall or spring budding. The rootstocks are smaller and have less stored foods than those used in fall or spring budding. The object behind the following procedures is to keep the rootstock (and later the budded top) actively and continuously growing so as to allow no check in growth, while at the same time changing the seedling shoot to a budded top. The bud should be inserted high enough on the stem so that a number of leaves, at least three or four, can be retained below the bud. The method of T-budding described on page 383 with the "wood out" should be used. Healing of the inserted bud should be very rapid at this time of year, since temperatures are relatively high and rapidly growing, succulent plant parts are used. By 3 to 4 days after budding, the top of the rootstock can be cut back somewhat—2 to 5 inches above the bud—leaving at least one leaf above the bud and several below it. This operation will check the terminal growth and stimulate shoot growth from basal buds of the rootstock which will produce additional leaf area. This continuous leaf area is necessary so that there always will be sufficient leaves to keep manufacturing foods for the small plant. Ten days to 2 weeks after budding, the rootstock can be cut back to the bud, which should be starting to grow. Other shoots arising from the rootstock should be headed back to retard their growth. After the inserted bud grows and develops a substantial leaf area, it can then supply the plant with the necessary nutrients. By the time the shoot from the inserted bud has grown 6 to 8 inches high, it should have enough leaves so that all other shoots and leaves can be removed.

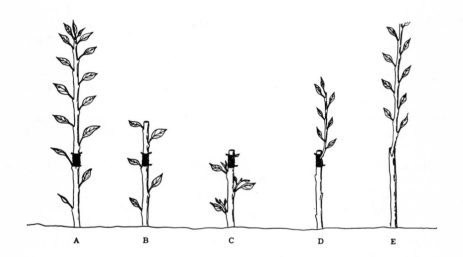

Figure 13–2. It is important in June budding that the stock be cut back to the bud properly. **(A)** The bud is inserted high enough on the stock so that there are several leaves below the bud. **(B)** Three or four days after budding, the stock is partially cut back—2 to 5 inches above the bud. **(C)** Ten days to 2 weeks after budding, the stock is completely removed just above the bud. **(D)** This forces the bud into growth as well as other buds on the stock; the latter must subsequently be removed. **(E)** Appearance of the budded tree after the new shoot has made considerable growth.

Another method which works well is to partially cut the stock just above the bud and break it over. Nutrients are still able to pass from the top of the stock to the roots, but this partial blocking forces the inserted bud into growth.

June budding is often of considerable value to nurserymen who find that their regular supply of fall or spring budded trees is insufficient to meet their expected demand. By this method they can, as late as mid-June, still propagate trees to be ready by fall, provided they have a supply of rootstock plants large enough to bud.

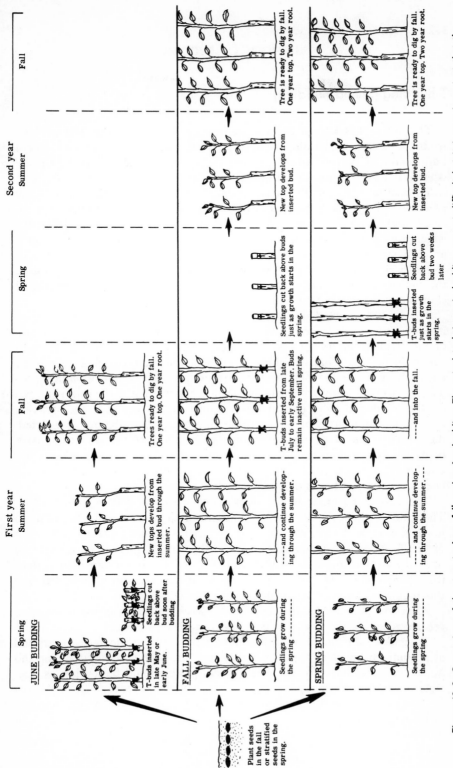

Figure 13-3. Comparison of the steps in **June, fall,** and **spring** budding. The actual techniques in budding are not difficult but it is very important that the various operations be done at the proper time.

METHODS OF BUDDING

T-Budding (Shield Budding)

This method is known by both names, the "T-bud" designation arising from the T-like appearance of the cut in the stock, whereas the "shield bud" name is derived from the shield-like appearance of the bud piece when it is ready for insertion in the stock.

T-budding is, by far, the most common method of budding and is widely used by nurserymen in propagating nursery stock of most fruit tree species, roses, and many ornamental shrubs. Its use is generally limited to stocks which are about $\frac{1}{4}$ to 1 inch in diameter, with fairly thin bark, and which are actively growing so that the bark will separate readily from the wood. If the bark is so tight on the wood that it has to be forcibly pried loose, the chances of the bud healing successfully are rather remote. The operation should then be delayed until the bark is slipping easily.

The bud is inserted into the stock 2 to 10 inches above the soil level in a smooth bark surface. There are different opinions as to the proper side of the stock to insert the bud. If extreme weather conditions are likely to occur during the critical healing period just following budding, it may be desirable to place the bud on the side of the stock where as much protection as possible may be obtained. Some believe that if the bud is placed on the windward side, there is less chance of the young shoot breaking off. Otherwise, it probably makes little difference where the bud is inserted, the convenience of the operator and the location of the smoothest bark being the controlling factors. When rows of closely planted rootstocks are budded, it is more convenient to have all the buds on the same side for later inspection and manipulations.

The cuts to be made in the stock plant are illustrated in Figure 13–4. There are various modifications of this technique; most budders prefer to make the vertical cut first followed by the horizontal crosscut at the top of the T. As the horizontal cut is made, the knife is given a twist to throw open the flaps of bark for insertion of the bud. It is important that neither the vertical nor horizontal cut be made longer than necessary, because this requires additional tying later to close the cuts.

After the proper cuts are made in the stock and the incision is ready to receive the bud, the shield piece is cut out of the budstick.

To remove the shield of bark containing the bud, a slicing cut is started at a point on the stem about $\frac{1}{2}$ inch below the bud, continuing under and about an inch above the bud. The shield piece should be as thin as possible but still thick enough to have some rigidity. A second horizontal cut is then made $\frac{1}{2}$ to $\frac{3}{4}$ inches above the bud, thus permitting the removal of the shield piece.

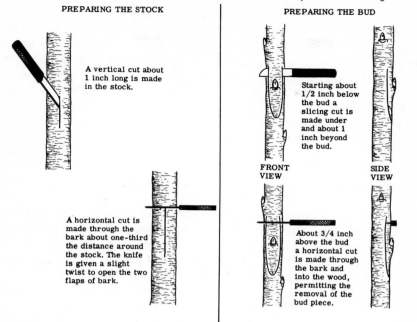

PREPARING THE STOCK

A vertical cut about 1 inch long is made in the stock.

A horizontal cut is made through the bark about one-third the distance around the stock. The knife is given a slight twist to open the two flaps of bark.

PREPARING THE BUD

Starting about 1/2 inch below the bud a slicing cut is made under and about 1 inch beyond the bud.

FRONT VIEW

SIDE VIEW

About 3/4 inch above the bud a horizontal cut is made through the bark and into the wood, permitting the removal of the bud piece.

INSERTING THE BUD INTO THE STOCK

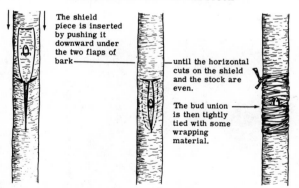

The shield piece is inserted by pushing it downward under the two flaps of bark

until the horizontal cuts on the shield and the stock are even.

The bud union is then tightly tied with some wrapping material.

Figure 13–4. Steps in making the T-bud (Shield bud). There are several variations of the procedure shown here.

There are two methods of preparing the shield—with the "wood in" or the "wood out." This refers to the little sliver of wood just under the bark of the shield piece and which will remain attached to it if the second horizontal cut is deep and goes through the bark and wood, joining the first slicing cut. Some professional budders believe it is best to remove this sliver of wood, but others retain it. In budding certain species, however, such as maples and walnuts, much better success is usually obtained with "de-wooded" buds. If it is desired to prepare the shield with the wood out, the second horizontal cut should be just deep enough to go through the bark and not the wood. Then if the bark is slipping easily, the bark shield can be snapped loose from the wood (which still remains attached to the budstick) by pressing it against the budstick and sliding it sideways. A small core of wood comprising the vascular tissues supplying the bud is present, and this should remain in the bud, rather than adhering to the wood and leaving a hole in the bud. If the shield is pulled outward rather than being slid sideways from the wood, this core usually pulls out of the bud, eliminating the chances of a successful take. In June budding of fruit trees, the shield piece is usually prepared with the wood out. In most instances, however, the wood is left in. In spring budding, using dormant budwood, this sliver of wood is tightly attached to the bark and cannot be removed.

The next step is the insertion of the shield piece containing the bud into the incision in the stock plant. The shield is pushed under the two raised flaps of bark until its upper horizontal cut matches the same cut on the stock. The shield should fit snugly in place, well covered by the two flaps of bark, but with the bud itself exposed.

No waxing is necessary, but the bud union must be wrapped to hold the two components firmly together until healing is completed. Rubber budding strips, especially made for wrapping, are widely used for this purpose. Their elasticity provides sufficient pressure to hold the bud securely in place. The rubber, being exposed to the sun and air, usually

Figure 13–5. Wrapping materials used in budding. **(left)** Nurserymen's adhesive tape. **(center)** Plastic resin tape. **(upper right)** Raffia. **(lower right)** Budding rubber strips.

Figure 13–6. Steps in the development of a T-bud. (left) Bud after being inserted and wrapped. (center) Bud has healed in place, the budding rubber has dropped off, and the stock cut back above the bud. (right) Shoot development from the inserted bud. All buds arising from the stock have been rubbed off.

deteriorates, breaks, and drops off after several weeks, at which time the bud should be healed in place. If the budding rubber is covered with soil, the rate of deterioration will be very much slower. This material has the advantage of eliminating cutting the wrapping ties, which can be a costly operation if thousands of plants have been budded. The rubber will expand as the rootstock grows so that there is little danger of constriction. Raffia (fiber-like leaf segments of certain *Raphia* species) has been used in the past for wrapping buds. However, it must be cut later (about 10 days to 2 weeks after budding) to prevent constriction at the bud union as the plant grows.

In tying the bud, the ends of the budding rubbers are held in place by inserting them under the adjacent turn. The bud itself should not be covered. The amount of tension given the budding rubber is quite important. It should not be too loose or there will be too little pressure holding the bud in place. On the other hand, if the rubber is stretched extremely tight there may be some harmful constriction; or it may be so thin that it will deteriorate rapidly and break too soon—before the bud union has taken place.

The next step, the cutting back of the rootstock, is described under "Time of Budding," page 377.

Inverted T-Budding

In localities where a great deal of rain occurs, water running down the stem of the rootstock will often enter the T-cut, soak under the bark, and cause rotting of the shield piece. Under such conditions an inverted T-bud may give better results, since it is more likely to shed excess water. In citrus budding, the inverted T method is widely used, even though the conventional method also gives excellent results. In species which bleed badly during budding, such as chestnuts, the inverted T-bud allows better drainage and better healing.

The techniques of the inverted T-bud method are the same as those already described except that the incision in the stock has the transverse cut at the bottom rather than at the top of the vertical cut, and in removing the shield piece from the budstick the knife starts above the bud and cuts downward below it. The shield is removed by making the transverse cut ½ to ¾ inches below the bud. The shield piece containing the bud is inserted into the lower part of the incision and pushed upward until the transverse cut of the shield meets that made in the stock.

It is important in using this inverted T-bud method that a normally oriented shield bud piece should not be inserted into an inverted incision in the stock. The bud would then have a reversed polarity. Although such upside down buds do live and grow, at least in some species, their use is not conducive to normal, rapid growth.

Patch Budding

The distinguishing feature of patch budding and related methods is that a rectangular patch of bark is removed completely from the stock and replaced with a patch of bark of the same size containing a bud of the variety to be propagated.

Patch budding is somewhat slower and more difficult to perform than T-budding, but it is widely and successfully used on thick-barked species, such as walnuts and pecans, where T-budding gives poor results, presumably due to the poor fit around the margins of the bud. Patch budding or one of its modifications, is also extensively used in propagating various tropical species, such as the rubber tree (*Hevea brasiliensis*).

Patch budding requires that the bark of both the stock and budstick be slipping easily. It is usually done in late summer or early fall but can also be done in the spring. In propagating nursery stock, the diameter of the rootstock and the budstick should preferably be about the same size, from ½ to 1 inch. Although the budstick should not be much larger than about 1 inch in diameter, the patch can be inserted successfully into stocks as large as 4 inches in diameter, although adequate healing of such large stubs may be a problem.

Special knives have been devised to facilitate the removal of the bark pieces from the stock and the budstick. Some type of a double-bladed

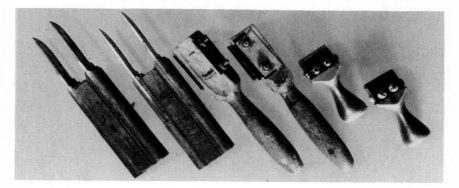

Figure 13–7. Tools used in patch budding and related methods. **(left)** Manufactured double-bladed knives. **(center)** Double-bladed knives made with two razor blades. **(right)** Manufactured patch budding tools consisting of four rectangular cutting blades.

knife that will make two transverse parallel cuts 1 to 1⅜ inches apart is necessary. These cuts, about an inch in length, are made through the bark to the wood in a smooth area of the rootstock several inches above the ground. Then the two transverse cuts are connected at each side by vertical cuts made with a single-bladed knife.

The patch of bark containing the bud is cut from the budstick in the same manner that the bark patch is removed from the stock. Using the same two-bladed knife, two transverse cuts are made through the bark, one above and one below the bud. Then two vertical cuts are made on each side of the bud so that the bark piece will be about an inch wide. The bark

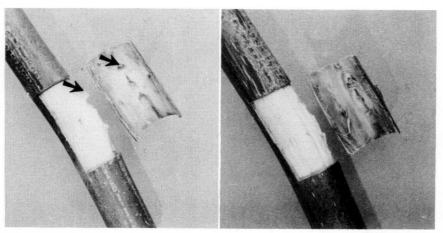

Figure 13–8. Removing the bud patch from the budstick in patch budding. **(left)** Incorrect. The core of wood in the bud, comprising the vascular tissues, has broken off leaving a hole in the bud. Such a bud is not likely to grow. **(right)** Correct. The patch was pushed off sideways and the core of wood has remained inside the bud.

piece containing the bud is now ready to be removed. It is important that it be slid off sideways rather than being lifted or pulled off. There is a small core of wood, the bud trace, which must remain inside the bud if a successful take is to be obtained. By sliding the bark patch to one side, this core is broken off and stays in the bud. If the bud patch is lifted off, this core of wood is likely to remain attached to the wood of the budstick, leaving a hole in the bud.

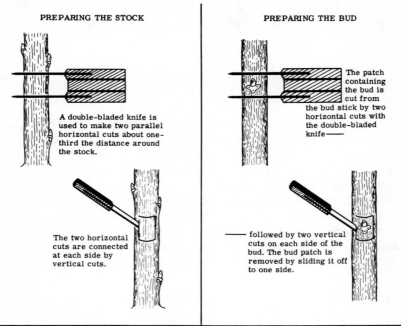

PREPARING THE STOCK

A double-bladed knife is used to make two parallel horizontal cuts about one-third the distance around the stock.

The two horizontal cuts are connected at each side by vertical cuts.

PREPARING THE BUD

The patch containing the bud is cut from the bud stick by two horizontal cuts with the double-bladed knife——

—— followed by two vertical cuts on each side of the bud. The bud patch is removed by sliding it off to one side.

INSERTING THE BUD INTO THE STOCK

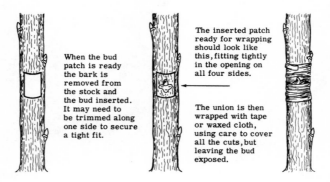

When the bud patch is ready the bark is removed from the stock and the bud inserted. It may need to be trimmed along one side to secure a tight fit.

The inserted patch ready for wrapping should look like this, fitting tightly in the opening on all four sides.

The union is then wrapped with tape or waxed cloth, using care to cover all the cuts, but leaving the bud exposed.

Figure 13–9. Steps in making the patch bud. This method is widely used for propagating thick-barked plants.

After the bud patch is removed from the budstick it must be inserted immediately on the stock, which should already be prepared, needing only to have the bark piece removed. The patch from the budstick should fit snugly at the top and bottom into the opening in the stock, since both transverse cuts were made with the same knife. It is more important that the bark piece fit tightly at top and bottom than along the sides.

The inserted patch is now ready to be wrapped. Often the bark of the stock will be thicker than the bark of the inserted bud patch so that upon wrapping it is impossible for the wrapping material to hold the bud patch tightly against the stock. In this case it is necessary that the bark of the stock be pared down around the bud patch so that it will be of the same thickness, or preferably slightly thinner, than the bark of the bud patch. Then the wrapping material will hold the bud patch tightly in place.

One type of tool, illustrated in Figure 13–7, has a pair of vertical cutting blades in addition to the horizontal blades. With this, all four cuts of the rectangle are made at once.

In cases where difficulty is experienced in obtaining successful unions with the patch bud method, it may help to make the four cuts of the rectangle in the stock 1 to 3 weeks ahead of the time the actual budding is to be done. This bark patch is not removed from the stock, however, until the patch containing the bud is ready to be inserted. By making the cuts ahead of time, the wounding causes the callusing process to start so that when the new bark patch is inserted it heals very rapidly.

In wrapping the patch bud, a material should be used which not only will hold the bark tightly in place but will cover all the cut surfaces to prevent the entrance of air under the patch with the subsequent drying and death of the tissues. The bud itself must not be covered during wrapping. The most satisfactory material is nurserymen's adhesive tape. Waxed cloth strips, prepared as described on page 355, are also satisfactory and have been used extensively. Another method is to tie the bud patch with heavy cotton string and cover the cut edges with grafting wax.

It is important in patch budding, especially with walnuts, that the wrapping not be allowed to cause a constriction at the bud union. When the stock is rapidly growing, it is necessary to cut the tape about 10 days after budding. A single vertical knife cut on the side opposite the bud is sufficient. The cut tape should not be pulled off.

Patch budding is best performed in late summer when both the seedling stocks and the source of budwood are growing rapidly and their bark slipping easily. The budsticks for patch budding done at this time should have the leaf blades cut 2 to 3 weeks before they are taken from the tree. The petiole or leaf stalk is left attached to the base of the bud, but by the time the budstick is taken this petiole has dropped off or is easily removed.

Patch budding can also be done in the spring after new growth has appeared on the stocks and it has been determined that the bark is slipping.

There is a problem, however, in obtaining satisfactory buds to use at this time of year, since it is necessary that the bark of the budstick separate readily from the wood. At the same time, the buds should not be starting to swell. There are two methods by which satisfactory buds can be obtained for patch budding in the spring. In one, the budsticks are selected during the dormant winter period and stored at low temperatures (about 32°F.) and wrapped in moist sphagnum or peat moss to prevent their drying out. Then, about 3 weeks before the time the spring budding is to be done, they are brought out into a warm room and set with their bases in a container of water or they may be left packed in damp peat or sphagnum moss. The increased temperature will cause the cambium layer to become active and soon the bark will slip sufficiently so that the buds

Figure 13–10. Steps in the development of a patch bud. **(upper left)** Patch bud after being inserted and wrapped with tape. **(upper right)** After about 10 days the tape is slit along the back side to release any constricting pressure. **(lower left)** The tape is completely removed after about 3 weeks at which time the patch should be healed in place. **(lower right)** Cutting back the stock above the bud forces it into growth.

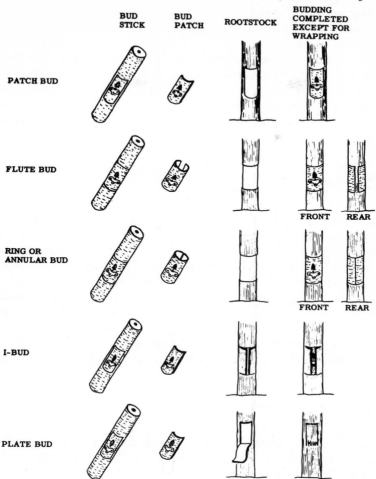

BUD STICK	BUD PATCH	ROOTSTOCK	BUDDING COMPLETED EXCEPT FOR WRAPPING

PATCH BUD

FLUTE BUD

FRONT   REAR

RING OR ANNULAR BUD

FRONT   REAR

I-BUD

PLATE BUD

Figure 13–11. There are many variations of the patch bud, some of which are shown here. The naming of these methods is somewhat confused but the most generally accepted names are as given here.

may be used. Although a few of the more terminal buds on each stick may start swelling in this time and cannot be used, there should be a number of buds in a satisfactory condition.

The second method of obtaining buds for spring patch budding is to obtain them directly from the tree which is the source of the budwood, but at the time the budding is to be done. If the trees are inspected carefully, it is seen that not all of the buds start pushing at once. The terminal ones are usually more advanced than the basal. There is a period when the bark is slipping easily throughout the shoot containing the desired buds, but when only a few of the buds have developed so far that they cannot be used. The remaining buds, which are still dormant but upon bark that can be removed readily, may be taken and used immediately for budding. It is easier to obtain suitable buds from young trees which made vigorous shoot growth the previous year than it is from old trees. The time that the budding is done will be governed then by the stage of development of the buds. This will vary considerably with the species and variety being used. Stage of development of the rootstock is not as critical. Its bark must be slipping well, and the budding should be done before the stock plant has made much new growth.

Flute Budding

This is made the same as the patch bud except that the patch of bark removed from the rootstock almost completely encircles it, leaving a narrow connection (about one-eighth of the circumference) between the upper and lower parts of the stock. In taking the bud patch from the budstick, a two-bladed knife is used with the two transverse cuts completely encircling the budstick. A single vertical cut connects the two horizontal cuts, permitting the bud patch to be removed. In fitting this bud patch to the stock, it may be necessary to shorten its circumference by a vertical cut to remove the surplus amount of bark. If the bud patch fails to unite, the narrow connecting strip of bark on the stock keeps the top of the stock alive.

Ring or Annular Budding

By this method, a complete ring of bark is removed from the stock and a complete ring from the budstick. In order for the two to match, the size of the stock and the budstick should be about the same. Since the stock is completely girdled, if the bud patch fails to heal in, the stock above the ring may eventually die. This method is not as widely used as the ordinary patch bud, since it has no particular advantages and it is rather cumbersome to perform.

I-Budding

In this type of budding, the bud patch is cut just as for patch budding; that is, in the form of a rectangle or square. Then using the same parallel-bladed knife, two transverse cuts are made through the bark of the stock. These are joined at their centers by a single vertical cut to produce the figure I. The two flaps of bark can then be raised for insertion of the bud patch beneath them. It may make a better fit to slant the side edges of the bud patch. In tying the I-bud, care should be taken to see that the bud patch does not buckle upward and fail to touch the stock.

This method should be considered for use when the bark of the stock is much thicker than that of the budstick. In such cases, if the patch bud was used, considerable paring down of the bark of the stock around the patch would be necessary. This operation is not necessary in the I-bud method.

Chip Budding

This is a budding method that can be done at times when the bark is not slipping, such as early in the spring before growth starts, or during the summer when active growth stops prematurely due to lack of water or some other cause. It is generally used with fairly small material, ½ to 1 inch in diameter. Although chip budding is quite successful, it is not as fast or simple as T-budding and is not likely to be done if conditions are favorable for the use of T-budding. Chip budding in the fall has given consistently excellent results, however, in budding vinifera grape varieties on phylloxera or nematode-resistant rootstocks. It is not commonly used on deciduous tree fruit species.

A chip of bark is removed from a smooth place between nodes near the base of the stock and replaced by another chip of the same size and shape from the budstick which contains a bud of the desired variety. The chips in both the stock and budstick are cut out in the same manner. The first cut is made just below the bud, cutting down into the wood at an angle of about 45 degrees. The second cut is started about ½ inch above the bud and goes inward and downward behind the bud until it intersects the first cut. The order of making these two cuts may be reversed. The chip is removed from the stock and replaced by the one from the budstick. If they have both been cut to the same size and shape—as they should be—a good close fit is obtained. It is important that the cambium layer of the bud piece be placed so as to coincide with that of the stock, preferably on both sides of the stem, but at least on one side.

There are no protective flaps of bark to prevent the bud piece from drying out, as there are in T-budding. It is very important, then, that the chip bud be wrapped to seal the cut edges as well as to hold the bud piece tightly into the stock. Nurseryman's adhesive tape works very well for this, although string can be used if all the cut edges are covered with grafting wax. If the bud is inserted in the stock close to the ground level, as it is in grape propagation, it is sufficient to wrap the bud with budding rubber and cover the whole bud union immediately with several inches of finely pulverized moist soil, which can be removed after the bud has united. Budding rubbers under the soil level are very slow to disintegrate so that they may need to be cut or removed before constriction occurs.

In chip budding, as in the other methods, the stock is not cut back above the bud until the union is completed. If the chip bud is inserted in the fall, the stock is cut back just as growth starts the next spring. If the budding is done in the spring, the stock is cut back about 10 days after the bud has been inserted.

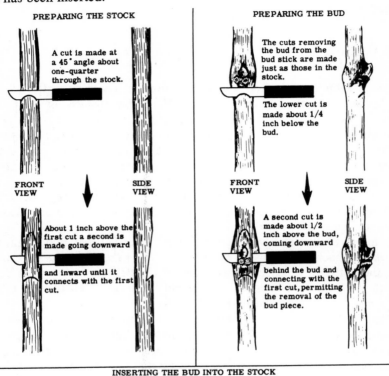

PREPARING THE STOCK

A cut is made at a 45° angle about one-quarter through the stock.

FRONT VIEW   SIDE VIEW

About 1 inch above the first cut a second is made going downward

and inward until it connects with the first cut.

PREPARING THE BUD

The cuts removing the bud from the bud stick are made just as those in the stock.

The lower cut is made about 1/4 inch below the bud.

FRONT VIEW   SIDE VIEW

A second cut is made about 1/2 inch above the bud, coming downward

behind the bud and connecting with the first cut, permitting the removal of the bud piece.

INSERTING THE BUD INTO THE STOCK

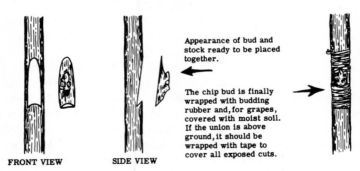

Appearance of bud and stock ready to be placed together.

The chip bud is finally wrapped with budding rubber and, for grapes, covered with moist soil. If the union is above ground, it should be wrapped with tape to cover all exposed cuts.

FRONT VIEW   SIDE VIEW

Figure 13–12. The chip bud is really a form of grafting, a variation of the side veneer graft, but with the scion reduced to a small piece of wood containing only a single bud. Chip budding is widely used in grape propagation.

Figure 13–13. Topworking a young tree by **top-budding.** T-buds were inserted in the positions shown by arrows and have grown for one season. All other shoots have been removed. From **Calif. Agr. Exp. Sta. Bul. 700.**

Top-Budding

In young trees where there is an ample supply of vigorous shoots at a height of 4 to 6 feet, top-budding provides a fast and certain method of topworking. It can be used in older trees, too, if they are cut back rather severely the year before to provide a quantity of vigorous watersprout shoots fairly close to the ground.

Depending upon the size of the tree, 10 to 15 buds are placed into vigorously growing branches ¼ to ¾ inches in diameter in the upper portion of the tree—about shoulder height. Although a number of buds could be placed in a single branch, usually only one will be saved to develop into secondary branches, which will then form the permanent new top of the tree. The T-bud method is used on thin-barked species and the patch bud on those with thick bark.

Top-budding is usually done from late June to late July, as soon as well-matured budwood can be obtained, and while the stock tree is still in active growth with the bark slipping easily. Orchard trees generally stop growth earlier in the season than young nursery trees; therefore the budding must be done earlier. When top-budding is done at this time of year, the buds will usually remain inactive until the following spring. At that time, just as vegetative growth starts, the stock branches are cut back just above the buds. This forces the buds into active growth, and they should develop into good-sized branches by the end of the summer. At the time the shoots are cut back to the buds, all other unbudded branches should be removed at the trunk. It is important that the trees be inspected carefully through the summer and any shoots removed that are arising other than from the inserted buds.

Top-budding can also be done in the spring just as the tree to be top-worked is starting active growth and the bark is slipping easily. The techniques for spring budding nursery stock, as described on page 378, are used. Although not commonly done, June budding could be used for top-budding, using the methods as described on page 379.

DOUBLE-WORKING BY BUDDING

In propagating nursery trees, some of the budding methods can be used in developing double-worked trees (see p. 362). As shown in Figure 13–14, the intermediate stock can be budded on the rootstock; then the following year the desired variety is budded on the interstock. Although quite successful, this is a rather lengthy process, taking 3 years. As illustrated in Figures 13–15 and 13–16, it is possible to develop a double-worked

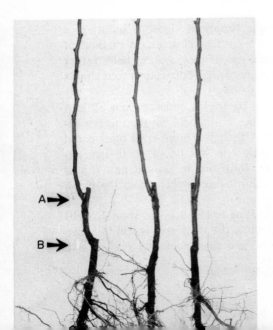

Figure 13–14. Double-working pears by budding. At **B** the Old Home pear was T-budded on a rooted quince cutting. A year later, at **A**, the Bartlett variety was budded on the Old Home. Three years were required to produce these nursery trees.

A➡

B➡

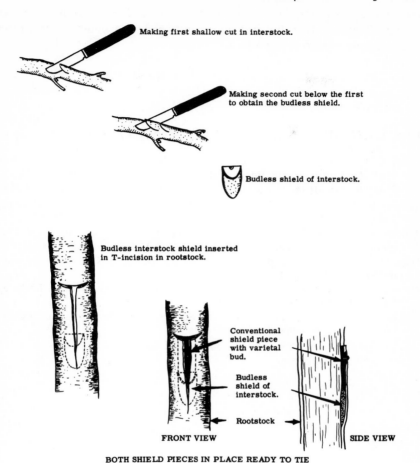

Making first shallow cut in interstock.

Making second cut below the first to obtain the budless shield.

Budless shield of interstock.

Budless interstock shield inserted in T-incision in rootstock.

Conventional shield piece with varietal bud.

Budless shield of interstock.

Rootstock

FRONT VIEW   SIDE VIEW

BOTH SHIELD PIECES IN PLACE READY TO TIE

Figure 13–15. Double shield-budding is double-working by budding in one operation. The intermediate stock is reduced to a small budless shield piece inserted under and just below the regular shield piece as used in T-budding.

Figure 13–16. Young pear trees double-worked by the "double-shield" bud method. **(A)** Bartlett directly on quince root. **(B)** Bartlett on quince but with an intermediate shield piece of Hardy pear. **(C)** With pressure the poor union of Bartlett on quince snaps off easily. **(D)** Strong union, having the intermediate shield piece, resists breaking. Courtesy R. J. Garner, East Malling Research Sta.

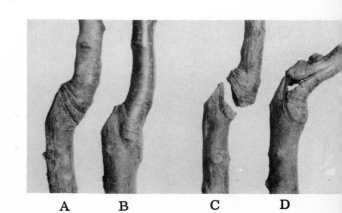

A   B   C   D

tree in one operation in 1 year by the double-shield bud method. An ordinary T-bud is used, but just under and below it a budless shield piece of the desired interstock is inserted.

• **Supplementary Reading**

Baltet, C., *The Art of Grafting and Budding,* 6th ed. London: Crosby, Lockwood, 1910.

Brase, K. D., "Propagation of Fruit Trees by Budding," *Farm Research* (New York Agricultural Experiment Station), Vol. 18, No. 3 (1952).

Duruz, W. P., "Grafting and Budding," *Oregon Extension Bulletin 528* (1953).

Garner, R. J., *The Grafter's Handbook,* 2nd ed. London: Faber and Faber, 1958.

Hansen, C. J., and H. T. Hartmann, "Propagation of Temperate Zone Fruit Plants," *California Agricultural Experiment Station Circular 471* (1958).

Reed, C. A., "Nut Tree Propagation," *U.S. Department of Agriculture Farmers' Bulletin 1501* (1926).

Webber, H. J., "Nursery Methods," in *The Citrus Industry,* Vol. II. Berkeley: University of California Press, 1948.

Yerkes, G. E., "Propagation of Trees and Shrubs," *U.S. Department of Agriculture Farmers' Bulletin 1567* (1945).

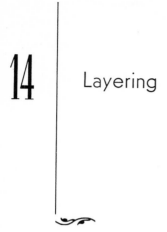

14 | Layering

Layering is the development of roots on a stem while it is still attached to the parent plant. The rooted stem is then detached to become a new plant growing on its own roots. A layered stem is known as a *layer*. This may be a natural means of reproduction, such as in black raspberries and trailing blackberries, or it may be induced by the "artificial" methods described in this chapter.

FACTORS AFFECTING THE PROPAGATION OF PLANTS BY LAYERING

Root formation during layering is stimulated by various stem treatments which cause an interruption in the downward translocation of organic materials—carbohydrates, auxin, and other growth factors—from the leaves and growing shoot tips. These materials accumulate near the point of treatment and rooting occurs in this general area even though the stem is still attached to the parent plant.

Water and minerals are supplied to the layered shoot, because the stem is not severed and the xylem remains intact. Thus, layering does not depend upon the length of time that a severed shoot (cutting) can be maintained before rooting occurs. This is an important reason why layering is more successful with many plants than is propagation by cuttings.

Etiolation is another means by which the internal condition of the developing shoot can be modified during layering to stimulate rooting. This

BEFORE ROOTING   AFTER ROOTING

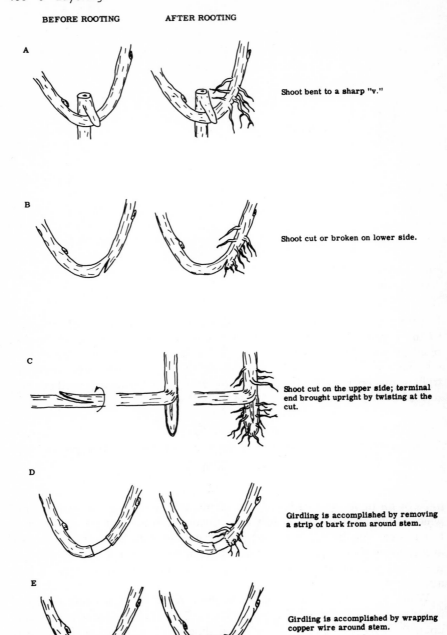

A   Shoot bent to a sharp "v."

B   Shoot cut or broken on lower side.

C   Shoot cut on the upper side; terminal end brought upright by twisting at the cut.

D   Girdling is accomplished by removing a strip of bark from around stem.

E   Girdling is accomplished by wrapping copper wire around stem.

Figure 14–1. Treatments used to stimulate rooting during layering.

factor is discussed on page 195 in relation to rooting of cuttings. It is accomplished in mound or trench layering by covering the newly developing shoot as it grows so that the basal part of the layered shoot is not exposed to the light. This apparently accounts in large measure for the success with which shy-rooting plants are rooted by these two methods.

Applying rooting substances during layering is sometimes beneficial as it is with cuttings, although the method of application may be somewhat different (5, 12, 20, 24). Applying the material as a powder, in lanolin, or as a 50 per cent alcohol solution are methods which could be utilized effectively (see p. 245).

Root formation on layers depends upon continuous moisture, good aeration, and moderate temperatures in the rooting zone. Prolonged dry spells and compact, heavy soils hinder root development, particularly during the initial stages of rooting. The addition of granulated peat moss to the soil mounded around apple and quince stock plants has been noted to promote rooting (23). Excessively high temperatures in the upper layers of soil during the spring and summer may reduce the moisture content and cause compaction, not only inhibiting rooting but injuring the shoots as well (22).

CHARACTERISTICS AND USES OF LAYERING

The principal advantage of layering is the success with which plants can be rooted by this method. Many clones which will not root easily by cuttings can be rooted by layering, enabling the plant to be established on its own roots. Most methods of layering are relatively simple to perform and can be practiced out-of-doors in the nursery or garden. When small numbers of plants are involved, layering can give a high degree of success with somewhat less skill, effort, and equipment than is necessary with cuttings. With those few kinds of plants in which layering occurs naturally, it is a simple and economical method of propagation.

In some cases, a larger plant can be produced in a shorter time than would be produced if started as a cutting. However, since transplanting becomes increasingly difficult as the size of the layer increases, special precautions are necessary to establish successfully the larger plant on its own roots.

On the other hand, layering tends to be an expensive method of propagation and does not lend itself to the large-scale techniques of mechanization used in modern nurseries. Part of the increased cost of propagation is due to the additional hand labor required. A layered plant requires a certain amount of individual attention, depending upon the particular method in use, even though the operations involved are in themselves simple. Also, the number of salable plants from a given number of stock plants is less than would be obtained with cuttings, buds, or scions. The methods tend to be cumbersome, and the stock plants take up a considerable area which is difficult to cultivate and maintain free of weeds.

Layering is usually limited by American nurserymen to those plants which propagate naturally in this manner—e.g., black raspberry, trailing blackberries, and those plants too difficult or impossible to propagate by other methods, yet of sufficient value to justify the cost. For instance, the filbert (*Corylus sp.*), Muscadine grape (*Vitis rotundifolia*), and litchi (*Litchi chinensis*) are propagated commercially in this manner. Layering is used in propagating certain clonal rootstocks such as the Malling apple stocks (see Chapter 16) which are not easily rooted as cuttings.

European nurserymen use layering extensively for the propagation of many ornamental shrubs and trees *(27)*. Nurseries of established plants to be used for layering (known as *stool beds*) have been in production for many years in some cases, and nurserymen have become skilled in their management.

Layering is perhaps best utilized by the amateur horticulturist who wishes to propagate a relatively small number of plants or by specialists involved with reproducing certain kinds of plants. In these cases, expense per plant and the individual attention necessary would not be factors in his choice of method.

PROCEDURES IN LAYERING

Tip Layering

In tip layering, rooting takes place near the tip of the current season's shoot which is bent to the ground. The shoot tip begins to grow downward into the ground but recurves to produce a sharp bend in the stem, from which roots develop. This natural method of reproduction is characteristic of trailing blackberries, dewberries, and black and purple raspberries.

Stems of these plants are biennial in that the canes are vegetative during the first year, fruitful the second, and pruned out after fruiting. "Summer topping" new canes by pinching off 3 to 4 inches of the tip after a growth of from 18 to 30 inches in length will encourage lateral shoot production. This will increase the number of potential tip layers and also next year's fruit crop. By late August or early September, the canes begin to arch over, and their tips assume a characteristic appearance in that the terminal ends appear elongated and the leaves small and curled to give a "snaky" or "rat-tail" appearance. The best time for layering is when only part of the lateral tips have attained this appearance. If the operation is done too soon, the shoots may continue to grow instead of forming a terminal bud. If done too late, the root system will be small.

Figure 14–2. Tip layer of boysenberry. In this method the entire tip of the cane should be covered with soil.

The tips are preferably layered by hand, using a spade or trowel to make a hole 3 to 4 inches deep. The end of the shoot is inserted into the hole and covered with soil. For large-scale operations, a shallow furrow may be plowed along the row into which the tips are placed. Rooting takes place rapidly, and the plants are ready for digging by the end of the same season. The rooted tip consists of a terminal bud, a large mass of roots, and 6 to 8 inches of the old cane to serve as a "handle" and to mark the location of the new plant. Since the tip layers are tender, easily injured, and subject to drying out, digging should preferably be done just before replanting.

A new planting is started from these rooted tip layers planted in the late fall or early spring. New canes develop rapidly during the first season.

Simple Layering

Simple layering (Figure 14–3) is performed by bending a branch to the ground, covering it partially with soil or rooting medium, but leaving the terminal end exposed. The end of the branch is sharply bent to an upright position about 6 to 12 inches back from the tip. The sharp bending of the shoot may be all that is necessary to induce rooting, although additional benefit may be gained by twisting to loosen the bark (14). Cutting or notching the underside of the stem is often practiced. Other methods are

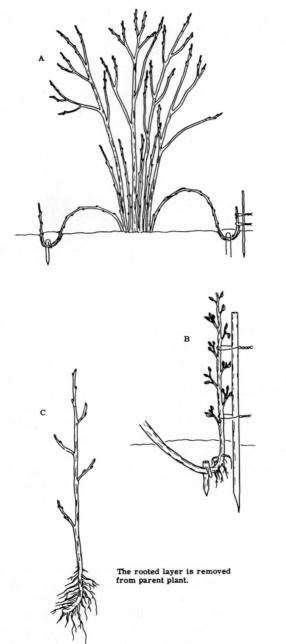

Shoots are bent over to the
ground in early spring or
fall. A second bend is made
in branch a short distance
from tip. It is covered with
soil and held in place with
wire or wood stakes. The
stem is sometimes injured.

Roots form on the buried
part of the shoot near the
bend.

The rooted layer is removed
from parent plant.

Figure 14–3. Steps in propagation by simple layering.

illustrated in Figure 14–1. The bent part of the shoot is next inserted into the soil so that it can be covered to a depth of 3 to 6 inches. A wooden peg, bent wire, or a stone may be used to hold the layer in place, and a vertical wooden stake should be inserted beside the layer to support the exposed shoot and hold it upright. If the branch is relatively inflexible and hard to bend, the tension may be lessened by notching the upper side of the shoot on the highest part of the bend back from the layer itself.

The usual time for layering is in the early spring, using dormant, 1-year-old shoots. Low, flexible branches of the plant which can be bent easily to the ground are used. In some cases, the suckers produced near the crown of the plant may serve as a source of shoots for layering. Layering could also be delayed until later in the growing season after the current season's shoots have attained sufficient length and become hardened. This timing would be used, perhaps, with some broad-leaved evergreens such as *Rhododendron* and *Magnolia*. As a general rule, shoots older than one year are not satisfactory for layering.

Shoots layered in the spring will usually be adequately rooted by the end of the first growing season and can be removed either in the fall or the next spring before growth starts. Mature shoots layered in summer should be left through the winter and either removed the next spring before growth begins or left until the end of the second growing season. When the rooted layer is removed from the parent plant, it is treated in essentially the same manner as a rooted cutting of the same plant. Evergreen plants should be potted and kept humid and cool for a time. It should be possible to plant a well-rooted layer of a dormant deciduous plant directly into a nursery row or permanent location if the top is reduced to a size corresponding to the root system. Rooted layers removed in the fall can be planted in a cold frame or shaded greenhouse in a peat-sand mixture. Although defoliation may occur, root activity often continues for several weeks so that by spring the root system may be well developed *(7)*.

A continuous supply of rooted layers can be produced over a period of years by establishing a stool bed composed of parent plants far enough apart to allow room for all shoots to be layered. This procedure has been used to produce commercially certain hard-to-root shrubs *(6, 14)*.

Compound or Serpentine Layering

Compound layering is essentially the same as simple layering except that the branch is alternately covered and exposed along its length. Generally, the stem is injured or girdled at the lower part of the stem and covered in the same manner as for simple layering. Roots develop at each of these buried sections. The exposed part of the stem should have at least one bud

Figure 14-4. Compound layering of a **Philodendron** vine.

to develop a new shoot. After rooting takes place or at the end of the growing season, the branch is cut in sections made up of the new shoot and the portion containing roots. Several new plants are thus possible from a single branch.

This method is used for propagating plants which have long, flexible shoots, such as the Muscadine grape. Ornamental vines, such as *Wistaria* and *Clematis,* can also be rooted this way, although such efforts are generally limited to use by amateurs rather than by commercial propagators.

Air Layering

In air layering, roots form on the aerial part of a plant after girdling or slitting the stem at an angle and enclosing it in a moist rooting medium at the point of injury. The method has been used for more than a thousand years, being known in various parts of the world as *Chinese layerage, pot layerage, circumposition, marcottage,* and *gootee.*

The principal limiting factor in air layering has been the difficulty in keeping the rooting medium properly moistened. The ancient Chinese gootee or marcottage method consists of plastering a ball of clay or other soil mixture about the ring or girdle, which is then covered with moss or fiber to hold it together. Above the gootee is a receptacle of water (perhaps a bamboo joint) from which extends a string leading to and wrapped about the gootee to keep it continuously moist *(9).* Various modifications of this technique have been made, but all require that the operation be carried out in greenhouses or in regions of very high humidity.

Enclosures used to surround the rooting medium have included metal or wooden boxes, split flower pots, paper cones, and rubber sheeting. Wrapping with moss alone may be adequate if the humidity is sufficiently high and daily syringing is practiced *(1).* These devices have been replaced to a large extent by sheets of plastic film which have the properties of high permeability to gases (carbon dioxide and oxygen), low transmission of water vapor, and sufficient durability to withstand weathering for long periods. By this means it is possible to keep the enclosed rooting medium moist for long periods of time without continuous attention *(11, 12, 26)*. Not all plastic films have the same degree of the necessary characteristics, so the one to be used should be selected carefully. The plastic film principally used is *polyethylene,* sold under various trade names.

Air layering is used to propagate a number of tropical and subtropical trees and shrubs *(9, 16, 25)*. In Florida, the litchi *(11)* and the Persian lime *(Citrus aurantifolia) (21)* are propagated commercially by this method. With plastic film for wrapping the layers, it is possible to extend the method of air layering out-of-door plants from the tropics to the Temperate Zone. However, its greatest application would appear to be to the amateur horticulturist or to the propagator of selected plants for cultural or for scientific purposes rather than for the commercial nurseryman.

Air layers are made in the spring on wood of the previous season's growth or, in other cases, in the late summer with partially hardened shoots. Wood older than one year can be used in some cases, but rooting is less satisfactory and the larger plants produced are somewhat more difficult to handle after rooting. With tropical greenhouse plants, layering should be done after several leaves have developed during a period of growth.

The first step in air layering is to girdle or cut the bark of the stem at a point 6 to 12 inches or more from the tip end. A strip of bark ½ to 1 inch wide, depending upon the kind of plant, is completely removed from around the stem. Scraping the exposed surface to insure complete removal of the cambium may be desirable to retard healing. Another procedure is to make a slanting cut about 2 inches long up and to the center of the stem, keeping the two surfaces apart by sphagnum or a piece of wood. Application of a rooting compound to the exposed stem, especially to the upper edges or between the two exposed surfaces of a cut, may be beneficial. About two handfuls of only *slightly* moistened sphagnum moss is placed around the stem to enclose the cut surfaces. If the moisture content of the sphagnum moss is too high, decay of the stem tissues may occur.

A piece of plastic film 8 to 10 inches square is wrapped carefully about the branch so that the sphagnum moss is completely covered. The ends of the sheet should be folded (as in wrapping meat) with the fold placed on the lower side. The two ends must be twisted to be sure that no water can seep inside. Adhesive tape, such as electricians' waterproof tape, works well to wrap the ends. Winding the tape around the twig should be started well above the end of the plastic film to be sure to enclose the ends, particularly the upper one, securely. Budding rubbers or florist's ties are other materials which can be used for this purpose.

The time for removal of the layer from the parent plant is best determined by observing root formation through the transparent plastic. In

The stem should be girdled for a distance of about one inch to induce adventitious root formation above the cut.

A ball of slightly damp sphagnum moss is placed around the girdled section.

A wrapping of polyethylene film is placed around the sphagnum moss and tied at each end.

Figure 14–5. Steps in making an air layer on a **Ficus elastica** plant using polyethylene film.

some plants, rooting occurs in 2 to 3 months or less. Layers made in spring or early summer may best be left until the shoot goes dormant in the fall and removed at that time. Holly, lilac, *Azalea,* and *Magnolia* should be left for two seasons *(7).* In general, it would be desirable to remove the layer during a time it is not actively growing. The period between the removal of the rooted layer from the plant and establishment on its own roots is very critical, and the plant may be lost at that time even though it rooted well. As a general rule, the root system is small in proportion to the top and is incapable of supporting the plant without special precautions. The difficulties of transplanting increase in proportion to the size of the top. Severe pruning usually is advisable to bring the top more in line with the size of the roots, but it may not be imperative if the following precautions are followed. The rooted layer should be potted into a suitable container and placed under cool, humid conditions, such as an enclosed frame, where the plants can be frequently syringed. If this operation is done in the fall, a sufficiently large root system may develop by spring to permit successful growth in the open. Placing the rooted layers under mist for several weeks, followed by gradually hardening-off, is probably the most satisfactory procedure *(18)*.

Mound (Stool) Layering

Mound or stool layering involves cutting a plant back to the ground during the dormant season and mounding soil or other media around the base of the newly developing shoots to encourage roots to form on them. Plants with stiff branches that do not bend easily and which are capable of producing an abundance of shoots from the crown year after year are particularly adapted to this method. Plants commonly propagated in this manner include the Malling apple stocks, currants, and gooseberries.

A stool bed can remain in use for 15 to 20 years; therefore, it should be on loose, fertile, well-drained soil and established 1 year before the operations begin. The mother plants should be set 12 to 15 inches apart in the row, but the spacing between rows varies under different conditions and the type of nursery equipment in use. Width between rows should be sufficient to allow for cultivation and hilling operations during the summer. In England 3½ foot rows are recommended *(10)*, but in New York a minimum of 8 feet was found to be desirable *(2)*. Planting in a shallow trench, as shown in Figure 14–6, will permit the shoots to arise from the crown at a low level. Plants are cut back to 15 to 18 inches from the ground and left to grow unchecked for a season, the space between the rows being kept cultivated.

Before new growth starts the next spring, all plants are cut back to an inch above the ground level. Two to five new shoots usually develop from the crown the second year, more in later years. When these shoots have grown 3 to 5 inches, loose soil is drawn up around each shoot to one-half of its height. When the shoots have grown to a total height of 8 to 10 inches, a second hilling operation takes place. Soil is again added but to

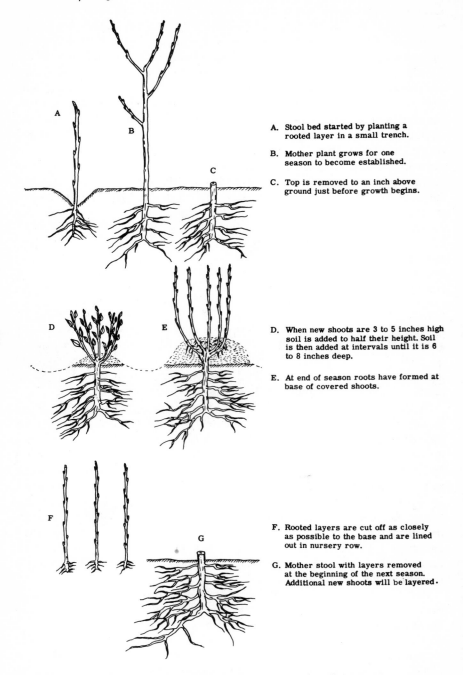

A. Stool bed started by planting a rooted layer in a small trench.

B. Mother plant grows for one season to become established.

C. Top is removed to an inch above ground just before growth begins.

D. When new shoots are 3 to 5 inches high soil is added to half their height. Soil is then added at intervals until it is 6 to 8 inches deep.

E. At end of season roots have formed at base of covered shoots.

F. Rooted layers are cut off as closely as possible to the base and are lined out in nursery row.

G. Mother stool with layers removed at the beginning of the next season. Additional new shoots will be layered.

Figure 14–6. Steps in propagation by mound (stool) layering.

cover no more than one-half the total height. Soil is drawn from the center of the row and mounded around the base of the shoots. In England, with a spacing of 3½ feet between the rows, a ridging plow is drawn between the rows so that two ridges of soil are produced about 15 inches apart. Each row of stools will thus have a ridge on each side. The trench made by the plow is kept cultivated, and the loose soil is shoveled around and between the shoots. The shoots arise close together and to prevent crowding should be spread apart by placing a shovel of soil in the middle of a cluster of shoots. A third and final hilling operation is made in mid-summer when the shoots have developed to a total length of approximately 18 inches. The base of the shoots will then have been covered with soil to a depth of 6 to 8 inches. Materials other than soil might be used to cover the developing shoots. In some areas sawdust is used extensively for this purpose.

Layered shoots of easily propagated plants should have rooted sufficiently by the end of the growing season to be separated from the parent stool for lining out in the nursery row. In regions of severe climate, the operation should be delayed until all danger of winter injury is past, or after removing the layers, the mother plant must be recovered by several inches of soil. The rooted layers are cut as close to their base as possible to keep the height of the stool plant low. After cutting away the shoots, the mother stool remains exposed until new shoots again reach a height of 3 to 5 inches, and the operation is repeated the following year. Shoots which do not root or which root poorly can often be cut off at the same time as the well-rooted ones and treated as hardwood cuttings ready for planting in the nursery row (2).

Several points which are important to the proper utilization of a stool bed should be kept in mind. To prolong the life of the stool bed and to maintain the plants in a vigorous condition, good fertility should be maintained by annual fertilizer application. Disease, insects, and weeds should be controlled. Supplementary overhead irrigation is essential in some areas to maintain proper moisture conditions in the rooting zone (4). Soil must be added around the base of the shoots while they are still soft and succulent, not delayed until the shoots have hardened. With some of the more difficult plants, such as certain plum varieties, it is best to add soil even before the shoots begin to grow so as to induce etiolation at their bases. Girdling the bases of the shoots by wiring about 6 weeks after they begin to grow will stimulate rooting in many plants (8, 13, 15, 16, 19).

Trench Layering

Trench layering consists of growing a plant or a branch of a plant in a horizontal position in the base of a trench and filling in soil around the

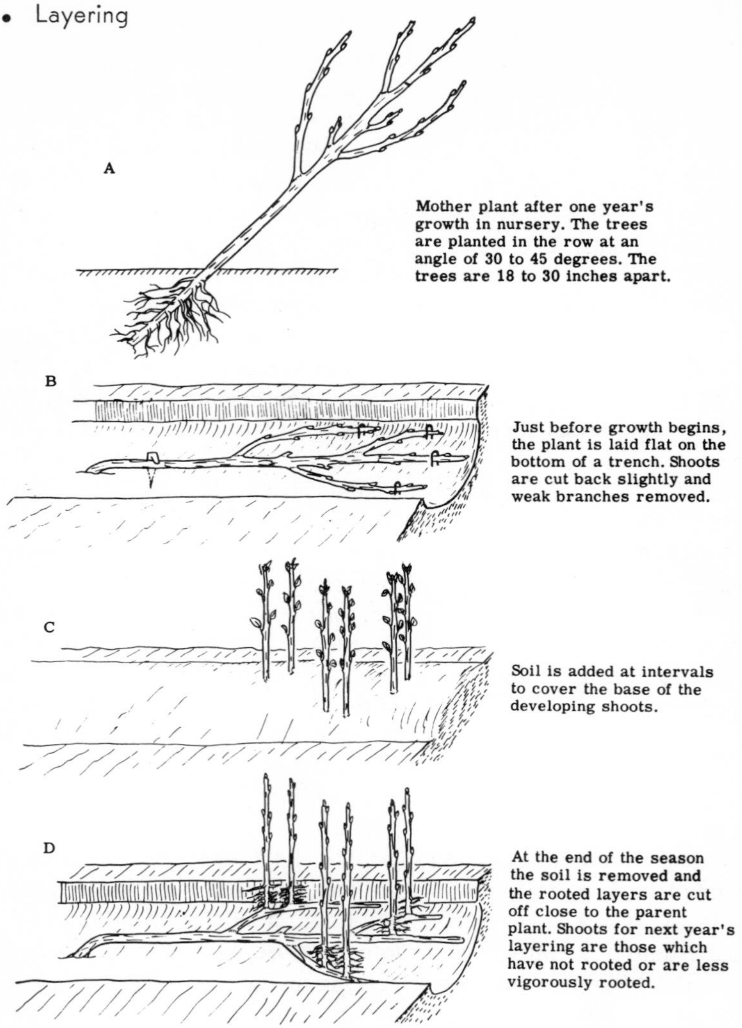

A

Mother plant after one year's growth in nursery. The trees are planted in the row at an angle of 30 to 45 degrees. The trees are 18 to 30 inches apart.

B

Just before growth begins, the plant is laid flat on the bottom of a trench. Shoots are cut back slightly and weak branches removed.

C

Soil is added at intervals to cover the base of the developing shoots.

D

At the end of the season the soil is removed and the rooted layers are cut off close to the parent plant. Shoots for next year's layering are those which have not rooted or are less vigorously rooted.

Figure 14–7. Steps in propagation by trench layering.

new shoots as they develop. Roots develop from the bases of these new shoots.

The first step in the procedure involves the establishment of the mother bed which, as in mound layering, can be used over a period of years. Rooted layers or 1-year-old nursery-budded or grafted trees are placed 18 to 30 inches apart at an angle of 30 to 45 degrees down a row. The rows should be 4 to 5 feet apart—wide enough to allow for cultivation and to draw soil up around the plants to a height of 6 inches. The plants are then cut back to a uniform length—18 to 24 inches—and left to grow one season. In some cases, in layering walnuts for instance, the plants are planted horizontally in the trench and the developing shoots layered the first year.

Before the beginning of growth in the spring, the parent layers are bent over and laid flat on the bottom of a trench dug along the row, about 2 inches deep and wide enough to receive the entire layer. Weak lateral branches are cut to ½ inch in length and strong laterals only tipped back. Wooden pegs may be used to hold the mother layer in place. Short lengths of wire bent to form a U are useful to hold down the small shoots. It is important that all parts of the shoot be completely flat on the floor of the trench.

Before the buds swell, the entire layer is covered with 1 to 2 inches of fine soil or other rooting medium such as peat moss, sawdust, or wood shavings. Another inch of soil is added when the developing shoots have pushed through the first soil layer but before their leaves have expanded. Several more additions of soil are made the first 2 or 3 weeks of the growing season to insure the etiolation of the basal 2 to 3 inches of the shoot. When the shoots have become exposed an additional 3 to 4 inches, soil is again added to half the height of the exposed shoot. Further additions are made at intervals until the bases of the shoots are finally covered to a depth of 6 to 8 inches by the end of July. Roots form on the base of the current season's shoot.

At the end of the growing season after the plants have become dormant —or the next spring—the soil is removed from around the layered shoots and rooted layers cut off from the original layered stock as close to the

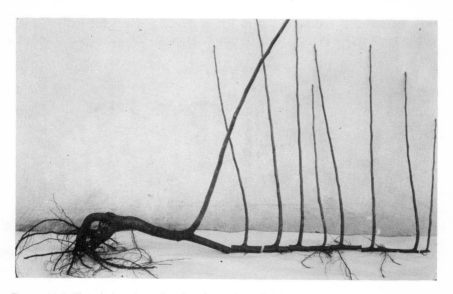

Figure 14–8. Trench layering of a Paradox walnut showing rooted shoots. Courtesy E. F. Serr.

base as possible. Unrooted shoots can be left to be pegged down the next year to produce a new crop of layers. If all have rooted, some of the vigorous shoots about a foot apart along the mother plant should be left to use in producing the next year's supply of rooted layers.

Trench layering is primarily a nursery method for propagating particular fruit tree rootstocks difficult to propagate by other methods. It could also be practiced on established shrubs or trees by bending long, flexible shoots or vines to the ground under the same conditions as is done in simple layering. The shoot is covered along its entire length, but the tip is left exposed. New shoots which develop from the buds along the stem grow upwards through the soil, with roots forming at their base. This latter procedure is sometimes known as *continuous layering*.

PLANT MODIFICATIONS SUITABLE FOR NATURAL LAYERING

Some plants exhibit modifications of their vegetative structure or method of growth which lead to their natural vegetative increase. Those listed below could be considered natural forms of layering and often can be utilized for propagation.

Runners

A *runner* is a specialized stem which develops from the axil of a leaf at the crown of a plant, grows horizontally along the ground, and forms a

Figure 14–9. Runners arising from the crown of a strawberry plant. New plants are produced at every second node. The daughter plants, in turn, produce additional runners and runner plants.

new plant at one of the nodes. The strawberry is a typical plant propagated in this way. Other plants also propagated by runners include bugle (*Ajuga*) and the strawberry geranium (*Saxifraga sarmentosa*). Each of these plants grows as a typical rosette or crown.

In most strawberry varieties, runner formation is related to the length of day, runners being produced after day lengths of 12 to 14 hours are reached. New plants are produced at alternate nodes. These take root but remain attached to the mother plant for some time. New runners may in turn be produced by the daughter plants. The connecting stems die in the late fall and winter, and each daughter plant becomes separate from the others.

To propagate by runners, the rooted daughter plants are dug when they have become well rooted and then transplanted to the desired location (see p. 492.

Stolons

A *stolon* is an aerial shoot which comes in contact with the ground and takes root. It may be a prostrate or sprawling stem which grows horizontally from the crown, as for instance from *Cornus stolonifera,* or from some grasses, such as Bermuda grass (*Cynodon dactylon*). Or it may be a shoot which grows upright for a time and then descends to the ground, such as the tip layers of black raspberry and blackberry.

A shoot rooted in this manner is merely cut from the parent plant and transplanted to the desired location.

Offsets

An *offset* is a characteristic type of lateral shoot or branch which develops from the base of the main stem in certain plants. This term is applied generally to a shortened, thickened stem of rosette-like appearance. Many bulbs (see Chapter 15 for details) reproduce by producing typical offset bulblets from their base. The term offset (or *offshoot,* as is sometimes used) also applies to lateral branches arising on stems of monocotyledons. The date palm produces lateral shoots from the base of the plant by which it is propagated. The pineapple is also propagated by offsets, although in commercial culture these are termed ratoons, suckers, or slips, depending upon the location on the plant where they are produced. Details of date and pineapple propagation are given in Chapter 16. Lateral shoots arising from

Figure 14–10. Offsets (offshoots) arising from the base of a date palm. Soil is mounded around the base of offsets to produce rooting; they are then removed from the parent plant (see page 474).

rhizomes, such as in the banana or orchid, could also be referred to as offsets or offshoots.

Offsets are removed by cutting them close to the main stem with a sharp knife. If it is well rooted, the offset can be potted as is done with any rooted cutting. If insufficient roots are present, the shoot is placed in a favorable rooting medium and treated as a leafy stem cutting.

In cases where offset development is meager, cutting off the main rosette may stimulate the development of offsets from the old stem in the same manner as removing the terminal bud stimulates lateral shoots in any other type of plant. For instance, in *Echeveria* the main stem may elongate so that the plant becomes a fleshy rosette borne on top of a fleshy, bare stem. The rosette, with a short piece of the stem, may be removed and rooted and new offsets will develop from buds at the base. It is desirable to do this operation while the stem is somewhat soft and succulent rather than allowing it to become hard and woody *(3)*.

Offshoots of the date palm do not root readily if separated from the parent plant. They are usually layered for a year prior to removing (see p. 473).

Suckers

A *sucker* is a shoot which arises on a plant from below ground. The most precise use of this term is to designate a shoot which arises from an adventitious bud on a root. However, in practice, shoots which arise from the vicinity of the crown are also referred to as suckers even though originating from stem tissue. Nurserymen generally designate any shoot produced from the rootstock below the bud union of a budded tree as a sucker and refer to the operation of removing them as "suckering." In contrast a shoot arising from a latent bud of a stem several years old, as for instance on the trunk or main branches, should be termed a *watersprout*.

Figure 14–11. Suckers arising adventitiously from the roots of a red raspberry plant. After rooting the suckers are cut from the parent plant and transplanted to their permanent location. From **Calif. Agr. Ext. Cir. 96.**

The tendency to "sucker" is a characteristic possessed by some plants and not by others. The ability of a plant to sucker and the ability of a plant to grow from root cuttings are closely related. Nurserymen would probably prefer to use root cuttings rather than depend on naturally produced suckers.

Suckers are dug out and cut from the parent plant. In some cases part of the old root may be retained, although most new roots will arise from the base of the sucker. It is important to dig the sucker out rather than pull it to avoid injury to its base. Suckers are treated essentially as a rooted layer or as a cutting, in case few or no roots have formed. They are usually dug during the dormant season.

Crowns

The term *crown* as used in horticulture designates that part of a plant stem at and below the surface of the ground from which new shoots are produced. In trees or shrubs with a single trunk, the crown is principally a point of location near the ground surface marking the general transition zone between stem and root. In herbaceous perennials, the crown is the part of the plant from which new shoots arise annually. The crown of many herbaceous perennials consists of many branches, each being the base of the current season's stem, which originated from the base of the preceding year's branch. These new shoots are stimulated to grow from the base of the old stem as it dies back after blooming. Adventitious roots develop along the base of the new shoots. These new shoots eventually flower either the same year they are produced or the one following. As a result of the annual production of new shoots and the dying back of old shoots, the crown may become extensive within a period of a relatively few years.

In certain plants, for example the strawberry or the African violet (*Saintpaulia*), the stem is a short and thickened structure from which the

Figure 14–12. African violet (**Saintpaulia**) with two crowns. These may be divided with a sharp knife and the two sections potted separately.

leaves are produced in a rosette-like arrangement. The entire body of the plant is often referred to as the crown. Lateral shoots or offsets are produced from the base of the crown. An old plant may be composed of a number of "crowns" or "crown divisions" which have been produced in this manner.

Multi-branched woody shrubs may develop extensive crowns. Although an individual woody stem may persist for a number of years, new vigorous shoots are continuously produced from the crown, which eventually crowd out the older shoots. If left undisturbed, such shrubs could develop into fairly extensive thickets. Under normal handling, the older shoots are regularly removed by pruning to give way to the younger, more vigorous shoots.

Division of the crown is an important method of propagation for herbaceous perennials and to some extent for woody shrubs because of its simplicity and reliability. Such characteristics make the method particularly useful to the amateur and professional gardener who is generally interested in only a modest increase of a particular plant. Many herbaceous perennials must be divided every 2 to 3 years to prevent the plant from becoming overcrowded.

The usual times of the year for dividing crowns of outdoor herbaceous perennials are in the spring just as growth begins or in the late summer or fall, at the end of the growing season. As a general rule, those plants which bloom in the spring and summer and produce new growth after blooming should be divided in the fall. Those which bloom in summer and fall and make little or no new growth until spring should be divided in early spring. Potted plants are divided when they become too large for the particular container in which they are growing.

Figure 14–13. Propagation by division as illustrated by dividing a clump of day lily. (Hemerocallis).

In division plants are dug and cut into sections with a knife. In herbaceous perennials such as the Shasta daisy or aster, where an abundance of new rooted offshoots are produced from the crown, each may be broken from the old crown and planted separately, discarding the older part of the plant clump. If a larger clump is desired, then a section of the old crown bearing a number of new shoots from its base may be used. In the case of plants where the crown consists of a number of rosettes or offsets, as occurs in the African violet, division should be made between each of the rosettes, being sure that roots are present on each section.

Shrubs may be divided in the same manner with a shovel or hatchet. Such an operation should be carried out at a time when the plant is dormant. The top should be cut back and the roots trimmed at the time of division and each section planted as a new shrub.

REFERENCES

1. Bailey, L. H., *The Nursery Manual*. New York: Macmillan, 1922.
2. Brase, K. D., Propagating fruit trees, *N.Y. Agr. Exp. Sta. Bul. 773, 1956.*
3. Butterfield, H. M., The propagation of Echeverias and related succulents, *Jour. Calif. Hort. Soc.,* 15:30–35. 1954.
4. Carlson, R. F., and H. B. Tukey, Cultural practices in propagating dwarfing rootstocks in Michigan, *Mich. Agr. Exp. Sta. Quart. Bul. 37:*492–497. 1955.
5. Ching, F., C. L. Hamner, and F. Widmoyer, Air-layering with polyethylene film, *Mich. Agr. Exp. Sta. Quart. Bul. 39:*3–9. 1956.
6. Congdon, M. L., Mass production of deciduous shrubs by layering, *Proc. 4th Ann. Mtg. Plant. Prop. Soc.,* pp. 39–45. 1954.
7. Creech, J. L., Layering, *Nat. Hort. Mag.,* 33:37–43. 1954.
8. Du Preez, D., Propagation of guavas, *Farming in South Africa,* 29:197–199. 1954.
9. Feilden, G. St. C., and R. J. Garner, Vegetative propagation of tropical and subtropical fruits, *Imp. Bur. Hort. and Plant. Crops, Tech. Comm. No. 13:*1–99.1940.
10. Garner, R. J., *The Grafter's Handbook*. London: Faber and Faber, 1947.
11. Grove, W. R., Wrapping air layers with rubber plastic, *Proc. Fla. State Hort. Soc.,* 60:184–189. 1947.
12. Hanger, F. E. W., V. M. H., and A. Ravenscroft, Air layering experiments at Wisley, *Jour. Roy. Hort. Soc.,* 79:111–116. 1954.
13. Hostermann, G., Versuche zur vegetativeen Vermehrung von Gehozen nach dem Dahlemer Drahtungsverfahren, *Ber. Deutsch. Bot. Ges.,* 48:66–70. 1930.
14. Knight, F. P., The vegetative propagation of flowering trees and shrubs, *Jour. Roy. Hort. Soc.,* 70: 319–330. 1945.
15. Maurer, K. J., Möglichkeiten der vegetativen Vermehrung der Walnuss, *Schweiz. Z. Obst. V. Weinb.,* 59:136–137. 1950.
16. Mowry, H., L. R. Toy, and H. S. Wolfe, Miscellaneous tropical and sub-tropical Florida fruits, *Fla. Agr. Ext. Serv. Bul. 156:* 1–110. 1953.
17. Modlibowska, I., and C. P. Field, Winter injury to fruit trees by frost in England, (1939–1940), *Jour. Pom. Hort Sci.,* 19:197–207. 1942.
18. Nelson, R., High humidity treatment for air layers of lychee, *Proc. Fla. State Hort. Soc.,* 66:198–199. 1953.
19. Oppenheim, J. E., A new system of citrus layers, *Hadar,* 5:2–4. 1932.
20. Singh, L. B., Vegetative propagation of mango (*Mangifera indica L.*) by air layering (gootee), *Science,* 117:158–159. 1953.
21. Sutton, N. E., Marcotting of Persian limes, *Proc. Fla. State Hort. Soc.,* 67:219–220. 1954.
22. Thomas, L. A., Stock and scion investigations. II. The propagation of own-rooted apple trees. *Jour. Counc. Sci. Industr. Res. Austral.,* 11:175–179. 1938.
23. Tukey, H. B., and K. Brase, Granulated peat moss in field propagation of apple and quince stocks, *Proc. Amer. Soc. Hort. Sci.,* 27:106–113. 1930.
24. Vieitez, E., Estudios sobre la reproduciion vegetativa del castano. I Enraizamiento en al acodo alto mediante el empleo de fitohormonas. *An Edaf. Fis. Veg. Madrid,* 12:337–356. 1953.
25. Watkins, J. V., Propagation of ornamental plants, *Fla. Agr. Exp. Bul. 150:*1–15. 1952.
26. Wyman, D., Air layering with polyethylene films, *Jour. Roy. Hort. Soc.,* 77:135–140. 1952.
27. ———, Layering plants in Holland, *Arnoldia,* 13:25–28. 1953.

• **Supplementary Reading**

Garner, R. J., "Propagation by Cutting and Layers. Recent Work and Its Application with Special Reference to Pome and Stone Fruits." *Imperial Bureau of Horticulture and Plantation Crops, Technical Communication No. 14* (1944).

Knight, R. C., et al., "The Vegetative Propagation of Fruit Tree Rootstocks," *Annual Report East Malling Research Station, Supplement A,* Vol. 10 (1927), pp. 11–30.

15

Propagation
by Specialized
Stems and Roots

This chapter deals with propagation by specialized vegetative structures —*bulbs, corms, tubers, tuberous roots, rhizomes,* and *pseudobulbs.* These organs are primarily modified plant parts specialized for food storage. Plants possessing them are invariably herbaceous perennials in which the shoots die down at the end of a growing season, and the plant lives over in the ground as a dormant, fleshy organ. These bear buds to produce new shoots the next season. Such plants are admirably suited to withstand periods of adverse growing conditions in their yearly growth cycle. The two principal climatic cycles for which such performance is geared are the warm-cold cycle of the temperate zones and the wet-dry cycle of tropical and sub-tropical regions.

The second function of these specialized organs is that of vegetative reproduction. The propagation procedure which utilizes the production of naturally detachable structures, such as the bulb and corm, is generally spoken of as *separation.* In cases where the plant is cut into sections, as is done in the rhizome, stem tuber, and tuberous root, the process is spoken of as *division.*

TABLE 15–1

FLOWERING PLANTS GROWN FROM SPECIALIZED STEMS OR ROOTS

Bulbs	Corms	Tubers	Tuberous Roots	Rhizomes

I

Hardy; spring-flowering; planted in the fall

Bulbs	Corms	Tubers	Tuberous Roots	Rhizomes
Camassia	*Crocus*		*Anemone*	*Convallaria*
Chionodoxa			(Wind flower)	(Lily-of-the-
(Glory-of-the-			*Arisaema*	valley)
snow)			(Jack-in-the-	*Iris* (bearded
Erythronium			pulpit)	types)
(Trout lily)			*Claytonia*	
Fritillaria			(Spring beauty)	
(Guinea hen			*Dicentra*	
flower)			(Bleeding heart)	
Galanthus			*Eranthis*	
(Snowdrop)			(Winter aconite)	
Hyacinthus			*Eremurus*	
(Hyacinth)			(Desert candle)	
Iris (bulbous)				
Leucojum				
(Snowflake)				
Muscari				
(Grape hya-				
cinth)				
Narcissus				
(Daffodil)				
Scilla				
(Squill)				
Tulipa				
(Tulip)				

II

Semi-hardy to hardy; summer- and fall-flowering; planted in the fall

Bulbs	Corms	Tubers	Tuberous Roots	Rhizomes
Lilium (Lily)	*Colchicum*		*Begonia evansiana*	
Lycoris	(Autumn			
(Hardy	crocus)			
amaryllis)	*Crocus*			
	Sternbergia			

III

Tender; summer- and fall-flowering; dug in the fall and stored over winter; planted in the spring when danger of frost is over; these can be kept out of doors over-winter and in mild climates

Bulbs	Corms	Tubers	Tuberous Roots	Rhizomes
Amaryllis	*Freesia*	*Caladium*	*Begonia*	*Canna*
belladonna	*Gladiolus*		(tuberous)	
Galtonia	*Ixia*		*Dahlia*	
(Summer	*Tritonia*		*Gloriosa*	
hyacinth)				
Hymenocallis				
Polianthes				
(Tuberose)				
Tigridia				
(Tiger flower)				
Watsonia				
Zephyranthes				
(Zephyr lily)				

IV

Tender; mostly grown under glass or as house plants; grown out of doors in mild climates

Bulbs	Corms	Tubers	Tuberous Roots	Rhizomes
Clivia (Kafir lily) *Crinum* *Eucharis grandiflora* (Amazon lily) *Haemanthus* (Blood lily) *Hippeastrum* (Amaryllis) *Nerine* *Oxalis* (bulbous types) *Vallota* (Scarborough lily) *Veltheimia*		*Caladium*	*Agapanthus* (Lily-of-the Nile) *Arum* (Black calla) *Colocasia* (Elephant's ear) *Cyclamen* *Ranunculus* (florist's types) *Sinningia* (Gloxinia)	*Achimenes* *Zantedeschia* (Calla lily)

BULBS

Definition and Structure

Bulbs are produced by monocotyledonous plants in which the usual plant structure is modified for storage and reproduction. A *bulb* is a specialized underground organ consisting of a short, fleshy, usually vertical, stem axis (*basal plate*) bearing at its apex a growing point or a flower primordium and enclosed by thick, fleshy scales.

Most of the bulb consists of the *bulb scales,* which morphologically are the continuous, sheathing leaf bases (see Figure 15–2.) The outer bulb scales are generally fleshy and contain reserve food materials, whereas the bulb scales toward the center function less as storage organs and are more leaf-like. In the center of the bulb, there will be either a vegetative growing point or an unexpanded flowering shoot. Growing points develop in the axil of these scales to produce miniature bulbs, known as *bulblets,* which when they grow to full size are known as *offsets.* In various species of lilies, bulblets may form in the leaf axils either on the underground portion or on the aerial portion of the stem. Aerial bulblets are called *bulbils.*

The two types of bulbs are:

(a) *Tunicate (laminate)* bulbs, represented by the onion and tulip. These bulbs have outer bulb scales which are dry and membranous. This covering, or *tunic,* provides protection from drying and mechanical injury to the bulb. The fleshy scales are in continuous, concentric layers, or *lamina,* so that the structure is more or less solid.

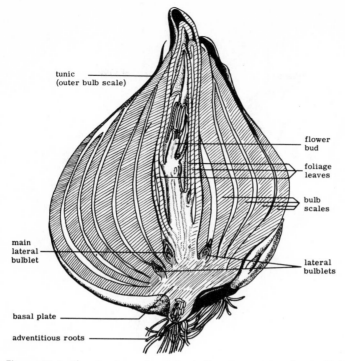

tunic
(outer bulb scale)

flower
bud

foliage
leaves

bulb
scales

main
lateral
bulblet

lateral
bulblets

basal plate

adventitious roots

Figure 15–1. The structure of a tulip bulb—an example of a typical laminate bulb. Redrawn from Mulder and Luyten **(28).**

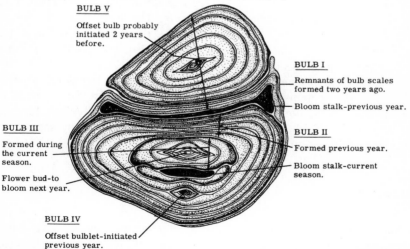

BULB V

Offset bulb probably
initiated 2 years
before.

BULB I

Remnants of bulb scales
formed two years ago.

Bloom stalk-previous year.

BULB III

Formed during
the current
season.

Flower bud-to
bloom next year.

BULB II

Formed previous year.

Bloom stalk-current
season.

BULB IV

Offset bulblet-initiated
previous year.

Figure 15–2. Cross-section of a daffodil bulb. The continuous, concentric leaf scales as found in the laminate bulb are shown. Also shown is the perennial nature of the daffodil bulb which continues to grow by producing a new bulb annually at the main growing point. Lateral offset bulbs are also produced, and parts of five individual differently aged bulbs are shown here. Redrawn from Huisman and Hartsema **(22).**

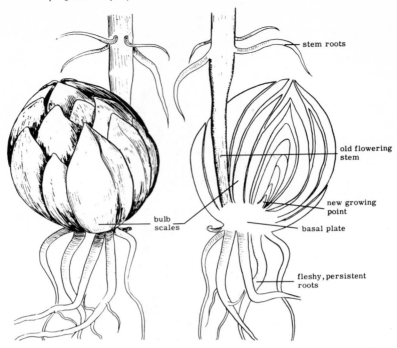

Figure 15–3. Structure of a scaly bulb (lily). This shows a new bulb being produced at the base of the flowering shoot.

(b) *Non-tunicate* (*scaly*) bulbs, represented by the lilies. These bulbs do not possess the enveloping dry covering. The scales are separate and give the bulb a scaly appearance. In general, the non-tunicate bulbs must be handled more carefully than the tunicate bulbs, because they are more easily injured and subject to drying.

Roots are not present on a dormant, tunicate bulb but develop adventitiously at the beginning of a growth period in a narrow band around the outside edge on the bottom of the basal plate. In the non-tunicate lily bulb, on the other hand, the roots persist during storage. Most lily species also form roots on the stem above the bulb.

Growth Behavior

An individual bulb goes through a characteristic cycle of development beginning with its initiation as a growing point and terminating in flowering and seed production. This general developmental cycle is composed of two fundamental stages: (a) the vegetative stage and (b) the reproductive stage. In the vegetative stage, the bulblet grows to flowering size and attains its maximum weight. The subsequent reproductive stage includes the induction of flowering, the differentiation of the floral parts, elongation of the flowering shoot, and finally flowering and (sometimes) seed production. Various bulb species have specific environmental requirements for the individual phases of this cycle which determine their seasonal behavior, environmental adaptations, and methods of handling. They can be grouped into classes depending upon their time of bloom and method of handling.

Spring-flowering bulbs. Important commercial crops included in this group are the tulip, daffodil, hyacinth, and bulbous iris, although other kinds are grown in gardens.

(a) *Bulb formation.* The vegetative stage begins with the initiation of the bulblet on the basal plate in the axil of a bulb scale. In this initial period which usually occupies a single growing season, the bulblet is relatively insignificant, since it is present within another growing bulb and can be observed only by dissecting the bulb. Its subsequent pattern of development and the time required for the bulblet to attain flowering size is somewhat different for different species. The bulb of the tulip and the bulbous iris, for instance, disintegrate upon flowering but leave a cluster of new bulbs and bulblets which were initiated the previous season. The largest of these may have attained flowering size at this time, but smaller ones will require several additional years growth (see Fig. 15–1 and 15–4). The flowering bulb of the daffodil, on the other hand, continues to grow from the center year by year, producing new offsets which may remain attached for several years (see Fig. 15–2 and 15–4). The hyacinth bulb also continues to grow year by year, but because the number of offsets produced is limited, artificial methods of propagation are usually used.

The size of the bulb and the amount of stored food which it contains determine the size and quality of bloom. Consequently, the size grade largely governs its commercial value *(2)*, although other factors, such as the condition of the bulb and freedom from disease, are also important. The greatest increase in size and weight of the developing bulb takes place in the period during and (mostly) after flowering, as long as the foliage remains in good condition *(10)*. Cultural operations that encourage vegetative growth include irrigation, weed, disease, and insect control, and fertilization, but their greatest benefit is to the next year's flower, because larger bulbs are produced. Conversely, adverse conditions, such as poor growing conditions, removal of foliage, premature digging of the bulb, and so forth, result in smaller bulbs and inferior flower production.

Moderately cool temperatures tend to prolong the vegetative period, whereas higher temperatures may cause the vegetative stage to cease and the reproductive stage to begin. Thus, a shift from cool to warm temperatures early in the spring, as occurs in mild climates, will shorten the vegetative period, result in smaller bulbs, and consequently produce inferior blooms the following year *(30)*. Commercial bulb-producing areas for hardy spring-flowering bulbs are largely in regions of cool springs and summers, such as Holland or the Pacific Northwest.

Photoperiod is another important factor which may affect bulb development in some species. It has been shown to be an important factor in the onion and garlic *(21, 27)*.

(b) *Flower bud formation and flowering.* The beginning of the reproductive stage and the end of the vegetative stage is indicated by the drying of the foliage and the maturation of the bulb. From then on, no additional increase in size or weight of the bulb takes place. The roots disintegrate, and the bulb enters a seemingly "dormant" period. However, important internal changes are taking place; the vegetative growing point is making a transition to a flowering shoot. It is necessary that the bulb attain sufficient size for this to occur; if it has not, it will remain vegetative.

Studies by workers in Holland have shown the importance of temperature in the progression from vegetative growth to flower bud formation *(36)*. The optimum temperature, as determined by the fact that the bulb would flower in the shortest time, was established for the various developmental phases. In general, a deviation from these temperatures or an increase in the period of time at any one temperature results in an increase in the time required to bloom and in some cases may prevent flower development entirely.

In the tulip, the differentiation of the flower parts takes place after the bulb becomes dormant in the summer. The optimum temperature for this process is 68°F. After 3 weeks of storage at this temperature, the optimum drops abruptly to 48°F. where it remains for 10 to 12 weeks, the cooler temperatures being necessary to overcome the rest period and to stimulate the flower shoot to elongate. The optimum temperature then gradually increases as the flower shoot elongates and a flower is produced.

In these studies *(36),* the hyacinth had somewhat more exacting requirements. The optimum temperature immediately upon digging was quite high (90° to 95°F.) for a week or two. When the first flower primordium on the raceme had appeared this shifted to 78°F., when the last flower primordium had appeared it had shifted to 63°F., and 3 weeks later had shifted to 55°F., where it remained for about 12 weeks. Maintaining the bulbs at a temperature above 86°F. or below 55°F. during this period inhibits flower bud development entirely *(30)*. For the hyacinth, a storage temperature of 78°F. is generally recommended for the flower forming period *(9)*.

The daffodil (King Alfred) has an optimum temperature of 62°F. for flower formation followed by a period of about 8 weeks at 48°F. *(36)*.

Holding the bulbs continuously at warm temperatures (86° to 90°F. or more) or at temperatures near freezing will stop bulb development and can be used to increase the period required for flowering. With a shift to normal temperatures, flower bud development will continue unimpaired. Such storage conditions can be used when shipping bulbs from the northern to the southern hemisphere *(36)*.

Lilies. The non-tunicate bulb of the lily exhibits certain important differences from the tunicate bulb of the spring-flowering bulbs. Different species of lily have different methods of bulb reproduction, some examples being given in the following section on propagation. The lily bulb exhibits a vegetative period during the summer in which the new bulb for next year is growing in size and accumulating reserve materials. Lily bulbs do not go dormant in the same manner as other bulbs, and the roots do not disintegrate. The bulb should be out of the ground as little as possible and, when it is for the purpose of propagation, should be handled carefully and kept from drying. The commercial value of the bulb depends not only on its size and weight but also on the condition of the fleshy roots and the freedom of the basal plate from rot.

The transition of the growing point to a flower bud does not take place until late fall in the Easter lily, apparently not until after the bulb is dug and replanted. Storing the mature bulbs at 45° to 50°F. for 6 weeks and then growing them at temperatures of 60°F. or more (night) will produce blooms within 80 to 100 days. Storing the mature bulbs at room temperatures or at low (31°F.) temperatures will keep the bulbs dormant and will delay flowering. In the latter case, the method of bulb storage is also important *(34)*. If they dry out they will deteriorate. If they absorb moisture from the packing material they may rot.

Tender, winter-flowering bulbs. There are a number of flowering bulbs from tropical areas whose growth cycle is geared to a wet-dry climatic cycle rather than a cycle related to cold-warm temperatures.

The amaryllis *(Hippeastrum vittata)* is an example of one of this type whose growth pattern has been examined in detail *(36)*. Its bulb is perennial, continuing to grow from the center, the outer scales disintegrating. A continuous series of new leaves are produced from the center during the vegetative period extending from late winter to the following summer. In the axil of every fourth leaf (or scale) that develops, a growing point is initiated. Thus, throughout the vegetative period a series of vegetative offsets are produced. By fall (August to October) the leaves mature and the bulb goes dormant, during which time the bulb should be dry. During this period, the *fourth* growing point from the center and any external to it differentiate into flower buds, and the shoot begins a slow elongation. When the bulbs are again watered after 2 to 3 months of dry storage, the flowering shoots elongate rapidly, and flowering takes place in January or February. Maximum foliage development and bulb growth are particularly important to produce a bulb large enough to form a flowering shoot.

This type of bulb represents one in which the various developmental stages are inherent within the bulb itself and are not brought about by external temperature changes.

Propagation

Offsets. The development of offsets provides a simple and reliable method for propagating many kinds of bulbs. It is sufficiently rapid for the commercial production of tulip, daffodil, bulbous iris, and grape hyacinth bulbs, but in general it is too slow for the lily, hyacinth, and amaryllis.

If undisturbed, the offsets may remain attached to the mother bulb for several years. They can also be removed at the time the bulbs are dug and replanted into beds or nursery rows to grow into flowering sized bulbs. This may require several growing seasons, depending upon the kind of bulb and size of the offset.

(a) *Tulip (9, 15).* Bulb planting takes place in the fall (September to November). Two systems of planting are used: the bed system, used mostly in Europe; and the row or field system, used mostly in the United States. Beds are usually 3 feet wide and separated by 12 to 18 inch paths. The soil is removed to a depth of 4 inches, the bulbs set in rows 6 inches apart, and the soil replaced. In the other system, single or double rows are used

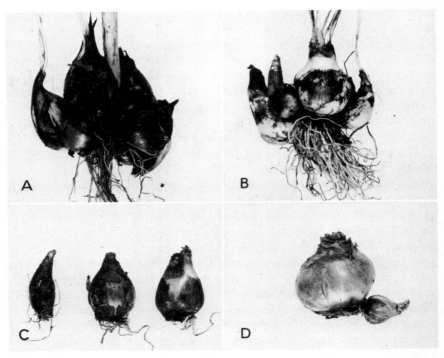

Figure 15–4. Propagation by offset bulbs. **(A)** Bulbous iris. The old bulb disintegrates leaving a cluster of bulbs. **(B) Narcissus.** Bulb continues to grow from the inside each year, but continuously produces lateral bulbs which eventually split away. **(C) Narcissus.** Three types of bulbs: "split" or "slab" bulb, "round" bulb, and "double-nose" bulb. **(D) Hyacinth.** Lateral bulblets produced, but old bulb continues to develop from inside.

that are wide enough apart to permit the use of machines. To improve drainage, two or three adjoining rows may be planted on a ridge. Bulbs are spaced one to two diameters apart, small bulbs scattered along the row. A mulch may be applied after planting but removed the following spring before growth.

Planting stock consists of those bulbs of the minimum size for flowering (9 to 10 cm. in circumference or smaller). Since the time required to produce flowering sizes varies with the size of the bulb, the planting stock will be graded so that those of one size can be planted together. For instance, an 8 cm. or larger bulb will normally require a single season to become of flowering size; a 5 to 7 cm. bulb, two seasons; and those 5 cm. or less, 3 years *(15)*.

During the flowering and subsequent bulb growing period of the next spring, good growing conditions should be provided so that the size and weight of the new bulbs will be at a maximum. Foliage should not be removed until it dries or matures. Important cultural operations include removal of competing weed growth, irrigation, fungicidal sprays to control *Botrytis* blight *(14)*, and fertilization. It is desirable to remove the flower heads at blooming time, because they may serve as a source of *Botrytis* infection and can lower bulb weight *(1)*.

Bulbs are dug in June or July when the leaves have turned yellow or the outer coats of the bulb have become dark brown in color. In the Pacific northwest where temperatures are cool and the leaves remain green for a longer period, digging may take place before the leaves dry. If the bulbs are dug too early or if warm weather causes early maturation, the bulbs may be small in size. The bulbs are dug by machine or by hand with a short-handled spade. After the loose soil is shaken from the bulbs, they are placed in trays in well-ventilated storage houses for drying, cleaning, sorting, and grading. General storage temperatures are 65° to 68°F. For early flowering, the bulbs should be held at 68°F. for 3 weeks and then placed at 48°F. for 8 weeks. Later flowering will be produced by holding bulbs at 72°F. for 10 weeks. For shipment to the Southern Hemisphere, the bulbs can be held at 31°F. until December 31, when they are shifted to a warm temperature *(9)*.

(b) *Daffodil (16)*. The daffodil represents a bulb which remains perennial and produces a new growing point at the center every year. In addition, offsets are produced which grow in size for several years until they break away from the original bulb, although they are still attached at the basal plate. An offset bulb, when it first separates from the mother bulb, is known as a "split," "spoon," or "slab" and can be separated from the mother bulb and planted. Within a year it becomes a "round," or "single-nose," bulb containing a single flower bud. One year later a new offset should be visible enclosed within the scales of the original bulb, indicating the presence of two flower buds. At this stage the bulb is known as a "double-nose." By the next year the offsets split away, and the bulb is known as a "mother bulb." Grading of daffodil bulbs is principally by age; that is, as to splits, round, double-nose, and mother bulbs. The grades marketed commercially are the round and the double-nose bulb. The mother bulbs are used as planting stock to produce additional offsets, and only the surplus are marketed. Offsets, or splits, are replanted for additional growth.

Storage should be at 55° to 60°F. with a relative humidity of 75 per cent. For earlier flowering, they can be stored at 48°F. for 8 weeks. To delay flowering, store at 72°F. for 10 weeks. For shipment to the Southern Hemisphere, bulbs can be held at 86°F. until October and then stored at 31°F. until December 31 *(9)*.

(c) *Lilies.* Lilies increase naturally, but except for a few species this increase is slow and of limited propagation value except in home gardens *(11, 18, 33, 37)*. Several methods of bulb increase are found among the different species. For instance, *Lilium concolor, L. hansoni, L. henryi,* and *L. regale* increase by bulb splitting. Two to four lateral bulblets are initiated about the base of the mother bulb, which disintegrates during the process, leaving a tight cluster of new bulbs. *Lilium bulbiferum, L. canadense, L. pardalinum, L. parryi, L. superbum,* and *L. tigrinum,* multiply from lateral bulblets produced from the rhizome-like bulb. This is sometimes spoken of as "budding-off" *(11)*.

Bulblet formation on stems. The production of *underground stem bulblets* is the usual commercial method of propagating the Easter lily (*Lilium longiflorum*) and some other lily species. Flowering of the Easter lily occurs in early summer. Bulblets form and increase in size from April on *(31)*. Between mid-August and mid-September, the stems are pulled from the bulbs and stacked upright in the field. Periodic sprinkling keeps the stems and bulblets from drying out. Similarly, the base of the stem can be "heeled in" the ground at an angle of 30 to 45 degrees or laid horizontally in trays at high humidity.

About mid-October the bulblets are planted in the field 4 inches deep and an inch apart in double rows which are spaced 36 inches apart. Here they remain for the following season. They are dug in the fall (September) as yearling bulbs and again replanted, this time 6 inches deep and 4 to 6 inches apart in single rows. At the end of the second year, they are dug and sold as commercial bulbs.

Digging is done in September after the stem is pulled. The bulbs are graded, packed in peat moss, and shipped. Commercial bulbs have a minimum size of 7 to 10 inches in circumference. Lily bulbs must be handled carefully so as not to injure them and must be kept from drying out. The fleshy roots should also be kept in good condition. For long term storage that will prevent flowering, the bulbs should be packed in polyethylene-lined cases containing peat moss at 30 to 50 per cent moisture and

Figure 15–5. Propagation of lily. **(left)** Underground stem bulblets are produced by some lily species. **(right)** Bulblets can be produced at the base of individual bulb scales; this method of propagation is possible for nearly all lily species.

stored at 31°F. *(34)*. To produce flowering in the shortest period of time, they should be stored at 45° to 50°F. for 6 weeks and then grown at temperatures of 60°F. (night) or more *(35)*.

Lilies are attacked by certain viruses, fungus diseases, and nematodes which can be carried in or on the bulbs. Their control during propagation is an important phase of bulb production. Methods of control include using disease-free stocks for propagation *(3, 7, 31)*, growing plants in disease-free locations with good sanitary procedures, and treating the bulbs with fungicides (see p. 135). A pre-planting dip of 2 pounds pentachloronitrobenzene (PCNB) plus 2 pounds ferbam in 100 gallons of water has been found to be useful *(5)*.

To obtain commercial planting stock of lilies free of *Rhizoctonia,* stem and bulb nematode, and root-lesion nematode: Cure bulbs at 95°F. and 95 per cent relative humidity for 1 to 2 weeks; presoak for 2 days in cool water; soak for 2 hours at 115°F. in water plus 37 per cent formaldehyde diluted 1:200; aftersoak the bulbs in Puratized Agricultural Spray 1:1000. Scale the bulbs, dust the bulblets with ferbam, and place in vermiculite for bulblets to form. Plant new bulblets in treated soil *(3,4)*.

Aerial stem bulblets, commonly known as *bulbils,* are formed in the axil of the leaves of some lily species, such as *Lilium bulbiferum, L. sargentiae, L. sulphureum,* and *L. tigrinum.* Bulbils develop in the early part of the season and fall to the ground several weeks after the plant flowers.

They are harvested shortly before they fall naturally and are then handled in essentially the same manner as underground stem bulblets. Increased bulbil production can be induced by disbudding as soon as the flower buds have formed. Likewise, some lily species which do not form bulbils naturally can be induced to do so by pinching out the flower buds and a week later cutting off the upper half of the stems. Species which respond to the latter procedure include *Lilium candidum, L. chalcedonicum, L. hollandicum, L. maculatum* and *L. testaceum (11)*.

Stem cuttings. Lilies may be propagated as stem cuttings. The cutting is made shortly after flowering. Instead of roots and shoots forming on the cutting, as would be true in other plants, bulblets form at the axils of the leaves and produce roots and small shoots while on the cutting.

Leaf-bud cuttings, made with a single leaf and a small‚heel of the old stem, may be used to propagate a number of lily species. A small bulblet will develop in the axil of the leaf. It is handled in the same manner as for any of the other methods here described.

Bulblet formation on scales (scaling). An efficient method for producing lily bulbs is the technique known as scaling, in which individual bulb scales are separated from the mother bulb and placed in growing conditions so that adventitious bulblets form at the base of each scale. Three to five bulblets will usually develop from each scale. This method is particularly useful for rapidly building up stocks of a new variety or to establish disease free stocks *(4)*. Almost any lily species can be propagated by scaling *(18)*.

Scaling is usually done soon after flowering in midsummer, although it might be done in late fall *(7)* or even in midwinter *(19)*. The bulbs are dug and the outer two layers of scales are removed. It is possible to remove the scales down to the core, but this will reduce subsequent growth of the mother bulb. The scales should be kept from drying and handled so as to avoid injury. Scales with evidence of rot should be discarded and the remaining ones dusted with a fungicide. Naphthaleneacetic acid has been found to stimulate bulblet formation. Mix 1000 parts of thiram or ferbam with 1 part of naphthaleneacetic acid and apply as a dust *(25)*. The PCNB-thiram mixture is also an effective fungicidal treatment *(5)*.

Although scales can be planted directly in the field, somewhat better results are obtained if they are placed in trays or flats of moist sand, peat moss, sphagnum moss, or vermiculite for 6 weeks at 65° to 70°F. The scales are inserted vertically to about half their length. Small bulblets and roots should form at the base within 3 to 6 weeks. The scales are transplanted either into the open ground or into pots or flats of soil and then planted in the field the following spring. Subsequent treatment is the same as described for underground bulblets.

Basal cuttage. The hyacinth is the principal plant propagated by this method, although others such as *Scilla* can be handled in this way. Specific methods include "scooping," "scoring," and "coring" *(9, 17)*. Mature bulbs which have been dug after the foliage has died down and are 17 to 18 cm. or more in circumference, are used. In *scooping,* the entire basal plate is scooped out with a special curve-bladed scalpel, a round-bowled spoon, or a small-bladed knife. Adventitious bulblets develop from the base of the exposed bulb scales. In *scoring,* three straight knife cuts are made across the base of the bulb, as shown in Figure 15–6, each deep enough to go through the basal plate and the growing point. Growing points in the axils of the bulb scales grow into bulblets. In *coring,* the growing point in the center of the bulb is removed entirely with an apple corer or a cork borer ⅜ to ½ inch in diameter. All of the growth potential is concentrated in the development of the bulblets which grow from the basal plate.

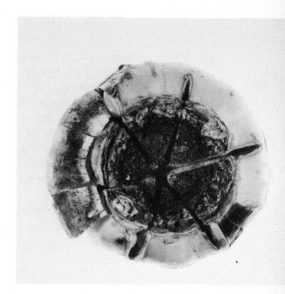

Figure 15–6. Basal cuttage. Hyacinth bulb which has been scored. Note the bulblets starting to appear.

To combat decay that may develop during the later incubation period, any infected bulbs should be discarded, the tools disinfected frequently with an alcohol, formalin, or mild carbolic acid solution, and the cut bulbs dusted with a fungicide. Most important is to callus the bulbs for a few days to a few weeks in dry sand or soil or in open trays cut side up. After callusing, the bulbs are incubated in trays or flats, in dark or diffuse light, at 70° to 90°F. and high humidity for 2½ to 3 months.

The mother bulbs are planted in nursery beds in mid-October. The next spring bulblets produce leaves profusely. Normally, the mother bulb disintegrates during the first summer. Annual digging and replanting of the graded bulblets is required until they reach flowering sizes. Bulbs for greenhouse forcing should be 17 cm. (6¾ inches) or more in circumference; bulbs for bedding should be 14 to 17 cm. (5½ to 6¾ inches) in circumference *(2)*. On the average, a scooped bulb will produce sixty bulblets, but 4 to 5 years will be required to produce flowering sizes; a scored bulb will produce twenty-four, requiring 3 to 4 years; and a cored bulb will produce ten, requiring 2 to 3 years *(9)*.

Leaf cuttings. This method has been reported successful for blood lily (*Haemanthus*), grape hyacinth (*Muscari*), hyacinth, and *Lachenalia (12, 13)*, although the range of species is probably wider than realized.

Leaves are taken at a time when they are well developed and green, generally near full bloom. An entire leaf is cut from the top of the bulb and may in turn be cut into two or three pieces. Each section is placed in a rooting medium with the basal end several inches below the surface, as described for rooting cuttings. The leaves should not be allowed to dry out, and bottom heat is desirable. Within 2 to 4 weeks small bulblets form on the base of the leaf and roots develop. At this stage the bulblets are planted in soil.

Bulb cuttings. Among those plants which have been reported to respond to this method of propagation are the *Albuca, Chasmanthe, Cooperia, Haemanthus, Hippeastrum, Hymenocallis, Lycoris, Narcissus, Nerine, Pancratium, Scilla, Sprekelia,* and *Urceolina (13)*.

A mature bulb is cut into a series of vertical sections (eight to ten), each containing a part of the basal plate. These sections are further divided by sliding a knife down between each third or fourth pair of concentric scale rings and cutting through the basal plate. Each of these fractions makes up a bulb cutting consisting of a piece of basal plate and segments of three or four scales.

The bulb cuttings are planted vertically in a rooting medium, such as peat moss and sand, with just their tips showing above the surface. The subsequent technique of handling is the same as for ordinary leaf cuttings. A moderately warm temperature, slightly higher than for mature bulbs of that kind, is required. New bulblets develop from the basal plate between the bulb scales within a matter of a few weeks, along with new roots. At this time they are transferred to flats of soil to continue development.

CORMS

Definition and Structure

A *corm* is the swollen base of a stem axis enclosed by the dry, scale-like leaves. In contrast to the bulb, which is predominantly leaf scales, a corm is a solid stem structure with distinct nodes and internodes evident. The bulk of the corm consists of storage tissue composed of parenchyma cells. In the mature corm, the dry leaf bases persist at each of these nodes and enclose the corm. This covering, known as the *tunic,* protects it against injury and water loss. At the apex of the corm is a terminal shoot bud which will develop into the leaves and the flowering shoot. Axillary buds are produced at each of the nodes. In a large corm, several of the upper buds may develop into flowering shoots, but those nearer the base of the corm are generally inhibited from growing. However, should something prevent the main buds from growing, these lateral buds would be capable of producing a shoot.

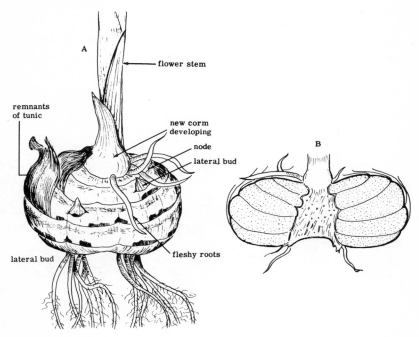

Figure 15–7. Gladiolus corm. **(A)** External appearance. **(B)** Longitudinal section showing solid stem structure.

Two types of roots are produced from the corm: a fibrous root system developing from the base of the old corm and enlarged, fleshy roots developing from the base of the new corm (see below).

Growth Behavior

Gladiolus and crocus are typical cormous plants. The gladiolus is a semi-hardy to tender plant which, in areas with severe winters, must be stored over winter and replanted in the spring. At the time of planting, the corm is a vegetative structure *(20, 29)*. New roots develop from the base of the corm and one or more of the buds begin to develop leaves. Differentiation of the inflorescence takes place within a few weeks after the bud begins to grow. At the same time the base of the shoot axis thickens, and a new corm for the succeeding year begins to form above the old corm. Root-like structures bearing miniature corms or cormels on their tip develop from the base of the new corm. The new corm continues to enlarge, and the old corm begins to shrivel and disintegrate as its contents are utilized in flower production. After flowering, the foliage continues to manufacture food materials, which are stored in the new corm. At the end of the summer, when the foliage dries, there are one or more new corms and perhaps a great number of the little cormels. The corms are dug and stored over winter until planting the following spring.

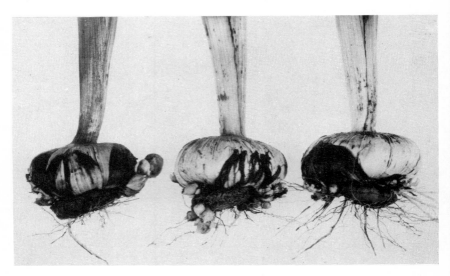

Figure 15-8. Stage of development of gladiolus corm during the latter part of the growing season. The remains of the originally planted corm can still be seen just below the newly formed corm. Many small cormels have also been produced.

Propagation

New corms. Propagation of cormous plants is principally by the natural increase of new corms. Flower production in corms, as in bulbs, depends upon the food materials stored in the corm the previous season, particularly during the period following bloom. In gladiolus, cool nights and long growing periods are favorable for the production of very large corms. Fertilization and other good management practices during bloom would have their greatest effect on the next year's flowers. Plants are left in the ground for

2 months following blooming, or until frost kills the tops. After digging, the plants are placed in trays with a screen or slat bottom arranged to allow air to circulate between them and cured at 95°F. at 80 to 85 per cent relative humidity. Then the new corms, old corms, cormels, and tops can be easily separated. The corms are graded according to size, sorted to remove the diseased ones, treated with a fungicide (Spergon wettable powder), and returned to a warm temperature for an additional week. This process suberizes the wounds and helps combat *Fusarium* infection. The corms are then stored at 40°F. with a relative humidity of 70 to 80 per cent in well aerated rooms to prevent excessive drying (6). It is also desirable to treat them immediately before planting with ½ per cent Lysol solution for 2 hours or with ⅛ per cent solution of New Improved Ceresan for 15 minutes (24).

Cormels. These are miniature corms which develop between the old and the new corms. One or 2 years growth is required for them to reach flowering size. Shallow planting of the corms, only a few inches deep, results in greater production of cormels; increasing the depth of planting will result in less cormel production (12).

Cormels are separated from the mother corms and stored over winter for planting in the spring. Dry cormels become very hard and may be slow to start growth the following spring, but if they are stored at about 40°F. in slightly moist peat moss, they will stay plump and in good condition. Soaking dry cormels in warm water for 2 to 5 days just prior to planting will hasten the onset of growth.

Disease free cormels can be produced by hot water treatment (6). Treatment should be done between 2 and 4 months after digging. The cormels are soaked in water at air temperature for 2 days, then placed in a 1:200 dilution of commercial 37 per cent formaldehyde for 4 hours, and then immersed in a water bath at 135°F. for 30 minutes. The temperature should be maintained within 1°F., plus or minus, of this temperature. At the end of the treatment, the cormels are cooled quickly, dried immediately, and stored at 40°F. in a clean area with good air circulation. Dusting the dry cormels with a fungicide at this time is also desirable.

The cormels are planted in the field in furrows about 2 inches deep in the manner of planting large seeds. Only grass-like foliage is produced the first season. The cormel does not increase in size but produces a new corm from the base of the stem axis, in the same manner as described for the full sized corm. At the end of the first growing season, the beds are dug and the corms separated by size. A few of the corms may attain flowering size, but most will require an additional year of growth.

Size grades in gladiolus are determined by diameter. These are in seven grades, the smallest ⅜ to ½ inch in diameter, the largest 2 inches or more (2).

Division of the corm. Large corms may be cut into sections, retaining a bud with each section. Each section should then develop a new corm. Segments should be dusted with a fungicide because of the great likelihood of decay of the exposed surfaces.

TUBERS

Definition and Structure

A *tuber* is the short, terminal portion of an underground stem which has become thickened because of the accumulation of reserve food materials. The most notable example of a plant which produces tubers by which it is propagated is the Irish potato (*Solanum tuberosum*). The *Caladium,* grown for its striking foliage, is also propagated by tubers, as is the Jerusalem artichoke (*Helianthus tuberosus*).

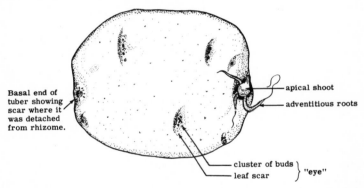

Basal end of tuber showing scar where it was detached from rhizome.

apical shoot

adventitious roots

cluster of buds ⎱ "eye"
leaf scar ⎰

Figure 15–9. Stem tuber of potato. Note nodes ("eyes"), and internodes.

A tuber shows all of the parts of a typical stem. The "eyes," present in regular order over the surface, represent nodes, each consisting of one or more small buds subtended by a leaf scar. The arrangement of the nodes is a spiral, beginning with the terminal bud on the end opposite the scar resulting from the attachment to the slender rhizome. The terminal bud represents the apical end of the tuber and shows apical dominance by being the first to grow, even though it is oriented farthest away from the crown of the plant.

Growth Behavior

A tuber is a storage and reproductive organ produced in one growing season; it remains dormant through the following winter, and is then utilized during the following season in the development of the new plant. If the tuber is planted whole, the terminal bud inhibits sprouting of the lateral buds. Apical dominance is destroyed by cutting the tuber into sections. New shoots develop from the buds on the tuber, but the new roots develop adventitiously from the base of the new shoot. Lateral shoots from the underground nodes of the new stem elongate for 3 to 4 inches, then begin to enlarge at their tip. These are the new tubers that are forming, which become evident about 3 to 4 weeks after planting, or approximately the same time as flower buds appear on the plant. Tuberization in the potato is most pronounced at cool temperatures and intermediate day lengths. Conditions which favor rapid and abundant plant growth above ground, such as an abundance of nitrogen or high temperatures, are not conducive to high tuber production *(26)*. In the fall, the tops of the plants die down and the tubers are dug. At this time, the buds of potato tubers are in a period of dormancy, which lasts 6 to 8 weeks. This condition must disappear before sprouting will take place.

Propagation

Division. Propagation by tubers can be carried out either by planting the tubers whole or by cutting them into sections, each containing a bud or eye. These small pieces of tuber which are to be used for propagation of the potato are commonly referred to as "seed." The weight of the tuber piece should be 1 to 2 ounces to provide sufficient stored food for the new plant to become well established.

Division of tubers is done with a sharp knife shortly before planting. The cut surfaces should be sealed by storing at warm (68°F.) temperatures and relatively high humidities (90 per cent) for 2 to 3 days prior to planting. During this time, the cut surfaces heal (*suberization*) and the "seed" piece is effectively protected against drying and rotting. Treatment of potato tubers prior to cutting for the control of *Rhizoctonia* and scab may be desirable *(26)*. Caladium tubers are produced commercially in Florida *(32)*. The tubers are cut into sections, usually two buds per piece. These are planted 3 to 4 inches deep, 4 to 6 inches apart in rows 18 to 24 inches apart. Harvest begins in November. After harvest, the tubers are dried in open sheds for 6 weeks or artifically dried for 48 hours. Further storage should be at a temperature of not below 60°F.

TUBERCLES

Begonia evansiana and the cinnamon vine (*Dioscorea batatas*) produce small aerial tubers, known as *tubercles,* in the axils of the leaves. These tubercles may be removed in the fall, stored over winter, and planted in the spring *(13)*.

TUBEROUS ROOTS

Definition and Structure

Certain herbaceous perennials produce thickened tuberous roots which contain large amounts of stored food. Although the appearance of such roots may vary considerably from one species to another, they have the internal and external features of a typical root. Thus, they differ from the true (stem) tuber in that they lack nodes and internodes; buds are present

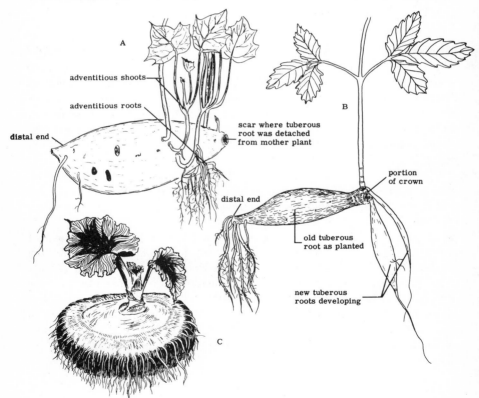

Figure 15–10. Types of tuberous roots. **(A)** Sweet potato showing adventitious shoots. **(B)** Dahlia during early stages of growth. The old root piece will disintegrate in the production of the new plant; the new roots can be used for propagation. **(C)** Tuberous begonia, showing its vertical orientation. This type continues to enlarge in size each year.

only at the crown or stem (proximal) end; fibrous roots are commonly produced towards the opposite (distal) end. The polarity of the tuberous root is consequently the reverse of that of the true tuber.

Growth Behavior

Three typical examples of these structures are shown in Figure 15–10. For instance, the sweet potato and dahlia produce swollen sections on lateral roots. In the latter case, these are borne in a cluster, each tuberous root attached to the crown of the plant. These roots are biennial. They are produced in one season, after which they go dormant as the herbaceous shoots die. The following spring, buds from the crown produce new shoots which utilize the food materials from the old root during their initial growth. The old root then disintegrates and new roots are produced which will in turn maintain the plant through the following dormant period.

In the tuberous begonia, on the other hand, the primary taproot becomes a single enlarged tuberous root. Buds are produced at the proximal end (the crown). Fibrous roots are produced from the distal portion of the swollen root. This tuberous root is perennial and lives for a number of years, continuing to increase in size and produce additional buds from the crown.

Figure 15–11. Propagation of sweet potato. The adventitious shoots or "slips" develop when the mother root is placed under moist conditions. The rooted slips are removed and planted.

Propagation

Adventitious shoots. The fleshy roots of a few species of plants such as sweet potato have the capacity to produce adventitious shoots if subjected to the proper conditions of temperature and moisture. The roots

Figure 15–12. Propagation of **Dahlia.** To produce a new plant each separate tuberous root must have a section of the crown, bearing a shoot bud as shown by the detached root on the left.

are laid in sand so that they do not touch one another and covered to a depth of about 2 inches. The bed is kept moist. The temperature should be about 80°F. at the beginning and about 70° or 75°F. after sprouting has started. As the new shoots, or *slips,* come through the covering, more sand is added so that eventually the stems will be covered 4 to 5 inches. Adventitious roots develop from the base of these adventitious shoots. After the slips are well rooted, they are pulled from the parent plant and transplanted into the field *(26).*

Division. Most plants with fleshy roots must be propagated by dividing the crown so that each section bears a shoot bud. This is necessary in the dahlia, for example. The plant is dug with its cluster of roots intact, dried for a few days, and stored at 40° to 50°F. in dry sawdust, dry peat, or dry shavings. Storage in the open may result in shriveling. The cluster of roots is divided in the late winter or spring shortly before planting. In warm, moist conditions the buds begin to grow, and division can be carried out with better assurance that each section will have a bud.

The perennial tuberous root of the tuberous begonia can also be divided as long as each section has a bud. To combat decay, the cut surface should be dusted with a fungicide and each section dried for several days after cutting and before placing in a moist medium *(8).*

Vegetative propagation in such plants as these can often be better carried out with stem, leaf, or leaf-bud cuttings. The cuttings will develop tuberous roots at their base. This process can be stimulated if the stem cutting initially includes a small piece of the fleshy root.

RHIZOMES

Definition and Structure

A *rhizome* is a horizontal stem growing either underground or along the surface of the ground. Typically, it is the main axis of the plant, produces roots on its lower surface, and extends leaves and the flowering shoots above the ground. It may be thick and fleshy or slender and elongated, but it is always made up of nodes and internodes. Lateral growing points arising at the nodes produce aerial shoots or lateral branches of the rhizome. Roots are adventitious and appear on the lower side of the rhizome, generally in the vicinity of a node.

Growth Behavior

The rhizome habit of growth is shown by a number of important plant groups. In general, most rhizomatous plants are monocotyledons, although

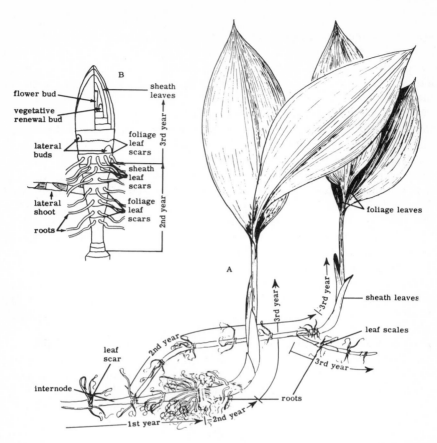

Figure 15–13. Structure and growth cycle of lily-of-the-valley **(Convallaria majalis)** **(A)** Section of rhizome as it appears in late spring or early summer with one-, two-, and three-year-old branches. A new rhizome branch begins to elongate in March or April and terminates in a vegetative shoot-bud by August. The following spring the leaves of the bud unfold; food materials manufactured in the leaves by photosynthesis are accumulated in the rhizome. Growth the second season is again vegetative. Early in the third season a flower bud begins to form, and at the same time a vegetative growing point forms in the axil of the last leaf. **(B)** Section of the three-year-old branch showing terminal flower bud and lateral shoot bud enclosed in leaf sheaths. Such a section is sometimes known as a "pip" or "crown" and is forced for spring bloom. In the early spring the flowering shoot expands, blooms and then dies down, the shoot bud beginning a new cycle of development. Redrawn from Zweede **(38)**.

a few dicotyledonous plants have analogous underground stems classed as rhizomes. Many of the ferns and lower plants also have rhizomes or rhizome-like structures. Rhizome length growth takes place from the terminal meristem, or growing point, and from lateral shoots arising at the nodes. As the shoot increases in length, the older part may die so that the several branches originating from one plant eventually become separated to form individual plants.

Rhizomes exhibit consecutive vegetative and reproductive stages similar to other plants discussed in this chapter. A rhizome depends upon photosynthesis in the leaves for continued growth of the underground stem, for food storage in the fleshy rhizome over winter or during dry periods, and for the production of a ·good flower bud. Consequently, foliage should not be removed after flowering or growth and flower development are inhibited.

Figure 15–14. Structure of an iris (rhizomatous type) plant as it appears about the time of flowering. A two-year-old section which had flowered the previous year and is now dying back is shown at **(D)**. The lateral branch arising from it consists of the one-year-old vegetative section **(B)**, the current season, lateral vegetative branches **(A)**, and the current season, terminal flowering shoot **(C)**. The vegetative shoot **(A)** will flower the following year.

Propagation

Division. Propagation of rhizomes consists of cutting or dividing the rhizome into sections, each of which is capable of producing a new shoot. Since the rhizome contains large amounts of stored food and produces adventitious roots readily, new plants are produced with little difficulty.

Each section removed for propagation, which is usually composed of several internodes, must have a vegetative bud or a growing point. The rhizome section can usually be transplanted directly into the desired location. The leaves should be reduced at this time.

Rhizomes are divided either at the end of a growing period or just before one begins, i.e., in the late summer, fall, or early spring. If the division is early enough in the summer, the rhizome section develops roots and becomes established before winter.

PSEUDOBULBS

Definition and Structure

A *pseudobulb* (literally "false bulb") is a specialized storage structure, consisting of an enlarged, fleshy section of the stem made up of one to several nodes, produced by certain orchid species. In general appearance the pseudobulb varies with different species of orchids, the differences being sufficiently characteristic to aid in identification of species.

Figure 15–15. Cattleya orchid showing rhizome structure and upright elongated pseudobulbs as basal part of shoots.

Growth Behavior

These pseudobulbs arise during the growing season on upright growths which develop laterally or terminally from the horizontal rhizome. Leaves and flowers form either at the terminal end or at the base of the pseudobulb, depending upon the species. During the growth period, they accumulate stored food materials and water and assist the plants in surviving the subsequent dormant period.

Propagation

Offshoots. In a few orchids, such as the *Dendrobium* species, the pseudobulb is long and jointed, being made up of many nodes. Offshoots develop at these nodes. From the base of these offshoots roots develop. The rooted offshoots are then cut from the parent plant and potted.

Division. Most important commercial species of orchids, including the *Cattleya, Laelia, Miltonia,* and *Odontoglossum,* may be propagated by dividing the rhizome into sections, the exact procedure used depending upon the particular kind of orchid. Division is done during the dormant season, preferably just before the beginning of a new period of growth. The rhizome is cut with a sharp knife back far enough from the terminal end to include four to five pseudobulbs in the new section, leaving the old rhizome section with a number of old pseudobulbs, or "back bulbs," from

Figure 15–16. A "back bulb" of a **Cymbidium** orchid was removed from the parent plant and placed in a rooting medium, whereupon the offshoot shown above developed. This offshoot is ready for removal and potting. When this is done, a second offshoot, or "break," should appear. Courtesy A. Kofranek.

Single Break — Cymbidium

Back Bulb Propagation

which the leaves have dehisced. The section is then potted, whereupon growth begins from the bases of the pseudobulbs and at the nodes. The removal of the new section of the rhizome from the old part stimulates new growth, or "back breaks," to occur from the old parts of the rhizome. These new growths grow for a season and can be removed the following year.

An alternate procedure is to cut partly through the rhizome and leave it for one year. New back breaks will develop which can later be removed and potted.

Back bulbs and green bulbs. "Back bulbs" (i.e., those without foliage) are commonly used to propagate clones of *Cymbidium*. These are removed from the plant, the cut surface painted with a grafting compound, and placed in a rooting medium for new shoots to develop. When the stage shown in Figure 15–16 is reached, the shoot can be removed from the bulb and potted. This back bulb can be repropagated and a second shoot developed from it.

"Green bulbs" (i.e., those with leaves) can also be used in *Cymbidium* propagation. Treatment with indolebutyric acid, either by soaking or by painting with a paste, has been shown to be beneficial *(23)*.

REFERENCES

1. Allen, R. C., Factors affecting the growth of tulips and narcissi in relation to garden practice, *Proc. Amer. Soc. Hort. Sci.*, 35:825–829. 1937.
2. Amer. Assoc. Nurserymen, Inc., Comm. on Hort. Stand., *American Standard for Nursery Stock*. Washington, D.C.: Amer. Assoc. Nurs., Inc. 1956.
3. Baker, K. F., and P. A. Chandler, Development and maintenance of healthy planting stock, Sec. 13 in *Calif. Agr. Exp. Sta. Man.* 23, 1957.
4. Bald, J. G., and P. A. Chandler, Reduction of the root rot complex on Croft lilies by fungicide treatment and propagation from bulb scales, *Phytopath.*, 47:285–291. 1957.
5. Bald, J. G., et al., Root rot of Easter lily, *Calif. Agr.*, 12(4):3, 14. 1958.
6. Bald, J. G., J. Ferguson, and B. B. Markley, Treatment of gladiolus cormels, *Calif. Agr.* 10(6):15–16. 1956.
7. Butterfield, H. M., Production of Easter lily bulbs, *Calif. Agr. Ext. Circ.* 132:1–34. 1947.
8. ———, Growing begonias in California, *Calif. Agr. Ext. Circ.* 162:1–41. 1950.
9. Crossley, J. H., Hyacinth culture; Narcissus culture; Tulip culture; *Handbook on Bulb Growing and Forcing,* Northwest Bulb Growers Assoc., pp. 79–84, 99–104, 139–144. 1957.
10. Curtis, A. H., Growth studies of King Alfred narcissus bulbs, *Proc. Amer. Soc. Hort. Sci.,* 36:781–782. 1938.
11. De Graaf, J., *The New Book of Lilies.* New York: Barrows, 1951.
12. Emsweller, S. L., Flowering bulbs, *Nat. Hort. Mag.,* 33:63–69. 1954.
13. Everett, T. H., *The American Gardener's Book of Bulbs.* New York: Random House, 1954.

14. Gould, C. J., Blights of lilies and tulips. *Plant Diseases. USDA Yearbook for 1953,* Washington, pp. 611–616. 1953.
15. Griffiths, D., The production of tulip bulbs, *USDA Bul. 1082,* 1922.
16. ———, Daffodils, *USDA Cir. 122,* 1930.
17. ———, The production of hyacinth bulbs, *USDA Cir. 112,* 1930.
18. ———, The production of lily bulbs, *USDA Cir. 102,* 1930.
19. ———, Artificial propagation of the lily, *Proc. Amer. Soc. Hort. Sci.* 29:519–521. 1932.
20. Hartsema, A. M., Periodieke ontwikkeling van *Gladiolus hybridum* var. Vesuvius, *Verh. Koninkl. Nederl. Akad. van Wetens.* 36(3):1–34. 1937.
21. Heath, O. V., and M. Holdsworth, Morphologenic factors as exemplified by the onion plant, *Symposia for the Soc. Exp. Biol.,* II:326–350. 1948.
22. Huisman, E., and A. M. Hartsema, De periodieke ontwikkeling van *Narcissus pseudonarcissus* L., *Meded. Landbouwhoogesch., Wageningen,* DL. 37 (*Meded.* No. 38, Lab. v. Plantenphys. onderz., Wageningen). 1933.
23. Kofranek, A. M., and G. Barstow, The use of rooting substances in *Cymbidium* green bulb propagation, *Amer. Orch. Soc. Bul.* 24(11):751–753. 1955.
24. Magie, R. O., Some fungi that attack gladioli. *Plant Diseases. USDA Yearbook for 1953,* Washington, pp. 601–607. 1953.
25. McClellan, W. D., and N. W. Stuart, Prevention of scale rot in propagation of Easter lily bulbs, *Florists' Review,* XCV (2467):19–20. 1944.
26. MacGillivray, J. H., *Vegetable Production.* Philadelphia: Blakiston, 1953.
27. Mann, L. K., Anatomy of the garlic bulb and factors affecting bulb development, *Hilgardia,* 21:195–251. 1952.
28. Mulder, R., and I. Luyten, De periodieke ontwikkeling van de Darwin tulip. *Verh. Koninkl. Nederl. Akad. van Wetens.,* 26:1–64. 1928.
29. Pfeiffer, N. E., A morphological study of *Gladiolus, Contrib. Boyce Thomp. Inst.* 3:173–195. 1931.
30. Post, K., *Florist Crop Production and Marketing.* New York: Orange Judd, 1949.
31. Roberts, A. N. and L. T. Blaney, Easter lilies. Culture. *Handbook on Bulb Growing and Forcing,* Northwest Bulb Growers Assoc., pp. 35–43. 1957.
32. Sheehan, T. J., Caladium production in Florida, *Fla. Agr. Ext. Cir. 128, 1955.*
33. Slate, G. L., *Lilies for American Gardens.* New York: Scribner, 1939.
34. Stuart, N. W., Moisture content of packing medium, temperature and duration of storage as factors in forcing lily bulbs, *Proc. Amer. Soc. Hort. Sci.,* 63:488–494. 1954.
35. ———, Easter lilies. Forcing. *Handbook on Bulb Growing and Forcing,* Northwest Bulb Growers Assoc., pp. 75–79. 1957.
36. Went, F. W., Thermoperiodicity, *In:* Murneek, A. E., and R. O. Whyte, *Vernalization and Photoperiodism,* Waltham, Mass.: Chronica Botanica. 1948.
37. Woodcock, H. B. D., and H. T. Stearn, *Lilies of the World.* New York: Scribner. 1950.
38. Zweede, A. K., De Periodieke ontwikkeling van *Convallaria majalis, Verh. Koninkl. Nederl. Akad. van Wetens.,* 27:1–72. 1930.

• ## Supplementary Reading

Everett, T. H., *The American Gardener's Book of Bulbs.* New York: Random House, 1954.

Handbook on Bulb Growing and Forcing. Mt. Vernon, Washington: Northwest Bulb Growers Assoc., 1957.

Rockwell, F. F., and E. C. Grayson, *The Complete Book of Bulbs.* Garden City, N.Y.: American Garden Guild and Doubleday, 1953.

IV

PROPAGATION OF
SELECTED PLANTS

16

Propagation Methods and Rootstocks for the Important Fruit and Nut Species

◄✦►

Few of the fruit or nut crops will reproduce true to variety when propagated by seed. It is necessary, therefore, that they be propagated by some asexual method. Most tree fruit and nut species are propagated by budding or grafting on rootstocks—seedlings, rooted cuttings, or layered plants. In many cases, cuttings would be the simplest and easiest method to use, but for other than a few species, such as the grape, fig, olive, quince, currant, and gooseberry, the fruit and nuts are so difficult to propagate by cuttings that other methods are used.

Almond (*Prunus amygdalus* Batsch). The almond is propagated by T-budding (see p. 382) the desired variety on seedling rootstocks. This is generally practiced as fall budding, but spring or June budding (see p. 374) may also be used. Root cuttings have given slight success. Layering can be done but with difficulty.

ROOTSTOCKS FOR ALMOND VARIETIES. Almond or peach seedlings are recommended. In order to obtain satisfactory germination, seeds of these species require cold stratification before planting—3 to 4 weeks for the almond and about 3 months for the peach—as described on page 127. The vegetatively-propagated Marianna 2624 plum (see p. 490) shows promise as a rootstock for almonds (except Nonpareil and Drake) on soils that are poorly drained or infected with oak root fungus (57).

Almond (*P. amygdalus*). Almond seedlings, particularly the bitter types, are widely used and are quite satisfactory. Seeds of the Texas (Mission) variety are also used. In poorly drained soils almond roots are often unsatisfactory, however, due to their susceptibility to infection by crown rot (*Phytophthora* sp.) and to their deep-rooting habit. This deep-rooting tendency is an advantage in orchards grown on unirrigated soils or where drought conditions occur. Almond seedlings can be used in soils of high lime content, where iron deficiency chlorosis may be expected, because of their tolerance to this condition. Almond roots are also the least affected by excess alkali and boron salts of any of the rootstocks available for almond varieties.

Peach (P. persica). Peach seedlings are satisfactory and widely used as rootstocks for almond varieties, especially in soils too wet for almond roots and where irrigation is practiced. The graft unions often are rough but are acceptable. Peach roots are not as susceptible to crown gall (*Agrobacterium tumefaciens*) as are almond roots. Almond varieties on peach roots in deep, irrigated soils will grow faster for the first several years and bear heavier crops during the first 15 to 20 years than those on almond roots, but trees on almond roots will tend to live longer than those on peach roots.

Anacardium occidentale. See Cashew.

Ananas comosus. See Pineapple.

Annona cherimola. See Cherimoya.

Apple (*Malus sylvestris* Mill.). T-budding (see p. 382) is successful either as fall budding or spring budding (see p. 374) on seedling or clonal vegetatively propagated rootstocks. Root grafting (see p. 358) is extensively used in some sections, either as whole-root or piece-root grafts. Propagation by hardwood cuttings, with the exception of certain clonal rootstocks, is generally unsuccessful. Rooting of softwood cuttings with the aid of root-promoting substances (see p. 244) has been reported *(74),* although this method is not used commercially.

All commercially successful apple rootstocks, either seedling or clonal, are in the genus *Malus,* although the apple will grow for a time and even come into bearing on pear (*Pyrus communis*) rootstocks. Most apple varieties will not grow much longer than a year on quince *(Cydonia oblonga)* roots. However, the Winter Banana variety seems to be successful on the quince, at least for a time, living as long as 20 years, although dwarfed. This offers possibilities of obtaining dwarfed trees by topworking the Winter Banana on quince to the desired variety. Apples have been grown also on roots of hawthorn (*Crataegus)* and mountain ash *(Sorbus)* species.

Rootstocks for Apple Varieties. **Seedling Rootstocks.** French Crab seeds and seedlings (*Malus sylvestris*) imported from France were widely used in the United States for many years in propagating apples. In 1930, United States quarantine regulations prohibited further importation of French Crab seedlings from Europe. Since then seedlings of such commercial varieties as Delicious, Winesap, and Rome Beauty have been used very successfully. These seedlings have shown considerable uniformity and no incompatibility problems have arisen. Selection in the nursery row tends to eliminate weak or off-type plants. In the colder portions of the United States—the Dakotas and Minnesota—the hardier Siberian crabapple *(Malus baccata)* and seedlings of such varieties as Antonovka, containing some *M. baccata* parentage, are used.

Fruits of apple varieties with the triploid number of chromosomes, such as Gravenstein, Baldwin, Stayman Winesap, Arkansas, Rhode Island Greening, Bramley's Seedling, and Tompkins King, produce seeds that are of low viability; consequently they are not recommended as a source of seed. For various reasons, seeds of Wealthy, Jonathan, or Hibernal have occasionally given unsatisfactory results.

The principal source of apple seeds is the pomace from cider presses. Apple seed require stratification (see p. 127) for 60 to 70 days at 32° to 45° F. before they will germinate. Seed for apple seedling rootstocks may be sown directly in the nursery row or planted in seedbeds. In the latter method they are transplanted to the nursery row after one season's growth. In order to obtain a branched root system, the seedlings are undercut while still small which prevents the development of a taproot. Seedlings that do not reach a satisfactory size in one year are graded out and eliminated.

Various Asiatic species of *Malus* appear promising as dwarfing or semi-dwarfing rootstocks or intermediate stocks for the cultivated apple (*121, 122*). Some of these, *Malus hupehensis, M. toringoides, M. sargenti,* and *M. sikkimensis,* are apomictic (see p. 43). These stocks are moderately hardy and are resistant to crown gall. *Malus sikkimensis* seems to be the most promising of this group. The seedlings are uniform (due to their apomictic character), and varieties worked on this stock are restricted in growth and start bearing at an early age. The seedlings are also resistant to powdery mildew *(Podosphaera leucotricha)* and the apple leaf hopper *(97).*

Clonal Rootstocks. There are numerous clonal, asexually propagated, apple rootstocks that have been developed for special purposes (*131*).

Northern Spy (72). This variety is resistant to woolly aphids (*Eriosoma lanigera*), an insect causing serious injury to apple trees by infesting the roots, particularly in areas with mild winters. By propagating Northern Spy nursery trees by layering (see p. 409) or by the nurse-root graft method (see p. 360) so that they are on their own roots, and then by working them to the desired variety, a woolly aphid-resistant tree can be obtained.

Because of its resistance to the woolly aphid, Northern Spy has been used to some extent as a rootstock, primarily in Australia and New Zealand. Results with seedlings as well as clonal selections of Northern Spy, however, have been generally unsatisfactory.

Hibernal. This is a very winter-hardy variety imported by the USDA from Russia in 1870. It has been widely used in the Midwestern states in developing the root, trunk, and primary scaffold system (or sometimes just the trunk and scaffold branches, a seedling root being used) where much of the winter injury occurs. After 1 to 3 years in the orchard, the Hibernal tree is topworked by budding or grafting to the desired variety (*153*). However, some orchards, particularly in the East and West Coast states, topworked on Hibernal roots have shown unfavorable symptoms, the trees being poorly shaped and unbalanced and leaning with the wind. It appears that the Hibernal clone has become mixed, other clones appearing in groups of stock trees which are supposedly the true Hibernal.

Robusta No. 5 (M. robusta [M. baccata × M. prunifolia], Cherry crabapple). This vigorous, very hardy clonal apple rootstock, propagated by layering or stem cuttings, was developed at the Central Experimental Farm, Ottawa, Canada. It is apparently resistant to fire blight and crown rot and it seems to be compatible with most apple varieties.

Virginia Crab. This stock originated as a chance seedling in a nursery in Iowa in 1862. It is propagated by vegetative methods in order to retain its desirable root and trunk characteristics. Virginia Crab is often used for the rootstock, trunk, and scaffold branches. It has a high resistance to at least one of the "collar rot" fungi (*Phytophthora cactorum*), is winter hardy, and grows vigorously with strong, wide-angled crotches (*93, 153*). It is usually topworked to the desired variety several years after setting in the orchard. Trees on this stock have often outyielded and have produced larger fruits than those on other roots (*96*). However, this stock has shown symptoms of incompatibility with certain varieties, resulting in dwarf trees, low vigor, premature bearing, small fruit, and abnormal longitudinal splits in the bark of the interstock. This behavior has been so erratic as to suggest the presence of a virus disease. Virginia Crab is not now considered a reliable stock for McIntosh,

Stayman Winesap, Rome Beauty or its sports, or for Clark Dwarf, Red Delicious, Golden Delicious, Grimes Golden, and perhaps others (*100, 150*).

Malling Series. Beginning in 1912, the East Malling Research Station in England selected and classified a series of sixteen vegetatively propagated apple rootstocks which ranged from very dwarfing to very invigorating in their effect on the scion variety. All these stocks are readily propagated by stool (mound) layering (*23*) and trench layering (see p. 409), and some by root cuttings (see p. 240) or hardwood cuttings (see p. 227). They apparently give completely compatible graft unions with most varieties. Trees on this series of rootstocks have been under trial, mostly on an experimental basis, for many years in America (*18*). Some, such as Malling IX, may be too dwarfing for the commercial apple grower. With the possible exception of Malling XVI, under American conditions they have not resulted in the increased tree uniformity over seedling rootstocks that was expected (*132, 152*). For the home gardener interested in dwarfed trees, Malling IX is of considerable value, whereas Malling II and VII deserve trials in commercial plantings (*19*). These stocks have proven to be winter hardy except in the extremely severe winters found in Minnesota and the Dakotas, and have done well on both heavy and light soils. All these stocks are susceptible to woolly aphid. A summary of the characteristics of the recommended rootstocks follows, grouped according to their effect on the vigor of the scion variety.

VERY DWARFING STOCKS. *Malling VIII (French Paradise, Clark Dwarf).* This is one of the most dwarfing of all the Malling stocks, but it is considered in England to be inferior to Malling IX, which has similar dwarfing characteristics. Trees on this stock require staking because the root system is weak and brittle and gives poor anchorage. It is best used as an intermediate stock, giving a dwarfing effect without the limitation of its weak, brittle root system. The amount of dwarfing seems to be proportional to the length of the interstock. It has been known in the United States for many years as Clark Dwarf (*16, 94*). This stock seems to be quite winter hardy.

Malling IX (Jaune de Metz). This originated as a chance seedling and was widely used in France and Germany as an apple rootstock. It is a valuable, very dwarfing rootstock much in demand for producing small trees for the home garden. Such trees are seldom over 6 feet tall when mature and usually start bearing in the first year or two after planting.

It has a weak root system with numerous thick, fibrous, brittle roots; the trees require staking for support. It is moderately hardy and resistant to

Figure 16–1. Dwarf growth habit of a 5-year-old Lane's Prince Albert apple on Malling IX rootstock. Courtesy Dept. of Pomology, Univ. of Calif.

crown rot (*Phytophthora*), but susceptible to crown gall. This stock seems to grow much better at relatively low soil temperatures (below about 60°F.) than at higher soil temperatures (*103*).

When used as an intermediate stock in double-working, (see p. 362) it will cause dwarfing of the scion variety but not as much as when it is used as the rootstock (*149*).

SEMI-DWARFING STOCKS. *Malling II (Doucin or English Paradise)*. This is the most commonly used apple understock in England. It is sometimes listed in the vigorous group. Trees on this stock tend to be vigorous and fruitful, come into bearing early, and have a spreading growth habit, but are slightly smaller than trees on seedling roots. It is moderately susceptible to crown gall, but quite resistant to crown rot. If the desired variety is budded high on this stock (3 or 4 inches above the soil level) so that the tree can be planted deeply, satisfactory root anchorage can be obtained. Malling II grows considerably better at low (below 60°F.) than at high soil temperatures (*103*). Trees are usually started by layering. This stock seems to tolerate excessively high or low soil moisture conditions better than any of the other Malling stocks.

Malling VII. This stock produces a tree somewhat larger than those on the very dwarfing Malling IX roots and may prove to be more suitable than IX as a stock for home fruit gardens in the United States. Malling VII has a stronger root system than IX and produces an early-bearing, semi-dwarf tree. It is tolerant of excessive soil moisture, but is susceptible to crown gall and crown rot. Malling VII seems to make good growth over a wide range of soil temperatures (*103*). Nursery trees are very winter hardy and are easily propagated by layering.

VIGOROUS STOCKS. *Malling I (Broad-leaved English Paradise)*. This originated in England as a chance seedling about 1860. It is a valuable rootstock, much in demand, but it is difficult to obtain, being mixed with other layered stocks. It is especially useful for weak varieties, poor soils, or severe winters. The onset of bearing is hastened for trees on this stock. It is quite susceptible to crown rot but somewhat resistant to crown gall. Malling I appears to make slightly better growth at low than at high soil temeratures (*103*). It is commonly propagated by layering, but can also be started by root cuttings and may be rooted by hardwood cuttings in sandy soils.

Malling I has not proven adaptable as a stock for certain American varieties for such reasons as breakage at the graft union and poor root anchorage (*5, 143, 151*), but it does seem particularly useful as a stock for the McIntosh and Delicious varieties.

Malling XIII (Doucin U 2). Trees on this stock are very vigorous when young but slow down as they grow older. They are intermediate in vigor between those on Malling I and XII. The trees have an erect growth habit, are well anchored, and tolerate heavy, wet soils, but fail completely on dry soils. Different scion varieties behave differently on this stock; it is almost semi-dwarfing with the Bramley's Seedling variety. It is well adapted for use with early-bearing varieties such as Golden Delicious and Cortland. It is very easily started by layering, root cuttings, and hardwood cuttings.

VERY VIGOROUS STOCKS. *Malling XII*. Trees on this rootstock are slow to come into bearing, are very strong growing, especially when young, and require wide spacing in the orchard. Fruit of varieties on this stock often have a poor color. It is not adapted to low soil moisture conditions. It produces a large, well-anchored tree of an erect growth habit, which spreads more as the tree grows older. It is somewhat resistant to crown gall and is rather difficult to propagate even by layering.

Malling XVI (*Ketziner's Ideal*). This is probably the best of the very vigorous group. Trees on this root are large and well anchored and will come into bearing sooner than those on seedling roots. Malling XVI seems to do well over a wide range of soil temperatures (*103*). It is usually propagated by layering but can also be started by root cuttings. In the United States, the Delicious and McIntosh varieties have performed exceptionally well on XVI (*132, 152*). Although this root is considered to produce very vigorous trees in England, in America such trees often do not reach the size of those propagated on seedling rootstocks.

Malling-Merton Series (*113, 114, 115*). Although the original Malling series of selected rootstocks has been widely used in propagating the apple throughout the world, even the recommended stocks have certain disadvantages, particularly their susceptibility to woolly aphids and their poor root anchorage.

The John Innes Horticultural Institution and the East Malling Research Station began work jointly in 1928 on breeding a new series of apple rootstocks to provide resistance to woolly aphids and to give a range in tree vigor. As a result of this work, five stocks were recommended for commercial trial in England. These are all highly resistant to woolly aphid, except one which had other such outstanding qualities that it was released but added to the original Malling series and named Malling XXV. Other improved tree characteristics associated with all these stocks include high yields, well anchored trees, freedom from the suckering habit, and good propagation qualities. The recommended stocks are listed below:

M.M. 104 (*Malling II × Northern Spy*). In England, trees on this stock have yielded heavy crops and have developed a strong root system. This is the easiest to propagate by layering of any in this group.

M.M. 106 (*Malling I × Northern Spy*). Trees on this stock are similar in size and yields to those on Northern Spy roots and on the semi-dwarfing Malling VII roots when grown on fertile loam soils. This stock produces a strong, well-anchored tree. On poorer sandy soils, the trees are smaller than those on VII, but larger than those on IX.

M.M. 109 (*Malling II × Northern Spy*). Trees on this stock are a little larger than those on Malling II, but the yields and root anchorage are about the same. It is propagated fairly easily by layering.

M.M. 111 (*Northern Spy × Merton 793* [*Malling II × Northern Spy*]). This root produces trees that are about the same size as the semi-dwarfing Malling II, but which yield heavier crops. If this stock is used instead of Malling II, larger crops may be expected from the same orchard area. It is fairly easy to propagate by layering.

Malling XXV (*Malling II × Northern Spy*). Although this is not as highly resistant to woolly aphids as the Malling-Merton stocks, it is more resistant than Malling XVI. It produces large, vigorous trees, induces early fruit bud formation, and gives excellent fruit set and yields. It is the most difficult of any in this group to propagate by layering.

Apricot (*Prunus armeniaca* L.). Apricot varieties are propagated commercially by T-budding (see p. 382) on various seedling rootstocks in the genus *Prunus*. Fall budding is the usual practice, but spring and June budding may be used (see p. 374).

Rootstocks for Apricot Varieties. Three stocks are commercially suitable for apricots—apricot seedlings, peach seedlings, and in some cases, myrobalan plum seedlings. Seeds of all these species require a low temperature (32° to 45° F.) stratification period (see p. 127) before planting in the spring—3 to 4 weeks for the apricot and about 3 months for the peach and myrobalan plum.

Apricot (P. armeniaca). Apricot seeds may be obtained from drying yards and canneries. Seeds of the Royal or Blenheim varieties produce excellent rootstock seedlings in California. Since the apricot root is almost immune to the root-knot nematode (*Meloidogyne* sp.), it should be used where this pest is present. It is also somewhat resistant to crown rot (*Phytophthora* sp.), but it is not tolerant of poor soil drainage conditions. Apricot roots are not as susceptible to crown gall (*Agrobacterium tumefaciens*), as are peach and plum roots.

Peach (P. persica). Seeds of the Lovell variety are usually used. Peach makes an entirely satisfactory rootstock for the apricot, but sometimes the union is enlarged or rough. Although the peach itself is short-lived, apricot trees 85 years old growing satisfactorily on peach roots are known. In unirrigated orchards or where drought conditions prevail, apricots on peach roots make better growth than those on apricot roots. Peach roots are not tolerant of wet soils, growing better on light or well-drained soils. If the trees are to be planted in a location formerly occupied by peaches, some stock other than peach should be used, because peach roots often grow poorly on soils formerly occupied by peach roots.

Myrobalan plum (P. cerasifera). Although there are successful apricot orchards grown on this rootstock, it cannot be unqualifiedly recommended. There are a few instances where the trees have broken off at the graft union in heavy winds, and die-back conditions have been noted. Nurserymen often have trouble getting apricots started on myrobalan roots, some of the trees failing to grow rapidly and upright or else having weak or rough unions. After these weaker trees are culled out, the remaining ones seem to grow satisfactorily. In older trees of this combination, the myrobalan root usually grows much larger than the apricot trunk, giving a "churn bottom" tree. The only time this stock is used for the apricot is when the trees are to be planted in heavy soils or under excessive soil moisture conditions, which the myrobalan root will tolerate. Rather than myrobalan plum seedlings, the related vegetatively propagated Marianna 2624 plum (see p. 490) may be used, on which apricots seem to do well.

Western sand cherry (P. besseyi). Although it is not used commercially, this rootstock will produce a semi-dwarf tree.

Asimina triloba. See Papaw.

Avocado *(Persea* sp.) *(80).* Nursery trees of the avocado are propagated commercially in California by T-budding and tip grafting avocado seedlings. In Florida and some of the Caribbean countries T-budding is occasionally done, but the usual nursery practice is to graft rather tender tip (terminal) scions, either as side grafts (see p. 325)—or sometimes the side-veneer (see p. 330)—or cleft grafts (see p. 331) on young succulent seedlings *(146, 159).* In South Africa, whip or tongue grafting (see p. 322) when the seedlings are ¼ inch in diameter is recommended. The grafted trees are raised in containers from which they are transplanted into the orchard *(92).*

The seeds for rootstocks are generally planted shortly after removal from the fruit, care being taken not to allow them to dry out. They can be stored for several months at 40° F. in dry peat moss if necessary, but it is better to use fresh seeds. Germination is hastened by removing the brown seed coats or by cutting a thin slice off the seed before planting. The seed coats can be removed by wetting the seeds and allowing them to dry in the sun. If the Mexican race is used, which ripens its fruit in the fall, the seeds may be planted in beds in October, November, or December. The sprouted seeds are lined-out in the nursery row the following March or April. The seeds should be planted with the large, basal end down, just deep enough to cover the tips. By fall, the seedlings will usually be large enough to permit T-budding; if not, they can be budded the following spring.

It is very important to select the budwood properly. The best buds are usually near the terminal ends of completed growth cycles with fully matured, leathery leaves. The leaves should be removed immediately when the budwood is taken to prevent drying.

In 4 to 6 weeks after budding, the seedling rootstocks should be cut off 8 to 10 inches above the bud or bent over a few inches above the bud. The remaining portion of the seedling above the bud is not cut off until the bud

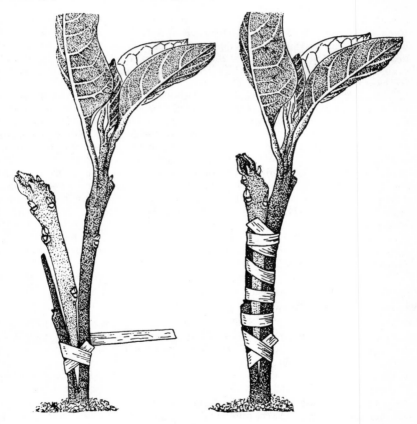

Figure 16–2. Side grafting the avocado. **(right)** Graft completed and tied with a rubber strip. Under Florida conditions no further protection is ordinarily used but under dry air conditions wrapping with vinyl plastic tape may be necessary. Courtesy S. J. Lynch and Dorothy Allen.

shoots have completed a cycle of growth. The new shoots are usually staked and tied. In digging, the nursery trees are usually "balled and burlapped" for removal to their permanent location. This is done just following the first or second growth cycle of the bud or sometimes just as the first flush starts.

The seedlings are sometimes grown in soil in containers made from 12 by 16 inch sheets of felt building paper, each stapled to form an open end cylinder. Following grafting, the trees can be planted directly in their permanent location in a prepared hole by slitting and removing the paper container.

Tip grafting is used by some nurserymen. It requires the use of a greenhouse or some similar structure. Open-bottom paper pots about 6 inches in diameter and 12 inches deep are set in greenhouse benches and filled with soil. One seed is planted in each pot in the fall and by January or February the seedlings are large enough to graft. The whip graft method (see p. 322) is used. The scion consists of a single-budded shoot about an inch long which is grafted near the base of each seedling. The scions are tied with rubber or plastic budding tape. The grafted trees are ready to set out in their permanent location at the end of their first growth cycle, which is about 3 months after grafting.

In Florida, side grafting on young, succulent West Indian seedlings is used as shown in Figure 16-2 (87). The seedlings, grown in gallon containers, are grafted when they are 6 to 10 inches high and ¼ to ⅜ inch in diameter. The scions are shoot terminals, 2 to 3 inches long with a plump terminal bud, taken just as it resumes growth.

Stem cuttings of young Mexican and Guatemalan avocado seedlings can be rooted (38), and cuttings taken from mature Mexican and Fuerte trees have also been rooted (50, 51), but with more difficulty. It is very difficult to root cuttings taken from mature trees of the Guatemalan race. Such cuttings can be rooted if the basal portion of the leafy shoot to be made into the cutting is etiolated; that is, allowed to grow only in complete darkness. The terminal portion of such a shoot develops in the light until 3 to 5 leaves have formed. Those shoots with etiolated bases can then be detached and rooted in a propagating case (42).

ROOTSTOCKS FOR AVOCADO VARIETIES. *Mexican race* (*P. drymifolia*). Seedlings of this race are preferred in California due to their cold-hardiness and their resistance to lime chlorosis and the diseases *Dothiorella* and *Verticillium*. The seeds are also available in the fall when they are needed for germination. In Florida, where seedlings of large diameter are preferred for grafting, the Mexican types are little used, due to their thin shoots.

Guatemalan race (*P. americana*). These are occasionally used in California when there is a scarcity of Mexican seeds. Guatemalan seedlings are often initially more vigorous than Mexican seedlings.

West Indian race (*P. americana*). These seedlings are too liable to frost injury to be used commercially under California conditions but are often used in Florida. The large seed produces a large, pencil-sized shoot suitable for side grafting in 2 to 4 weeks after germination.

West Indian × *Guatemalan hybrids.* Seedlings of this hybrid are occasionally used in Florida.

Banana (*Musa* sp.) (*112*). The banana "tree" is not a tree at all but a large perennial herb. The "stem" is not a stem but compressed, curved leaf stalk bases arranged spirally in strips. The bases of the leaf stalks are attached to the true stem, a rhizome (a horizontal, underground stem—see p. 445). New "suckers" grow from buds on the rhizome and soon develop their own roots and a base as large as the parent plant, which dies and deteriorates shortly after the fruit bunch is harvested. A banana planting may live for a considerable time but it really is a succession of new plants, each arising as a sucker from a rhizomatous bud; any given sucker fruits only once, then dies.

Since the best varieties do not produce seeds, commercial propagation of the banana plant is entirely asexual, consisting essentially of division of the rhizome and replanting the pieces or the suckers. A large rhizome is cut into pieces weighing 3 to 10 pounds, depending on the variety, which are termed "heads." These should contain at least two buds capable of growing into suckers. Each sucker produces two branches in the first crop. Fairly large "sword" suckers 3 to 6 feet high with well-developed roots are also used, but the leaves must be shortened considerably to reduce water loss after the sucker is cut from the parent plant. These suckers are removed with a sharp cutting tool inserted vertically about half way between the parent stalk and stem of the sucker. These sword suckers only produce one bunch of fruit in the first crop, but they are often preferred due to the large size of the bunch.

Blackberry (*Rubus* sp.). The upright type of blackberry produces suckers readily, its propagation consisting of digging up a sucker with an attached root piece during early spring and replanting it in a new location. The suckers are often grown an additional year in the nursery row to develop stronger plants before being set out in a new planting (see p. 417).

The trailing type of blackberry, such as the youngberry, boysenberry, loganberry, or dewberry, does not produce many suckers. This type is propagated by tip layering (see p. 402).

All blackberries can be propagated by root cuttings, but some thornless forms, such as the thornless youngberry and thornless loganberry, revert to the thorny type if propagated in this manner (see p. 168).

Both the upright and trailing types of blackberries may be started easily by leaf-bud cuttings (see p. 239) taken from succulent, leafy shoots in the spring and rooted under high humidity, particularly in mist propagating beds (see p. 251). Treatment of such cuttings with root-promoting chemicals is beneficial.

Blueberry, Highbush (*Vaccinium corymbosum* L.) *(32, 36, 129)*. Stem cuttings, both dormant hardwood and leafy softwood, are commonly used. The blueberry can also be started by leaf-bud cuttings. Softwood cuttings are probably easier to root than the hardwood type, but are little used commercially. Most blueberry cuttings are grown in nursery rows for 1 year after the year of rooting and then sold as 2-year plants for setting in their permanent location.

Blueberry varieties can also be propagated by T-budding to seedling plants or to rooted cuttings. In addition, older plants can be divided.

HARDWOOD CUTTINGS. The blueberry is difficult to propagate by hardwood cuttings, but with care very good results can be obtained. The cutting material should be taken from dormant plants in late winter or early spring before the buds start to swell. It should consist of vigorous, firm, unbranched shoots of the previous season's growth, about the size of a pencil. Only vegetative wood, without fruit buds, should be used. The cuttings should contain three or four buds and be 4 to 5 inches long.

Glass covered frames in a lathhouse, or otherwise protected from the full sun, are suitable rooting structures. Bottom heat is very helpful, but root-promoting chemicals have generally failed to improve rooting. A mixture of half sand and half peat moss is a satisfactory rooting medium.

Cuttings should be spaced about 2 inches apart in the rooting bed and set with the top bud just showing. When leaves appear, the glass frame should be raised slightly to allow for ventilation. Watering must be frequent enough to maintain a high humidity. Roots should start to form after about 2 months.

SOFTWOOD CUTTINGS. These are leafy cuttings made during the growing season from lateral shoots about 6 inches long which are still growing actively but with the basal portion firm. These are made as heel cuttings with a portion of the old wood attached. It is very important that such cuttings be rooted under high humidity conditions.

Rooted blueberry cuttings are best handled by allowing them to remain in the rooting frame until early the following spring when they are lined-out in the nursery row. Fertilizing the cutting beds with nitrogen (see p. 32) after roots start forming will produce larger and thriftier plants.

Cacao (*Theobroma cacao* L.). Almost all established commercial cacao plantings consist of seedling trees, which are highly variable in their characteristics. Cacao can be propagated vegetatively, however, and with the development of new, superior clones and the use of modern techniques for rooting softwood cuttings, it is likely, especially in the West Indies and Central America, that in the future more vegetatively-propagated plantings will be made.

In the large cacao-producing areas of West Africa and South America, however, emphasis is on seedling propagation with seed taken from selected clonal material. Vegetative propagation is used to produce the seed bearers. Cross-pollination between high yielding clones and the use of the resultant seeds to produce bearing trees is becoming an important propagation method in these countries.

SEEDLING PROPAGATION. Freshly harvested seeds are usually planted immediately, but they can be stored for a time at 60° to 70°F. if necessary. Lower storage temperatures are harmful. A common practice is to plant three or four seeds in a hole. If they all germinate they are allowed to grow, treating the plants as branches of one tree. Another method is to start the seedlings in a nursery bed and transplant the small trees to their permanent location; or the seedlings may be started in baskets, bamboo or paper cyclinders, or clay pots, from which they are removed later and planted.

ASEXUAL PROPAGATION. After the young seedling trees have attained sufficient size, they can be used as rootstocks on which superior clones are budded. The patch bud (see p. 386) is most successful, but T-budding (see p. 382) may be used *(25)*. In areas where unfavorable soil conditions occur, superior clones are sometimes grafted on specially selected resistant clonal rootstocks. In the entire world industry, however, budding and grafting is done on only a negligible scale.

Hardwood stem cuttings and root cuttings have generally been unsuccessful, but satisfactory methods of rooting leafy softwood cuttings have been developed and may become an important commercial propagation method *(25, 39, 40)*.

Carica papaya. See Papaya.

Carya illinoensis. See Pecan.

Carya ovata. See Hickory.

Cashew (*Anacardium occidentale* L.). This is generally propagated by seeds which germinate readily in 3 to 4 weeks. The seedlings are started in beds and are transferred to the orchard when they are 4 or 5 inches tall. Several seedlings may be planted in one position and thinned to one plant after they become well established. Although not done commercially, the cashew can also be propagated by rooting leafy cuttings under glass, or by air layering.

Castanea mollissima. See Chestnut, Chinese.

Cherimoya (*Annona cherimola* Mill.). This is propagated by cleft grafting or T-budding selected varieties on cherimoya seedlings or on seedlings of the related sugar apple (*Annona squamosa*), which gives a dwarf plant, or on custard apple (*Annona reticulata*). These latter two species should not be used as rootstocks in cold areas or on poorly drained soils where they are subject to root rot.

Some of the seedling forms developed in Mexico and parts of South America are said to come nearly true from seed, and in many regions seed propagation is used exclusively. The seeds will retain their viability for many years if kept dry, but will germinate in a few weeks after planting. After the young seedlings are 3 or 4 inches high, they should be transferred from flats to small pots, and when they are about 8 inches high, moved to larger pots or to the open ground.

Cherry (*Prunus avium* L., *P. cerasus* L.) *(27, 95, 111)*. Cherry nursery trees are generally propagated by T-budding (see p. 382) the desired variety on a seedling rootstock. The rootstock seedlings are often grown closely planted in a seed bed for one year, then the seedlings are lined-out about 4 inches apart in the nursery row and grown a second year before budding. If growing conditions are good, however, the seeds may be planted directly in the nursery row in early spring, and the seedlings will become large enough for budding by late summer or early fall of the same season.

ROOTSTOCKS FOR CHERRY VARIETIES *(34)*. The two most common stocks are Mazzard (*Prunus avium*) and Mahaleb (*P. mahaleb*). A third stock, the vegetatively propagated Stockton Morello (*P. cerasus*) is occasionally used. These three rootstocks are used for sweet cherry (*P. avium*) varieties. Sour cherry (*P. cerasus*) and Duke cherry (hybrids between sweet and sour cherries) varieties are propagated on both Mazzard and Mahaleb roots.

Mazzard (*P. avium*). Mazzard seedlings used in the United States were formerly imported from Europe, but for many years they have been available from domestic sources, largely in Oregon and Washington. There is considerable variation among the sources of Mazzard seeds, some undoubtedly being better than others. In England, where this is the most common cherry stock, vegetatively propagated clonal rootstocks—such as the bacterial canker-resistant F 12/1—have been developed *(48)*. These are propagated by trench layering (see p. 411).

Mazzard seeds require a stratification period (see p. 127) of about 100 days at 35° to 40°F.

Sweet cherry varieties make an excellent graft union with Mazzard roots. Trees on this stock are vigorous and long-lived, but under ideal conditions they often become so large that harvesting costs may be excessive. Mazzard roots are not particularly suitable for heavy, poorly-aerated, wet soils, but will tolerate such conditions better than Mahaleb. Under dry, unirrigated, drought conditions Mahaleb is more likely to survive than Mazzard, presumably due to the deep, vertical rooting habit of Mahaleb in contrast to Mazzard's shallow, horizontal root system. Mazzard is semi-resistant to oak root fungus (*Armillaria mellea*), whereas Mahaleb and Stockton Morello are quite susceptible.

Mahaleb (*P. mahaleb*). The seeds require stratification (see p. 127) for about 100 days at 35° to 40°F. Mahaleb is less subject to defoliation in the nursery row by leaf spot fungus (*Coccomyces hiemalis*) and usually gives a higher percentage of bud "takes" than Mazzard stocks. The graft union between cherry varieties and Mahaleb roots is strong but not as smooth as with Mazzard roots.

It is often believed that Mahaleb roots produce a somewhat dwarfed tree, but there is evidence that in good soils the trees will become just as large as those on Mazzard roots. Mahaleb-rooted trees cannot be grown satisfactorily where heavy, wet soils with high water tables occur, being more suitable for sandy, well-drained areas. This rootstock should be used where nonirrigation or drought conditions prevail. Trees on Mahaleb roots have more cold-hardiness than those on Mazzard or Stockton Morello. Sweet cherries on Mahaleb often grow faster for the first few years than on Mazzard roots, and some varieties start heavy bearing rather early, which may result in some dwarfing of the tree. Although there is evidence, especially in England, that trees on Mahaleb roots are relatively short-lived, in the United States good, productive trees over 50 years old on this rootstock are known. Mahaleb roots give the trees more resistance to the buckskin virus disease than Mazzard, but they are more subject to injury from root-knot nematodes and gophers than Mazzard. Mahaleb roots, however, are distinctly more resistant to the lesion, or meadow nematode (*Pratylenchus vulnus*), than are Mazzard or Stockton Morello roots and should be used where this pest is prevalent *(35)*.

Stockton Morello (*P. cerasus*). This clonal stock is particularly useful for growing cherries in heavy, wet soils or for producing semi-dwarf trees. It is propagated by suckers arising under trees worked on this stock. All sweet cherry varieties tend to overgrow the Stockton Morello root at the graft union, but the union is strong. The Chapman variety is reported to be incompatible with Stockton Morello, requiring the use of an intermediate stock.

Stockton Morello (and Mahaleb) rootstocks can be propagated by leafy softwood cuttings using intermittent mist and root-promoting chemicals (see p. 244). Cuttings should be made in the spring of current season's growth, 8 to 12 inches long, when they have attained some degree of maturity, but *while they are still actively growing*. In preparing the cuttings, the terminal growing point should be included to obtain satisfactory rooting.

Chestnut, Chinese (*Castanea mollissima* Blume.) *(59)*. This species has in the past been propagated only by seed, many orchards consisting entirely of seedling trees. Improved selections have been made, however, and named clonal varieties are available.

Chestnut seeds should be prevented from drying, because this quickly destroys their capacity to germinate. The nuts should be gathered as soon as they drop and either be planted in the fall or kept in moist storage over winter for spring planting. Seed nuts are satisfactorily stored in tight tin cans, with only one or two very small holes for ventilation, at 32°F. or slightly higher *(99)*. Weevils in the nuts, which will destroy the embryo, can be killed by a hot water treatment at 120°F. for 30 minutes.

After one year's growth, the seedlings should be large enough to transplant to their permanent location or be grafted to the desired variety *(110)*.

Although the chestnut is difficult to graft or bud, bark grafting (see p. 336) and inverted T-budding (see p. 385) have given very good results. In regular T-budding, the buds tend to "drown" due to excessive bleeding. The splice graft (which is similar to the whip graft except that no tongue is made) has been widely used with chestnuts.

The seedling rootstock should be pure *C. mollissima* if a permanently successful graft union is to be obtained. It is likely that many of the graft union failures are due to the use of hybrid seedling rootstocks. In grafted trees, the union sometimes becomes defective and the tree dies, even after it has been in bearing for some years *(117)*.

Softwood cuttings rooted under mist (see p. 251) with the use of root-promoting chemicals may offer possibilities for propagating selected varieties without the difficulties encountered in grafting *(109)*. The subsequent behavior of such trees on their own roots is not known, however.

Citrus (*Citrus* sp.) *(8, 22, 76, 81, 107)*. The various citrus species are propagated by the same methods. The members of this genus are readily inter-grafted and can also be grafted to other closely related genera such as *Fortunella* (kumquat) and *Poncirus* (trifoliate orange). Citrus varieties are propagated commercially by T-budding (see p. 382) on seedling rootstocks.

Many of the citrus species can be propagated by rooting leafy cuttings, although nursery trees are not commonly propagated in this manner, since such trees on their own roots have no particular advantages and in some cases are distinctly inferior to those worked on seedling stocks *(53)*.

In Florida, the Persian lime (*C. aurantifolia*) is propagated to some extent by air layering (see p. 406).

Although not used commercially probably the most rapid method of obtaining a citrus variety worked on a given rootstock is by the use of "twig-graft cuttings" *(52, 54)*. Two small, leafy shoots—one the scion and one the rootstock—several inches long, such as would be used for cuttings, are grafted together using the whip or tongue graft (see p. 322). Leaves are left attached to both parts of the graft and the union wrapped with tape. Development of roots is hastened if the base of the cutting is treated with a root-promoting solution (see p. 244). The twig-graft cuttings are then inserted in a rooting medium and placed under high humidity such as a mist propagating bed (see p. 251).

GROWING CITRUS NURSERY STOCK. It is important to avoid using soils infested with citrus nematodes (*Tylenchulus semipenetrans*) or soil-borne diseases. It is preferable to use virgin soil or at least a soil that has not been formerly planted to citrus. For small operations, raised seed-beds enclosed by 12 inch boards can be used. A soil mixture of ¾ sandy loam and ¼ peat moss is satisfactory. Treating the soil with a fumigant such as DD (dichloropropane-dichloropropene) at the rate of 700 to 1000 lbs. per acre will insure against nematode infestations. Planting should be delayed for 6 to 8 weeks to allow the fumigant to dissipate. The seed-bed should be in a lathhouse, or some other provision should be made for screening the young seedlings from the full sun.

Since there is considerable variation in the performance of seedlings taken from different trees, it is best to select the seeds from healthy, virus-free, old trees which have a history of producing vigorous, uniform seedlings and which result in satisfactory nursery trees after being budded to the desired variety.

Citrus seeds generally have no dormancy conditions but are injured by being allowed to dry; they should, therefore, be planted immediately after being extracted from the ripe fruit. Certain species, such as the trifoliate orange or its hybrids, mature their fruits in the fall. If the seeds are to be planted at that time they should be held in moist storage between 30° and 40°F. for at least a week before planting. The seeds may be stored until spring under low temperature (40°F.) and high humidity conditions.

The best time to plant the seed is in the spring after the soil has warmed up—above 60°F. Soaking the seed in water for at least 24 hours before planting promotes germination. The seeds should be planted in rows 2 to 3 inches apart, 1 inch apart in the row. They are pressed lightly in the soil and covered with a ½ to ¾ inch layer of clean, sharp river sand. This prevents crusting and aids in the control of "damping off" fungi. To further aid in controlling these organisms apply aluminum sulfate to the surface of the seed-bed just before the seeds are planted at the rate of 1¼ ounces per square foot. The material may be either scattered over the surface and raked in or dissolved in water and sprinkled over the seed-bed. The soil should be kept moist at all times until the seedlings emerge. Either extreme, allowing the soil to become dry and baked or overly soggy, should be avoided. Electric soil-heating cables (see p. 18) below the seed-bed to maintain a soil temperature of 80° to 85°F. will hasten germination. By this method, seeds may be planted in the winter months and the seedlings will be large enough to line-out in the nursery that spring. Many can be budded by fall or the following spring. This will often shorten the propagation time by 6 to 12 months.

After the seedlings are 8 to 12 inches tall, they are ready to be transplanted from the seed-bed to the nursery row. This is best done in the spring after danger of frost has passed. The seedlings are dug with a spading fork after the soil has been wet thoroughly to a depth of 18 inches. They can then be loosened and removed with little danger of root injury. All stunted seedlings or those with crooked, misshapen roots should be discarded.

The nursery site should be in a frost-free, weed-free location on a light clay loam soil at least 24 inches deep and with irrigation water available. Old citrus soils should be avoided unless it is heavily fumigated with DD before planting. The seedlings should be planted at the same depth that they were in the seed-bed and spaced about 12 inches apart in four foot rows.

Citrus seedlings are usually budded in the spring following transplanting to the nursery row. Fall budding, sometimes done in California, is started in mid-September, early enough so that warm weather will insure a good bud union, yet late enough so that bud growth does not start.

Budwood should be taken only from known high-producing, disease-free trees. It is desirable to select the budsticks from a single tree, avoiding any off-type "sporting" branches. The best type of budwood is that next to the last flush of growth, or the last flush after the growth hardens. A round budstick will give more good buds than an angular one. The best buds are those

Figure 16–3. Budded citrus seedlings are often "lopped over" just above the inserted bud. This forces the bud into growth yet the top continues to provide nourishment for the plant. Courtesy Dept. of Pomology, Univ. of Calif.

in the axils of large leaves. The budsticks are usually cut at the time of budding, the leaves removed, and protected against drying. Budsticks may be stored for several weeks if kept moist and held under refrigeration at 40° to 50°F.

The T-bud method (see p. 382) is very successful with citrus, the bud piece being cut to include a sliver of wood beneath the bud. Fall buds are unwrapped in 6 to 8 weeks after budding—spring buds in about 3 weeks.

Buds inserted in the fall are forced into growth in the spring by "lopping" the top of the seedlings 2 or 3 inches above the bud. This is done just before spring growth starts and consists of partly severing the top, allowing it to fall over on the ground. The top thus continues to nourish the seedling roots, but the bud is forced into growth. Lopping of spring buds is done when the bud wraps are removed—about 3 weeks after budding. If possible the "lops" should be left until late summer, at which time they are cut off just above the bud union. Although lopping is satisfactory, it makes irrigation and cultivation difficult. An alternative practice is to first cut the seedling completely off 12 to 14 inches above the bud, then later cut it back immediately above the bud.

Young citrus nursery trees may be dug "balled and burlapped" or bare root. Bare-rooted trees should be defoliated and whitewashed before digging. Transplanting of such trees is best done in early spring, but balled trees can be moved any time during the spring before hot weather starts.

A marked variation occurs among the several citrus species in regard to the vigor and growth habit of their seedlings. Sweet orange and grapefruit seedlings are somewhat bushy and difficult to handle, as are those of the Sampson tangelo which are also slow growing. Rough lemon, sour orange, Cleopatra mandarin, and Troyer citrange seedlings are vigorous, rapid growers with a uniform, upright growth habit which makes them easy to use.

Polyembryony (see p. 45) frequently occurs in citrus seeds. The sexual seedling is often weak and makes a poor rootstock. The other seedlings arising from the nucellus are entirely asexual and have the same characteristics as the seed-bearing plant. Consequently, they are very uniform and make good rootstocks if the parent tree is desirable. Nucellar seedlings are vigorous, thorny, upright-growing, but slow to start bearing if used as an orchard tree. These undesirable qualities (thorniness and delayed bearing) are less pronounced in nursery trees propagated from the nucellar seedling itself. Such trees are free from the usual citrus virus diseases. Nucellar varieties have been developed for all the commercial citrus varieties and are promising due to their increased vigor, tree size, and yields (21).

ROOTSTOCKS FOR CITRUS. (12, 83). *Sweet orange (C. sinensis)*. In California this is the most commonly used citrus rootstock, and it is considered to be excellent for all commercial citrus varieties, producing large, vigorous trees. It is adapted to well-drained, light to medium loam soils, but due to its susceptibility to gummosis (*Phytophthora* sp.), it is not suited to poorly-drained, heavy soils. It tends to produce smaller fruits than some of the other stocks, but the fruits are thin-skinned, juicy, and of high quality. The seeds, which are 70 to 90 per cent nucellar, germinate readily, but the seedlings are relatively slow growers and tend to produce low-branched, bushy trunks.

Sour orange (C. aurantium). This stock was long considered to be excellent for most citrus species due to its vigor, hardiness, deep root system, resistance to gummosis diseases, and to the high quality, smooth, thin-skinned, and juicy fruit produced by varieties worked on it. However, it has been found that sweet orange varieties on sour orange roots are affected by a disease long prevalent in Java and South Africa and later known as the "bud union decline" in Australia, "tristeza" disease in Argentina and Brazil, and orange "quick decline" in California *(13, 55)*. This is a virus disease transmitted by an insect vector or by using infected budwood. The sweet orange top is itself tolerant to the virus, but in combination with sour orange root the stock is affected due to death of the phloem tissues in the bud union area which then results in starvation of the root. Grapefruit as well as orange varieties on sour orange roots are subject to quick decline. *Sour orange is no longer recommended as a rootstock for orange or grapefruit varieties.*

Rough lemon (C. limon). This stock is widely used in Florida since the advent of the tristeza disease, but it is not recommended for general use in California, although it has been satisfactory for oranges in the lighter soil types of the desert regions. In California the vigor of this stock causes the tree and the fruit to grow rapidly, but the trees tend to be short lived. Both the trees and their fruits on this stock are more susceptible to cold injury than those on other commonly used rootstocks. Fruit from trees on Rough lemon roots are early maturing, but have a thick rind and are low in both sugar and acid and are often coarse textured. The Valencia orange on this stock tends to produce granulated fruits of low juice content. Rough lemon is easily propagated—numerous seeds are produced which germinate well. Ninety to 100 per cent of the seedlings are nucellar. They are upright growing with single, unbranched trunks which are easy to bud and handle in the nursery. The Rough lemon also can be easily propagated by cuttings. Sweet orange varieties are tolerant to quick decline when worked on Rough lemon roots. The chief advantages of this stock are its vigor and its ability to produce a bearing tree quickly, particularly on light sandy soils.

Grapefruit (C. paradisi). This has been used occasionally as a rootstock, especially for lemons, with conflicting reports on its behavior. Good quality fruits of excellent size are produced on this stock, but the trees require liberal fertilization. It is unsatisfactory for light, sandy soils and is less cold resistant than sour orange and sweet orange. Because sweet orange on this stock is susceptible to quick decline and production is variable, grapefruit finds limited use as a rootstock.

Trifoliate orange (Poncirus trifoliata). This dwarfing citrus rootstock has been used to some extent for many years. In Florida, it has long been used as a stock for Satsuma oranges and kumquats, for which it is excellent. The dwarfing effect has been variable, however, due perhaps to the use of genetically different clones. Dwarfing has been particularly marked with lemon and grapefruit varieties. Trifoliate orange is commonly used as a stock for ornamental citrus varieties and in home orchards for dwarfed trees. Trees on this stock yield heavily and produce high quality fruits, although they are somewhat small in size. Trifoliate orange is a deciduous species noted for its winter hardiness and nematode resistance. Both the tree and its fruits when worked on this stock are more resistant to cold than other rootstock-top combinations, making it particularly adaptable to the colder citrus growing regions. A citrus variety worked on trifoliate orange is one of the few examples of an evergreen top on a deciduous rootstock.

Trees on trifoliate roots are often affected by exocortis or "scaly butt." This may be overcome by careful selection of better varieties of trifoliate orange for seed and by using uncontaminated nucellar buds or by taking buds from trees on trifoliate stock that are free of the disease and show no indication of stunted growth. This stock is quite resistant to gummosis, but it is very susceptible to citrus canker (*Phytomonas citri*) and moderately so to scab. Eureka lemon is reported to develop a graft union disorder when worked on this stock.

Trifoliate orange fruits produce large numbers of plump seeds which germinate easily.˙ The upright-growing, thorny seedlings, about 70 per cent of which are nucellar, are easy to bud and handle in the nursery, but their slow growth often necessitates an extra year in the nursery before salable trees are produced.

Mandarin (C. reticulata). The Cleopatra mandarin is widely used as a citrus rootstock in some localities, particularly in Florida, and is coming into greater use in California and Texas as a replacement for sour orange *(9).* Its resistance to gummosis, compatibility with most citrus varieties, salt tolerance, and resistance to the quick decline virus seemingly justifies its greater use. In addition, trees on this stock show good yields of high quality fruits. Its chief disadvantages are the slow growth of the seedlings, slowness in coming into bearing, and susceptibility to *Phytophthora* root rot. From 80 to 100 per cent of the seedlings are nucellar.

Citrange (trifoliate orange × sweet orange) hybrids. This stock is believed, both in California and Florida, to be promising. There are several named varieties—Savage, Morton, and Troyer.

Savage is especially suitable as a dwarfing stock for grapefruit and is also satisfactory for the mandarins. It is resistant to gummosis, and trees on this stock are more cold hardy than when the conventional stocks are used *(11).*

Morton citrange is not particularly dwarfing. Trees worked on it are very heavy producers of excellent quality fruits. It produces so few seeds, however, that it is difficult to get quantities of nursery trees started; in addition, orange varieties on this stock appear to be susceptible to quick decline.

Sweet orange on Troyer citrange is vigorous, cold hardy, resistant to gummosis, and produces high quality fruit. In replanting citrus on old citrus soils, trees on the Troyer citrange have shown outstanding vigor in comparison with other stocks *(9).* Troyer is relatively fruitful and produces 15 to 20 plump seeds per fruit, facilitating the propagation of nursery trees. It is also readily propagated by leafy cuttings, especially if they are taken from young, vigorous trees and root-promoting chemicals are used *(106).* Troyer is not generally recommended as a stock for lemons, particularly the Eureka variety *(154).* As other citrus rootstocks, it is not adaptable to soils with a high salt content or where the irrigation water is high in boron *(14).*

Seedlings of most citrange varieties are almost entirely nucellar and develop strong single trunks, easily handled in the nursery. As with trifoliate orange, only exocortis-free buds should be used on citrange rootstocks; otherwise, dwarfing—and eventual low production—will result.

Coconut *(Cocos nucifera* L.). The trees are propagated entirely by seed. There are some named seedling varieties which reproduce their characteristics quite dependably. It is important to select seeds from trees that produce large crops of high quality nuts.

The nuts are usually germinated in seed-beds. Those that germinate rapidly and have strong, vigorous shoots are selected. The nuts, still in the husk or hull, are set at least 12 inches apart in the bed, and laid on their sides with the stem end containing the "eyes" slightly raised. The sprout emerges through the eye on the side that has the longest part of the triangular hull. As soon as this occurs (about a month after planting), the sprout sends roots downward through the hull and into the soil.

Cocos nucifera. See Coconut.

Coffee (*Coffea arabica* L.). The most common method of propagation is by seed, preferably obtained from selected superior trees. Coffee seeds can be stored for several months in sand in a cool place. They are usually planted in seed beds under shade. Germination takes place in 6 to 7 weeks. When the seedlings have their first pair of true leaves, they are transplanted to the nursery row and set 12 inches apart. After about 18 months, when they have formed 6 to 8 pairs of laterals, the young trees are ready to set out in the plantation.

Coffee can be propagated asexually by almost all methods, but leafy cuttings probably hold the most promise for commercial practice. The cutting material should be taken only from upright-growing shoots in order to produce the desired type of upright-growing tree.

Leafy cuttings of partially hardened wood can be rooted fairly easily, especially if treated with root-promoting chemical (see p. 244). High humidity conditions, such as those obtained in a mist propagator (see p. 251), must be maintained, and the cuttings should be kept partially shaded *(49)*.

Corylus avellana. See Filbert.

Crabapple. Siberian crabapple (*Malus baccata* Borkh.), Western crabapple (*M. ioensis* Britt.), and other *Malus* species. The usual propagation method is to bud or graft the desired varieties on seedling rootstocks, either one of the crabapple species or the common apple, *Malus sylvestris*. In areas where winter hardiness is important, *M. baccata* seedlings should be used.

Crabapples can be propagated, although with difficulty, by softwood or hardwood cuttings, especially if root-promoting chemicals are used.

Cranberry (*Vaccinium macrocarpon* Ait.). This vine type of evergreen plant produces trailing runners upon which are numerous upright branches. Propagation is by cuttings made from both the runners and upright branches. The cutting material is obtained by mowing the vines in early spring before new growth has started. The cuttings are then set in April or May directly in place in their permanent location without previous rooting at distances of 6 to 18 inches apart each way. Two to four cuttings are set in sand in each "hill." The cuttings are 5 to 10 inches long and set deep enough so that only an inch is above ground. A more rapid method of starting a cranberry bog is to scatter the cuttings along the ground and disc them in. This is justifiable when there is an abundance of cutting material and a scarcity of labor for setting the cuttings by hand *(30, 41)*. Water is applied to the bog immediately after planting. The cuttings root during the first year and make some top growth, but the plants do not start bearing until they are 3 or 4 years of age.

Currant (*Ribes* sp.). Currants are readily propagated by hardwood cuttings prepared from 1-year wood. The plants will be ready for transplanting to their permanent location in 1 or 2 years, depending upon their rate of growth *(31)*. Currants can also be propagated by mound layering (see p. 409).

Cydonia oblonga. See Quince.

Date (*Phoenix dactylifera* L.) *(1, 2, 105)*. Propagation of the date is either by seed or by offshoots (see p. 415). This is a monocotyledonous plant having no continuous cambial cylinder, so it cannot be propagated by budding or grafting. In commercial plantings, most of the trees are female, but a few male trees are necessary for pollination purposes.

In seed propagation, about half of the trees produced are males, whereas the seedling female trees produce fruits of variable and generally inferior types. The commercial grower is, therefore, little interested in seedling trees, preferring the superior named clonal varieties, even though the latter must be propagated by the vegetative offshoot method.

The offshoots arise from axillary buds near the base of the tree. If they are near the ground level, they will develop roots in the soil after 3 to 5 years on the parent tree. Large, well-rooted offshoots, weighing 40 to 100 lbs., are more likely to grow than smaller ones. Other offshoots higher up can be induced to root by mounding soil up to their bases. Unrooted offshoots arising higher on the stem can be cut off and rooted in the nursery, but in relatively low percentages.

Considerable skill is required to properly cut off a date offshoot. The soil is dug away from the rooted offshoot, retaining if possible a ball of moist earth 2 or 3 inches thick attached to the roots. The connection with the parent tree should be exposed on each side by removing loose fibre and old leaf bases. A special chisel, as shown in Figure 16–4, having a blade flat on one side and beveled on the other is used to sever the offshoot. The first cut is made to the side of the base of the offshoot close to the main trunk.

Figure 16–4. Removing a date offshoot showing the use of chisel and sledge hammer. From **USDA Cir. 728, Date Culture in the United States.**

The beveled side of the chisel is toward the parent tree, which gives a smooth cut on the offshoot. A single cut may be sufficient, but usually one or more cuts from each side are necessary to remove the offshoot. The offshoot should never be pried loose but cut off cleanly. After removal it should be handled carefully and replanted as soon as possible, care being taken to prevent the roots from drying out.

Dewberry. See **Blackberry.**

Diospyros sp. See **Persimmon.**

Eriobotrya japonica. See **Loquat.**

Feijoa (*Feijoa sellowiana* Berg.). Propagation is mainly by seeds, which germinate without difficulty. They should be started in flats of soil and later transplanted to the nursery row. Named varieties can be grafted on feijoa seedlings, although it is difficult to obtain a high percentage of successful unions. Leafy softwood cuttings treated with root-promoting substances and started under closed frames can sometimes be rooted.

Ficus carica. See Fig.

Fig (*Ficus carica* L.). The fig is easily propagated by hardwood cuttings (see p. 227). Two- or 3-year-old wood or basal parts of vigorous 1-year shoots with a minimum of pith are suitable for cuttings. These are grown for one or two seasons in the nursery then transplanted to their permanent location. A common method in European countries is to plant long cuttings (3 to 4 feet) their full length in the ground where the tree is to be located permanently; sometimes two cuttings are set in one location to increase the chance of having one grow.

The fig can be budded, using either T-buds (see p. 382) inserted in vigorous 1-year-old shoots on heavily pruned trees or patch buds (see p. 386) on older shoots.

Fig roots show considerable resistance to oak root fungus (*Armillaria mellea*) but are quite susceptible to both root-knot (*Meloidogyne* sp.) and lesion nematodes (*Pratylenchus vulnus*) *(35)*.

Propagation of figs by seeds is practiced for breeding new varieties. The small seeds can be germinated easily in flats of well-prepared soil. The fertile seeds should first be separated from the sterile ones by placing all of them in water; fertile seeds sink whereas the sterile ones float *(29)*.

Figs can be air-layered (see p. 406) successfully. One-year-old branches, if layered in early spring, are usually well rooted by midsummer.

Filbert (*Corylus avellana* L.) *(127, 140)*. Layering is the usual method of commercial filbert propagation, either simple, trench, or mound (see Chapter 14). In simple layering—the most important method—the suckers arising from the base of vigorous young trees, 4 to 8 years old, are layered in early spring. After one season's growth, a well-rooted tree 2 to 6 feet tall may be obtained, ready to set out in the orchard.

Budding or grafting filbert varieties on seedling stocks is rarely practiced due to the difficulty usually encountered in obtaining successful unions. When done, cleft or whip grafting (see p. 322) or T-budding (see p. 382) is used.

Filbert nuts are easily germinated, but they require a stratification period (see p. 127) of several months at 32° to 40°F. before planting.

Fragaria sp. See Strawberry.

Gooseberry (*Grossularia* or *Ribes sp.*). Mound layering (see p. 409) is used commercially. The layered shoots of American varieties will usually root well after one season. They are then cut off and transferred to the nursery row for a second season's growth before they are set out in their permanent location. The slower-rooting layers of European varieties may have to remain attached to the parent plant for two seasons before they develop enough roots to be detached from the parent plant *(31)*.

Some varieties, such as the Houghton, Poorman, and Van Fleet, can be started fairly easily by hardwood cuttings *(116)*.

Grape (*Vitis sp.*) *(78, 79, 101)*. The grape can be propagated by seeds, cuttings, layering, budding, or grafting. Seeds are used chiefly in producing new varieties. Cuttings are most often used commercially. For varieties difficult to root by cuttings, such as the Muscadine (*Vitis rotundifolia*), layering is necessary. Budding or grafting on rootstocks is used occasionally to increase vine life, plant vigor, and yields. Where noxious soil organisms, as phylloxera (*Dactylosphaera vitifoliae*), rootknot nematodes (*Meloidoyne* sp.), or cotton root rot (*Phymatotrichum*) are present and varieties of susceptible species, such as *V. vinifera* are to be grown, it is necessary to graft or bud the desired variety on a resistant rootstock.

CUTTINGS. Most varieties of grapes are easily started by hardwood cuttings (see p. 227). The cutting material should be collected during the dormant season from healthy, vigorous, mature vines. Well-developed, current season's canes should be used which are of medium size and have moderately short internodes. Cuttings ⅓ to ½ inch in diameter and 12 to 16 inches long are generally used. One season's growth in the nursery should produce plants large enough to set in the vineyard.

Root-promoting chemicals have not been particularly helpful with grape cuttings, adequate rooting of most varieties being obtained without this added stimulation *(62)*. However, the difficult-to-root Muscadine types (*V. rotundifolia*) have been rooted in commercially satisfactory percentages in mist propagating beds (see p. 251), when succulent, immature tip cuttings were used *(130)*.

LAYERS. Grape varieties which are difficult to start by cuttings can be propagated by layering, using either air *(90)* or simple, trench, or mound layering (see Chapter 14).

GRAFTING. Bench grafting (see p. 359) is used to some extent; scions are grafted on either rooted or unrooted disbudded cuttings by the whip or tongue method (see p. 322). Machine grafting is sometimes used, giving very satisfactory results (see Fig. 12–24 and 12–25). The grafts are made in late winter or early spring from previously collected, completely dormant, scion and stock material. The stocks are cut to a length of about 11 inches with the lower cut just below a node and the top cut an inch or more above a node. All the buds are completely cut away from the stock to prevent subsequent suckering. Scion wood should be selected which has the same diameter as the stock.

After grafting, the union is wrapped with raffia, waxed string, or budding rubber. In the grape, the presence of air at the graft union is essential for adequate healing; therefore, no grafting wax is used and the wrapping material is not overlapped.

Following grafting, proper callusing or healing of the graft union is very important. The grafts should be held for 3 or 4 weeks in moist sand at a temperature of about 75°F. It is very important that the grafts be planted in the nursery row as soon as the graft unions have healed but before there is much shoot or root growth. Before planting, it is best to harden the callused grafts by holding them for about 10 days at a temperature 10°F. lower than the callusing temperature.

Before planting, all suckers from the stock and all roots arising from the scion should be removed. Scion shoots and stock roots longer than an inch should be cut back to that length. The grafts are planted at such a depth that the unions are just above the soil level. Immediately after planting, the graft is covered with a wide ridge of soil so that the scions are covered to a depth of 2 or 3 inches.

After the grafts are growing vigorously each one should be examined carefully. Roots arising from the scion should be removed, although some scion roots are not undesirable for a time to help the graft get started. Removing the scion roots too late will retard root growth from the stock. Suckers from the stock should also be removed. At this time, the tying material should be cut if it has not already rotted.

GREENWOOD GRAFTING. Greenwood grafting is a simple, and rapid, procedure for propagating vinifera grapes on resistant rootstocks *(63, 64)*. A one-budded greenwood scion is grafted during the active growing season on new growth arising from either a one-year-old rooted cutting or from a cutting during midseason of the first or root-forming year. A splice graft is used which is similar to the whip or tongue graft (see p. 322) except that no tongue is made. For this method to be successful, only cuttings making a strong growth should be used, and the soil should be kept well supplied with moisture. Four to 7 days before grafting, the leaves and buds should be removed from the stock below the point of the intended graft union. In collecting the green, herbaceous scion wood, the leaf blades should be removed immediately and the wood kept cool and moist until used. The cut surfaces on the graft—¾ to 1½ inches long—should fit together well and be wrapped tightly with budding rubbers that are left on for a month. In this case, it is not necessary to wax or otherwise protect the graft union.

BUDDING. A satisfactory method of establishing grape varieties on resistant rootstocks is by fall budding on rapidly growing, well-rooted cuttings which were planted in their permanent vineyard location the previous winter or spring. A form of chip budding (see p. 393) is commonly performed in late summer or early fall just as soon as mature buds from wood with light brown bark can be obtained.

The bud is inserted in the stock near the soil level, preferably on the north or east side. It is tied in place with raffia, waxed string, or budding rubber, but it is not waxed. The bud is then covered with 5 to 10 inches of well-pulverized, *moist* soil to prevent drying. In areas of extremely hot summers, or in soils of low moisture, poor results are likely to be obtained, and bench or nursery grafted vines should be used.

T-budding is not usually practiced with grapes due to the relatively large size of the buds or "eyes," but small buds such as would be found on small seedling plants inserted in actively growing shoots in the spring may give a high percentage of successful unions *(61)*.

ROOTSTOCKS FOR AMERICAN GRAPE VARIETIES *(86)*.

Dogridge, Champanel, Lukfata (V. champini). These stocks have been very effective in the southern Coastal region of the United States in increasing yields and in prolonging vine life of the "bunch" type grapes.

Constantia, V. riparia × V. rupestris 3309, V. cordifolia × V. riparia 125–1, Cynthiana, Wine King, Lenoir. These stocks have been useful in the inland states of the United States in increasing yields, plant vigor, and evenness of ripening.

ROOTSTOCKS FOR VINIFERA GRAPE VARIETIES *(77, 137, 138, 139)*.

Rupestris St. George (V. rupestris). This vigorous, phylloxera-resistant stock is especially suitable for nonirrigated soils, although it is not resistant to nematodes or to cotton root rot. It is readily propagated by cuttings and easily grafted. It tends to sucker profusely, so disbudding before planting should be carefully done.

Aramon × Rupestris No. 1. This is a phylloxera-resistant rootstock recommended for irrigated soils that are free of nematodes. Vines on this stock under such conditions generally become larger and more productive than those on St. George. It is very susceptible to nematodes and does not seem to do well on dry, hillside soils.

Solonis × Othello 1613. This stock has proven to be very resistant to phylloxera in some plantings but only moderately so in others. It has the added advantage of being quite resistant to the root-knot nematode. Although this stock is suitable for fertile, irrigated sandy loam soils, it produces weak, unproductive vines in nonirrigated or sandy soils of low fertility.

Dogridge (V. champini) and Salt Creek (V. doaniana). These are extremely vigorous, nematode-resistant stocks being tested for their value under various conditions. In fertile soils, the vines are often so vigorous that they are unproductive. Dogridge is resistant to both phylloxera and cotton root rot, but it is somewhat difficult to start by cuttings.

Grapefruit. See Citrus.

Grossularia sp. See Gooseberry.

Guava (*Psidium cattleianum* Sabine—the Cattley or strawberry guava—and *Psidium guajava* L.—the common, tropical, or lemon guava) (*56, 87*). The Cattley guava has no named varieties, and most nursery plants are propagated by seed. This species seems to come nearly true from seed, large-fruited, superior trees being used as the seed source. It is very difficult to propagate by vegetative methods.

The common guava does have several named varieties, but they are not propagated extensively, probably due to the difficulties of asexual propagation. Most trees of this species are propagated by seeds which germinate easily and in high percentages. Seeds should be taken from the best type of tree available, and the flowers to produce the seeds should be self-pollinated which, in this species, reduces the amount of variability.

The seedlings are somewhat susceptible to damping off organisms, so they should be started in sterilized soil or otherwise protected by fungicides. When the seedlings are about 1½ inches high, they should be transplanted into individual containers. In 6 months, the plants should be about 12 inches high and can then be transplanted to their permanent location.

For large scale propagation of the guava, grafting is necessary. Although these species are considered to be difficult, grafting can be successfully accomplished (*102*).

Air layering (see p. 406) gives good results with the use of sphagnum moss and plastic wrapping.

Simple and mound layering are effective methods of starting new plants, provided the layer is tightly wrapped with wire just below the point where roots are wanted (*37*).

Hickory (*Carya ovata* Koch—Shagbark hickory). Hickory varieties are propagated by grafting or budding on seedlings of the Shagbark hickory (*C. ovata*), bitternut (*C. cordiformis*), or pecan (*C. illinoensis*) (*108, 155*). However, due to grafting and transplanting difficulties and slow growth of the trees, there is little widespread planting of grafted trees.

To avoid transplanting failure caused by the long taproot, several stratified nuts are planted in the spring where the trees are to be located permanently. The best tree is saved and topworked, usually by the bark graft method (see p. 336), to the desired variety (*89*). If grafted nursery trees are to be used, the taproot should be cut a year previous to digging or the tree transplanted in the nursery row once or twice to force out lateral roots.

Hickory nuts will germinate without stratification but should be kept in moist, cool storage until planting. Fall planting is successful if the soil in cold climates is well mulched to prevent excessive freezing and thawing.

Patch budding (see p. 386) is commonly used by nurserymen in the commercial propagation of hickories and is usually performed in late summer. The seedling stocks are grown for 2 years or more before they are large enough to bud.

Juglans sp. See Walnut.

Jujube (*Zizyphus jujuba* Mill.)—Chinese date. The two important named jujube varieties—Lang and Li—are propagated by budding or grafting on.

jujube seedlings, which are started without difficulty. They may also be propagated by root cuttings or hardwood stem cuttings.

Lemon. See Citrus.

Lime. See Citrus.

Litchi chinensis. See Lychee.

Loganberry. See Blackberry.

Loquat (*Eriobotrya japonica* [Thunb.] Lindl.). This is propagated by budding or grafting on young loquat seedlings or by top-grafting on older, established trees, using the cleft graft method (see p. 331). The quince can be used as a rootstock, producing a very dwarfed tree.

Lychee (*Litchi chinensis* Sonn.). The many varieties of this species are propagated by asexual methods, the most important being air layering (see p. 406). This can be done at any time of the year, but the best results are obtained in the spring and summer *(87)*.

Branch tip cuttings taken during the active flush of growth in the spring have been started experimentally in fairly high percentages when rooted under mist (see p. 251) in the full sun. Treatments with root-promoting chemicals are beneficial. Hardwood cuttings taken from an active flush of new vegetative growth have been observed to root more readily than dormant hardwood cuttings.

Various grafting methods have been successful in working one-year-old seedling to named varieties, but they are not used to any extent commercially. The cleft (see p. 331), side tongue, and side veneer (see p. 328) grafts can be used as well as the approach graft (see p. 340). Scions should be taken from vigorous flushes of terminal wood still showing some green color and which have prominent axillary buds. T-budding (see p. 382) and chip budding (see p. 393) have also been successful.

Lychee seeds germinate in 2 to 3 weeks if planted immediately upon removal from the fruit, but they lose their viability in a few days if not planted. Seedling trees are rarely grown for their fruit, because they require 10 to 15 years to start bearing, and the fruit is quite likely to be of inferior quality *(26)*.

Macadamia (*Macadamia ternifolia* F. Muell.) Most trees of this sub-tropical evergreen nut tree have been grown in California as seedlings, but vegetative propagation of a few superior selections is practiced.

Seeds may be planted as soon as they mature in the fall either directly in the nursery row or started in sand boxes in a lathhouse and transplanted to the nursery row after the seedlings are 4 to 6 inches tall. It is very important not to crack the seed, because they are readily attacked by fungi.

Selected clones are propagated by one of the side graft methods (see p. 326). Leaves should always be retained for a time on the rootstock. Rapid healing of the union seems to be promoted if the rootstock is checked in growth prior to grafting by a water or nitrogen deficiency so as to permit carbohydrate accumulation. In the same manner, ringing the branches that are to be the source of the scions several weeks to several months before they are taken increases their carbohydrate content and promotes healing of the union.

Cuttings can be rooted in moist sand, especially if they are made 1 or 2 feet long from mature wood and rooted with leaves attached in a very humid, shady propagation bench held at a temperature of 65° to 70°F. Such long, leafy cuttings may root outdoors in the nursery row in localities where the air remains humid for long periods of time. Leaf-bud cuttings (see p. 239) and terminal leafy, semi-hardwood stem cuttings of some clones can also be rooted easily in a closed propagating case or under intermittent mist, especially if a root-promoting substance is used.

Air layering (see p. 406) is also a successful propagation method, but it is believed by some that a much better type of root system develops when grafted seedlings are used than when the propagation is by cuttings or air layering *(10)*.

Malus baccata. See **Crabapple.**

Malus ioensis. See **Crabapple.**

Malus sylvestris. See **Apple.**

Mandarin. See **Citrus.**

Mango (*Mangifera indica* L.). Most trees of this evergreen sub-tropical fruit in cultivation are seedlings, although many superior selections are perpetuated vegetatively. Polyembryony (see p. 45) occurs commonly in mango. The seedlings may be sexual or nucellar in origin, either or both conditions occurring simultaneously in the seed. However, growth of several shoots from one seed does not necessarily indicate the presence of nucellar embryos, since in certain varieties shoots develop from below ground, arising in the axils of the cotyledons of one embryo, which may or may not be of zygotic origin *(6)*.

Mango seeds are used either to produce a true-to-type nucellar seedling of some superior clone or as a rootstock on which is budded or grafted the desired clone. They should be planted as soon as they are mature or stored at temperatures above 50°F. Excessive drying should be prevented. Re-

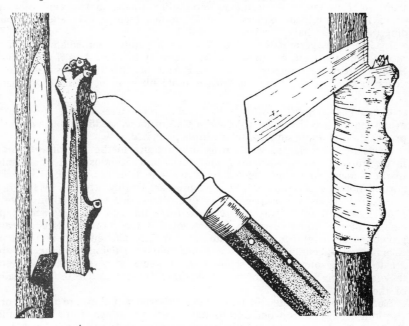

Figure 16–5. Veneer grafting the mango. **(left)** Scion cut and ready for placing on the stock. **(right)** Graft wrapped with vinyl plastic tape, leaving only the bud exposed. Courtesy S. J. Lynch and Dorothy Allen.

moving the tough endocarp which surrounds the seed, followed by planting in a sterilized medium should result in good germination in 2 to 3 weeks. Soon after the seedlings start to grow, they should be transplanted to cans or pots or to the nursery row.

Mangos are commonly propagated in Florida by chip budding (see p. 393) or a modified chip bud method. A week after budding, the stock is cut off two to three leaves above the bud, with a final removal to the bud when the bud shoot is 3 or 4 inches long. The best budwood is prepared from terminal growths, ¼ to ⅜ inch in diameter, that have been hardened. All the leaves are removed with the exception of two or three terminal ones. The buds will swell in 2 to 3 weeks when they are ready to use. If the buds are to be used on stocks older than 3 weeks, ringing the base of the shoots from which the buds are to be taken about 10 days before they are used increases their carbohydrate supply and seems to promote healing. Budding is best done when the rootstock seedlings are 2 to 3 weeks old—in the succulent red stage. In 4 to 6 weeks after budding, the inserted bud should start growth *(87)*.

The side veneer graft (see p. 328) is also successful in propagating the mango, using a vigorous, plump terminal bud as the scion. Approach grafting (see p. 340) has been used since ancient times in India.

Air layering is sometimes successful but is not used commercially *(134)*. The mango is not commonly propagated by cuttings, but it can be done, root-promoting chemicals being of some benefit *(104, 133)*.

Morus sp. See Mulberry.

Mulberry (*Morus* sp.). The mulberry is readily started by hardwood cuttings (see p. 227) 8 to 12 inches long, made from wood of the previous season's growth and planted in early spring.

Musa sp. See Banana.

Nectarine (*Prunus persica*). See Peach.

Olea europaea. See Olive.

Olive (*Olea europaea* L.). Olive varieties can be propagated in a number of ways, such as by budding or grafting on seedling or clonal rootstocks, by hard- or semi-hardwood cuttings, or by suckers from old trees.

Germinating olive seeds in high percentages is rather difficult, although seeds of small-fruited varieties germinate much easier than those of large-fruited ones. Often germination will be prolonged over a period of 1 or even 2 years. The usual practice is to plant a great many more seeds than will be needed as seedlings so as to offset the low germination percentage. The true olive seed is enclosed in a hard endocarp or "pit." Removing, clipping, or cracking this endocarp will materially hasten germination, although even when this is done germination is still slow and erratic.

The seedlings grow rather slowly, and it may take a year or two for them to become large enough to be grafted or budded. Many propagation methods have been used successfully, such as T-budding (see p. 382), patch budding (see p. 386), whip grafting (see p. 322), and side tongue grafting (see p. 328). The latter method, in which the stock is not cut back until the union is well healed and the scion starts growth, gives a high percentage of successful unions. In Italy, a widely used method is to bark graft (see p. 336) small seedlings in the nursery row in the spring. The stocks are cut off several inches above ground, and one small scion is inserted in each seedling, followed by tying and waxing. After grafting or budding, one or possibly two more years are required before a nursery tree large enough for transplanting to the orchard is produced.

Hardwood cuttings may be made from 2- or 3-year-old wood about an inch in diameter and 8 to 12 inches long. All leaves are removed. Slow-growing wood from the upper portion of the tree should be used rather than succulent, fast-growing suckers or watersprouts taken from around the base of the tree. It is often helpful to soak the basal ends of the cuttings in a solution of indolebutyric acid (15 ppm for 24 hours), followed by storage in moist sawdust at a temperature of 60° to 70°F. for a month preceding planting in the nursery *(65)*.

Semi-hardwood cuttings from vigorous, 1-year-old wood about ¼ inch in diameter can be successfully rooted. The cuttings should be 4 to 6 inches long with two to six leaves retained on the upper portion of the cutting. Such cuttings must be started under high humidity conditions. They root especially well under intermittent mist (see p. 251) and respond markedly to treatments with indolebutyric acid (see p. 244).

Suckers from the base of own-rooted trees may be carefully cut away (taking with each one a small piece of old root) and then planted in the early spring in the nursery row.

The characteristic swellings, sometimes called "ovuli," usually found on the trunks of old olive trees may be cut off and planted in early spring. These contain both adventitious root initials and dormant buds so that new root and shoot systems can be regenerated. This practice is somewhat damaging to the parent tree, however, and is not widely used.

Another method of propagating olives is to saw large branches, 3 or 4 inches in diameter, into pieces about 12 inches long and plant them horizontally several inches below the surface of the soil. Sometimes they are split into several pieces. These are called "truncheons." Usually several shoots, each with an accompanying root system, will grow from each piece; the truncheon may then be cut apart to form several small plants which are grown separately another year in the nursery row to produce a tree.

ROOTSTOCKS FOR OLIVE VARIETIES. *Olea europaea* seedings are ordinarily used where propagation by budding or grafting is practiced, although considerable variation in tree vigor often results from this practice. A more suitable rootstock, giving uniform trees, is rooted cuttings of a strong-growing variety such as Mission.

Orange. See Citrus.

Papaya (*Carica papaya* L.) *(60)*. Propagation by seed is the usual method. They are sown in flats of soil or in seed-beds in the open and germinate in 2 to 3 weeks. The seeds do equally well if taken from fresh fruit or stored dry. When the seedlings have reached a height of about 4 inches, they are ready for transplanting. This is generally done once or twice before they are put in their permanent location.

A method of growing the seedlings without transplanting is to plant four to eight seeds in a container and then thin to two to four of the strongest seedlings when they are about 4 inches tall. They can then be set in the field without disturbing the root system. Young papaya seedlings are very susceptible to damping off organisms; therefore, the soil in which they are started should be sterilized if possible (see p. 30).

In Florida, the usual practice is to plant the seed in January and set the young plants in the field by late March or April. They grow during the spring and summer and will usually mature their first fruits by October or November, the plants bearing all winter and the following season.

Papaya cuttings are not difficult to root if bottom heat at 85°F. is maintained and entire branches with the basal swelling are used (*145*). Due to the nonbranching growth habit of the plant, the amount of cutting material is limited. Scions from particularly good plants may be grafted on seedlings, but this is not done commercially (*160*).

Papaw (*Asimina triloba*. Dun.). Propagation is entirely by seed, which should be removed from the fruits as soon as they mature. The seeds are either planted in the fall or are given a rather long stratification period (see p. 127) and planted in early spring. The seeds are slow to germinate, some starting in the second year. The young seedlings are slow growing, and because they are quite sensitive to strong sunlight, they are usually started under partial shade. The seedlings are somewhat difficult to transplant successfully after the first year's growth due to their long taproot (*46*).

Passiflora edulis. See Passion Fruit.

Passion Fruit (*Passiflora edulis* Sims.). This sub-tropical, evergreen fruit is propagated chiefly by seed which germinates readily in 2 to 3 weeks after planting. Propagation by cuttings of mature wood is also practiced occasionally.

Peach and **Nectarine** (*Prunus persica* Batsch). Nursery trees of the peach are propagated by T-budding (see p. 382) on seedling rootstocks. Fall budding is most common, but spring budding or—in regions with long growing seasons —June budding is also done.

Some varieties of the peach can be propagated by leafy, succulent softwood cuttings taken in the spring, treated with a root-promoting material, and rooted in a mist type propagating bed (see p. 251) (*67*).

Rootstocks for Peach Varieties. Most peach varieties are propagated on peach seedlings. Apricot and almond seedlings are sometimes used and, in Europe, certain clonal strains of the Brompton and Common Mussel plum. Peach seeds must be stratified for about 3 months and almond and apricot for 3 to 4 weeks before they are planted.

Peach (*P. persica*). Peach seedlings are the most satisfactory rootstock for peach varieties and should be used unless certain special conditions warrant trials with other stocks. Seeds of the Lovell freestone variety are obtained in large quantities from drying yards and canneries in California and are widely used in the United States, since they usually germinate well and produce vigorous seedlings. Seeds should not be taken from varieties whose fruits mature early in the season, because their germination percentage is usually low.

Peach roots are quite susceptible to the root-knot nematode (*Meloidogyne* sp.), especially in sandy soils. There is much interest, therefore, in nematode-resistant types. For example, seedlings of the S-37 peach (U.S. Plant Patent 904)* show high resistance to attacks of *M. incognita* var. *acrita* as do seedlings of the Shalil peach variety, an introduction by the USDA from northern India. However, neither of these rootstocks shows a similar amount of resistance to another widely distributed nematode species, *M. javanica* (*58*). Trees on Shalil roots in soils not infested with root-knot nematodes seem to grow more slowly than those on Lovell seedling roots. Shalil seedlings are not considered to be particularly desirable to use in spite of their nematode resistance.

---

*Introduced and distributed by Stribling's Nurseries, Merced, California.

Nursery trees on peach roots often make unsatisfactory growth when planted in soils previously planted to peaches.

Apricot (P. armeniaca). Apricot seedlings are occasionally used as a rootstock for the peach. The graft union is not always successful, but numerous trees and commercial orchards of this combination have produced fairly well for many years. Seedlings of the Blenheim apricot variety seem to make better rootstocks for peaches than those of the Tilton variety. Since the apricot root is highly resistant to root-knot nematodes, its use may be justified as a peach rootstock on sandy soils so heavily infested with nematodes as to preclude the use of peach roots.

Almond (P. amygdalus). Almond seedlings have been used successfully as a rootstock for peaches, and there are orchards of this combination growing well; in general, however, this is not a satisfactory combination, and few commercial peach orchards on almond roots are planted. The trees are often dwarfed and tend to be short lived.

Western sand cherry (P. besseyi). When this was used in limited experiments as a dwarfing rootstock for several peach varieties, it was found that although the bud unions were excellent, about 40 per cent of the nursery trees failed to survive. The remainder grew well, however, and developed into typical dwarf trees with healthy dark green foliage. The trees bore normal size fruit in the second or third year after transplanting to the orchard *(17).*

Pear *(Pyrus communis L.).* Pear varieties are commonly propagated by fall budding, using the T-budding method (see p. 382), on either seedling pear rootstocks or on rooted quince cuttings. Pear trees are also started by whole-root grafting (see p. 358), using the whip or tongue method (see p. 322). Pear seeds must be stratified (see p. 127) for 45 to 90 days before planting. They are then planted thickly about ½ inch deep in a well-prepared seedbed where they are allowed to grow during one season. The following spring they are dug up, the roots and top cut back, and then transplanted to the nursery row where they are grown a second season, ready for budding in the fall.

Although the pear can be propagated by trench and stool layering (see p. 409), this is seldom done commercially. Propagation by hardwood cuttings is successful with some varieties, such as Pineapple, Garber, Keiffer, and Old Home *(68).*

ROOTSTOCKS FOR PEAR VARIETIES. *French pear (P. communis).* These are seedlings of the common pear, taking their name from the fact that until about 1915 seeds were imported into the United States in large quantities from France. French pear seedlings as used now are generally grown from seeds of such varieties as the Winter Nelis or, perhaps, Bartlett. This rootstock is vigorous and produces uniform trees with a strong, well-anchored root system. It forms an excellent graft union with all pear varieties and will tolerate relatively wet (but not waterlogged) and heavy soils. French pear roots are quite resistant to oak root fungus (*Armillaria mellea*), growing in soils where stone fruit trees have been killed by this disease. They are, however, susceptible to the somewhat similar *Dematophora* root rot. This stock is also fairly resistant to crown gall and to the root-knot nematode.

The two serious defects of French pear roots are their susceptibility to pear root aphid, *Eriosoma languinosa,* and to fire blight (pear blight), *Erwinia amylovora.* The latter fault is especially serious, because the roots can be infected and the disease can become far advanced before it is detected. The tendency of French pear roots to sucker freely increases the chances of the disease moving into the root system from the suckers. Although infected branches can be cut out, it is almost impossible to cut away infected portions of the root system. Millions of pear trees on French pear roots have died from fire blight due to the high susceptibility of this stock.

Blight-resistant French pear rootstocks—Pear varieties resistant to blight, such as Old Home and Farmingdale *(118)*, are sometimes used as an intermediate stock budded or grafted on seedling rootstocks. Topworking with the desired variety takes place after the trunk and primary scaffold branches develop. If a blight attack occurs in the top of the tree, it will stop at the resistant body stock, which can subsequently be regrafted after the blight has been cut out.

At the Oregon Agricultural Experiment Station, some *P. communis* clones have been developed which are highly resistant to blight *(119)*. Cross pollination, using certain resistant clones as parents, gave seedling trees which were completely resistant to blight. Therefore, by using such seedlings as rootstocks, complete root blight resistance can be obtained together with all the other desirable characteristics of French pear roots.

Japanese pear (P. pyrifolia). This was widely used as a pear rootstock from about 1900 to 1925. It does not have the bad habit typical of French pear of sending up suckers which become infected with blight. It is almost free from attacks of the pear root aphid and grows vigorously in the nursery. However, it is not much more resistant to fire blight than French pear roots and is more susceptible to winter injury and to oak root fungus. It will not tolerate wet soils or drought conditions as well as French root. But the most serious defect of this root—which has caused its elimination as a recommended stock—is the physiological disease "black end" or "hard end" which may occur in the Bartlett, Anjou, Winter Nelis, Comice, Colonel Wilder, Easter, and Claireau varieties when propagated on it *(73)*. The severely affected fruits are entirely unsalable due to a hardening and cracking of the flesh at the blossom end, often with the development of blackened areas. Fruit with mild symptoms may also be undesirable because of failure to soften and ripen normally.

Callerya pear (P. calleryana). This stock is blight resistant, produces vigorous trees with a strong graft union, and seems to produce little, if any, black-end fruits. Several entirely satisfactory Bartlett orchards on this rootstock have produced well in California, and it is a popular rootstock in the southern part of the United States for Keiffer and other hybrid pears. On the other hand, in Michigan and New York it is reported *(82, 147)* to be of little value due, principally, to lack of winter hardiness.

Ussurian pear (P. ussuriensis). This oriental stock has been tested to some extent, but it is not promising since many varieties on this root develop black-end, although not to the extent found with Japanese roots. It is vigorous, very winter hardy, and is somewhat resistant to fire blight and to pear root aphid.

Birch-leaf pear (P. betulaefolia). This is characterized by vigorous seedlings, resistance to leaf spot and woolly aphid, tolerance to alkali soils, and an adaptability to a wide range of climatic conditions. It is, however, susceptible to fire blight. Certain pear varieties, for instance Anjou, are not compatible with it, necessitating the use of a compatible interstock such as Old Home. In New York, the Bartlett, Seckel, and Kieffer varieties on *P. betulaefolia* were outstanding in size, vigor, and early fruiting *(147)*. Bartlett fruits on this rootstock have developed black-end, however, which precludes its general use, at least with this variety.

Quince (Cydonia oblonga). This has been used for centuries as a dwarfing stock for the pear. Some varieties, however, fail to make a strong union directly on the quince, hence double-working, (see p. 362) using an inter-mediate stock such as Hardy or Old Home is necessary. Varieties which re-quire such a compatible interstock when worked on quince roots include Bartlett, Bosc, Winter Nelis, Seckel, Easter, Clairgeau, Comice, and Guyot (Early Bartlett).

Quince roots are resistant to pear root aphids and nematodes and are tolerant of excess soil moisture, but they are not resistant to oak root fungus, fire blight, or excess lime and are not winter hardy in areas where extremely low temperatures occur *(148)*. The black-end trouble has not developed with pear varieties on quince roots. There are a number of varieties of quince, most of which are quite easily propagated by hardwood cuttings or layering. Angers quince is commonly used as a pear rootstock, because it roots readily by cuttings, grows vigorously in the nursery, and does well in the orchard.

The East Malling Research Station in England has selected several types of quince suitable as pear rootstocks and designated them as Quince A, B, and C *(69)*. Quince A, an Angers type, proved to be the most satisfactory stock. Quince B is somewhat dwarfing, whereas Quince C produces very dwarfed trees *(70)*.

Pecan (*Carya illinoensis* Koch) *(15)*. Pecan varieties are propagated by budding or grafting on seedling rootstocks *(136)*. Leafy, softwood cuttings have been rooted experimentally under mist *(45)*. New plants have also been started by root cuttings *(7)* and by both trench and air layering, the latter with the aid of indolebutyric acid treatments *(44)*.

Pecan seeds will often start growth in the hulls even before the nuts are harvested. The seeds will lose their viability, however, in warm, dry storage *(98)*. To prevent this, they should be placed at 32°F. immediately after harvest until planted in the spring. Alternative methods are to plant the seeds in the fall or to store them out-of-doors through the winter in moist sand. If the nuts have been allowed to dry, it is often helpful to soak them in water for several days before planting. Young seedlings are very tender and should be shaded against sunburn. Toward the end of the second growing season, the seedlings are large enough to bud to the desired commercial variety. Patch budding, or sometimes ring budding (see p. 392), is the usual method employed. After the top grows for one, or sometimes two, seasons, the nursery tree is ready to transplant to its permanent location. Young pecan trees have a long taproot which must be handled carefully in digging and replanting.

Occasionally the smaller pecan seedlings in the nursery row are changed to the desired variety by crown grafting (see p. 362) in late winter or early spring, using the whip or tongue method (see p. 322).

Rootstocks for Pecan Varieties. Commercially, pecan varieties are propagated almost entirely on pecan (*C. illinoensis*) seedlings. Wild seedling trees that are large and vigorous are generally used as a source of the seeds. The Halbert variety is reported to produce seedlings of exceptional vigor and uniformity. As a possible rootstock for wet soils, seedlings of one of the hickory species, *C. aquatica,* have been used experimentally. Although scions of pecan varieties will grow on the hickory species, the nuts generally do not attain their normal size.

Persea sp. See Avocado.

Persimmon (*Diospyros* sp.) *(47, 120)*. American persimmon (*D. virginiana* L.). The named varieties of this species are commonly propagated by budding or grafting on *D. virginiana* seedlings. Root cuttings (see p. 240) are also successful.

Germination of persimmon seeds is rather slow due mainly to their slow rate of water absorption. Fall sowing or stratification (see p. 127) at about 50°F. for 60 to 90 days is advisable. In transplanting any but small seedlings, the taproot should be cut 12 inches below ground a year before moving to force out lateral roots.

Oriental persimmon (*D. kaki* L.). The named varieties of this fruit are propagated by grafting on seedling rootstocks. Crown grafting (see p. 362) by the whip or tongue method (see p. 322) in early spring when both scion wood and stock are still dormant is a common practice, although bench grafting (see p. 359) is also used. Budding can be done, but it is less successful than grafting.

The usual practice in germinating seeds of both *D. lotus* and *D. kaki* is to stratify the seeds from fall until early spring. If the seeds have dried out, they should be soaked in warm water for 2 to 3 days before stratification. Excessive drying of the seed is harmful, especially for *D. kaki*. The seeds are planted either in flats or in the nursery row. Young persimmon seedlings require shading.

ROOTSTOCKS FOR ORIENTAL PERSIMMON VARIETIES *(75)*. *Diospyros lotus*. This has been widely used in California; it is very vigorous, drought resistant, and produces a rather fibrous type of root system which transplants easily. This stock is quite susceptible to crown gall and will not tolerate poorly drained soils. The Hachiya variety does not produce well on *D. lotus* stock due to the excessive shedding of fruit in all stages *(126)*. Fuyu scions usually do not form a good union with *D. lotus*.

Diospyros kaki. This stock is the one most favored in Japan and is probably best for general use, because it develops a good union with all varieties and is somewhat resistant to crown gall. Trees worked on it grow well and yield satisfactory commercial crops. The seedlings have a long taproot with few lateral roots, making transplanting somewhat difficult.

Diospyros virginiana. Seedlings of this species are most favored in the southern part of the United States and seem to be adapted to a wide range of soil conditions. It has not proven satisfactory in some localities, however. In California, the Hachiya variety on this stock is distinctly dwarfed and yields poorly due to the sparse bloom *(126)*. Most oriental varieties make a good union with this stock, but there are diseases carried by *D. kaki* scions that will move into the *D. virginiana* roots, causing them to die. This stock seems to be quite tolerant of excess soil moisture conditions, and it produces a fibrous type of root system easy to transplant.

Phoenix dactylifera. See Date.

Pineapple (*Ananas comosus* Merr.) *(28, 91, 144)*. All commercial propagation of the pineapple is by asexual methods. There are three main types of planting material—*suckers, slips,* and *crowns.* Suckers coming from below ground are rarely used as planting material. Those above ground are cut from the mother plant about 1 month after the peak fruit harvest. Slips are taken from the plant 2 to 3 months following the peak harvest. Crowns, when used in propagation, are taken either before or at the time of harvest.

Slips are the most popular type of planting material. A larger number of these are produced by the plant than either suckers or crowns. After removal from the mother plant, slips can be stored for a relatively long time and still retain sufficient vigor for replanting. If the slips are all about the same

crown

slips

suckers

peduncle

main stem of
mother plant

ground
sucker

Figure 16–6. Parts of the pineapple plant showing the three major types of asexual planting material—**crowns, suckers** and **slips.** In Hawaii **slips** are, by far, the type most commonly used. Courtesy Pineapple Research Institute of Hawaii.

size and age when planted, they will flower and fruit at approximately the same time.

Slips will produce fruit in 18 to 20 months after planting, suckers about

15 months, and crowns about 22 months. Due to these differences, the three types of planting material are never mixed in one field.

In South Africa, "stumps" are also used as propagating material. These are fruit stems which have borne and have been removed from the parent plant during pruning.

All types of planting material must be cured or dried for one to several weeks after they are cut from the mother plant before planting. This allows a callus layer to develop over the cut surface which reduces losses from decay organisms after they are planted.

Pistachio (*Pistacia vera* L.) *(84, 156, 158)*. The pistachio nut is usually propagated by T-budding (see p. 382) on seedling rootstocks of *Pistacia* species. Budding may be carried out over a considerable period of time, but if done before mid-spring, when sap flow is likely to be excessive, the percentage of takes is apt to be low. A marked improvement in bud union occurs as the time of budding is extended through the summer and fall.

Pistacia seeds are collected in the fall and stored dry at about 70° F. until time to plant. Planting can be done from late fall to early spring.

With the early planting of seed and good care in watering and supplying ample nutrients throughout the summer, part or all of the more vigorous seedlings may reach budding size by fall. Buds of both male and female *P. vera* trees are quite large, requiring a fairly large seedling to accommodate them. Because of their large taproot, nursery trees should be transplanted to their permanent planting site as early as possible.

ROOTSTOCKS FOR PISTACHIO VARIETIES. *Pistacia atlantica* and *P. terebinthus* are recommended rootstocks. Although seedlings of these species make a slower growth in the nursery than those of *P. vera,* or its hybrids with other species, they tend to be more nematode resistant than *P. vera.* Only the most vigorous seedlings should be used.

Plum (*Prunus* sp.). Plums are almost always propagated by T-budding (see p. 382) in the fall on seedling rootstocks or, with certain stocks, on rooted cuttings or layers. T-budding in the spring (see p. 378) can also be done. Some plum varieties can be propagated by hardwood cuttings *(68)* and some by leafy, softwood cuttings under intermittent mist *(67)*.

ROOTSTOCKS FOR PLUM VARIETIES *(71)*. *Myrobalan plum, (P. cerasifera).* This is the most widely used plum rootstock, being particularly desirable for the European plums (which includes the commercially important prune varieties). It is also a very satisfactory stock for the Japanese plums. Three varieties of plums—President, Kelsey, and Robe de Sergeant—are not entirely compatible with this stock, however.

Myrobalan roots are well adapted to a wide range of soil and climatic conditions. They will endure heavy soils and excess moisture and are quite resistant to crown rot. They also grow very well on light and sandy soils.

Myrobalan seeds require stratification for about 3 months at 32° to 40°F. They may then be planted thickly in a seedbed for one season, then transplanted to the nursery row and grown for a second season before budding. The seeds may also be planted directly in the nursery row and grown there for one season before budding in late summer or fall.

Certain very vigorous myrobalan selections are propagated vegetatively as cuttings or layers. One of these was introduced in California as Myro 29. This is a mixture of several selections, the better ones of which have been isolated and given distinctive letters, such as Myro 29C. Myro 29 is resistant to root-knot nematodes and somewhat resistant to oak root fungus. In

England two selections, Myrobalan A and B, were developed at the East Malling Research Station and are propagated vegetatively by hardwood cuttings. Type B is particularly valuable in producing vigorous trees, although there are varieties not completely compatible with it *(70)*.

Marianna plum (P. cerasifera × P. munsoniana?). This is a clonal rootstock which originated in Texas as an open-pollinated cross between the myrobalan plum and, supposedly, *P. munsoniana*. It is propagated by hardwood cuttings *(66, 68)*. Some plum varieties have grown well on it, others not. Several exceptionally vigorous seedling selections of the parent Marianna plum were made by the California Agricultural Experiment Station in 1926 and introduced under the identifying numbers of Marianna 2623 and 2624. These two stocks are adaptable to heavy, wet soils and are quite resistant to root-knot nematodes and crown gall. They are somewhat resistant to oak root fungus, 2624 more so than 2623. Both of these Marianna selections are quite resistant to *Dematophora* root rot *(Dematophora necatrix) (85)*.

Peach (P. persica). Over 50 per cent of the plum and prune orchards in California are on peach seedling rootstocks. This stock has proven to be very satisfactory, but some plum varieties are not compatible with it. Peach should be avoided if the young trees are to be planted on a site formerly occupied by a peach orchard.

Apricot (P. armeniaca). Apricot seedlings are a desirable plum stock in nematode-infested sandy soils for those varieties which are compatible with apricot. Japanese plum varieties tend to do better on apricot roots than do European plum varieties.

Almond (P. amygdalus). Some plum varieties can be grown successfully on almond seedlings. The French prune does very well on this stock, the trees growing faster and bearing larger fruit than when myrobalan roots are used. Plum varieties on almond roots tend to overbear sometimes to the detriment of the tree.

Brompton, and Common plum (P. domestica). These two vegetatively propagated, clonal plum stocks are used chiefly in England. Brompton seems to be compatible with all plum varieties and tends to produce medium to large trees. Common plum, which produces small to medium trees, has shown incompatibility with some varieties.

St. Julien, Common Mussel, Damas, and Damson (P. insititia). The first three stocks are used mostly in England. Damas C produces medium to large trees, whereas Common Mussel generally produces small to medium trees. The latter stock seems to be compatible with all plum varieties. St. Julian A produces small to medium trees for all compatible scion varieties. Results have been variable with these stocks, since they vary widely in type. At the East Malling Research Station in England, the more promising types of St. Julien, Mussel, and Damas have been selected and kept true to type by vegetative propagation and listed as clones A, B, C, D, and so forth. St. Julien has been used to some extent as a plum stock for the *P. domestica* varieties in the United States.

Florida sand plum (P. angustifolia). This may be useful as a dwarfing stock for compatible plum varieties. In California, after 16 years, the Giant, Burbank, and Beauty varieties on this stock were healthy and very productive with a dwarf type of growth.

Japanese plum (P. salicina). Seedlings of this species are used in Japan as plum stocks but apparently not elsewhere. European plum varieties (*P. domestica*) when topworked on Japanese plum stocks result in very short-lived trees; the reverse combination, though, produces perfectly compatible unions.

Western sand cherry (*P. besseyi*). This stock has produced satisfactory dwarfed plum trees of the Japanese and European types, but poor bud unions and shoot growth developed when it was used as a stock for varieties of *P. insititia (17)*.

Pomegranate (*Punica granatum* L.). The pomegranate is easily propagated by hardwood cuttings (see p. 227). After one season's growth, the plants are usually large enough to move to their permanent location. Softwood cuttings (see p. 232) taken during the summer are also easily rooted if maintained under high humidity conditions. The pomegranate forms suckers readily, and these may be dug up during the dormant season with a piece of root attached.

Prunus amygdalus. See Almond.

Prunus armeniaca. See Apricot.

Prunus persica. See Peach.

Psidium sp. See Guava.

Punica granatum. See Pomegranate.

Pyrus communis. See Pear.

Quince (*Cydonia oblonga* Mill.). The quince is usually propagated by hardwood cuttings (see p. 227), because those of most varieties root readily. "Heel" cuttings (see p. 228) root more readily than those made entirely from 1-year-old wood. Cuttings made from 2- or 3-year-old wood also root easily. The burrs or knots found on this older wood are masses of adventitious root initials. Cuttings made from the basal portion of 1-year-old wood root better than those made from the terminal end. The cuttings usually make sufficient growth in one season to transplant to their permanent location. The quince can also be propagated by mound layering (see p. 409).

Occasionally, commercial quince varieties are T-budded (see p. 382) on rooted cuttings (such as the Angers rootstock variety) or sometimes on seedlings.

Raspberry, Black (*Rubus occidentalis* L.) and **Purple** (*R. occidentalis* × *R. idaeus*). Tip layering (see p. 402) is the usual method of propagating these species, the black rooting more easily than the purple *(142)*. The black raspberry can be propagated also by leaf-bud cuttings (see p. 239), roots forming in about 3 weeks. The cuttings should be taken in early summer and rooted under high humidity conditions or in a mist propagating frame (see p. 251) *(3, 141)*.

Raspberry, Red (*Rubus strigosus* Michx., *R. idaeus* L.). The red raspberry is very easily propagated by removing suckers (see p. 417) of one-year-old growth. These are usually dug in early spring, using care to leave a piece of the old root attached. Also young, green suckers of new wood may be dug in the spring shortly after they appear when they are only a few inches tall. When these plants are dug, they should have some new roots starting. A piece of the old root is taken with them. Such suckers should be dug and transplanted during cool, cloudy weather and irrigated well after re-setting; otherwise they will not survive. Sucker production can be stimulated by inserting a spade deeply at intervals in the vicinity of old plants to cut off roots, each root piece then sending up a shoot. Production of suckers can also be stimulated by mulching with straw or sawdust.

The red raspberry can be propagated by root cuttings (see p. 240). Very small root pieces are used and, if given good care, will produce strong nursery plants in one year.

While new plants of most *Rubus* species can be started by leaf-bud cuttings (see p. 239), such cuttings of the red raspberry do not form roots *(141)*.

Ribes sp. See Currant, Gooseberry.

Rubus sp. See Blackberry; Raspberry, Black; Raspberry, Red.

Strawberry (*Fragaria* sp.). Strawberries are propagated by runners (see p. 414) or, in everbearing types—which produce few runners—by crown division (see p. 417). Seed propagation is used only in breeding programs for the development of new varieties.

Figure 16–7. Equipment used for large-scale digging of strawberry nursery plants. The entire row is scooped up and elevated to a revolving tunnel which separates the dirt from the roots. The plants are then packed in wet burlap bags and taken to sheds for further cleaning. Courtesy Wheeler's Nursery, Los Molinos, Calif.

The nursery field is set out in early spring and the runner plants are ready for digging the following winter. They may be dug any time after they have had sufficient winter chilling to overcome the rest period of the buds. The digging should be completed in the spring before the plants start to grow, particularly if they are to be held in cold storage. Special machine diggers have been developed which handle great quantities of plants. The plants are hauled immediately after digging to packing sheds where they are cleaned and all but the youngest leaves removed. They are packed in fairly tight wood or cardboard boxes for storing or shipping. A polyethylene lining in the boxes is beneficial in keeping the plants in good condition *(161)*. They are usually handled in one thousand plant units and packed firmly in the boxes with the roots to the center. Such plants can be stored and kept in good condition for as long as one year if held at temperatures between 28° and 30°F.

Crown division is the usual method of propagating everbearing varieties. Some varieties, such as the Rockhill, may produce ten to fifteen strong crowns per plant by the end of the growing season. In the spring, such plants are dug and carefully cut apart; each crown may then be used as a new plant.

Certification programs have been established so that nursery sources of disease and insect-free, true-to-name plants of most varieties are available *(4, 33, 128)*. Strawberry plants can be freed of nematodes by hot water bath treatments, dormant plants being immersed for 2 minutes in water at 127°F. *(43)*.

Tangerine. See Citrus.

Theobroma cacao. See Cacao.

Vaccinium corymbosum. See Blueberry, Highbush.

Vaccinium macrocarpon. See Cranberry.

Vitis sp. See Grape.

Walnuts *(Juglans* sp.). Persian (English) walnut *(J. regia* L.). Walnut varieties are propagated either by patch budding (or one of its variations—see p. 386)—or crown grafting (see p. 362) 1-year-old seedling rootstocks, or by topworking seedling trees, 1 to 4 years or more old, planted in place in the orchard. Bark grafting (see p. 336) in late spring or patch budding in the spring or summer works well for the latter method.

Rootstocks for Persian Walnut Varieties. Nuts of most of the *Juglans* species used as seedling rootstocks should be stratified for about 3 months before they are planted to obtain good germination. Although Persian walnut seeds will germinate without any cold treatment, a stratification period hastens germination. Drying of the nuts should be prevented. It is better to plant the seeds before they start sprouting in the stratification boxes, but with care sprouted seeds can be successfully planted. At the end of one season, the seedlings should be large enough to bud.

Northern California black walnut (*J. hindsii*). This is the stock most commonly used in California. The seedlings are vigorous, make a strong graft union, and will withstand adverse soil conditions. They are resistant to oak root fungus (*Armillaria mellea*) and the root-knot nematode (*Meloidogyne* sp.), but they are susceptible to crown rot (*Phytophthora* sp.) and the lesion nematode (*Pratylenchus vulnus*) *(123)*.

A very serious defect, known as "blackline," appears occasionally in Persian walnut trees on this rootstock after the trees are 15 to 30 years old. It is characterized by a breakdown of the tissues in the cambial region at the graft union, leading to a girdling effect on the trees. The cause of this defect has not yet been established. Symptoms are an unhealthy, yellowish-green leaf color, a reduction in leaf area and crop, black lesions at the graft union, and a heavy production of watersprouts or suckers from the black walnut stock below the graft union.

Southern California black walnut (J. californica). Seedlings of this species were once popular as rootstocks but have been little used in recent years. It is highly susceptible to crown rot, the crown below the union usually becomes greatly enlarged, and the roots sucker badly. It is not as vigorous as *J. hindsii.* Sometimes this stock is mistakenly used in place of *J. hindsii,* thus producing trees very susceptible to crown rot troubles.

Eastern black walnut (J. nigra). Rootstocks of this species produce good trees, but they grow slowly when young, delaying the age when the trees reach full bearing. This stock is commonly used in the eastern part of the United States and in Europe for Persian walnut varieties. Its long taproot tends to make transplanting nursery trees difficult.

Persian walnut (J. regia). Seedlings of this species produce good trees with an excellent graft union and are the most resistant of any walnut stock to crown rot. The roots are not resistant to oak root fungus or tolerant of salt accumulations in the soil and are not as resistant to root-knot nematodes as *J. hindsii.* Nurserymen object to the slow initial growth of the seedlings. Trees on this stock should be quite satisfactory in soils free of oak root fungus and salt accumulation. Its use is recommended in some localities as a means of avoiding the blackline disease.

Paradox walnut (J. hindsii × J. regia). This is a hybrid stock, the seedlings being obtained from seed taken from *J. hindsii* trees, whose pistillate (female) flowers have been wind pollinated with pollen from nearby *J. regia* trees. When the seeds from such a *J. hindsii* tree are planted in a nursery, some of the seedlings may be the hybrid progeny. The amount varies widely, from 0 to almost 100 per cent, depending upon the individual mother tree. The hybrids are easily distinguished by their large leaves in comparison with the smaller-leaved, self-pollinated *J. hindsii* seedlings (see Fig. 4-3). Although the seedlings are variable, most of them exhibit hybrid vigor and make excellent rootstocks for the Persian walnut. They are resistant to root lesion

Figure 16–8. Steps in the modified cleft graft used in propagating the Eastern black walnut. **(left to right)** Scion cut to a wedge. Stock cut diagonally with the scion inserted. Waxed cloth placed over cut surfaces and the union tied with raffia. Scion and stub after waxing. From **Cornell Ext. Bul. 701, Nut Growing.**

nematodes *(123)* and crown rot and are tolerant of excess water. Trees on this stock grow and yield as well or better than those on *J. hindsii* roots and may produce larger sized nuts with better kernel color *(124)*. In very heavy or low fertility soils, trees on Paradox roots will grow faster than those on *J. hindsii.*

Since it is difficult to secure Paradox seeds in quantity, vegetative propagation methods would be very desirable in order to establish superior Paradox clones from which large numbers of rootstock plants could be obtained. Propagation by cuttings and trench layering (see p. 411) seems promising *(88; 125).*

Royal walnut (J. nigra × J. hindsii or *J. californica).* This is used to a limited extent as a rootstock for Persian walnuts. It is more tolerant of excessive soil moisture than *J. hindsii,* but probably not more than *J. nigra* or Paradox.

Chinese wing nut (Pterocarya stenoptera) (157). The strongly growing seedlings of this species are under trial as rootstocks for the Persian walnut. Although they are not thoroughly tested, some walnut varieties, especially Eureka, seem to make a compatible union with it. This stock has a high degree of resistance to the root lesion nematode *(123),* but is not as resistant to oak root fungus as *J. hindsii.*

Eastern black walnut *(J. nigra* L.). The several named black walnut varieties are propagated by patch or ring budding (see p. 392) and grafting (especially the modified cleft graft) on eastern black walnut seedlings *(J. nigra),* which seems to be a satisfactory rootstock *(20, 24, 89, 135).*

The modified cleft graft, as illustrated in Figure 16-8, is suitable for seedling stocks up to about one inch in diameter. The scion is cut to a wedge, slightly thicker on one side than the other. The stock is cut diagonally rather than being split. The scion is inserted into this cleft, the thicker part out, with the cambium of stock and scion matching.

Zizyphus jujuba. See **Jujube.**

REFERENCES

1. Albert, D. W., Propagation of date palms from offshoots, *Ariz. Agr. Exp. Sta. Bul. 119,* 1926.

2. Aldrich, W. W., G. H. Leach, and W. A. Dollins, Some factors influencing the growth of date offshoots in the nursery row, *Proc. Amer. Soc. Hort. Sci.,* 46:215–221. 1945.

3. Angelo, E., Experiences in propagating *Rubus* and other species by leaf-bud cuttings, *Proc. Amer. Soc. Hort. Sci.,* 35:448–450. 1938.

4. Anonymous, Development of virus-free and nematode-free strawberry plant stocks, *Rpt. Hort. Crops Res. Branch. Agr. Res. Ser. USDA,* 1955.

5. Anthony, R. D., and W. S. Clarke, Jr., Performance of clonal understocks at the Pennsylvania State College, *Proc. Amer. Soc. Hort. Sci.,* 48:212–226. 1946.

6. Arndt, C. H., Mango polyembryony and other multiple shoots, *Amer. Jour. Bot.,* 22:26. 1935.

7. Bailey, J. E., and J. G. Woodroof, Propagation of pecans, *Ga. Agr. Exp. Sta. Bul. 172,* 1932.

8. Batchelor, L. D., and H. J. Webber, *The Citrus Industry,* Vol. II, Berkeley: Univ. of Calif. Press, 1948. Chs. 1, 2, and 3.

9. Batchelor, L. D., and W. P. Bitters, High quality citrus rootstocks, *Calif. Agr.,* 6(9):3–4. 1952.

10. Beaumont, J. H., and R. H. Moltzau, Propagating macadamia, *Hawaii Agr. Exp. Sta. Cir. 13, 1937.*

11. Bitters, W. P., Rootstocks with dwarfing effect, *Calif. Agr.,* 4(2):5, 14. 1950.

12. Bitters, W. P., and L. D. Batchelor, Citrus rootstock problems, *Calif. Agr.,* 6(2):8, 12. 1952.

13. Bitters, W. P., and E. R. Parker, Quick decline of citrus as influenced by top-root relationships, *Calif. Agr. Exp. Sta. Bul. 733, 1953.*

14. Bitters, W. P., *et al.,* Limitations in the use of Troyer citrange rootstock, *Citrus Leaves,* 35:10–11, 26. 1955.

15. Blackmon, G. H., and R. H. Sharpe, Pecan growing in Florida, *Fla. Agr. Exp. Sta. Bul. 437, 1951.*

16. Brase, K. D., Similarity of the Clark Dwarf and East Malling Rootstock VIII, *Proc. Amer. Soc. Hort. Sci.,* 61:95–98. 1953.

17. ———, Western sand cherry—a dwarfing stock for prunes, plums, peaches, *Farm Research* (N.Y. Agr. Exp. Sta.), 19(1):4. 1953.

18. ———, Ten years' results with size-controlling rootstocks, *Farm Research.* (N.Y. Agr. Exp. Sta.), 19(4):8–9. 1953.

19. ———, Dwarf fruit trees for the serious amateur, *Nat. Hort. Mag.,* 32(4):211–217. 1953.

20. Brierley, W. G., Effects of hormone and warm temperature treatments upon growth of black walnut root grafts, *The Nutshell,* Northern Nut Growers' Assoc., 7(2):6–8. 1955.

21. Cameron, J. W., and R. K. Soost, Nucellar lines of citrus, *Calif. Agr.,* 7(1):8, 15, 16. 1953.

22. Camp, A. F., Citrus propagation, *Fla. Ext. Bul. 139, 1950.*

23. Carlson, R. F., and H. B. Tukey, Cultural practices in propagating dwarfing rootstocks in Michigan, *Mich. Agr. Exp. Sta. Quart. Bul 37*(4):492–497. 1955.

24. Chase, S. B., Budding and grafting eastern black walnut, *Proc. Amer. Soc. Hort. Sci.,* 49:175–180. 1947.

25. Cheeseman, E. E., The vegetative propagation of cacao, *Trop. Agr.,* 12:240–246. 1935.

26. Cobin, M., The lychee in Florida, *Fla. Agr. Exp. Sta. Bul. 546, 1954.*

27. Coe, F. M., Cherry rootstocks, *Utah Agr. Exp. Sta. Bul. 319, 1945.*

28. Collins, J. L., History, taxonomy, and culture of the pineapple, *Econ. Bot.,* 3:335–359. 1949.

29. Condit, I. J., *The Fig.* Waltham, Mass.: Chronica Botanica, 1947. Chap. 12.

30. Crowley, D. J., The cultivated cranberry in Washington, *Wash. Agr. Exp. Sta. Bul. 349, 1937.*

31. Darrow, G. M., and S. B. Detwiler, Currants and gooseberries: their culture and relation to white pine blister rust. *USDA Farmers' Bul. 1398, 1940.*

32. Darrow, G. M., Blueberry growing, *USDA Farmers' Bul. 1951. 1957.*

33. Darrow, G. M., A. C. Goheen, and P. W. Miller, The importance of virus diseases in the cultivation of strawberries in the United States, *Proc. Amer. Soc. Hort. Sci.,* 63:547–552. 1954.

34. Day, L. H., Cherry rootstocks in California, *Calif. Agr. Exp. Sta. Bul. 725, 1951.*

35. Day, L. H., and E. F. Serr, Comparative resistance of rootstocks of fruit and nut trees to attack by root lesion or meadow nematode, *Proc. Amer. Soc. Hort. Sci.,* 57:150–154. 1951.

36. Doehlert, C. A., Propagating blueberries from hardwood cuttings, *N.J. Agr. Exp. Sta. Cir. 551, 1953.*

37. duPreez, D., Propagation of guavas. *Fmg. South Afr.,* 29:297–299. 1954.

38. Eggers, E. R., and F. F. Halma, Propagating the avocado by means of stem cuttings, *Calif. Avocado Assoc. Yearbook,* pp. 63–66. 1936.

39. Evans, H., Investigations on the propagation of cacao, *Trop. Agr.,* 28:147–203. 1951.

40. ———, Physiological aspects of the propagation of cacao from cuttings, *Rpt. 13th Int. Hort. Cong.,* Vol. 2, 1179–1190. 1953.

41. Franklin, H. J., Cranberry growing in Massachusetts, *Mass. Agr. Exp. Sta. Bul. 447,* 1948.

42. Frolich, E. F., Rooting Guatemalan avocado cuttings, *Calif. Avocado Assoc. Yearbook,* pp. 136–138. 1951.

43. Goheen, A. C., and J. R. McGrew, Control of endoparasitic root nematodes in strawberry propagation stocks by hot water treatments. *USDA Plant Disease Rptr.,* 38:818–826. 1954.

44. Gossard, A. C., Rooting pecan stem tissue by layering, *Proc. Amer. Soc. Hort. Sci.,* 38:213–214. 1941.

45. ———, The rooting of pecan softwood cuttings under continuous mist, *Proc. Amer. Soc. Hort. Sci.,* 44:251–254. 1944.

46. Gould, H. P., The native papaw, *USDA Leaflet 179,* 1939.

47. ———, The Oriental persimmon, *USDA Leaflet 194,* 1940.

48. Grubb, N. H., *Cherries.* London: Crosby, Lockwood, 1949. Chap. IV.

49. Guiscafre-Arrillage, J., The propagation of coffee (*Coffea arabica* L.) by cuttings, *Proc. Amer. Soc. Hort. Sci.,* 48:279–290. 1946.

50. Haas, A. R. C., Propagation of the Fuerte avocado by means of leafy-twig cuttings, *Calif. Avocado Assoc. Yearbook,* pp. 126–130. 1937.

51. Haas, A. R. C., and J. N. Brusca, Zutano avocado cuttings rooted, *Calif. Agr.,* 7(10):11–12. 1953.

52. Halma, F. F., The propagation of citrus by cuttings, *Hilgardia,* 6:131–157. 1931.

53. ———, Own-rooted and budded lemon trees, *Proc. Amer. Soc. Hort. Sci.,* 50:172–176. 1947.

54. Halma, F. F., and E. R. Eggers, Propagating citrus by twig-grafting, *Proc. Amer. Soc. Hort. Sci.,* 34:289–290. 1937.

55. Halma, F. F., K. M. Smoyer, and H. W. Schwalm, Quick decline associated with sour rootstocks, *Calif. Citrogr.,* 29:245. 1944.

56. Hamilton, R. A., and H. Seagrave-Smith, Growing guava for processing, *Univ. of Hawaii Ext. Bul. 63,* 1954.

57. Hansen, C. J., and D. Kester, Almond varieties on plum roots, *Calif. Agr.,* 9(9):9. 1955.

58. Hansen, C. J., B. F. Lownsbery, and C. O. Hesse, Nematode resistance in peaches, *Calif. Agr.,* 10(9): 5, 11. 1956.

59. Hardy, M. B., The propagation of Chinese chestnuts, *40th Ann. Rpt. Northern Nut Growers' Assoc.,* pp. 121–130. 1949.

60. Harkness, R. W., Papaya growing in Florida, *Fla. Agr. Ext. Cir. 133,* 1955.

61. Harmon, F. N., and E. Snyder, The "T" bud method, an aid to grape propagation, *Proc. Amer. Soc. Hort. Sci.,* 37:663–665. 1940.

62. Harmon, F. N., Influence of indolebutyric acid on the rooting of grape cuttings, *Proc. Amer. Soc. Hort. Sci.,* 42:383–388. 1943.

63. Harmon, F. N., and E. Snyder, Some factors affecting the success of greenwood grafting of grapes, *Proc. Amer. Soc. Hort. Sci.,* 52:294–298. 1948.

64. Harmon, F. N., A modified procedure for greenwood grafting of vinifera grapes, *Proc. Amer. Soc. Hort. Sci.,* 64:255–258. 1954.

65. Hartmann, H. T., Further studies on the propagation of the olive by cuttings, *Proc. Amer. Soc. Hort. Sci.,* 59:155–160. 1952.

66. ———, Auxins for hardwood cuttings. *Calif. Agr.,* 9(4):7, 12, 13. 1955.

67. Hartmann, H. T., and C. J. Hansen, Rooting of softwood cuttings of several fruit species under mist, *Proc. Amer. Soc. Hort. Sci.*, 66:157–167. 1955.

68. ———, Rooting pear, plum rootstocks, *Calif. Agr.*, 12(10):4, 14–15. 1958.

69. Hatton, R. G., Rootstocks for pears. *in* Apples and pears, varieties and cultivation in 1934. *Rpt. Conf. Roy. Hort. Soc.*, pp. 154–166. 1935.

70. ———, Rootstocks for pears, *Ann. Rpt. East Malling Res. Sta. for 1934*, pp. 75–86. 1935.

71. ———, Plum rootstock studies: their effect on the vigor and cropping of the scion variety, *Jour. Pom. and Hort. Sci.*, 14:97–136. 1936.

72. Hearman, J., The Northern Spy as a rootstock, *Jour. Pom. and Hort. Sci.*, 14: 246–275. 1936.

73. Heppner, M. J., Pear black-end and its relation to different rootstocks, *Proc. Amer. Soc. Hort. Sci.*, 24:139–142. 1927.

74. Hitchcock, A. E., and P. W. Zimmerman, Root-inducing substances effective on apple cuttings taken in May, *Proc. Amer. Soc. Hort. Sci.*, 40:292–297. 1942.

75. Hodgson, R. W., Rootstocks for the Oriental persimmon, *Proc. Amer. Soc. Hort. Sci.*, 37:338–339. 1940.

76. Hume, H. H., *Citrus Fruits*. New York: Macmillan, 1957. Chs. XIV and XV.

77. Husmann, G., E. Snyder, and F. Husmann, Testing vinifera grape varieties grafted on phylloxera-resistant rootstocks in California, *USDA Tech. Bul. 697*, 1939.

78. Jacob, H. E., Propagation of grape vines, *Calif. Agr. Ext. Cir. 101*, 1936.

79. ———, Vineyard planting stock, *Calif. Agr. Exp. Sta. Cir. 360*, 1944.

80. Johnston, J. C., and E. F. Frolich, Avocado propagation, *Calif. Agr. Exp. Sta. Cir. 463*, 1957.

81. Johnston, J. C., Growing citrus seedlings, *Calif. Agr. Exp. Sta. Leaflet 22*, 1954.

82. Johnston, S., Oriental pear stocks tested in Michigan, *Quart. Bul. Mich. Agr. Exp. Sta. 13:*67–68. 1930.

83. Joiner, J. N., Citrus rootstocks, *Fla. Agr. Ext. Cir. 132*, 1955.

84. Joley, L. E., and W. E. Whitehouse, Rootknot nematode susceptibility—a factor in the selection of pistachio nut rootstocks, *Proc. Amer. Soc. Hort. Sci.*, 61: 99–102. 1953.

85. Khan, A. H., *Dematophora* root rot, *Calif. Dept. Agr. Bul. 44:*167–170. 1955.

86. Loomis, N. H., Rootstocks for grapes in the south, *Proc. Amer. Soc. Hort. Sci.*, 42:380–382. 1943.

87. Lynch, S. J., and R. O. Nelson, Current methods of vegetative propagation of avocado, mango, lychee, and guava in Florida, *Cieba* (Escuela Agricola Panamericana, Tegucigalpa, Honduras), 4:315–337. 1956.

88. Lynn, C., and H. T. Hartmann, Rooting cuttings under mist—Paradox walnut, *Calif. Agr.*, 11(5):11, 15. 1957.

89. MacDaniels, L. H., Nut growing, *Cornell Ext. Bul. 701*, 1952.

90. Magoon, C. A., and I. W. Dix, On aerial propagation of grapes, *Proc. Amer. Soc. Hort. Sci.*, 38:388–392. 1941.

91. Malan, E. F., Pineapple production in South Africa, *South Afr. Dept. Agr. Bul. 339*, 1954.

92. Malan, E. F., and A. van der Meulen, Propagation of avocados, *Fmg. South Afr.*, 29:499–502. 1954.

93. Maney, T. J., and H. H. Plagge, Three apple stocks especially well adapted to the practice of double-working, *Proc. Amer. Soc. Hort. Sci.*, 32:330–333. 1935.

94. Maney, T. J., Dwarfing stocks, *Proc. Iowa State Hort. Soc.*, 72:126–130. 1942.

95. Marshall, R. E., *Cherries and Cherry Products*. New York: Interscience, 1954.

96. McClintock, J. A., The effect of stocks on the yield of Grimes apple, *Proc. Amer. Soc. Hort. Sci.*, 35:369–371. 1938.

97. McDaniel, J. C., The present status of apple and pear understocks, *Trans. Ill. State Hort. Soc.,* 87:45–55. 1953.

98. McHatton, T. H., and J. G. Woodroof, Some factors influencing pecan germination, *Proc. Amer. Soc. Hort. Sci.,* 24:125–129. 1927.

99. McKay, J. W., and H. L. Crane, Chinese chestnut. A promising new orchard crop. *Econ. Bot.,* 7:228–242. 1953.

100. Miller, V. J., A trunk disorder of Virginia Crab interstocks, *Proc. Amer. Soc. Hort. Sci.,* 64:159–164. 1955.

101. Mortensen, E., and V. A. Randolph, Grape production in Texas, *Tex. Agr. Exp. Sta. Cir. 89,* 1940.

102. Nelson, R. O., Propagation of guavas by graftage, *Proc. Fla. State Hort. Soc.,* 67:228–231. 1954.

103. Nelson, S. H., and H. B. Tukey, Root temperature affects the performance of East Malling apple rootstocks, *Quart. Bul. Mich. Agr. Exp. Sta.,* 38:46–51. 1955.

104. Naik, K. C., Mango propagation studies, *Indian Jour. Agr. Sci.,* 11:736. 1941.

105. Nixon, R. W., Date culture in the United States, *USDA Cir. 728,* 1951.

106. Opitz, K., Troyer citrange rootstock propagation, *Calif. Citrograph,* pp. 454, 456. Sept., 1951.

107. Opitz, K., and J. C. Johnston, Growing better citrus nursery trees, *Calif. Agr. Exp. Sta. Leaflet 38,* 1954.

108. O'Rourke, F. L., Propagation of the hickories, *44th Ann. Rpt. Northern Nut Growers' Assoc.,* pp. 122–127. 1953.

109. Pease, R. W., Rooting chestnuts from softwood cuttings, *Nat. Hort. Mag.,* 32(4):259–264. 1953.

110. ———, Growing chestnuts from seed, *W. Va. Agr. Exp. Sta. Cir. 90,* 1954.

111. Philp, G. L., Cherry culture in California, *Calif. Agr. Ext. Cir. 46,* 1947.

112. Popenoe, W., Banana culture around the Caribbean, *Trop. Agr.,* 18:33–38. 1941.

113. Preston, A. P., Some new apple rootstocks, *Rpt. 13th Int. Hort. Cong.,* Vol. 1, 267–281. 1953.

114. ———, Some improved apple rootstocks, *The Fruit Yearbook,* No. 7, pp. 43–46. 1954.

115. ———, Apple rootstock studies: Malling-Merton rootstocks, *Jour. Hort. Sci.,* 30:25–33. 1955.

116. Rake, B. A., The propagation of gooseberries. I. Some factors influencing the rooting of hardwood cuttings. *Ann. Rpt. Long Ashton Res. Sta. for 1953,* pp. 79–88. 1954.

117. Reed, C. A., The present status of chestnut growing in the United States, *Proc. Amer. Soc. Hort. Sci.,* 39:147–152. 1941.

118. Reimer, R. C., Blight resistance in pears and characteristics of pear species and stocks, *Ore. Agr. Exp. Sta. Bul. 214,* 1925.

119. ———, Development of blight-resistant French pear rootstocks, *Ore. Agr. Exp. Sta. Bul. 485,* 1950.

120. Ryerson, K., Culture of the Oriental persimmon in California, *Cal. Agr. Exp. Sta. Bul. 416,* 1927.

121. Sax, K., The use of *Malus* species for apple rootstocks, *Proc. Amer. Soc. Hort. Sci.,* 53:219–220. 1949.

122. ———, Interstock effects in dwarfing fruit trees, *Proc. Amer. Soc. Hort. Sci.,* 62:201–204. 1953.

123. Serr, E. F., and L. H. Day, Lesion nematode injury to California fruit and nut trees, and comparative tolerance of various species of Juglandaceae, *Proc. Amer. Soc. Hort. Sci.,* 53:134–140. 1949.

124. Serr, E. F., and H. I. Forde, Comparison of size and performance of mature Persian walnut trees on Paradox hybrid and *J. hindsii* seedling rootstocks, *Proc. Amer. Soc. Hort. Sci.,* 57:198–202. 1951.

125. Serr, E. F., Rooting Paradox walnut hybrids, *Calif. Agr.,* 8(5):7. 1954.

126. Schroeder, C. A., Rootstock influence on fruit set in the Hachiya persimmon, *Proc. Amer. Soc. Hort. Sci.,* 50:149–150. 1947.

127. Schuster, C. E., Filberts, *Ore. Agr. Ext. Bul. 628,* 1945.

128. Schwartz, C. D., and A. S. Myhre, Results of grafting Northwest and Marshall strawberry plants to a virus indicator, *Proc. Amer. Soc. Hort. Sci.,* 58:80–90. 1951.

129. ———, Blueberry propagation, *Wash. Agr. Exp. Sta. Cir. No. 124,* 1954.

130. Sharpe, R. H., Rooting of muscadine grapes under mist, *Proc. Amer. Soc. Hort. Sci.,* 63:88–90. 1954.

131. Shaw, J. K., The propagation and identification of clonal rootstocks for the apple, *Mass. Agr. Exp. Sta. Bul. 418,* 1944.

132. ———, The influence of Malling clonal rootstocks on the growth of certain apple varieties, *Proc. Amer. Soc. Hort. Sci.,* 48:171–179. 1946.

133. Sherwood, H. M., Propagating sub-tropical fruits, *Proc. Fla. State Hort. Soc.,* 53:169. 1940.

134. Singh, L. B., Vegetative propagation of mango (*Mangifera indica* L.) by air-layering, (Gootee), *Science,* 117:158–159. 1953.

135. Sitton, B. G., Vegetative propagation of the black walnut, *Mich. Agr. Exp. Sta. Tech. Bul. 119,* 1931.

136. ———, Pecan grafting methods and waxes, *USDA Cir. 545,* 1940.

137. Smith, L. M., and E. M. Stafford, Grape pests in California, *Calif. Agr. Exp. Sta. Cir. 445,* 1955.

138. Snyder, E., Susceptibility of grape rootstocks to rootknot nematode, *USDA Cir. 405,* 1936.

139. Snyder, E., and F. N. Harmon, Comparative value of nine rootstocks for ten vinifera grape varieties, *Proc. Amer. Soc. Hort. Sci.,* 51:287–294. 1948.

140. Snyder, J. C., Filbert growing in Washington, *Wash. Agr. Ext. Bul. 263,* 1945.

141. Stoutemyer, V. T., T. J. Maney, and B. S. Pickett, A rapid method of propagating raspberries and blackberries by leaf-bud cuttings, *Proc. Amer. Soc. Hort. Sci.,* 30:278–282. 1934.

142. Sudds, R. H., A study of the morphological changes and the origin of roots in tip-layered Cumberland raspberry plants, *Proc. Amer. Soc. Hort. Sci.,* 32:401–406. 1935.

143. ———, Twelve years' results of orchard tests with apple trees on selected rootstocks, Kearneysville, W. Va., *Proc. Amer. Soc. Hort. Sci.,* 48:180–186. 1946.

144. Topper, B. F., How to grow pineapples, *Dept. Agr. Jamaica B. W. I. Ext. Cir. 49,* 1952.

145. Traub, H. P., and L. C. Marshall, Rooting of papaya cuttings, *Proc. Amer. Soc. Hort. Sci.,* 34:291–294. 1937.

146. Traub, H. P., et al., Avocado production in the United States, *USDA Cir. No. 620,* 1941.

147. Tukey, H. B., and K. D. Brase, Trials with pear stocks in New York, *Proc. Amer. Soc. Hort. Sci.,* 30:361–364. 1934.

148. ———, Random notes on fruit-tree rootstocks and plant propagation, II, *N.Y. Agr. Exp. Sta. Bul. 657,* 1935.

149. ———, The dwarfing effect of an intermediate stem-piece of Malling IX, *Proc. Amer. Soc. Hort. Sci.,* 42:357–364. 1943.

150. Tukey, R. B., R. L. Klackle, and J. A. McClintock, Observations on the uncongeniality between some scion varieties and Virginia Crab stocks, *Proc. Amer. Soc. Hort. Sci.,* 64:151–155. 1955.

151. Upshall, W. H., Malling stocks and French Crab seedlings as stocks for five varieties of apples, III, *Sci. Agr.,* 23:537–545. 1943.

152. ———, Malling stocks and French Crab seedlings as stocks for five varieties of apples, IV, *Sci. Agr.*, 28:454–460. 1948.

153. Waring, J. H., and M. T. Hilborn, Hardy stocks in the apple orchard, *Me. Agr. Ext. Bul. 355,* 1947.

154. Weathers, L. G., et al, Lemon on Troyer citrange root, *Calif. Agr.*, 9(11):11–12. 1955.

155. Weschcke, C., *Growing Nuts in the North.* St. Paul: Webb, 1953.

156. Whitehouse, W. E., C. L. Stone, and L. E. Jones, Vigor of *Pistacia* seedling progenies during first season in nursery, *Proc. Amer. Soc. Hort. Sci.*, 48:137–140. 1946.

157. Whitehouse, W. E., and L. E. Joley, Notes on the growth of Persian walnut propagated on rootstocks of the Chinese wingnut, *Pterocarya stenoptera*, *Proc. Amer. Soc. Hort. Sci.*, 52:103–106. 1948.

158. ———, Propagation of the pistachio nut, *Amer. Nurs.*, 97:10–11, 90. 1953.

159. Wolfe, H. S., L. R. Toy, and A. L. Stahl, Avocado production in Florida, *Fla. Agr. Exp. Sta. Bul. 272,* 1934.

160. Wolfe, H. S. and S. J. Lynch, Papaya culture in Florida, *Fla. Agr. Ext. Bul. 113,* 1943.

161. Worthington, T., and D. H. Scott, Strawberry plant storage using polyethylene liners, *Amer. Nurs.*, 105(9):13, 56–57. 1957.

• **Supplementary Reading**

Brase, K. D., "Propagating Fruit Trees," *New York Agricultural Experiment Station Bulletin 773.* 1956.

Chandler, W. H., *Deciduous Orchards,* 3rd ed. Philadelphia: Lea and Febiger, 1957.

———, *Evergreen Orchards,* 2nd ed. Philadelphia: Lea and Febiger, 1958.

Day, L. H., "Apple, Quince, and Pear Rootstocks in California," *California Agricultural Experiment Station Bulletin 700.* 1947.

———, "Rootstocks for Stone Fruits," *California Agricultural Experiment Station Bulletin 736.* 1953.

Feilden, G. S., and R. J. Garner, "Vegetative Propagation of Tropical and Sub-Tropical Plantation Crops," *Imperial Bureau of Horticulture and Plantation Crops, Tech. Comm. No. 13.* 1940.

Hansen, C. J., and H. T. Hartmann, "Propagation of Temperate-Zone Fruit Plants," *California Agricultural Experiment Station Circular 471.* 1958.

Popenoe, W., *Manual of Tropical and Sub-Tropical Fruits.* New York: Macmillan, 1934.

Reed, C. A., and J. Davidson, *The Improved Nut Trees of North America and How to Grow Them.* New York: Devin-Adair. 1954.

Ruehle, G. D., "Miscellaneous Tropical and Sub-Tropical Fruit Plants," *Florida Agricultural Extension Bulletin 156A.* 1958.

Shoemaker, J. S., *Small Fruit Culture,* 3rd ed. New York: McGraw-Hill, 1955.

United States Department of Agriculture, "Dwarf Fruit Trees," *U.S. Dept. of Agr. Leaflet 407.* 1956.

Wallace, T., and R. G. W. Bush, *Modern Commercial Fruit Growing.* London: Country Life, 1956.

17

Propagation of Certain Ornamental Trees, Shrubs, and Woody Vines

This chapter is limited to propagation methods of those woody perennial ornamentals in which there seems to be the greatest amount of interest. It is beyond the scope of this book to attempt to discuss propagation of all plants used as ornamentals.

Abelia (*Abelia* sp.). Leafy cuttings from partially matured current season's growth can be rooted easily under glass in summer or fall. Such cuttings do well under mist and respond markedly to treatments with indolebutyric acid (see p. 244). Hardwood cuttings may also be rooted in fall or spring.

Abies sp. See Fir.

Abutilon (*Abutilon* sp.). Flowering maple, Chinese bell flower. Started by leafy cuttings rooted under glass in the spring or fall.

Acacia (*Acacia* sp.). This is usually propagated by seeds. The impervious seed coats must be softened before planting. This is done by soaking in concentrated sulfuric acid for 20 minutes to 2 hours. Another method is to pour

Figure 17–1. Effect of wounding and treatments with indolebutyric acid on rooting of **Abelia grandiflora** cuttings taken in mid-summer after four weeks under intermittent mist in the greenhouse. **(left)** Wounded and treated with IBA, 4000 ppm, by the concentrated-solution-dip method. **(right)** Wounded but not treated with IBA.

boiling water over the seeds and allow them to soak for 12 hours in the gradually cooling water. Leafy cuttings of partially matured wood can be rooted. Transplanting plants more than a year or two old should be avoided, because of a pronounced taproot.

Acer sp. See Maple.

Aesculus sp. See Buckeye.

Ailanthus (*Ailanthus altissima* Swingle). Tree of Heaven. Seed propagation is easy, and self sowing usually occurs when both male and female trees are grown close together. Embryo dormancy apparently is present in freshly harvested seed. Stratification at about 40°F. for 2 months will aid germination. Seed propagation produces both types of trees, but planting male trees should be avoided, since the staminate flowers produce an obnoxious odor. Propagaagation of the more desirable female trees can easily be done by root cuttings which will sprout readily when planted in the spring.

Albizzia (*Albizzia julibrissin* Durazz.). Silk tree. Started by seeds with some treatment to overcome the impermeable seed coat, such as scarification or brief soaking in sulfuric acid (see p. 126). Root cuttings several inches long and ½ inch or more in diameter may be planted in early spring.

Arborvitae (American [*Thuja occidentalis* L.] and Oriental [*T. orientalis* L.]).

SEEDS. Germination is relatively easy but stratification of seeds for 60 days at about 40°F. may be helpful.

CUTTINGS. *Thuja occidentalis.* These may be taken in midwinter and rooted in frames in the greenhouse. The best rooting is often found with cuttings taken from older plants which are no longer making rapid growth. The cuttings should be about 6 inches in length and may be taken either from succulent, vigorously growing terminals or from more mature side growths several years old. Wounding (see p. 243) and treating with root-inducing chemicals (see p. 244) is beneficial.

Cuttings may also be made in midsummer, rooted out-of-doors in a shaded, closed frame. They should be several inches long and of current season's growth with somewhat matured wood at the base. With good care, they should be rooted by fall.

Thuja orientalis. Cuttings of this species are often more difficult to root than those of *T. occidentalis.* Small, soft cuttings, several inches long, taken in late spring can be rooted in out-of-door mist beds if treated with a root-promoting chemical (see p. 244) (*65*).

GRAFTING. The side graft (see p. 328) is used frequently in propagating selected clones of *T. orientalis,* with 2-year-old potted *T. orientalis* seedlings as the rootstock. Grafting is done in late winter in the greenhouse. After making the graft unions, the potted plants are set in open benches filled with moist peat moss just covering the graft union. The grafted plants should be ready to set out in the field for further growth by midspring.

Arbutus menziesi. See Madrone.

Ash (*Fraxinus* sp.). Seeds of most species germinate readily if stratified for 2 to 4 months at about 40°F. Seeds of *F. excelsior, F. nigra,* and *F. quadrangulata* should have a warm, followed by a cold, stratification period; that is, 2 to 4 months moist storage at room temperature, followed by 2 to 4 months at about 40°F.

Aspen. See Poplar.

Azalea (*Rhododendron* sp.). (*9, 29, 31, 46, 47, 50, 59*). **Evergreen and Semievergreen Types.** Although evergreen azaleas can be propagated by seeds, grafting, and layering, almost all nursery plants are started by cuttings.

SEEDS. The seed capsules should be gathered in the fall after they turn brown and then stored at room temperature in a container that will hold the seed when the capsules open. The seeds have no dormancy problems but will lose viability if held for extended periods in open storage. Sealed, low-temperature storage is preferable for long storage. The seeds can be germinated satisfactorily in a thin layer of screened sphagnum moss over an acid soil mixture. Seed planting is usually done in the greenhouse from midwinter to early spring. Optimum germinating temperatures are about 70°F. during the day and 55°F. at night. Germination is rapid, usually occurring within a month. In areas having hard water, the seedlings should be watered with distilled or rain water because the alkaline salts will soon cause injury.

CUTTINGS. Azalea cuttings of the evergreen and semi-evergreen types are not difficult to propagate, roots forming in 3 to 4 weeks under proper conditions. They are best taken in midsummer after the new current season's growth has become somewhat hardened but before the wood has turned red or brown. The root-promoting growth regulators are often beneficial *(46)*. Azaleas seem to do very well under mist (see p. 251) and will tolerate considerable water during rooting if the medium is well drained. After roots commence forming, excessive water is detrimental, and the mist should be rapidly reduced and finally discontinued.

After rooting, the cuttings may be potted in a mixture suitable for azaleas such as equal parts of leaf mold, sand, and sphagnum or peat.

Deciduous Types. SEEDS. Deciduous azaleas are often propagated by seed due to the difficulty in rooting cuttings. Germination procedures are the same as described for the evergreen types. Growth of the seedlings is sometimes very slow, but with early spring seed germination and early transplanting to a good growing medium, it is possible to have plants large enough to set flower buds in their second year. The seedlings should be partially shaded during all phases of growth.

CUTTINGS. With a few notable exceptions deciduous azaleas are difficult to propagate by cuttings, but by taking soft, succulent material early in the season, particularly from stock plants brought into the greenhouse and forced, cuttings can be rooted. Timing is very important; it is much better to take the cuttings in the spring than during the summer.

The use of root-promoting chemicals is almost essential in obtaining good rooting. Treatment with indolebutyric acid has been found to be effective. Closed frames with bottom heat and a rooting medium of a sand-peat mixture provide good rooting conditions.

It is not only difficult to root deciduous azalea cuttings, but it is also a problem to get them to survive through the winter even after they are rooted. Following rooting, the cuttings should be set in a cold frame where they will make some growth during the summer. They are best left in the cold frame throughout the winter, then transplanted the following spring.

GRAFTING. This is the chief propagation method for most Holland-imported Ghent and Mollis hybrids. *R. luteum* (*Azalea pontica*) seedlings, 2 or 3 years old, are used as the understock. This method has the disadvantages of undesirable suckering from the understock and a general lack of plant vigor, perhaps due to an unsatisfactory graft union or to a lack of adaptability of the seedling stocks to some climates. The seedlings are potted in early spring with the grafting being done during late summer. A side veneer graft (see p. 328) may be used. The grafted plants are set in closed frames in the greenhouse during healing of the union.

LAYERING. Azaleas are easily layered. For obtaining a limited number of new plants, especially of the deciduous types difficult to start by cuttings, it is a method worth using. Simple, mound, trench, and air layering have all been used satisfactorily.

Bamboo (*Arundinaria, Phyllostachys, Sasa* sp.). This is easily propagated by division of the rhizomes (see p. 445), which grow horizontally at or just below the soil level.

Barberry (*Berberis* sp.). These are propagated without difficulty by fall sowing or spring sowing seeds which have been stratified for 2 to 6 weeks at about 40°F. Leafy cuttings taken from late spring to fall can be rooted under glass. Greenhouse grafting of some selected types is also practiced, and layering is done occasionally.

Beech (*Fagus* sp.). Seeds germinate readily in the spring from fall planting or after being stratified for 3 months at about 40°F. Selected clones are grafted, either by the cleft, whip, or side veneer methods, on seedlings of *F. sylvatica,* the European beech. Frequent transplanting or root pruning of nursery trees is necessary to prevent development of a single long tap root which, if present, makes subsequent transplanting very difficult.

Berberis sp. See Barberry.

Betula sp. See Birch.

Birch (*Betula* sp.). Seeds should either be fall planted or spring planted following stratification at about 40°F. for 1 to 3 months. *B. nigra* matures its seeds in the spring and if planted promptly, the seed will germinate at once without treatment. Some of the selected, weeping forms are grafted on European birch (*B. pendula*) seedlings. Birch is difficult to propagate by cuttings, but leafy cuttings will root to some extent in summer under glass if treated with indolebutyric acid at about 50 ppm for 24 hours (see p. 244). Low growing species can be propagated by layering.

Bittersweet (*Celastrus* sp.). These twining vines have male flowers on one plant and female on another, and both types must be near each other for production of the attractive berries. Seeds should be stratified for about 3 months at 40°F. for good germination. Some nurseries propagate the bittersweet asexually and can supply plants of known sex. Softwood cuttings taken in midsummer root readily under glass. Treatments with indolebutyric acid (see p. 244) will hasten rooting. Hardwood cuttings are also easily rooted and show the same benefits of treatments with root-promoting substances as do the softwood cuttings.

Bottle Brush (*Callistemon* sp.). Although seeds germinate without difficulty, seedlings should be avoided because many of them will prove to be worthless as ornamentals. The preferred method of propagation is by leafy cuttings of partially matured wood which will root under glass quite easily.

Bougainvillea (*Bougainvillea* sp.). This showy evergreen vine, growing out-of-doors only in mild climates, is propagated by cuttings of young wood under glass at any time of the year.

Boxwood (*Buxus sempervirens* L. and *B. microphylla* Sieb. and Zucc.). Cuttings are commonly used, either softwood taken in summer or semi-hardwood taken in the fall. In the latter case, which is ordinarily used, the cuttings are rooted in a cool greenhouse or cold frame during the winter and spring. The rooted cuttings are ready for digging at the end of the summer. Seeds are rarely used due to the very slow growth of the seedlings. Young plants should always be transplanted with a ball of soil around their roots.

Broom (*Cytisus* sp.). Seeds of many of the species germinate satisfactorily if gathered as soon as mature and treated with sulfuric acid to soften the hard seed coat before planting. The seeds are best germinated in a warm location and then transferred to a cooler place when the seedlings are several inches high. The various *Cytisus* species crossbreed readily, so stock plants for seed sources should be kept isolated.

Cuttings can be rooted rather easily if taken from nearly mature wood in late summer or fall.

Buckeye (*Aesculus* sp.). Horse chestnut. This may be propagated by seeds, but prompt sowing or stratification after gathering in the fall is necessary. If the seeds lose their waxy appearance and become wrinkled, their viability will be reduced. For the best germination, seeds should be stratified for 4 months at about 40°F. immediately after collecting. In propagating the low growing species, simple layering (see p. 403) either in spring or fall is often used.

Butterfly Bush (*Buddleia* sp.). Softwood cuttings can be taken in the summer or fall and rooted under glass. Seeds started in the greenhouse in early spring will provide flowering plants by fall, although reproduction is not genetically true by seed.

Buddleia sp. See Butterfly Bush.

Buxus sp. See Boxwood.

Callistemon sp. See Bottle Brush.

Calluna vulgaris. See Heather.

Camellia (*Camellia* sp.). (*6, 18, 23, 24*). Camellias can be propagated by seed, cuttings, grafting, and layering. To perpetuate selected and named varieties, cuttings, grafts, or layers must be used. Seedlings are used in breeding new varieties, as rootstock for grafting, or in growing hedges where foliage is the only consideration.

SEEDS. In the fall when the seed capsules begin to turn reddish-brown and split, they should be gathered before the seeds become scattered. The seed should not be allowed to dry out before planting—in fact the best germination is obtained if they are planted before the seed coat hardens. If the seeds must be stored for long periods, they will keep satisfactorily mixed with ground charcoal and stored in an air-tight container placed in a cool location. After the hard seed coat develops, germination is hastened by pouring boiling water over the seeds and allowing them to remain in the cooling water for 24 hours. Germination presents no particular problem, but well-drained acid soil high in organic matter should be used. It normally takes 4 to 7 years to bring a camellia into flowering from seed.

CUTTINGS. Most *C. japonica* and *C. sasanqua* plants are produced commercially from cuttings which are not particularly difficult to root. *C. reticulata* cuttings do not root easily, however, and this species is generally propagated either by cleft or approach grafting (see p. 331).

Cuttings are best taken in midsummer from the spring flush of growth after the wood has become somewhat matured and has changed from green to light brown in color. Tip cuttings are used, 3 to 6 inches long, with two or three terminal leaves retained. Rooting will be much improved if the cuttings are treated with indolebutyric acid (see p. 244) used at 20 ppm for 24 hours. Wounding (see p. 243) the base of the cuttings before they are treated is also likely to improve rooting. The cuttings root best under high humidity; either a closed frame or under mist (see p. 251). In high humidity climates, open beds can be used if frequent, careful syringing is given.

Camellias may also be started as leaf-bud cuttings (see p. 239), which are handled just as stem cuttings. In this case, excessive concentrations of a root-promoting substance should be avoided because this may inhibit development of the single bud.

GRAFTING. Camellias are frequently grafted, not only to produce nursery plants but to change varieties of older established plants. Seedlings or rooted cuttings of either *C. japonica* or *C. sasanqua* can be used as stocks for grafting, but they should be strong, well-rooted plants before grafting is attempted. In propagating such nursery plants in the greenhouse, one of the side graft methods (see p. 328) is suitable.

Both the cleft and bark graft methods (see pp. 331 and 336) are used for grafting larger, established plants. This is best done in the spring, 2 or 3 weeks before new vegetative growth starts. The stock and the scion should be dormant at the time of grafting. Scions several inches long from terminal shoots containing one or two leaves and several dormant buds are used, inserted into the stock plant which is cut off 2 or 3 inches above the soil level. In cleft grafting, stocks smaller than ½ inch should be wrapped securely with string to hold the scions firmly in place. This is not necessarily with larger stocks. After the graft is completed, the union is usually waxed, but sometimes not. In either case, it should be covered with well-pulverized, moist soil or sand up to the base of the leaves on the scion. A gallon can with both ends removed may be set around the graft, which will hold the soil in place more securely. Following this, a large inverted glass jar should be set over the leafy scion, but it should be shaded to prevent excessively high temperatures inside. After the buds on the scions start growth, the jar is gradually lifted and finally removed.

LAYERING. To obtain a few additional plants from a single mother plant, simple layering (see p. 403) performed in the spring may be done. To do this, branches must be present close to the ground which, preferably, are young and not over about ½ inch in diameter. One or 2 years may be required for sufficient roots to form before the layer can be removed.

Campsis sp. See **Trumpet Creeper.**

Cape Jasmine. See **Gardenia.**

Carob (*Ceratonia siliqua* L.). This is commonly propagated by seeds. They should be soaked in concentrated sulfuric acid for about 30 minutes and then stratified at 32° to 36°F. for 3 months to obtain good germination. Selected varieties are propagated by budding on seedlings.

Catalpa (*Catalpa* sp.). Seeds germinate readily without any previous treatment. They are stored dry over winter at room temperature and planted in late spring. For ornamental purposes, *C. bignonioides nana* is often budded or grafted high on stems of *C. speciosa,* giving the "umbrella tree" effect. A strong shoot is forced from a 1-year-old seedling rootstock, which is then budded with several buds in the fall at a height of about 6 feet. Catalpa species can also be propagated in summer by softwood cuttings rooted under glass.

Ceanothus (*Ceanothus* sp.). Propagation is by seeds, cuttings, layering, and sometimes grafting. Seeds must be gathered shortly before the capsules open or they will be lost. Those of *C. arboreus, C. jepsoni, C. megacarpus, C. oliganthus,* and *C. rigidis* have only seed coat dormancy. Soaking in hot water, as described on page 125, or even boiling in water for 5 minutes will aid germination. To secure germination of other *Ceanothus* species, which have both seed coat and embryo dormancy, the seeds should be covered with hot water (170° to 212°F.) and allowed to soak overnight, then stratified at about 40°F. for 2 to 3 months.

Leafy cuttings may be rooted under glass at any time from spring to fall, especially if treated with a root-promoting substance (see p. 244). Some species root well under mist.

C. americanus seedlings are often used as rootstocks for grafting selected clones.

Cedar (*Cedrus* sp.). Seedlings are easily started either in the fall or spring. No dormancy conditions occur, although soaking the seeds in water several hours before planting is helpful. Cuttings do not root easily, but if taken in late summer or fall some rooting may be obtained. Side veneer grafting (see p. 328) of selected forms on 1- or 2-year-old potted seedling stocks may be done in the spring. Scions should be taken from vigorous terminal growth of current season's wood rather than from lateral shoots.

Celastrus sp. See **Bittersweet.**

Celtis sp. See **Hackberry.**

Chaenomeles sp. See **Quince, Flowering.**

Chamaecyparis (*Chamaecyparis* sp.). False cypress. After collection in the fall, the seeds should be carefully dried in a warm room or in a kiln at 90° to 110°F. Stratification at about 40°F. for 2 to 3 months will aid germination. Cuttings of most species are not difficult to root, particularly if juvenile forms are used (see p. 197). They may be taken in fall or winter and rooted in a closed frame in the greenhouse, using lateral shoots of current season's wood. Indolebutyric acid treatments (see p. 244) are helpful.

Ceratonia siliqua. See **Carob.**

Cercis sp. See **Redbud.**

Cherry, Flowering (*Prunus* sp.) (*55*). Varieties of *P. serrulata, P. serotina, P. sargenti, P. sieboldi, P. yedoensis, P. campanulata,* and *P. subhirtella* comprise the flowering cherries. Seedlings of *P. avium,* the Mazzard cherry, or *P. serrulata* are suitable as rootstocks upon which these ornamental forms may be T-budded (see p. 382), either in the fall or spring. If cross-pollination can be avoided, *P. sargenti, P. campanulata,* and *P. yedoensis* will reproduce true from seed.

Chionanthus sp. See **Fringe Tree.**

Clematis (*Clematis* sp.). Seeds of some clematis species have embryo dormancy, so stratification for 1 to 3 months at about 40°F. is likely to aid germination. Clematis is probably best propagated by cuttings. Young wood with short internodes in the spring often gives satisfactory results, but partially matured wood taken in late spring to late summer is more commonly used. Treatments with indolebutyric acid (see p. 244) are likely to be helpful. Some of the large-flowering hybrids are root grafted by the cleft or side veneer methods (see pp. 331 and 328) in the spring on *C. flammula, C. vitalba,* or *C. viticella* seedlings. The grafts are planted deeply with scion roots forming, the rootstock acting as a nurse-root (see p. 360). When only a few plants are needed, layering (see p. 405) the long canes gives satisfactory results.

Cornus sp. See **Dogwood.**

Cotoneaster (*Cotoneaster* sp.). Seeds should be soaked for about 90 minutes in concentrated sulfuric acid and then stratified for 3 to 4 months at about 40°F. As a substitute for the acid treatment, a moist, warm (60° to 75°F.) stratification treatment for 3 to 4 months may be used. This must be followed by the cold stratification treatment. Leafy cuttings of most species taken from late spring into fall will root under glass without much difficulty. Treatments with indolebutyric acid (see p. 244) are helpful. Simple layering is useful in starting a limited number of plants.

Cottonwood. See Poplar.

Crabapple, Flowering (*Malus* sp.) (*45, 67*). Four species of crabapples—*M. toringoides, M. hupehensis, M. sikkimensis,* and *M. florentina*—will reproduce true from seed. Selected forms of all other crabapple species should propagated by asexual methods and not by seed. Nursery trees are commonly propagated either by root grafting, using the whip or tongue method (see p. 322) or by T-budding (see p. 382) seedlings in the nursery row; the latter is done either as spring or fall budding (see p. 374). Fall budding is considered by most nurserymen to be the fastest and most desirable method of propagating crabapples. In addition, older *Malus* trees may be topworked (see p. 364) to the desired flowering crab variety. Various seedling rootstocks are used such as *M. sylvestris* (common apple), *M. baccata, M. ionensis,* and *M. coronaria.* The flowering Bechtel's Crab is said to show delayed incompatibility, appearing in 10 to 15 years, when worked on *M. sylvestris* seedlings.

Crape Myrtle (*Lagerstroemia indica* L.). This is propagated by cuttings, either hardwood started in the spring or leafy cuttings under glass or under mist in the summer. Transplanting is somewhat difficult, so all but very small plants should be moved with a ball of soil.

Crataegus sp. See Hawthorn.

Cupressus sp. See Cypress.

Cypress (*Cupressus* sp.). It is likely that the seeds of most species have some embryo dormancy, so stratification for several months at about 40°F. would improve germination. Cuttings can be rooted if taken during the winter months. Treatments with indolebutyric acid (see p. 244) at about 60 ppm for 24 hours have aided rooting. Side veneer grafting (see p. 328) of selected forms on seedlings rootstocks in the spring is often practiced.

Cytisus sp. See Broom.

Daphne (*Daphne* sp.). This is generally propagated by leafy cuttings under glass, which are probably best taken in late spring from a partially matured flush of growth. Root-promoting substances (see p. 244) have often been helpful. Layering (see p. 403) is successful using previous season's canes layered in the spring and removed the following spring. The daphnes do not transplant easily and should be moved only when young.

Deutzia (*Deutzia* sp.). This is easily propagated either by hardwood cuttings lined-out in the nursery row in spring or by softwood cuttings under glass in summer.

Dogwood (*Cornus* sp.). The seeds have various dormancy conditions; those of the popular flowering dogwood (*C. florida*) require either fall planting or a stratification period of about 4 months at 40°F. The best germination is obtained if the seeds are gathered as soon as the fruit starts to color and sown or stratified immediately. Other species require, in addition, a treatment to soften the seed covering. Two months in moist sand at diurnally fluctuating temperatures (70° to 85°F.), followed by 4 to 6 months at 32° to 40°F. is effective. With some species, the warm stratification period may be replaced by mechanical scarification or soaking in concentrated sulfuric acid.

Some dogwoods are not difficult to start by cuttings. Those of *C. florida* probably are best taken in late spring or early summer from new growth after flowering, then rooted under glass. Treatments with indolebutyric acid (see p. 244) at 10 to 25 ppm for 24 hours have been helpful. Hardwood cuttings in the spring are successful with certain species, such as *C. alba.*

Choice selected types, such as the red flowering dogwood, *C. florida rubra,* and the weeping forms, are difficult to start by cuttings and are ordinarily propagated by T-budding (see p. 382) in late summer on *C. florida* seedlings. Cuttings of *C. florida rubra* have, however, been successfully rooted in 30 days by taking them in early summer after the second flush of growth and rooting them under intermittent mist (see p. 251) in 1 part peat moss and 3 parts sand (*20*). To insure survival through the following winter in cold climates, the potted cuttings should be kept in a heated cold frame which will hold the temperature between 32° and 45°F.

Douglas Fir (*Pseudotsuga taxifolia* Britt.). Seeds exhibit varying degrees of embryo dormancy. For satisfactory, prompt germination, it is best to sow the seeds in the fall or stratify them for 2 months at about 40°F.

Douglas fir cuttings are rather difficult to root, but by taking them in late winter, treating them with indolebutyric acid at about 50 ppm (see p. 244), and rooting them in a sand-peat moss mixture, it is possible to obtain fairly good rooting.

Elaeagnus (*Elaeagnus* sp.). Russian olive. Silverberry. Seeds planted in the spring germinate readily following a stratification period of 3 months at about 40°F. The Russian olive, *E. angustifolia,* can be started by hardwood cuttings planted in spring. The use of root cuttings or layering is also successful. Leafy cuttings of the evergreen, *E. pungens,* will root if taken in the fall and started under glass.

Elder (*Sambucus* sp.). Seed propagation is somewhat difficult due to complex dormancy conditions involving both the seed coat and embryo. Probably the best treatment is a warm (70° to 85°F.), moist stratification period for 2 months, followed by a cold (40°F.) stratification period for 3 to 5 months. These conditions could be obtained naturally by planting the seed in late summer, after which germination should occur the following spring.

Since softwood cuttings can be rooted rather easily under glass if taken in the spring or summer, this method is generally practiced.

Elm (*Ulmus* sp.). Seed propagation is commonly used. Elm seed loses viability rapidly if stored at room temperature, but it can be kept for several years in sealed containers if held at 32° to 40° F. Seeds ripening in the spring should be sown immediately, germination usually taking place promptly. For those species which ripen their seed in the fall, either fall planting or stratification for 2 months at about 40° F. should be used. To eliminate seedling variation when trees are to be propagated for street planting, some nurserymen bud selected clones on seedlings of the same species.

Although it is not often done commercially, softwood cuttings of several elm species have been successfully rooted under glass when taken in the spring. In some instances, treatments with indolebutyric acid (see p. 244) at about 50 ppm for 24 hours have been beneficial.

Erica sp. See Heath.

Escallonia (*Escallonia* sp.). This is easily started by leafy cuttings following a flush of growth. The cuttings root well under mist (see p. 251) and respond markedly to treatments with indolebutyric acid (see p. 244).

Eucalyptus (*Eucalyptus* sp.). This is almost entirely propagated by seeds planted in the spring. No dormancy conditions occur, the seed being able to germinate immediately following ripening. Mature capsules are obtained just before they are ready to open. Eucalyptus seedlings are very susceptible to damping off, so they should be planted in flats of sterilized soil placed in a shady location. From this they are transplanted into small pots from which they are later lined-out in nursery rows. The roots of young trees will not tolerate drying, so the young plants should be handled as container-grown stock.

Euonymus *(Euonymus* sp.*)*. Stratification for 3 to 4 months at 32° to 50° F. is required for satisfactory seed germination. Euonymus is easily started by cuttings, hardwood in early spring for the deciduous species and leafy semi-hardwood under glass after a flush of growth has partially matured for the evergreen types. Layering is also successful.

False Cypress. See **Chamaecyparis.**

Fir *(Abies* sp.*)*. Seed propagation is not difficult, but fresh seed should be used because those of most species lose their viability after one year in ordinary storage. Embryo dormancy is generally present, fall planting or stratification at about 40° F. for 1 to 3 months being necessary for good germination. Fir seedlings are very susceptible to damping off attacks. They should also be given partial shade during the first season, since they are injured by excessive heat and sunlight.

Fir cuttings are difficult to root, but if they are taken during the winter and treated with indolebutyric acid (see p. 244), quite good percentages can be obtained.

Firethorn. See **Pyracantha.**

Forsythia *(Forsythia* sp.*)*. This is easily propagated by hardwood cuttings set in the nursery row in early spring or by leafy, softwood cutings under high humidity conditions during late spring or summer.

Fraxinus sp. See **Ash.**

Fringe Tree *(Chionanthus virginicus* L. and *C. retusus* L.) *(52)*. Seed propagation can be used, but it is very slow. Dormancy of the embryo as well as some endosperm inhibition seem to be present. Probably the best practice is moist stratification for 30 days or more at room temperature followed by 1 or 2 months stratification at about 40°F. With fall planted seed, germination will not often occur until the second spring.

Cutting propagation of the Chinese fringe tree (*C. retusus*) has generally been considered almost impossible, but by taking softwood cuttings in early June, together with mist sprays (see p. 251), treatments with indolebutyric acid (see p. 244), and the use of a mixture of sand and vermiculite as the rooting medium, excellent rooting percentages can be obtained.

Gardenia *(Gardenia jasminoides* Ellis). Cape jasmine. Leafy terminal cuttings can be rooted in the greenhouse under glass from fall to spring. A mixture of one-half sand and one-half peat moss is a good rooting medium. Gardenias are difficult to transplant and should be moved only when small.

Ginkgo *(Ginkgo biloba* L.). Seed propagation is commonly used. The seeds require a stratification period of several months at about 40°F. for good germination. Seedlings produce either male or female trees. The plum-like fruits on the female trees have a very disagreeable odor, so only male trees are desirable for ornamental planting. For this reason, propagation by cuttings taken from male trees is advisable. Softwood cuttings in midsummer can be rooted under glass.

Gleditsia triacanthos. See **Honeylocust.**

Goldenrain Tree *(Koelreuteria* sp.*)*. This is usually propagated by seed, but root cuttings or softwood cuttings of new growth rooted under glass in the spring can also be used. The seeds have double dormancy (see p. 129), germinating best if the seed coats are softened by soaking for about 60 minutes in concentrated sulfuric acid and followed by stratification for about 90 days at 32° to 40°F. to overcome the embryo dormancy.

Hackberry (*Celtis* sp.). Seeds are ordinarily used, sown either in the fall or stratified for 2 or 3 months at about 40°F. and planted in the spring. Treatments prior to stratification to soften the seed coat, such as soaking in concentrated sulfuric acid, may hasten germination. There is a noticeable variation in the behavior of seedling trees, especially when they are young. A better propagation method would be to use cuttings taken from selected vigorous trees. At least two species, *C. occidentalis* and *C. laevigata,* can be started by cuttings.

Hawthorn (*Crataegus* sp.). These tend to reproduce true by seed. Pronounced seed dormancy is present due to a combination of an impermeable seed coat plus embryo conditions. Probably the best procedure for rapid germination is stratification of freshly collected and cleaned seed in moist peat moss for 3 or 4 weeks at 70° to 80°F. (or treatment with sulfuric acid), followed by stratification for 3 months at about 40°F. Seeds of some *Crataegus* sp. do not have an impermeable seed coat, so the initial high temperature storage period is unnecessary. Untreated seed may require 2 or 3 years to germinate. Since the hawthorn develops a long taproot, transplanting is successful only with very young plants.

Selected clones may be T-budded (see p. 382) or root grafted (see p. 358) on seedlings, usually those of the English hawthorn (*C. oxyacantha*).

Heath (*Erica* sp.) and **Heather** (*Calluna vulgaris* Hull). The propagation of these two closely related genera is about the same. Seeds may be germinated in flats in the greenhouse in winter or in a shaded outdoor cold frame in spring. Leafy, partially matured cuttings taken almost any time of year, but especially in early summer, can be rooted readily under glass. Treatments with indolebutyric acid at about 50 ppm for 24 hours (see p. 244) are likely to be helpful.

Hemlock (*Tsuga* sp.). Hemlocks are propagated by seed without difficulty. Seed dormancy is variable, some lots exhibiting embryo dormancy whereas others do not. To insure good germination, it is advisable to stratify the seeds for 2 to 4 months at about 40°F. Fall planting out-of-doors will generally give satisfactory germination in the spring. The seedlings should be given partial shade during the first season. Hemlock cuttings are somewhat difficult to root, but success has been reported with cuttings taken at all times of the year. They seem to respond to treatments with root-promoting substances (see p. 244). Layering has also been used successfully.

Hibiscus (*Hibiscus syriacus* L.) Shrub-althea. Rose-of-Sharon. This is easily propagated, either by hardwood cuttings set out in the nursery row in the spring, or by softwood cuttings in midsummer under glass. Lateral shoots make good cutting material. The softwood cuttings respond well to treatments with indolebutyric acid (see p. 244).

Hibiscus, Chinese (*Hibiscus rosasinensis* L.) (*10*). A number of methods can be used—seeds, cuttings, budding and grafting, division, and air layering.

CUTTINGS. These are not difficult to root; terminal shoots of partially matured wood of most varieties taken in late spring or early summer usually form roots in about 6 weeks. Leaf-bud cuttings (see p. 239) can also be used if propagating wood is scarce. Rooting should take place under high humidity, such as in a glass-covered frame. The rooted cuttings are generally transferred to some type of container where they are grown to salable size.

GRAFTING. Strongly growing varieties, resistant to soil pests and which can be started easily by cuttings, such as Single Scarlet, Dainty, Euterpe, or Miami Lady, are used as rootstocks. Some varieties develop into much better plants grafted on these rootstocks than when they are on their own roots and propagated by cuttings. Whip grafting in the spring (see p. 322) or side grafting (see p. 328) in late spring or early summer is successful. Scions of current season's growth, about pencil size, are grafted on rooted cuttings of about the same size with the union covered by grafting wax or paraffin.

BUDDING. T-budding using an inverted T (see p. 385) is sometimes practiced, generally in the spring, although it is successful at any time during the year when the bark is slipping.

AIR LAYERING (see p. 406). This is practiced during the spring or summer, particularly for varieties difficult to start by cuttings. Roots will usually form in 6 to 8 weeks.

Holly (*Ilex* sp.) (*25, 41, 43, 44*). Holly can be propagated by seeds, cuttings, grafting, budding, layering, and division.

Most hollies are dioecious. The female plants produce the very desirable decorative berries if male plants are nearby for pollination. In seed propagation, both male and female plants are produced in the ratio of one female to three, or sometimes up to ten, male plants. Sex cannot be determined, however, until the seedlings start blooming, which may be at 4 to 12 years.

SEEDS. Germination of holly seed is very erratic; those of some species, *I. crenata, I. cassine, I. glabra,* and *I. myrtifolia,* germinate promptly and should be planted as soon as they are gathered. Seeds of other species, including the ones of most interest, do not germinate until a year after planting even though stratified.

Seeds of *Ilex aquifolium* (English holly), *I. opaca* (American holly), and *I. cornuta* (Chinese holly) should be collected and cleaned as soon as the fruit is ripe in the fall and then stratified until spring in a mixture of moist sand and peat moss. Germination of these species generally does not occur until a year later, and then growth is very slow, two seasons being required to bring seedlings of *I. opaca* to a size large enough to be used for grafting.

CUTTINGS. This is the method most in use at present by commercial nurserymen, permitting large scale production of choice clones. Semi-hardwood tip cuttings made from well-matured current season's growth will produce the best plants, but lateral shoots can also be used.

Timing is important; the best rooting is usually obtained from mid- to late summer, but cuttings are successfully taken on into January (*56, 68*).

Wounding (see p. 243) the base of the cuttings seems to help induce root formation. The wounding induced by stripping off the lower leaves may be sufficient, especially with *I. crenata*.

The use of a root-promoting chemical, particularly indolebutyric acid, is almost essential in obtaining rooting of some varieties, whereas in others this is not needed (*53*).

A rooting medium of one-half sand and one-half peat moss has generally proved to be satisfactory, and the application of bottom heat is beneficial. In fact, air temperatures of 95° to 110°F., provided 100 per cent humidity was maintained, have given excellent rooting (*32*). The use of intermittent mist (see p. 251) in greenhouse propagation where high temperatures can be maintained provides good rooting conditions.

The cuttings will root in 1 to 3 months and can then be potted. It is very important that they be gradually hardened off during removal from the rooting bed to out-of-door conditions.

GRAFTING AND BUDDING. Hollies are easily grafted, the cleft, whip, and side grafts (see pp. 331, 322, and 328) being used. The operation is best performed during the dormant season for field grafting. Grafting is often done on greenhouse potted stock. Callusing is rapid under such conditions, especially if the union is coated with lanolin (*34*). T-budding (see p. 382) is also suitable, being done in late summer or early spring. The inverted T-bud is commonly used in Florida. *Ilex opaca* is a satisfactory stock for its own varieties and those of *I. aquifolium,* but probably the best stocks for English holly are *I. aquifolium* and *I. cornuta.*

AIR LAYERING (see p. 406). This method has been found to be successful for a number of *Ilex* species. The layers are best started in June and early July; after 10 to 14 weeks, plants 1 to 2 feet high can be produced (*34*).

Honeylocust, Common (*Gleditsia triacanthos* L.). This is readily propagated both by seeds planted in the spring or by cuttings. The thornless honey locust, *G. triacanthos,* var. *inermis,* and the thornless and fruitless patented Moraine locust, are usually propagated by grafting on seedlings of the thorny type. In seed propagation, some treatment just before planting is necessary to soften the impermeable seed coat (see p. 94). There is no embryo dormancy, thus stratification is unnecessary. Hardwood cuttings planted in the spring have been rooted successfully.

Honeysuckle (*Lonicera* sp.). The seed show considerable variation in their dormancy conditions; some species having both seed coat and embryo dormancy, some only embryo dormancy, and some no dormancy. This variability also occurs among different lots of seeds of the same species. In *L. tatarica* some lots have no seed dormancy, stratification even retarding germination. In general, however, for prompt germination, stratification for 2 to 3 months at about 40°F. is recommended. Seeds of *L. hirsuta* and *L. oblongifolia* should have 2 months warm (70° to 85°F.) stratification, followed by 2 to 3 months stratification at about 40°F.

Most honeysuckle species are propagated easily by either hardwood cuttings in the spring or leafy softwood cuttings of summer growth under glass. Layering of the vine types, such as Hall's honeysuckle, is very easy, roots forming wherever the canes touch moist ground.

Horse chestnut. See Buckeye.

Hydrangea (*Hydrangea* sp.). This is easily rooted by leafy, softwood cuttings which do well under mist and respond markedly to indolebutyric acid treatments (see p. 244). Leaf-bud cuttings can be used if propagating material is scarce, two cuttings being obtained from the two opposite leaves at each node. Hardwood cuttings planted in early spring are often used in propagating *H. paniculata grandiflora.*

Hypericum sp. See St. Johnswort.

Jasmine (*Jasminum* sp.). This is propagated without difficulty by leafy, semi-hardwood cuttings taken in late summer and rooted under glass. Layers and suckers can also be used.

Juniper (*Juniperus* sp.) (*21, 30, 51, 69*). The junipers are usually propagated by cuttings, but in some cases difficult-to-root types are grafted on seedlings. The low-growing, prostrate forms are easily layered.

SEEDS. Seedlings of the red cedar, *Juniperus virginiana* or *J. chinensis,* are ordinarily used as stocks for grafting ornamental clones.

The seeds should be gathered in the fall as soon as the berry-like cones become ripe. For the best germination, the seeds should be removed from the fruits and then treated with sulfuric acid for 30 minutes before being stratified, which should last about 4 months at 40°F. As a substitute for the acid treatment, 2 to 3 months warm (70° to 85°F.) stratification or summer planting could be used. As an alternative for cold stratification, the seed may be sown in the fall. Germination is delayed at temperatures above 60°F. Viability of the seeds varies considerably from year to year and among different lots, but it never seems to be much over 50 per cent. Planting of treated seed is usually done in the spring, either in out-of-door beds or in flats in the greenhouse. Two or 3 years are required to produce plants large enough to graft.

CUTTINGS. The spreading, prostrate types of junipers are more easily rooted than upright kinds. Cuttings are often made about 6 inches long from new lateral growth tips stripped off older branches. A small piece of old wood —a heel—is thus left attached to the base of the cutting. Some propagators believe this to be advantageous. In other cases, very good results are obtained when the cuttings are just clipped without the heel from the older wood. Terminal growth of current season's wood has rooted well in some instances.

Juniper cuttings to be rooted in the greenhouse are best taken during the winter, from November through February (66). Taking the cuttings after the stock plants have been exposed to some sub-freezing temperatures seems to give better rooting. For propagating in an out-of-door cold frame, cuttings are usually taken in late August or early September. Lightly wounding (see p. 243) the base of the cuttings is helpful, and the use of root-inducing chemicals, especially indolebutyric acid, (see p. 244) is also beneficial, as shown in Figure 10–14.

GRAFTING. Vigorous seedling understocks with straight trunks, about pencil size, are dug in the fall from the seedling bed and potted in small pots set in peat moss in a cool, dry greenhouse. Seedlings potted earlier—in the spring—may also be used. After about 30 days, the greenhouse is heated and the plants kept well watered. This stimulates growth activity so that after 1 or 2 weeks the plants resume root activity and are in a suitable condition for grafting.

The scions should be selected from current season's growth taken from vigorous, healthy plants and preferably of the same diameter as the stock to be grafted. Scion material can be stored at temperatures of 30° to 40°F. for several weeks until used if it is kept in a saturated atmosphere.

The side veneer or side graft (see pp. 328 and 326) are the methods ordinarily used. The grafts are best tied with budding rubber strips. The grafted plants are set deep enough in a greenhouse bench filled with peat moss to keep the union covered. The temperature around the graft union should be kept as constant as possible at 75°F., with a relative humidity of 85 per cent or above around the tops of the plants. A lightly shaded greenhouse should be used to avoid burning the grafts. Adequate healing will take place in 2 to 8 weeks, after which the temperature and humidity can be lowered. The stock plant is then cut off above the graft union, allowing the scion to develop.

Koelreuteria sp. See Goldenrain Tree.

Lagerstromia indica. See Crape Myrtle.

Larch (*Larix* sp.). Most of these deciduous conifers are propagated easily by fall planted seeds. They have a slight embryo dormancy, so for spring planting stratification for 1 to 2 months at about 40°F. is advisable. *Larix lyalli,* the Alpine larch, germinates poorly, however, regardless of the seed treatment. Cutting propagation of the larches seems to be very difficult.

Ligustrum sp. See Privet.

Lilac (*Syringa* sp.) (*7, 28*). Grafting or budding on California privet (*Ligustrum ovalifolium*) or Amur privet (*L. amurense*) cuttings or on lilac or on green ash seedlings is used commercially in lilac propagation. Cuttings can be rooted, however, if close attention is given to proper timing. Layering or division of old plants is quite satisfactory when only a limited number of new plants are needed. Suckers can also be removed from the base of old plants and grown in the nursery for a year or two.

SEEDS. Seedlings are used mostly as an understock for grafting named varieties. They require a stratification period (see p. 97) of 40 to 60 days at about 40°F. for good germination.

CUTTINGS. Ordinarily, good rooting of lilac cuttings can be obtained only if they are taken within a rather narrow period shortly after growth commences in the spring. When the new, green shoots have reached a length of several inches, they snould be cut off and trimmed into cuttings. Since they are very succulent at this stage, it is difficult to prevent wilting. A mist propagating bed (see p. 251) should give excellent results. The use of a root-promoting substance is helpful; indolebutyric acid (see p. 244) at about 50 ppm for 24 hours gives good rooting. Hardwood cuttings are generally unsuccessful.

GRAFTING AND BUDDING. Due to the difficulty in rooting lilac cuttings and the fact that they must be taken at a definite time in the spring at the peak of the nurseryman's busy season, some commercial propagators practice grafting.

When rooted privet cuttings are used as the understock, the lilac may show incompatibility symptoms with the privet, but if the grafts are planted deeply, scion roots rapidly develop from the lilac scion and soon become the predominant root system of the plant. *Syringa vulgaris* seedlings are sometimes used as the stock, but if suckers arise from this stock, there is difficulty in distinguishing them from the selected hybrid lilac top. The plant thus becomes a mixture of growth from the scion and rootstock. Should privet understock produce suckers, however, they can be easily identified and removed. It is best in any case, to plant lilacs "on their own roots," either started as cuttings or with the privet or lilac nurse root already removed.

Grafting is done during the winter season, using rooted privet cuttings which have been dug and brought inside. Vigorous, 1-year-old scion wood is used, taken from plants that have been heavily pruned and well fertilized to induce such growth. Different grafting methods can be used such as the side (see p. 328) or whip or tongue graft (see p. 322). Cleft grafting (see p. 331) on pieces of privet root is also practiced, which tends to eliminate subsequent suckering from the rootstock.

T-BUDDING (see p. 382). T-budding in late summer or early fall is sometimes practiced, the lilac buds being inserted below ground on 1-year-old privet cuttings. The following spring the privet stock is cut off above the bud and soil mounded around the shoot as it develops so as to encourge subsequent rooting from the lilac.

LAYERING. Simple layering (see p. 403) of 1-year shoots arising from the base of plants on their own roots provides an easy propagation method where only a few plants are needed. Air-layering of 1- or 2-year-old branches is also successful.

Linden *(Tilia* sp.). Basswood. The seeds have a dormant embryo and an impermeable seed coat, which in some species is surrounded by a hard, tough pericarp. Such seeds are slow and difficult to germinate. For *T. americana*, removing the pericarp mechanically or by soaking in concentrated nitric acid for ½ to 2 hours, rinsing thoroughly and drying, then soaking the seeds for about 15 minutes in concentrated sulfuric acid to etch the seed coat, followed by stratification for 4 months at 35°F., should give fairly good germination. For *T. cordata,* warm (60° to 80°F.) stratification for 4 to 5 months followed by an equal period at 35° to 40°F. is necessary.

Suckers arising around the base of trees cut back to the ground have been successfully mound layered (see p. 409).

Liquidambar *(Liquidambar styraciflua* L.). American Sweet Gum. Propagation is usually by seed which is collected in the fall. Stratification for 1 to 3 months at about 40°F. is recommended to overcome the dormancy conditions.

Leafy, softwood cuttings of partially matured wood made with a heel of old wood at the base can be rooted under glass in midsummer.

Liriodendron tulipifera. See Tulip Tree.

Lonicera sp. See Honeysuckle.

Madrone, Pacific *(Arbutus menziesi* Pursh.). This Pacific Coast evergreen tree is usually propagated by seed which has been stratified for 3 months at 35° to 40°F. Seedlings are started in flats then transferred to pots. They are difficult to transplant and should be set in their permanent location when not over 18 inches tall. Propagation can also be done by cuttings, layering, and grafting.

Magnolia *(Magnolia* sp.) *(1, 11, 16, 19, 35, 62).* Seeds, cuttings, grafting, and layering are utilized in propagating magnolias. The use of cuttings is becoming more widely practiced since the development of the root-promoting chemicals, which permits good rooting percentages. Magnolia nursery trees are difficult to transplant, so they should be set out from containers or balled and burlapped, but only in early spring.

SEEDS. Magnolia seeds are gathered in the fall as soon as possible after the fruit is ripe. After cleaning, the seeds should either be sown immediately in the fall or—prior to spring planting—stratified for 3 to 6 months at about 40°F. Allowing the seeds to dry out at any time seems to be harmful. After sowing, the germinating medium must not become dry. *M. grandiflora* seeds, and perhaps others, will lose their viability if stored through the winter at room temperature. If prolonged storage is necessary, the seeds should be held in sealed containers at 32° to 41°F.

Magnolia seedlings grow very rapidly and generally are large enough to graft by the end of the first season. Transplanting should be kept at a minimum since this retards the plants.

CUTTINGS. Some species, such as *M. soulangeana* and *M. stellata,* have been successfully propagated commercially by leafy, softwood cuttings. These may be taken from late spring to late summer after terminal growth has stopped and the wood has become partly matured, although some propagators, especially in the southern states, use very soft, succulent material taken in early April. Use of such immature wood presents a problem in the control of damping off fungi, particularly if rooting is done in a hot, humid greenhouse. Frequent applications of a fungicide are usually necessary under such conditions.

Excellent rooting can be obtained if the cuttings are taken from very young plants, the bases wounded (see p. 243) and treated with a root-promoting substance (see p. 244), and rooted in sand in outdoor mist beds (see p. 251). Under such conditions, rooting is rapid and in high percentages, and there is little trouble from diseases.

To obtain survival of the rooted cuttings through the following winter, they should be rooted early enough in the season so that some resumption of growth will occur before fall.

GRAFTING. *Magnolia kobus* is probably the best rootstock for the oriental magnolias, whereas *M. acuminata* can be used as a stock for either oriental or American species. *Magnolia grandiflora* seedlings or rooted cuttings are used for *M. grandiflora* varieties.

One-year-old seedlings are potted in early spring and then grafted while the understocks are in active growth during mid- to late summer. Side or side veneer grafts (see pp. 326 and 328) are satisfactory, with the union and scion waxed after grafting. Some propagators pot the seedlings in the fall and then bring them in the greenhouse and do the grafting in midwinter. The newly grafted plants may be set on open benches in the greenhouse or placed in closed propagating frames where they stay for 7 to 10 days while the union is healing. Air is gradually given until after 6 weeks they can be removed from the case and the understock cut off above the union.

LAYERING. Simple layering (see p. 403) gives good results. One- or 2-year-old shoots arising from the base of stock plants are started in early spring, but often two seasons are required to produce well-rooted layers.

Mahonia (*Mahonia* sp.). Seeds of most species should be stratified through the winter to obtain satisfactory germination. On the other hand, dry seeds of red mahonia (*M. haematocarpa*) will germinate promptly after planting in the spring.

Leafy cuttings of partially matured wood under glass will root, but not easily. Root-promoting substances may be helpful. Removal of the suckers permits easy propagation when only a few plants are needed.

Malus sp. See **Crabapple, Flowering.**

Maple (*Acer* sp.) (*4, 36, 40, 63*). Various methods of propagation are in use —seeds, grafting, budding, cuttings, and layering.

SEEDS. Most maples ripen their seed in the fall, but two species—*A. rubrum* and *A. saccharinum*—produce seed in the spring. Such spring-ripening seeds should be gathered promptly when mature and sowed immediately without drying. For other species stratification, usually for 90 days at 41° F., followed by spring planting, gives good germination. Dry seeds of the Japanese maple, *A. palmatum*, will germinate satisfactorily if they are placed in warm water (about 110° F.) and allowed to soak for 2 days. Soaking seeds of *A. rubrum* and *A. negundo* in cold running water for 5 days and 2 weeks respectively before planting may increase germination.

Varieties of some maples, such as *A. palmatum,* var. *atropurpureum,* will reproduce fairly true from seed, especially if the stock plants are isolated. Removal of the few off-type plants can easily be done in the nursery row.

CUTTINGS. Leafy Japanese maple cuttings will root readily in a sand-peat moss medium if they are made from sturdy growth taken from the tips of vigorous shoots in early June and placed under mist (see p. 251). Wounding (see p. 243) and relatively strong applications of indolebutyric acid (see p. 244) are helpful. This material at 1000 ppm, applied by the concentrated-dip method, gave good results in rooting softwood sugar maple (*A. saccharum*) cuttings under constant mist in the greenhouse (*12*). It is often a problem, however, to successfully over-winter rooted *Acer* cuttings.

GRAFTING AND BUDDING. *Acer palmatum* seedlings are used as the understock for Japanese maple varieties, *A. saccharum* for the sugar maples, *A. rubrum* for red maple varieties, and *A. platanoides* for such Norway maple types as Crimson King, Schwedler, and the pyramidal forms. There is some evidence of delayed incompatibility in using *A. saccharinum* as a stock for red maple varieties.

Seedling rootstock plants are grown for 1 year in a seed-bed, and then in the fall or early spring they are dug and transplanted into small pots in which they grow, plunged in propagating frames, through the second summer. In late winter, the stock plants are brought into the greenhouse preparatory to grafting. As soon as roots show signs of growth, the stock is ready for grafting. Dormant scions are taken from outdoor plants. The side graft or side veneer graft (see pp. 326 and 328) is ordinarily used. While the union is healing, the plants are set in a grafting case with peat moss covering the union. Sometimes grafting wax is used, covering both the scion and graft union.

Maples are also successfully T-budded (see p. 382) on 1-year seedlings in the nursery row, the buds being inserted from mid- to late summer. The wood is removed from the bud shields, which then consists only of the actual bud and attached bark. The seedling is cut back to the bud the following spring just as growth is starting.

Metasequoia (*Metasequoia glyptostroboides* Hu and Cheng.). Dawn redwood *(8)*. Seeds germinate without difficulty, and both softwood and hardwood cuttings root readily. The leafless hardwood cuttings may be lined-out in the nursery row in early spring, but the leafy softwood cuttings taken in late spring should be rooted under glass.

Mock Orange (*Philadelphus* sp.). The many varieties of mock orange are best propagated by cuttings, which root easily. Hardwood cuttings planted in early spring or leafy, softwood cuttings under glass in early summer can be used. Removing rooted suckers arising from the base of old plants is an easy means of obtaining a few new plants.

Mulberry, Fruitless (*Morus* sp.). Some mulberry trees produce only male flowers and hence do not bear fruits. Propagated vegetatively, these are suitable as ornamental shade trees. Some strains are very rapid growers. They may be propagated by cuttings or by budding or grafting on mulberry seedling rootstocks.

Myrtle (*Myrtus* sp.). These are usually propagated in summer by leafy, softwood cuttings of partially matured wood under glass. Treatments with indolebutyric acid (see p. 244) have been helpful in some instances.

Nandina (*Nandina domestica* Thun.). Propagation is usually by seed. The embryos in the mature fruits are rudimentary, so storage under warm, moist conditions for several months prior to planting is necessary to permit complete development of the embryo. No low temperature stratification period is necessary. Germination occurs in about 90 days, but growth of the seedlings is slow, taking several years to produce salable plants. Suckers arising at the base of old plants may be removed for propagation.

Nerium oleander. See Oleander.

Oak (*Quercus* sp.) *(49)*. Seed propagation is generally practiced. Wide variations exist in the germination requirements of oak seed, particularly between the black oak (acorns maturing the second year) and white oak (acorns maturing the first year) groups. Seeds of the white oak group have little or no dormancy and, with few exceptions, are ready to germinate as soon as they mature in the fall. Seeds of most species of the black oak group do have an embryo dormancy condition, requiring either stratification (30° to 35° F. for 1 to 2 months) or fall planting. Seeds of the following species will germinate without a low temperature stratification period: *Quercus agrifolia, Q. alba, Q. arizonica, Q. bicolor, Q. chrysolepis, Q. douglasii, Q. dumosa, Q. garryana, Q. lobata, Q. macrocarpa, Q. montana, Q. petraea, Q. prinus, Q. robur, Q. stellata, Q. suber,* and *Q. virginiana.*

Acorns of many species tend to lose their viability rapidly when stored dry at room temperature. They should be held under cool, moist conditions or stored dry in sealed containers at 32° to 36° F.

Attempts to propagate oaks by cuttings or by layering have been unsuccessful. Budding has also proven unsatisfactory.

Bench grafting of potted seedling stocks in the greenhouse in late winter or early spring is moderately successful. Side grafting or the whip or tongue method (see pp. 326 and 322) is ordinarily used, taking dormant 1-year-old wood for scions. Crown grafting (see p. 362) seedlings in place in the nursery row is also practiced occasionally. This is done in the spring just after the the stock plants start to leaf out. Scions are taken from wood gathered when dormant and stored under cool, moist conditions until used. Various grafting methods are satisfactory—whip, cleft, or bark (see pp. 322, 331, and 336). In grafting, only seedlings of the black oak group should be used for scion varieties of the same group and, in the same manner, only seedlings of the white oak group should be used as stocks for other members of the white oaks. Although some distantly related species of the oaks will unite satisfactorily, incompatibility symptoms often appear.

Oleander (*Nerium oleander* L.). Seedlings reproduce fairly true to type, although a small percentage of plants with different flower colors will appear. The seeds should be collected in late fall after a frost has caused the seed pods to open. Rubbing the seeds through a coarse mesh wire screen will remove most of the fuzzy coating. The seeds are then planted immediately in the greenhouse in flats without further treatment. Germination occurs in about 2 weeks.

Cuttings root easily under glass if taken from rather mature wood during the summer. Simple layering (see p. 403) is also successful.

Parthenocissus. Virginia Creeper (*P. quinquefolia* Planch.). Boston Ivy (*P. tricuspidata* Planch.). These two ornamental vines can be propagated by seeds planted in the fall or stratified for 2 months at about 40°F. before planting in the spring.

Softwood cuttings taken in late summer root easily under glass as do hardwood cuttings planted out-of-doors in early spring. A limited number of plants may be started by compound layering (see p. 405).

Philadelphus sp. See **Mock Orange.**

Picea sp. See **Spruce.**

Pine (*Pinus* sp.). These are ordinarily propagated by seeds. Considerable variability exists among the species in regard to seed dormancy conditions. Seeds of many species have no dormancy and will germinate immediately upon collection, whereas others have embryo dormancy. With the latter, stratification at 35° to 40°F. for 1 to 3 months will increase or hasten germination. Seed coat dormancy seems to be present also in *P. cembra* and *P. monticola*. With these, concentrated sulfuric acid treatment for 3 to 5 hours and 45 minutes respectively, followed by stratification for 3 months at 36°F., will aid germination. Species which have no dormancy conditions and can be planted without treatment include *Pinus aristata, P. banksiana, P. canariensis, P. caribaea, P. clausa, P. contorta, P. edulis, P. griffithi, P. halepensis, P. jeffreyi, P. latifolia, P. mugo, P. nigra, P. palustris, P. pinaster, P. ponderosa, P. pungens, P. radiata, P. resinosa, P. roxburghi, P. sylvestris, P. thunbergi,* and *P. virginiana.* However, if seeds of the above species are used which have been stored for any length of time, it would be advisable to give them a cold stratification period before planting as described above. Pine seeds can be stored for considerable periods of time without losing viability if held in sealed containers between 5° and 32°F.

Pinus cuttings are difficult to root. Success is more likely if cutting material is taken from low-growing lateral shoots on young trees in late winter. Treatments with root-inducing substances (see p. 244) may give some benefit.

Side veneer grafting (see p. 328) is used for propagating selected clones; well-established, 2-year-old seedlings of the same or closely related species should be used as rootstocks.

Pittosporum (*Pittosporum* sp.). These are started by seeds or cuttings. The seeds are not difficult to germinate; dipping a cloth bag containing the seeds for several seconds in boiling water may hasten germination. Leafy, semi-hardwood cuttings taken after a flush of growth has partially matured will root readily, particularly under mist (see p. 251). Indolebutyric acid treatments (see p. 244) are also beneficial.

Plane Tree (*Platanus* sp.). Sycamore. Seed propagation is ordinarily used. The best procedure is to allow the seed to over-winter in the seed balls right on the tree. They may then be collected in late winter or early spring and planted immediately, with prompt germination usually occurring. If the seeds are collected in the fall, then stratification over winter at about 40°F. should be used.

Platanus sp. See **Plane Tree.**

Plumbago (*Plumbago* sp.). Seeds sown in late winter usually germinate easily. Leafy cuttings taken from partially matured wood can be rooted without difficulty under glass. Root cuttings can also be used and old plants can be divided.

Poplar (*Populus* sp.). Cottonwood. Aspen. These are propagated either by seeds or hardwood cuttings. Seed should be collected as soon as the capsules begin to open and planted at once, because they lose viability rapidly. However, if held in sealed containers near 32°F., seeds of some species can be stored for as long as 3 years. There are no dormancy conditions, and seeds germinate within a few days after planting. The seedlings are highly susceptible to damping off fungi and will not tolerate excessive heat or drying.

Hardwood cuttings of *Populus* (except the aspens) planted in the spring will root fairly easily. Treatments with indolebutyric acid (see p. 244) are likely to improve rooting. Leafy, softwood cuttings taken in midsummer (of some species at least) will also root well, especially if treated as indicated above.

Populus sp. See **Poplar.**

Privet (*Ligustrum* sp.). Seed propagation is easily done. The cleaned seed should be stratified for 2 to 3 months at 32° to 50°F. before planting. Hardwood cuttings of most species planted in the spring root easily, as do softwood cuttings in summer under glass. Japanese privet (*L. japonicum*) is somewhat difficult to start from cuttings, the best results being obtained with the use of actively growing terminal growth rather than more mature wood.

Prunus campanulata, P. sargenti, P. serotina, P. serrulata, P. sieboldi, P. subhirtella, P. yedoensis. See **Cherry, Flowering.**

Pyracantha (*Pyracantha* sp.) Firethorn. Propagation by cuttings is almost always used. Partially matured, leafy current season's growth taken in late spring and rooted under high humidity conditions gives satisfactory results. Rooting may be poor with dormant cuttings taken in winter. Treatments with root-promoting substances (see p. 244) are beneficial.

Quercus sp. See Oak.

Quince, Flowering (*Chaenomeles* sp.). These are easily started by seeds, which should be stratified for 2 or 3 months at 40°F. before sowing. Root cuttings can be taken in late fall, cut into 2 to 4 inch lengths, and stored at 35° to 40°F. until spring, when they can be lined-out horizontally in the nursery row. Leafy cuttings of partially matured wood may be rooted under glass in late spring. Treatment with indolebutyric acid (see p. 244) at about 15 ppm for 24 hours is beneficial. Older plants tend to produce suckers freely at the base, which may be removed and used if they are well rooted.

Redbud (*Cercis* sp.). Seed propagation is successful, but seed treatments are necessary due to dormancy resulting from an impervious seed coat plus a dormant embryo. Probably the most satisfactory treatment is a 30 to 60 minute soaking period in concentrated sulfuric acid, followed by stratification for 2 months at about 40°F. The fall sowing out-of-doors of untreated seeds may also give good germination.

Softwood cuttings of some *Cercis* species will root readily under glass if taken in spring or early summer. Simple layering (see p. 403) is used successfully also.

Redwood. Redwood. (*Sequoia sempervirens* Endl.). Giant sequoia (*Sequoia gigantea* Decne.). Both species are ordinarily propagated by seed. Seeds of *S. sempervirens* are mature at the end of the first season, but those of *S. gigantea* require two seasons for maturity of the embryos. Cones are collected in the fall and allowed to dry for 2 to 4 weeks after which the seeds can be separated. Seeds may be kept for several years in sealed containers under cold storage without losing viability. Although it is not absolutely necessary, germination is likely to be improved by stratification for 2 months at about 40°F. Fall planting may also be done, sowing the seed about 1/8 inch deep in a well-prepared seed-bed. A burlap cover on the seed-bed, which is removed when germination starts, is helpful. The young seedlings should be given partial shade for the first 60 days.

S. sempervirens may also be propagated by sprouts arising from the burls taken from the base of older trees.

Rhododendron (*Rhododendron* sp.) *(15, 39, 47, 48, 61)*. These plants can be propagated by seeds, cuttings, grafting, and layering.

SEEDS. Seedlings may be used as rootstocks for grafting desirable hybrid varieties or for the propagation of the ornamental species. *R. ponticum* is the principal rootstock for grafting. The seed should be collected just when the capsules are beginning to dehisce, and they may be stored dry and planted in late winter or early spring in the greenhouse. Seed to be kept for long periods should be put in sealed bottles and held under refrigeration. A good germinating medium is a layer of shredded sphagnum moss or vermiculite over a mixture of sand and acid peat. The very small seeds are sifted on the surface of the medium and watered with a fine spray. The flats should be covered with glass and always kept shaded. Very careful attention must be given to provide adequate moisture and ventilation as well as even heat—60° to 70°F. The plants grow slowly, taking about 3 months to reach transplanting size. After two or three true leaves form, they are moved to another flat and spaced 1 to 2 inches apart, where they remain through the winter in a cool greenhouse or in cold frames. In the spring the plants are set out in the field in an acid soil, and by fall they are ready to be dug and potted preparatory to grafting in the winter.

CUTTINGS. Hybrid rhododendron cuttings have always been considered to be very difficult to root, but with the use of root-promoting growth regulators together with proper attention to other factors, this method is entirely practical for many species and garden hybrids. Both stem and leaf-bud cuttings are used commercially. Although leaf-bud cuttings root more easily than stem cuttings, they have the disadvantage in some cases of prolonged bud dormancy even though the cutting is well rooted.

The cuttings are best taken from late summer into the fall, but the optimum time will vary with the variety and season, many hybrids rooting well from cuttings taken in December and January. Leaf-bud cuttings should be taken in late June or early July, using vegetative rather than flowering wood. Ideal cutting material is the lateral shoots which are induced to form by removing terminal buds. Making a rather severe wound (see p. 243) at the base of the

Figure 17–2. Propagation of Rhododendron by leaf-bud cuttings. **(left)** Cutting when made. **(center)** Root development after several weeks. **(right)** Appearance of root ball and new shoot after five months. Courtesy H. T. Skinner.

cutting is helpful in securing rooting. Treatments with indolebutyric acid (see p. 244) at relatively strong concentrations are also beneficial. Rooting can be done in closed frames in the greenhouse or in outdoor cold frames. Bottom heat at 70° to 75°F. is helpful. Rhododendrons respond well to rooting under mist (see p. 251), but they should be lifted soon after roots are well formed, otherwise the roots will deteriorate. Plants started from cuttings usually develop rapidly and are free of the disadvantage of suckering from the rootstocks which occurs in grafted plants.

GRAFTING. A side veneer graft (see p. 328) is most successful. The best scionwood is taken from straight, vigorous current season's growth. After grafting, the plants are kept in closed frames under high humidity and a temperature near 70°F. until the union has healed. The plants should then be moved to cooler conditions—50° to 60°F.—and the top of the stock removed above the graft union. After the plant has hardened, it is transplanted to the nursery row in acid soil and grown for 2 years when it is ready to dig as a salable nursery plant.

LAYERING. Rhododendrons are easily reproduced by trench and simple layering (see pp. 411 and 403).

Rhus sp. See Sumac.

Rose (*Rosa* sp.) (*3, 5, 13, 42, 57*). All the selected rose varieties are propagated by asexual methods. T-budding on vigorous rootstocks is most common, although the use of softwood or hardwood cuttings or grafting, layering, or the use of suckers is sometimes practiced. Seed propagation is used in breeding new varieties and occasionally in growing rootstock plants of some species, such as *Rosa multiflora, R. rugosa,* or *R. canina.*

SEEDS. As soon as the rose fruits ("hips") are fully ripe but before the flesh starts to soften, they should be collected and the seeds extracted. It is best to stratify them immediately at about 40°F. A few weeks is sufficient for *Rosa multiflora,* but others—*R. rugosa* and *R. hugonis*—require 4 to 6 months. *R. canina* has been found to germinate best if the seeds are held at room temperatures for 2 months in moist vermiculite and then transferred to 32°F. for an additional 2 months (54). Hybrid rose seeds usually respond best to a stratification temperature of 34° to 36°F. for 6 to 12 weeks. The seeds may be planted either in the spring or fall in seed beds or in the nursery row. In areas of severe winters, seedlings are likely to be winter killed if they are smaller than 4 inches by the onset of cold weather.

CUTTINGS. HARDWOOD CUTTINGS. Hardwood cuttings are widely used commercially in the propagation of rose rootstocks, and to some extent in propagating the strong growing polyanthas, pillars, climbers, and hybrid perpetuals. The hybrid teas and other similar everblooming roses can also be started by cuttings, but more winter-hardy and nematode-resistant plants are produced if they are budded on selected vigorous rootstocks. In mild climates, the cuttings are taken and planted in the nursery row from late fall to late winter. In areas with severe winters, cuttings may be made in late fall or early winter, tied in bundles, and stored in damp peat moss or sand at about 40°F. until spring when they are planted in the nursery row. The rootstock types are ready to bud to the named variety by the following spring, summer, or fall. The cuttings are made into 6 or 8 inch lengths from previous season's canes ¼ to ⅜ inch in diameter. In commercial practice, large bundles of canes are run through band saws to cut them to the correct length. Disbudding is usually done in rootstock propagation; all buds except the top one or two are removed so as to prevent subsequent sucker growth in the nursery row.

SOFTWOOD CUTTINGS. Softwood cuttings (see p. 232) are ordinarily made from current season's growth, from midspring to late summer, depending upon the time the wood becomes partially mature. Rooting is fairly rapid, occurring in 10 to 14 days. At the end of the season the cuttings may be transplanted to their permanent location, potted and over-wintered in a cold frame, or transferred to the nursery row for another season's growth or to be budded to the desired variety.

BUDDING. T-budding (see p. 382) is the method ordinarily used. The buds are inserted into ³⁄₁₆ to ⅜ inch diameter rootstock plants. In California, budding can be done during a long period, from late February until November. Early buds will make some growth during the summer and produce a salable plant by fall. Some propagators break over the top of the rootstock about 2 weeks after budding to force the bud out. After the bud has reached a length of 4 to 8 inches, the top of the stock is entirely removed. Buds inserted late in the summer either make little growth or remain dormant until the following spring. In this case, the rootstock is cut off just above the bud in late winter or early spring, forcing the inserted bud into growth. Shoots from buds which started in the fall are cut back to ½ inch in the spring. The shoot then grows through the following entire summer, producing a well-developed plant by fall. After the shoot has grown about 6 inches, it is generally cut back to 2 or 3 inches to force out side branches.

Budwood may be obtained during the budding season from current season's growth of the desired variety, only a day's supply being taken at a time.

It is best collected early in the morning, clipping off the leaves immediately and leaving about ¼ inch of the petiole attached to the bud. Lateral buds from the stems producing the flowers are the best to use. Plump but dormant buds three or four nodes below the flower are the most desirable. The wood should be at a stage of maturity in which the thorns are easily removed.

An alternative method for obtaining budwood, which has been widely and successfully used, is to store dormant wood under refrigeration just below freezing (30° to 32°F.) until time for budding. The budwood is collected in late fall after the flowers are shed and the thorns become dark. The leaves are removed by hand, but the thorns are left intact. Sticks 10 to 15 inches long are put up in bundles of 30 or 40 each. The bundles are wrapped tightly as possible in waterproof paper over which a layer of moist wrapping —such as wet newspapers—is placed. Finally, the bundles are covered with another layer of waterproof paper. Budwood stored in this manner has kept satisfactorily for 23 months *(33)*.

Buds are inserted in the wood of the original cutting rather than into new growth arising from the rootstoc! .

ROOTSTOCKS FOR ROSE VARIETIES *(2)*. *Rosa multiflora.* This is a widely used rootstock, especially its thornless forms, for out-of-door roses. Cuttings of this species root readily, develop a vigorous, nematode-resistant root system, and do not sucker excessively. It is adaptable to a wide range of soil and climatic conditions, but it does not seem to do well in the southern United States. Seedlings are used in the eastern part of the United States and cuttings in the South and the Pacific Coast. The bark often becomes so thick late in the season that budding is impossible.

Rosa canina (Dog rose). Although this has not done well under American conditions, it is the most commonly used stock in Europe. The cuttings do not root easily and the prominent thorns make it difficult to handle. It also tends to sucker somewhat. Young plants on this stock grow slowly, but they are long-lived. *Rosa canina* is adaptable to alkaline soil conditions.

Ragged Robin (Gloire des Rosomanes). This French stock is popular in California for out-of-door roses, resisting heat and dry conditions well. It is also resistant to nematodes and does not sucker if the lower buds on the cuttings are removed. This stock grows steadily through the summer permitting budding at any time. The fibrous root system is easy to transplant but requires good soil drainage. In some areas, however, it is difficult to propagate and is injured by leafspot. Due to its susceptibility to *Verticillium* wilt, land previously planted to tomatoes or cotton should be avoided.

Dr. Huey (Shafter). This is the principal rootstock in California rose districts, replacing Ragged Robin to a large extent. It is especially useful for late season budding because of its thin bark. It is very vigorous, well adapted to irrigated conditions, and its cuttings root readily. It is very good as a stock for weak growing varieties. Defects are its injury from sub-zero temperatures and susceptibility to blackspot and mildew.

Rosa manetti (R. noisettiana Manetti *(38).* This is a very old stock now commonly used for greenhouse forcing roses. It is also of value for dwarf roses and for planting in very sandy soil types. It is easily started from cuttings and produces a plant of moderate vigor but one which is susceptible to *Verticillium* wilt and tends to be short lived.

Rosa odorata (Odorata 22449). This is an excellent stock for greenhouse forcing roses. It roots easily from cuttings under suitable conditions, and produces a large symmetrical root system. It is adapted to both excessively dry or wet soil conditions. Since it is not cold-hardy, it should be used only in areas with mild winters. Many clones of this stock are badly diseased and do not root well. The plants are not adaptable to cold storage handling.

IXL (Tausendschon × Veilchenblau). This stock is used primarily as a trunk for tree roses. It is very vigorous and has no thorns. The canes tend to sunburn and are somewhat susceptible to low temperature injury.

Multiflore de la Grifferaie. This is useful as a trunk for tree roses, producing desirable straight canes. It is vigorous, extremely hardy, and resistant to borers, but it is very susceptible to mite injury.

Rosa rugosa. The form which is used as an understock bears purplish-red, single flowers. For bush roses it is propagated by cuttings and for tree roses by seeds. The root system is shallow and fibrous and tends to sucker badly, but the plants are very long lived.

PROPAGATION OF TREE (STANDARD) ROSES. A satisfactory method of producing this popular form of rose is to use·*Rosa multiflora* as the rootstock, which is budded in the first summer to IXL, or preferably to the Grifferaie stock. These are trained to an upright form and kept free of suckers. In the second summer, at a height of about 3 feet, three or four buds of the desired flowering variety are inserted into the trunk stock. During the winter, the cane above the inserted buds is removed. The buds grow out during the following summer as do buds from the stock, which must be removed. In the fall, the plants may be dug and moved to their permanent location. Tree roses are sometimes dug as balled and burlapped plants due to the extensive root system formed during the 2 years the top is being developed.

Rose-of-Sharon. See Hibiscus syriacus.

Russian Olive. See Elaeagnus.

St. Johnswort (*Hypericum* sp.). These are rather easily started by softwood cuttings taken in late summer from the tips of current growth and rooted under high humidity.

Salix sp. See Willow.

Sambucus sp. See Elder.

Sequoia sp. See Redwood.

Shrub Althea. See Hibiscus syriacus.

Silk Tree. See Albizzia.

Silver Berry. See Elaeagnus.

Spirea (*Spiraea* sp.). This is usually propagated by cuttings, although some species, such as *S. thunbergi,* are more easily started by seeds. Leafy, softwood cuttings taken in midsummer and rooted under high humidity are generally successful. Treatments with one of the root-promoting substances (see p. 244) are often of considerable benefit. Some species, such as *S. vanhouttei,* can be started readily by hardwood cuttings planted in early spring.

Spruce (*Picea* sp.). These are ordinarily propagated without difficulty by seeds, either fall planted or stratified over winter. Most species have embryo dormancy, requiring 1 to 3 months' stratification at about 40°F. for good germination. Seeds of *P. abies, P. engelmanni,* and *P. glauca,* var. *albertiana,* are among those giving good germination without stratification.

Spruce cuttings are difficult to root. In making cuttings of upright-growing species terminal shoots should be selected rather than lateral branches, since the latter, if rooted, tend to produce abnormal, sprawling plants rather than the desired upright form.

Colorado blue spruce (*Picea pungens glauca*) grown from seed produces trees which usually have a greenish color with a slight bluish cast. Only a small percentage of the seedlings have the very desirable bright blue color. Several exceptionally fine blue seedling specimens have been selected as clones and are perpetuated by grafting. The two best known are the Koster blue spruce (*Picea pungens kosteriana*), developed at the Koster Nursery in Holland many years ago, and the Moerheim spruce (*Picea pungens moerheimi*), which also originated in Europe about 1930.

These selected clones of the blue spruce are quite difficult to propagate by cuttings, but there are instances where high percentages of the cuttings have been rooted. Timing is important; cuttings taken in February or March apparently root best. Treatments with root-inducing chemicals (see p. 244) and wounding (see p. 243) are also beneficial.

The Koster blue spruce is propagated commercially by grafting scions on Norway spruce (*Picea abies*) seedlings. Norway spruce seeds are sown in the spring; no previous stratification treatment is necessary. Seedlings are grown through two seasons, at which time they should be about 6 inches high. They may be dug and potted preparatory to grafting, either in the fall of the second season or the following spring. After potting, the plants are set in cold frame beds with peat moss covering the tops of pots. By late summer of the third season, the understocks should be about pencil size or thicker and be ready to graft. This may be done in the fall or in early spring of the fourth season. Scions about 6 inches long are used with the needles removed from the basal 2 inches. Either the side or the side veneer graft (see p. 328) is used. The completed graft is wrapped with waxed string, then coated with grafting wax or paraffin. The grafted plants are set in benches in a cool greenhouse (50° to 65°F.) until the union is completed, which should be in 30 to 45 days.

The top of the understock is gradually cut back to the graft union, although some propagators retain a portion of the understock above the graft union throughout the first season after grafting. By midspring the plants should be set out in the field and staked. Two or three seasons' growth after grafting is required to produce plants of a salable size. The entire grafting procedure is very slow, often with a low percentage of survivals (30, 64).

Star Jasmine, Chinese (*Trachelospermum jasminoides* Lem.). Leafy cuttings of partially matured wood root without difficulty, especially when placed under mist (see p. 251) and treated with a root-promoting substance (see p. 244).

Sumac (*Rhus* sp.). These are commonly propagated by seeds which are collected in the fall. For prompt germination they should be soaked in concentrated sulfuric acid for 1 to 6 hours, depending upon the species, then stratified for 2 months at about 40°F. Not all species have embryo dormancy, however, and the latter treatment may sometimes be omitted. Some sumac plants bear only female flowers and others only male flowers, whereas still others have both flower types on the same plant. To insure fruiting, plants of the latter type should be propagated asexually. In seed propagation many of the seedlings produced will not bear fruit.

For those species which sucker freely, such as *R. typhina* and *R. copallina,* root cuttings several inches long planted in the nursery row in early spring may be used. Leafy, softwood cuttings, at least of some species, taken in midsummer, root well under glass. The Smoke Bush, *Rhus cotinus* (*Cotinus coggygria*), can be rooted but with difficulty either by softwood cuttings or by hardwood cuttings in spring. This popular ornamental should not be propagated by seeds, since many of the seedlings are staminate plants, thus lacking the showy flowering panicles. Only vegetative methods should be used, with the propagating wood being taken from plants known to produce large quantities of the desirable fruiting clusters.

Sycamore. See Plane Tree.

Syringa sp. See Lilac.

Tamarisk (*Tamarix* sp.). These are easily rooted by hardwood cuttings which are usually made about 12 inches long and planted deeply. Softwood cuttings taken in early summer will also root readily under glass.

Taxus sp. See Yew.

Thuja sp. See Arborvitae.

Tilia sp. See Linden.

Tulip Tree (*Liriodendron tulipifera* L.). Yellow-poplar. Seed propagation is ordinarily used, the seed being stratified for about 2 months. A daily varying stratification temperature between freezing and about 50°F. has given good results, although a constant temperature around 40°F. would probably be equally satisfactory. Fall planting and out-of-door stratification through the winter has also given good germination. Although not often done commercially, leafy stem cuttings taken in the summer have been rooted in fairly good percentages. Root cuttings also have been used successfully.

Young tulip trees are very difficult to transplant, so they should always be propagated into containers from which they can be taken or else dug, balled and burlapped, for transplanting from the nursery row.

Trachelospermum jasminoides. See Star Jasmine, Chinese.

Trumpet Creeper. (*Campsis* sp.). This is usually propagated by cuttings, but seeds can also be used. With the latter method, stratification for 2 months at 40° to 50°F. hastens but does not increase germination. Both softwood and hardwood cuttings root readily. *C. radicans* can be started by root cuttings. Layering is also successful.

Tsuga sp. See Hemlock.

Ulmus sp. See Elm.

Viburnum (*Viburnum* sp.) (*14, 17, 22, 27*). This large group of desirable shrubs can be propagated by a number of methods, including seeds, cuttings, grafting, and layering. At least one species (*V. dentatum*) is readily started from root cuttings.

SEEDS. The viburnums have rather complicated seed dormancy conditions. Seeds of some species, such as *V. sieboldi*, will germinate after a single ordinary low temperature (41°F.) stratification period, but for most species a period of 2 to 9 months at high temperatures (68° to 86°F.) followed by a 2 to 4 month period at low temperatures (41°F.) is required. The initial warm temperatures cause root initiation, whereas the subsequent low temperature causes shoot development. Cold stratification alone will not result in germination. Such rather exacting treatments may best be given by planting the seeds in summer or early fall (at least 60 days before the onset of winter), thus providing the first high temperature requirement; the subsequent winter period fulfills the second low temperature requirement. After this, the seeds should germinate readily in the spring. Often collecting the seeds early, before a hard seed coat has developed, will hasten germination. Viburnum seed can be kept for 1 or 2 years if stored dry in sealed containers and held just above freezing.

CUTTINGS. Although some viburnum species (*V. opulus, V. dentatum,* and *V. trilobum*) can be propagated by hardwood cuttings, softwood cuttings rooted under glass or in intermittent mist are successful for most species. Soft, succulent cuttings taken in late spring root faster than those made from more mature tissue in midsummer, but the latter type is more likely to grow on into sturdy plants that will survive through the following winter. In fact, one of the chief problems with viburnum cuttings is to keep them growing after rooting. Cuttings made from succulent, rapidly growing material often die in a few weeks after being potted. This trouble may be overcome by not digging the cuttings too soon, allowing a secondary root system to form which will better stand the transplanting shock. It may help, too, to feed the rooted cuttings with a nutrient solution about 10 days before the cuttings are to be removed. Cuttings of some species root much easier than others. *Viburnum carlesi,* for example, is considered difficult to root but *V. burkwoodi* roots readily.

GRAFTING. Selected types of viburnum are often propagated by grafting on rooted cuttings, layers, or seedlings of *V. dentatum* or *V. lantana.* Often, grafted viburnums will develop more quickly into vigorous plants than those started as cuttings. It is important that all buds be removed from the root-stock so that subsequent suckering from the stock does not occur. The understocks are potted in the fall and brought into the greenhouse where they are grafted in midwinter by the side graft method (see p. 328), using dormant scionwood. After grafting, the potted plants are placed in a closed, glass-covered frame with the unions buried in damp peat moss.

Sometimes, rather than plunging them in peat moss the scion and graft union are dipped in melted paraffin, which is satisfactory if only a very thin coating is applied. Close attention must be given the graft during the healing period, avoiding either excessive humidity or high temperatures from too much direct sunlight.

Grafting can also be done in late summer, using potted understock plants and scion material which has stopped growing and become hardened. The grafted plants are placed in the greenhouse and plunged in slightly damp peat moss in closed frames until the unions heal, after which they are moved to outdoor glass-covered cold frames for hardening off for the winter.

LAYERING. Simple layering (see p. 403) is widely used, especially in Europe, for propagating most viburnum species. Wood of the previous season's growth will produce roots in 18 to 24 months if layered in the spring. Some species are best layered in midsummer, using current season's wood.

Weigela (*Weigela* sp.). This is easily propagated either by hardwood cuttings planted in early spring or by softwood tip cuttings under glass taken any time from late spring into fall. Treatment with a root-promoting substance (see p. 244) seems to promote rooting of the softwood cuttings.

Willow (*Salix* sp.). Willow seeds must be collected as soon as the capsules mature (when they turn from green to a yellowish color) and planted immediately, since at room temperature they retain their viability for only a few days. Even under the most favorable conditions, maximum storage is 4 to 6 weeks. No dormancy occurs, germination taking place 12 to 24 hours after planting if the seeds are kept constantly moist.

Willows root so readily by either root or stem cuttings that there is little occasion to use other methods. Hardwood cuttings planted in the soil in early spring root promptly.

Wisteria (*Wistaria* sp.). These may be started by softwood cuttings under glass taken in midsummer. Indolebutyric acid treatments (see p. 244) at about 25 ppm for 24 hours will often aid rooting. Some species can be started by hardwood cuttings set in the greenhouse in the spring. Root cuttings are also used occasionally. Simple layering of the long canes is quite successful. Choice types are often grafted on rooted cuttings of less desirable types. Suckers arising from roots of such grafted plants should be removed promptly. Wisterias do not transplant easily, so young nursery plants are best started in containers.

Yellow Poplar. See **Tulip Tree.**

Yew (*Taxus* sp.) *(26, 37, 58, 60).* Most clonal selections of yews are propagated by cuttings, which root without much difficulty. Seedling propagation is little used due to the variation appearing in the progeny, the complicated seed dormancy conditions, and the slow growth of the seedlings. Side or side veneer grafting (see p. 328) is practiced for those few varieties which are especially difficult to start by cuttings, easily rooted cuttings being used as the rootstock.

SEEDS. This method is confined in commercial practice almost entirely to the Japanese yew, *Taxus cuspidata capitata,* which comes fairly true from seed if isolated plants can be located as sources of seed. Seed imported from Japan is believed to produce uniform offspring.

To produce good germination, the seeds should be given a warm temperature (68°F.) stratification period in moist peat moss or other medium for 3 months followed by 4 months at a lower temperature (41°F.). Seedling growth is very slow. Two years in the seed bed, followed by 2 years in a lining-out bed, then 3 or 4 years in the nursery row are required to produce a plant of salable size of the Japanese Yew.

CUTTINGS. Taxus cuttings may be rooted out-of-doors in cold frames or in the greenhouse, the latter giving much faster results.

For the cold frame, fairly large cuttings, 8 to 10 inches long, are made in early fall from new growth with a section of old wood at the base. *Taxus* cuttings seem to respond well to treatments with a root-inducing chemical (see p. 244), indolebutyric acid at relatively high concentrations being particularly effective.

Cuttings may be kept in closed frames through the winter; in climates with severe winters, the frames should be kept covered especially at times when the ground is frozen but the sun is shining. Rooting takes place slowly during the following spring and summer.

For greenhouse propagation the cuttings should be taken in late November or early December, after several frosts have occurred, and rooted in sand with bottom heat at about 70°F. and an air temperature of 50° to 55°F. A high humidity, such as provided by a mist system (see p. 251), seems to be particularly suitable for *Taxus* cuttings. Rooting is fairly rapid in the greenhouse, taking about 2 months, although the cuttings should not be dug too soon. This allows time for secondary roots to develop from the first-formed primary roots.

REFERENCES

1. Afanasiev, M., A physiological study of dormancy in seed of *Magnolia acuminata., N.Y.* (Cornell) *Agr. Exp. Sta. Mem. 208,* 1937.
2. Buck, G. J., Varieties of rose understocks, *Amer. Rose Ann.,* 36:101–116. 1951.

3. Buck, G. J., and E. C. Volz, A handbook for rose growers, *Iowa Agr. Ext. Bul. P117, 1955.*

4. Burton, J. H., The grafting of some maples, *Proc. 2nd Ann. Mtg. Plant Prop. Soc.,* pp. 71–73. 1952.

5. Butterfield, H. M., Rose culture in California, *Calif. Agr. Ext. Cir. 148,* 1950.

6. ———, Camellia culture for the home gardener, *Calif. Agr. Exp. Sta. Man. 5,* 1952.

7. Chester, K. S., Graft-blight; a disease of lilac related to the employment of certain understocks in propagation, *Jour. Arn. Arb.,* 12:79–146. 1931.

8. Chu, K., and W. S. Cooper, An ecological reconnaissance in the native home of *Metasequoia glyptostroboides, Ecology,* 31:260–278. 1950.

9. de Wilde, R., Azaleas from cuttings, *Proc 4th Ann. Mtg. Plant Prop. Soc.,* pp. 143–145. 1954.

10. Dickey, R. D., Hibiscus in Florida, *Fla. Agr. Exp. Sta. Bul. 467,* 1952.

11. Dodd, T., Jr., Propagation of oriental magnolias from softwood cuttings, *Proc. 3rd Ann. Mtg. Plant Prop. Soc.,* pp. 108–110. 1953.

12. Dunn, S., and R. J. Townsend, Propagation of sugar maple by vegetative cuttings, *Jour. Forest.,* 52:678–679. 1954.

13. Emsweller, S. L., W. D. McClellan, and F. F. Smith, Roses for the home, *USDA Home and Garden Bul. 25,* 1953.

14. Fillmore, R., Propagation of viburnums from cuttings, *Proc. 2nd Ann. Mtg. Plant Prop. Soc.,* pp. 17–20. 1952.

15. ———, Growing rhododendrons from seed, *Arnold Arboretum Garden Book.* New York: Van Nostrand, 1954, pp. 42–49.

16. Galle, F., The propagation of magnolias by seed, *Proc. 3rd Ann.Mtg. Plant Prop. Soc.,* pp. 105–107. 1953.

17. Giersbach, J., Germination and seedling production of species of viburnum, *Contrib. Boyce Thomp. Inst.,* 9:79–90. 1937.

18. Hertrich, W., *Camellias in the Huntington Gardens.* San Marino, Calif.: Huntington Botanical Gardens, 1954.

19. Hess, C., Sr., Magnolias from grafts, *Proc. 3rd Ann. Mtg. Plant Prop. Soc.,* pp. 113–115. 1953.

20. Hess, C. E., Propagating and overwintering *Cornus florida rubra* cuttings, *Proc. 5th Ann. Mtg. Plant Prop. Soc.,* pp. 43–44. 1955.

21. Hill, J. B., Juniper grafting—practical and technical aspects, *Proc. 3rd Ann. Mtg. Plant Prop. Soc.,* pp. 86–93. 1953.

22. Hoogendoorn, C., The grafting of viburnum, *Proc. 2nd Ann. Mtg. Plant Prop. Soc.,* pp. 32–35. 1952.

23. Hume, H. H., *Camellias in America.* New York: Macmillan, 1946.

24. ———, *Camellias, Kinds and Culture.* New York: Macmillan, 1951.

25. ———, *Hollies.* New York: Macmillan, 1953. Chap. 11.

26. Keen, R. A., The propagation of *Taxus*—a review, *Proc. 4th Ann. Mtg. Plant Prop. Soc.,* pp. 63–68. 1954.

27. Kern, C. E., The propagation of viburnum from seed, *Proc. 2nd Ann. Mtg. Plant Prop. Soc.,* pp. 23–27. 1952.

28. Kirkpatrick, H., Propagation of lilacs on their own roots, *Amer. Nurs.,* 69(6):3–4. 1939.

29. Kraus, E. J., Rooting azalea cuttings, *Nat. Hort. Mag.,* 32(3):163–164. 1953.

30. Kumlien, L. L., *The Friendly Evergreens,* Dundee, Ill.: D. Hill Nursery, 1946.

31. Lee, F. P., et al. (eds.), *The Azalea Handbook.* Washington, D.C.: Amer. Hort. Soc., 1952. Chap. XI.

32. Lindberg, W. H., Studies in the propagation of several deciduous and evergreen plants, *Ohio Nursery Notes,* Vol. 21, No. 9. 1952.

33. Lyle, E. W., Preservation of rose budwood, *Amer. Rose Ann.,* 41:61–63. 1956.

34. Mattoon, H. G., Vegetative propagation of holly by grafting, *Proc. 2nd Ann. Mtg. Plant Prop. Soc.,* pp. 91–93. 1952.

35. Meahl, R. P., Recorded work on the propagation of magnolias—a review, *Proc. 3rd Ann. Mtg. Plant Prop. Soc.,* pp. 98–102. 1953.

36. McGill, W., The selection of maple understock, budwood, and the timing and placement of buds, *Proc. 2nd Ann. Mtg. Plant Prop. Soc.,* pp. 64–69. 1952.

37. Mitiska, L. J., The propagation of *Taxus* by seeds, *Proc. 4th Ann. Mtg. Plant Prop. Soc.,* pp. 69–73. 1954.

38. Morey, D. H., Jr., and W. M. Annis, The Manetti understock, *Amer. Rose Ann.,* 38:177–179. 1953.

39. Nearing, G. G., and C. H. Conners, Rhododendrons from cuttings, *N.J. Agr. Exp. Sta. Bul. 666,* 1939.

40. Nordine, R. M., Collecting, storage, and germination of maple seed, *Proc. 2nd Ann. Mtg. Prop. Soc.,* pp. 62–64. 1952.

41. Pease, R. W., and J. L. Creech, Propagating hollies, in *Handbook of Hollies.* Washington, D.C.: Amer. Hort. Soc., 1957.

42. Poulsen, S., *Poulsen on the Rose.* London: MacGibbon and Kee, 1955.

43. Roberts, A. N., and C. A. Boller, Holly production in Oregon, *Ore. Agr. Exp. Sta. Bul. 455,* 1953.

44. Roller, J. B., Propagation of *Ilex cornuta Burfordi, Proc. 3rd Ann. Mtg. Plant Prop. Soc.,* pp. 48–50. 1953.

45. Simpson, R. C., The propagation of *Malus* by budding and grafting, *Proc. 5th Ann. Mtg. Plant Prop. Soc.,* pp. 99–105. 1955.

46. Skinner, H. T., Rooting response of azaleas and other ericaceous plants to auxin treatments, *Proc. Amer. Soc. Hort. Sci.,* 35:830–838. 1937.

47. ———, Further observations on the propagation of rhododendrons and azaleas by stem and leaf-bud cuttings, *Proc. Amer. Soc. Hort. Sci.,* 37:1013–1017. 1939.

48. ———, A new propagation method for hybrid rhododendrons, *Jour. N.Y. Bot. Gard.,* 40(472):83–89. 1939.

49. ———, Vegetative propagation of oaks and suggested research techniques, *Proc. 2nd Ann. Mtg. Plant Prop. Soc.,* pp. 81–85. 1952.

50. ———, Fundamentals of azalea propagation, *Proc. 4th Ann. Mtg. Plant Prop. Soc.,* pp. 129–136. 1954.

51. Snyder, W. E., The fundamentals of juniper propagation, *Proc. 3rd Ann. Mtg. Plant Prop. Soc.,* pp. 67–77. 1953.

52. Stoutemyer, V. T., The propagation of *Chionanthus retusus* by cuttings, *Nat. Hort. Mag.,* pp. 175–178. Oct., 1942.

53. Stuart, N. W., and P. C. Marth, Composition and rooting of American holly cuttings as affected by treatment with indolebutyric acid, *Proc. Amer. Soc. Hort. Sci.,* 35:839–844. 1937.

54. Rowley, G. D., Germination in *Rosa canina, Amer. Rose Ann.,* 41:70–73. 1956.

55. Russell, P., The Oriental flowering cherries, *USDA Cir. 313,* 1934.

56. Thomas, C. C., Some factors influencing the rooting of cuttings of the Chinese holly (*Ilex cornuta*), *Nat. Hort. Mag.* July, 1935.

57. Tincker, M. A. H., Rose seeds; their after-ripening and germination, *Jour. Roy. Hort. Soc.,* 60:399–417. 1935.

58. Vermeulen, J., The propagation of *Taxus* by cuttings, *Proc. 4th Ann. Mtg. Plant Prop. Soc.,* pp. 76–79. 1954.

59. Warner, Z. P., Azaleas from seed, *Proc. 4th Ann. Mtg. Plant Prop. Soc.,* pp. 137–139. 1954.

60. Wells, J. S., Propagation of *Taxus, Amer. Nurs.,* 96(11):13, 37–43. 1952.

61. ———, Propagation of rhododendrons from stem cuttings, *Amer. Nurs.,* 97(9):10–11, 60–73. 1953.
62. ———, Outdoor propagation under constant mist, *Amer. Nurs.,* 97(11):14, 51–58. 1953.
63. ———, Rooting *Acer palmatum, Amer. Nurs.,* 98(7):15, 59–64. 1953.
64. ———, Pointers on propagation: propagating Koster spruce, *Amer. Nurs.,* 98(9):13, 48–53. 1953.
65. ———, *Plant Propagation Practices.* New York: Macmillan, 1955. Chap. 31.
66. Wyman, D., The time of year to make cuttings of narrow-leaved evergreens, *Florists Exch.,* 75(11):27. 1930.
67. ———, *Crab Apples for America.* Rockford, Ill.: Amer. Assoc. Bot. Gard. and Arb., 1955.
68. Zimmerman, P. W., and A. E. Hitchcock, Vegetative propagation of holly, *Amer. Jour. Bot.,* 16:556–570. 1929.
69. Zorg, P. G., The propagation of junipers from cuttings, *Proc. 3rd Ann. Mtg. Plant Prop. Soc.,* pp. 81–84. 1953.

• **Supplementary Reading**

American Association of Nurserymen, Inc., Committee on Horticultural Standards, *American Standard for Nursery Stock.* Washington: American Association of Nurserymen, Inc., 1956.

Hottes, A. C., *The Book of Shrubs.* New York: De La Mare, 1939.

———, *The Book of Trees.* New York: De La Mare, 1946.

Plant Propagator's Society, *Proceedings of Annual Meetings.*

Sheat, W. G., *Propagation of Trees, Shrubs, and Conifers.* London: Macmillan, 1948.

U.S. Department of Agriculture, *Woody Plant Seed Manual,* Miscellaneous Publication No. 654. Washington, D.C.: U.S. Government Printing Office (1948).

Wells, J. S., *Plant Propagation Practices.* New York: Macmillan, 1955.

Wyman, D., *Shrubs and Vines for American Gardens.* New York: Macmillan, 1949.

———, *Trees for American Gardens.* New York: Macmillan, 1951.

Yerkes, G. E., "Propagation of Trees and Shrubs," *U.S. Department of Agriculture Farmers' Bulletin* 1567, 1945.

18

Propagation of Selected Annuals and Herbaceous Perennials Used as Ornamentals

The number of herbaceous plants used as ornamentals is very large. The following list (pages 536–543) is by no means complete nor does it indicate all of the many species and hybrids which are available in any one of the genera listed. It would be desirable for the reader to have some familiarity with the range of plant species represented *(2, 3, 4, 5, 7, 8)*. The methods listed may serve as a guide for the usual means of propagation, but some variation from those indicated may be necessary with specific selections.

Many of these plants can be readily propagated by seed. Annuals and biennials obviously would be propagated only in that way, but many of the perennials can also be propagated by seed. The germination temperature requirement, the period of time required for germination, and the necessity for any pre-germination treatment are important items of information supplied in the following table. The temperatures given are those which experience has shown give the best and quickest germination, although other temperatures may also give reasonably good results *(6)*.

Seeds of many flower species show sensitivity to high temperatures and fail to germinate at temperatures over 75°F. Note that seeds of many of the following species have a relatively low germination temperature requirement. Also, many respond markedly to alternating temperatures and to light. These requirements would be particularly applicable to fresh seed. The Rules for Seed Testing *(1)* also include specific suggestions for environmental conditions which will stimulate germination of such seed.

Seeds of annual plants are planted in the spring, either in their permanent location or in flats for later transplanting into beds in the garden.

Although seeds of some perennials can be directly seeded, it is usually better to start them in a cold frame or in a flat in a greenhouse and later transplant them into the garden. Some plants may produce flowers the first year if they are started sufficiently early, but most do not bloom until the second year. Plants are put into the garden in the fall or potted and held over winter in a cold frame and planted in the spring.

Most herbaceous perennial plants can be propagated vegetatively and in some cases, where selected hybrids and special forms are involved, this method must be utilized to preserve the particular variety of plant being grown. The easiest method is simple division (see p. 417) when a plant which has grown for at least a season will enlarge sufficiently so that it can be divided into sections. This is usually done in the spring or fall, and each section is then used to produce a new plant. Different kinds of plants vary considerably in regard to the extent to which they may be increased. In many cases division is not sufficiently rapid for commercial propagation purposes, although it would be desirable for the modest increase required by the home gardener. For the large-scale commercial propagation of those perennials which do not reproduce true by seeds, the use of stem, leaf, or root cuttings is necessary. (See Chap. 10).

REFERENCES

1. Assoc. Off. Seed Anal., Rules for seed testing, *Proc. Assoc. Off. Seed Anal.*, 44:31–78. 1954.
2. Bailey, L. H., and E. Z. Bailey, *Hortus Second*. New York: Macmillan, 1941.
3. Booth, C. O., *An Encyclopedia of Annual and Biennial Garden Plants*. London: Faber and Faber, 1957.
4. Hottes, A. C., *The Book of Perennials,* 6th ed. New York: De La Mare, 1948.
5. Laurie, A., and L. C. Chadwick, *The Modern Nursery*. New York: Macmillan, 1931.
6. Northen, H. T., and R. T. Northen, *Complete Book of Greenhouse Gardening.* New York: Ronald, 1957.
7. Post, K., *Florist Crop Production and Marketing*. New York: Orange Judd, 1949.
8. Taylor, N., *Encyclopedia of Gardening,* 3rd ed. Boston: American Garden Guild and Houghton Mifflin, 1957.

PROPAGATION OF SELECTED ANNUAL AND HERBACEOUS
PERENNIAL ORNAMENTAL PLANTS

Plant					
Scientific name	Common name	Annual, biennial or perennial	Optimum temperature for seed germination*	Weeks required for seeds to germinate*	Vegetative methods
Achillea ptarmica	Yarrow	P	68	1–2	Spring or fall division
Aconitum spp.	Monkshood	P	Needs light; store in damp sand below 40°F. for six weeks		Division
Ageratum houstonianum	Ageratum	A	68–86†	3	
Agrostemma githago	Corncockle	P	68	2–3	
Althaea rosea	Hollyhock	P	68	2–3	
Alyssum maritimum	Alyssum	A	68	2–3	
A. saxatile	Golden tuft	P	68–86	3–4	Spring or fall division
Amaranthus spp.	Amaranth	P	68–86	3–4	
Amaryllis spp.	Amaryllis	P	68–86	Slow, uneven	Bulb cuttings; offsets
Anchusa spp.	Bugloss	P	68–86	3–4	Spring or fall division; root cuttings
Anemone coronaria	Poppy anemone	P	68	5–6	Division
A. japonica and hybrids	Japanese anemone				Root cuttings in fall
A. pulsatilla	Pasqueflower	P	68	5–6	Division
Anthemis tinctoria	Golden marguerite	P	68	3–4	Division
Antirrhinum majus	Snapdragon	A	54 60–65 (hybrids)	1–2	
Aquilegia spp.	Columbine	P	68–86	3–4	Spring division

Botanical name	Common name	Type	Temperature	Weeks	Remarks
Arabis spp.	Rockcress	P	68	3–4	Spring or fall division; stem cuttings
Arctotis stoechadifolia	African daisy	A	68	2–3	Division
Armeria spp.	Thrift	P	68	3–4	Division
Asclepias tuberosa	Butterfly milkweed	P	68–86 Fresh seeds need chilling	3–4	Division
Asparagus asparagoides	Smilax asparagus	P	68–86	3–4	
A. plumosus	Fern asparagus	P	68–86	4–6	
A. sprengeri	Sprenger asparagus	P	68–86	4–6	
Aster spp.	Michaelmas daisy	P	68	2–3	Spring or fall division necessary for varieties
Aubrieta deltoidea	Aubrieta	P	54	2–3	Stem cuttings
Baptisia spp.	Wild indigo	P	68	Slow, uneven	Division
Begonia spp. Tuberous and fibrous rooted	Begonia	P	68 Needs light	2–3	Various methods depending on species: leaf, stem cuttings; division of roots.
Bellis perennis	English daisy	P	68	1–2	Division
Bocconia (Macleaya) spp.	Plume poppy	P	54–90	1–4	Division
Boltonia asteroides	Boltonia	P	68	2–3	Spring or fall division
Browallia spp.	Browallia	A	68	2–3	
Calceolaria spp.	Calceolaria	A	68	2–3	
Calendula officinalis	Pot marigold	A	68–86	2–3	
Callistephus chinensis	China aster	A	68	2–3	
Campanula carpatica	Carpathian harebell	P	68–86	2–3	Spring or fall division

537

Scientific name	Common name	Annual, biennial or perennial	Optimum temperature for seed germination*	Weeks required for seeds to germinate*	Vegetative methods
C. lactiflora coerulea	Bellflower	P	55–90	2–3	Spring or fall division
C. medium	Canterbury bells	B	68–86	2–3	Spring or fall division
C. persicifolia	Peach bells	P	55–90	2–3	Spring or fall division
C. pyramidalis	Chimney bellflower	P	68–90	2	Spring or fall division
Canna generalis	Canna	P	Notch or file before planting		Division of rhizome
Catananche caerula	Cupidsdart	P	68–86	2–4	
Celosia argentea cristata	Cockscomb	A	68–86	1–2	
Centaurea spp.	Dusty miller; Cornflower, Sweet-sultan	A & P	68–86	3–4	
Cerastium tomentosum	Snow-in-summer	P	68	2–4	Division
Cheiranthus cheiri	Wallflower	P	54	2–3	
Chrysanthemum spp.	Chrysanthemum	A & P	68	2–4	Selected varieties by softwood cuttings in spring; division.
Clarkia spp.	Clarkia	A	54–90	1–2	
Cleome spinosa	Spiderflower	A	54–90	1–2	
Coreopsis spp.	Coreopsis	P	68	2–3	
Cosmos bipinnatus	Cosmos	A	68–86	1–2	
Cucurbita pepo var. ovifera	Ornamental gourds	A	68–86	2–3	
Cyclamen indicum	Cyclamen	P	68	3–4	
Cymbalaria muralis	Kenilworth ivy	P	54	1–4	
Cynoglossum spp.	Hounds tongue	A	68	2–3	
Delphinium grandiflorum	Delphinium	P	54	3–4	Division; cuttings of young shoots in spring
D. ajacis	Larkspur	A	54	3–4	
Dianthus spp.	Pink, Carnation	A & P	68	2–3	Herbaceous stem cuttings; layering; division

Dicentra spectabilis	Bleedingheart	P	Store in damp sand below 40°F. for 6 weeks		Division in spring; stem cuttings in early spring or after flowering; root cuttings after growth stops
Dictamnus albus	Dittany, Gasplant	P	Same as *Dicentra*		Division in spring
Digitalis	Foxglove	B & P	68–86	2–3	Division in spring
Dimorphotheca spp.	Cape marigold	A	68	2–3	
Doronicum spp.	Leopard bane	P	86	2–3	Division
Echinops spp.	Globe thistle	P	68–86	1–4	Division; root cuttings
Euphorbia spp.	Spurge	A & P	68–86	2–3	Division
Fern spores	Fern	P	70–90	Slow, uneven	Division
Freesia spp.	Freesia	P	54	4–6	Corms
Gaillardia spp.	Blanketflower	A & P	68	2–3	Division; root cuttings; stem cuttings
Gentiana spp.	Gentian	P	68 Freeze for 10 days before planting	1–4	
Geranium spp.	Cranesbill	A & P	54–90	1–6	Division
Gerbera jamesonii	Transvaal daisy	P	68	2–3	Division
Geum spp.	Avens	P	68–86	3–4	Division
Godetia spp.	Godetia	A	68	2–3	
Gypsophila spp.	Baby's breath	A & P	68	2–3	Division; double-flowered grafted to *G. paniculata* seedling roots during winter
Helenium autumnale	Sneezeweed	P	68	1–2	Division
Helianthemum nummularium	Sunrose	P	68–86	2–3	Summer cuttings; division
Helianthus annuus	Sunflower	A	68–86	2–3	
Heliopsis spp.	Heliopsis	P	68	1–2	Division
Heliotropium spp.	Heliotrope	A	68–86	3–4	

Plant		Annual, biennial or perennial	Optimum temperature for seed germination*	Weeks required for seeds to germinate*	Vegetative methods
Scientific name	Common name				
Helleborus spp.	Hellebore	P	Stratify 6 weeks		Division in fall
Hemerocallis spp.	Daylily	P	Stratify 6 weeks		Named varieties by division
Hesperis matronalis	Rocket	P	68–86	3–4	
Heuchera sanguinea	Coral Bells	P	68–86	2–3	Division; leaf cuttings
			Treatment with Arasan or Spergon recommended		
Hippeastrum (See *Amaryllis*)					
Hunnemannia fumariaefolia	Goldencup	A	68	2–3	
Iberis spp.	Candytuft	A	68–86	1–2	
			needs light		
Impatiens balsamina	Snapweed; Balsam	A	68	2–4	
Incarvillea spp.	Incarvillea	P	68	1–2	Division
Ipomoea purpurea	Morning-glory	A	68–86	1–3	
	Cracking seed coat may increase germination				
Iris spp.	Iris	P	54		Varieties by division of rhizome or bulb separation
	Stratify 6 weeks; embryo culture gives immediate germination				
Kniphofia uvaria	Torch lily	P	68–86	3–4	Division
Lantana sellowiana	Lantana	P	68–86	6–7	Cuttings in fall or winter
Lathyrus latifolius	Perennial pea vine	P	68–86	2–3	
L. odoratus	Sweet pea	A	68	2	
Lavandula officinalis	Lavender	P	52–90	2–3	
Liatris spp.	Gayfeather	P	68–86	3–4	Division
Lilium spp.	Lily	P	68	3–5	(see Chapter 15)
			(also see page 101)		
Linaria spp.	Toadflax	A	54	2–3	Division
Linum spp.	Flax	P	54	3–4	Division

540

Lobelia erinus	Lobelia	A	68–86	2–3	Division
Lobelia spp.	Lobelia	P	68–86	3–4	Division
Lunaria rediviva	Honesty	P	68	2–3	Division in early spring
Lupinus spp.	Lupine	A & P	68	2–3	Division
Lychnis spp.	Campion	P	68	3–4	
Mathiola incana	Stock	A	54–90	2	
Matricaria spp.	Mayweed, Camomile	P	68–86	2–3	
Mesembryanthemum spp.	Fig marigold	P	68	1–3	Cuttings
Mimulus spp.	Monkeyflower	A	54	1–2	
Molucella laevis	Bells of Ireland	A	86	2–3	
Myosotis spp.	Forget-me-not	P	68	2–3	Cuttings; division
Nemesia spp.	Nemesia	A	55	2–3	
Nepeta spp.	Nepeta	P	68	2–3	Division, layering
Nierembergia spp.	Cupflower	P	68–86	2–3	Division, cuttings in fall
Oenothera spp.	Evening primrose	P	68–86	1–3	Division
Paeonia spp.	Peony	P	(see p. 101)		Division of fleshy roots in fall, 1–3 buds per section
Papaver nudicaule	Iceland poppy	P	54	1–2	
P. orientale	Oriental poppy	P	54	1–2	Root cuttings in late summer
P. rhoeas	Corn poppy	A	55	1–2	
Penstemon spp.	Beard tongue	A	68–80	2–3	
Penstemon spp.	Beard tongue	P	68–86	Slow, uneven	Division
Petunia hybrida	Petunia	A	68	1–2	
	Doubles, and some **F₁** petunia hybrids may need light and higher temperatures for good germination; if not successful, try 80–85°F.				
Phlox drummondii	Annual phlox	A	68	2–3	
P. divaricata	Sweet William	P	Over winter freezing		Division; root cuttings

(see p. 101)

541

Plant

Scientific name	Common name	Annual, biennial or perennial	Optimum temperature for seed germination*	Weeks required for seeds to germinate*	Vegetative methods
P. paniculata	Garden phlox	P			Division; root cuttings; spring, summer, or fall cuttings
Physalis alkekengi	Chinese lantern plant	P	54–90	3–4	Division in spring
Physostegia virginiana	False dragonhead	P	54–90	2–3	Division
Platycodon grandiflorum	Balloon flower	P	68–86	2–3	Division in spring
Polemonium spp.	Polemonium	P	68–86	3–4	Division
Portulaca grandiflora	Moss rose	A	68–86	2–3	
Potentilla spp.	Cinquefoil	A	68	1–3	
Primula obconica	Top primrose	A	55–90 light	3–4	
P. malacoides	Fairy primrose	A	68–86	2–3	
P. sinensis	Chinese primrose	A	68	3–4	
P. (perennial species)	Primrose	P	68 Some species may require lower temperatures	3–6	Division; cuttings in spring
Ranunculus spp.	Buttercup	P	68	1–4	Division; *R. asiaticus* by division of tuberous roots.
Reseda odorata	Mignonette	A	54	2–3	
Rudbeckia spp.	Coneflower	P	69–86	2–3	Division
Saintpaulia ionantha	African violet	P	85	3–4	Leaf cuttings; division
Salpiglossis sinuata	Painted tongue	A	68–86	2	
Salvia splendens	Scarlet sage	A	68–86	2–3	
Salvia spp.	Sage	P	68–86	2–3	Division
Sanvitalia procumbens	Creeping zinnia	A	68	1–2	
Saponaria officinalis	Bouncing bet	P	68	2–3	Division; cuttings
S. vaccaria	Soapwort	A	68	2–3	
Scabiosa spp.	Pincushion flower	A & P	68–86	2–3	Division

Schizanthus spp.	Butterfly flower	A	54	1–2
Senecio cruentus	Cineraria	A	68	2–3
Sinningia speciosa	Gloxinia	P	68	Needs light	Leaf cuttings
Stokesia laevis	Stokes daisy	P	68–86	4–6	Division
Tagetes spp.	Marigold	A	68–86	1–2	
Thalictrum spp.	Meadow rue	P	68	4–6	Division in spring
Thermopsis spp.	Thermopsis	P	68–86	2–3	Division in spring
Thunbergia spp.	Clockvine	A	68–86	2–3	
Thymus spp.	Thyme	P	54–90	1–2	
			needs light		
Tithonia spp.	Mexican sunflower	A	68–86	2–3	
Torenia fournieri	Torenia	A	68–86	2	
Trachymene caerulea	Laceflower	P	68	2–3	
Trollius europaeus	Globeflower	P	Slow, stratify 6 weeks		Division
Tropaeolum majus	Nasturtium	A	68	1–3	
Tunica saxifraga	Tunicflower	P	68–86	1–2	Division
			Needs light		
Valeriana officinalis	Valerian	P	54–90	3–4	Division
Venidium fastuosum	Venidium	A	68–86	4–6	
Verbascum spp.	Mullein	P	86	Slow	
Verbena hortensis	Verbena	A	68–86	3–4	
V. canadensis	Clump verbena	P	54–90	2–4	Cuttings
Veronica spp.	Speedwell	P	54–90	2	Division
Vinca minor	Periwinkle	P	68	2–3	Cuttings
Viola cornuta	Violet	P	54–90	2–3	Cuttings in spring; division; runners
			Some varieties need light		
V. tricolor hortensis	Pansy	A	55–90	2–3	Cuttings of young growth
Yucca spp.	Yucca	P	68	Slow	Offsets
Zinnia elegans	Zinnia	A	68–86	1–2	

INDEX

Index